BEGINNING ALGEBRA

CUSTOM EDITION FOR HEALD COLLEGE

Taken from:

Beginning Algebra, Sixth Edition
by John Tobey and Jeffrey Slater

Cover photo: *Zakim Bridge 3*, by S. Olsen and K. Mira

Excerpts taken from:

Beginning Algebra, Sixth Edition
by John Tobey and Jeffrey Slater

Published by Prentice Hall
Upper Saddle River, New Jersey 07458

Printed in the United States of America

10 9 8 7 6 5 4 3 2

ISBN 0-536-20872-7

2006360143

RG

Please visit our web site at *www.pearsoncustom.com*

PEARSON CUSTOM PUBLISHING
75 Arlington Street, Suite 300, Boston, MA 02116
A Pearson Education Company

To the Student

As authors our highest goal has been to write a solid mathematics textbook that will truly help you succeed in your mathematics course. After years of refining our textbooks, we have now developed a feature that we think will help ensure your success in mathematics. It is called the ***How Am I Doing? Guide to Math Success.***

The ***How Am I Doing? Guide to Math Success*** shows how you can effectively use this textbook to succeed in your mathematics course. This clear path for you to follow is based upon how our successful students have utilized the textbook in the past. Here is how it works:

EXAMPLES and PRACTICE PROBLEMS: When you study an Example, you should immediately do the Practice Problem that follows to make sure you understand each step in solving a particular problem. The worked-out solution to every Practice Problem can be found in the back of the text starting at page SP-1 so you can check your work and receive immediate guidance in case you need to review.

EXERCISE SETS—Practice, Practice, Practice: You learn math by *doing* math. The best way to learn math is to *practice, practice, practice*. The exercise sets provide the opportunity for this practice. Be sure that you complete every exercise your instructor assigns as homework. In addition, check your answers to the odd-numbered exercises in the back of the text to see whether you have correctly solved each problem.

HOW AM I DOING? MID-CHAPTER REVIEW: This feature allows you to check if you understand the important concepts covered to that point in a particular chapter. Many students find that halfway through a chapter is the point of greatest need because so many different types of problems have been covered. This review covers each of the types of problems from the first half of the chapter. Do these problems and check your answers at the back of the text. If you need to review any of these problems, simply refer back to the section and objective indicated next to the answer. Before you go further into the chapter, it is important to understand what has been learned so far.

HOW AM I DOING? CHAPTER TEST: This test (found at the end of every chapter) provides you with an excellent opportunity to both practice and review for any test you will take in class. Take this test to see how much of the chapter you have mastered. By checking your answers, you can once again refer back to the section and the objective of any exercise you want to review further. This allows you to see at once what has been learned and what still needs more study as you prepare for your test or exam.

HOW AM I DOING? CHAPTER TEST PREP VIDEO CD: If you need to review any of the exercises from the *How Am I Doing? Chapter Test,* this video CD found at the back of the text provides worked-out solutions to each of the exercises. Simply insert the CD into a computer and watch a math instructor solve each of the Chapter Test exercises in detail. By reviewing these problems, you can study any points of difficulty and better prepare yourself for your upcoming test or exam.

These steps provide a clear path you can follow in order to successfully complete your math course. More importantly, the ***How Am I Doing? Guide to Math Success*** is a tool to help you achieve an understanding of mathematics. We encourage you to take advantage of this new feature.

John Tobey
Jeffrey Slater
North Shore Community College

MORE TOOLS FOR SUCCESS

In addition to the ***How Am I Doing? Guide to Math Success,*** your Tobey/Slater textbook is filled with other tools and features to help you succeed in your mathematics course. These include:

Blueprint for Problem Solving

The Mathematics Blueprint for Problem Solving provides you with a consistent outline to organize your approach to problem solving. You will not need to use the blueprint to solve every problem, but it is available when you are faced with a problem with which you are not familiar, or when you are trying to figure out where to begin solving a problem.

Chapter Organizers

The key concepts and mathematical procedures covered in each chapter are reviewed at the end of the chapter in a unique Chapter Organizer. This device not only lists the key concepts and methods, but provides a completely worked-out example for each type of problem. The Chapter Organizer should be used in conjunction with the ***How Am I Doing? Chapter Test*** and the ***How Am I Doing? Chapter Test Prep Video CD*** as a study aid to help you prepare for tests.

Developing Your Study Skills

These notes appear throughout the text to provide you with suggestions and techniques for improving your study skills and succeeding in your math course.

RESOURCES FOR SUCCESS

In addition to the textbook, Prentice Hall offers a wide range of materials to help you succeed in your mathematics course. These include:

Student Study Pack

Includes the *Student Solutions Manual* (fully worked-out solutions to odd-numbered exercises), access to the *Prentice Hall Tutor Center,* and the CD *Lecture Series Videos* that accompany the text. The *Student Study Pack* is available at no charge when packaged with a new textbook.

MyMathLab

MyMathLab offers the entire textbook online with links to video clips and practice exercises in addition to tutorial exercises, homework, and tests. *MyMathLab* also offers a personalized Study Plan for each student based on student test results. The Study Plan links directly to unlimited tutorial exercises for the areas you need to study and re-test so you can practice until you have mastered the skills and concepts. *MyMathLab* is available at no charge when packaged with a new textbook.

*This book is dedicated to the memory of Lexie Tobey and John Tobey, Sr.
They have left a legacy of love, a memory of four decades of faithful teaching,
and a sense of helping others that will influence generations to come.
For their grandchildren they have left an inspiring model of a loving family,
true character, and service to God and community.*

Contents

CHAPTER 2

Equations and Inequalities 133

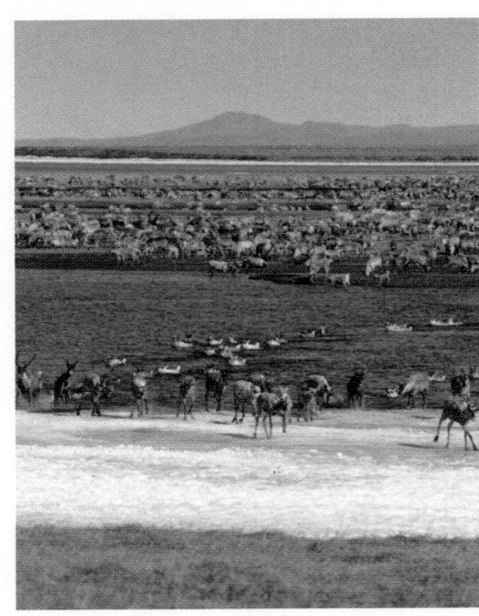

CHAPTER 3

Solving Applied Problems 191

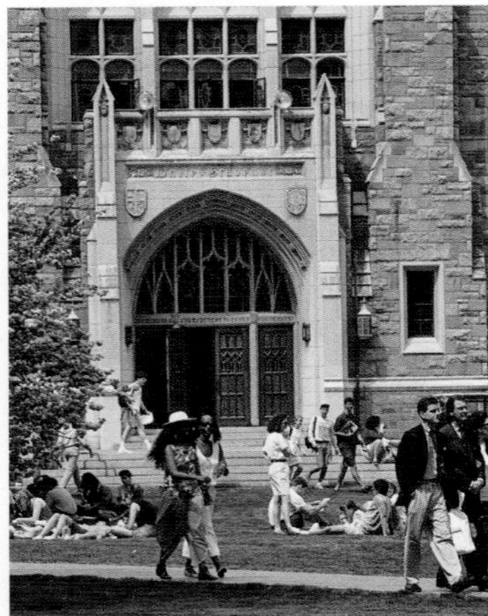

CHAPTER 4

Exponents and Polynomials 251

CHAPTER 5

Factoring 303

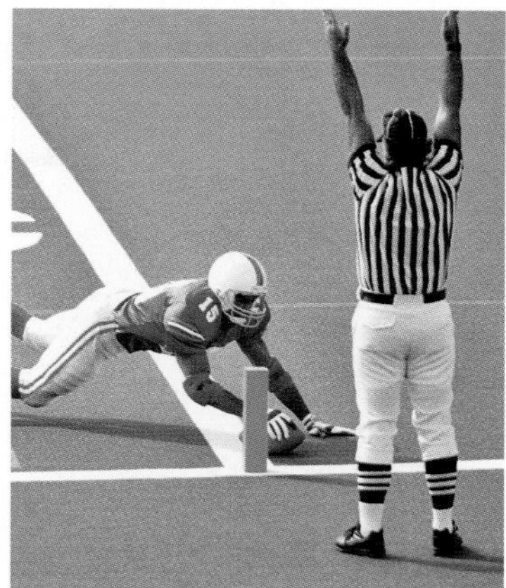

CHAPTER 6

Rational Expressions and Equations 355

Preface

TO THE INSTRUCTOR

We share a partnership with you. For over thirty-three years we have taught mathematics courses at North Shore Community College. Each semester we join you in the daily task of sharing the knowledge of mathematics with students who often struggle with this subject. We enjoy teaching and helping students—and we are confident that you share these joys with us.

Mathematics instructors and students face many challenges today. *Beginning Algebra* was written with these needs in mind. This textbook explains mathematics slowly, clearly, and in a way that is relevant to everyday life for the college student. As with previous editions, special attention has been given to problem solving in the sixth edition. This text is written to help students organize the information in any problem-solving situation, to reduce anxiety, and to provide a guide that enables students to become confident problem solvers.

One of the hallmark characteristics of *Beginning Algebra* that makes the text easy to learn and teach from is the building-block organization. Each section is written to stand on its own, and each homework set is completely self-testing. Exercises are paired and graded and are of varying levels and types to ensure that all skills and concepts are covered. As a result, the text offers students an effective and proven learning program suitable for a variety of course formats—including lecture-based classes; discussion-oriented classes; distance learning centers; modular, self-paced courses; mathematics laboratories; and computer-supported centers. The book has been written to be especially helpful in online classes. The authors teach at least one course online each semester.

Beginning Algebra is part of a series that includes the following:

Tobey/Slater, *Basic College Mathematics,* Fifth Edition

Tobey/Slater, *Essentials of Basic College Mathematics*

Blair/Tobey/Slater, *Prealgebra,* Third Edition

Tobey/Slater, *Beginning Algebra,* Sixth Edition

Tobey/Slater/Blair, *Beginning Algebra: Early Graphing*

Tobey/Slater, *Intermediate Algebra,* Fifth Edition

Tobey/Slater/Blair, *Beginning and Intermediate Algebra,* Second Edition

We have visited and listened to teachers across the country and have incorporated a number of suggestions into this edition to help you with the particular learning delivery system at your school. The following pages describe the key continuing features and changes in the sixth edition.

NEW! AND IMPROVED FEATURES IN THE SIXTH EDITION

How Am I Doing? Guide to Math Success

The ***How Am I Doing? Guide to Math Success*** shows how students can effectively use this textbook to succeed in their mathematics course. This clear path for them to follow is based upon how successful students have utilized this textbook in the past.

EXAMPLES and PRACTICE PROBLEMS The design of the text has been enhanced so the Examples and Practice Problems are clearly connected in a cohesive unit. This has been done to encourage students to immediately do the Practice Problem associated with each Example to make sure they understand each step in solving a particular problem. The worked-out solution to every Practice Problem can be found in the back of the text starting at page SP-1 so students can check their work and receive immediate guidance in case they need to review.

Enhanced Exercise Sets

- First, *each* exercise set has been:
  - enhanced to have a **better progression from easy to medium to challenging** problems, with appropriate quantities of each.
  - restructured to have **better matching of even and odd** problems.
  - rewritten to ensure that **all concepts are fully represented** with every example from the section covered by a group of exercises.
- In addition, the **number and frequency of *Mixed Practice* problems have been increased,** when appropriate, throughout the exercise sets. These *Mixed Practice* problems require the students to identify the type of problem and the best method they should use to solve it. **More *Verbal and Writing Skills* exercises have also been added,** where appropriate, to allow students more time to interact with new concepts and to explain them fully in their own words.
- Lastly, throughout the text the **application exercises have been updated and labeled** to better indicate the scope and relevance of each real-world and real-data problem at-a-glance. These applications relate to everyday life, global issues beyond the borders of the United States, and other academic disciplines. Many include source citations. Roughly 30 percent of the applications have been contributed by actual students based on scenarios they have encountered in their home or work lives.

How Am I Doing? Mid-Chapter Review

This feature allows you to check if your students understand the important concepts covered to that point in a particular chapter. Many students find that halfway through a chapter is the point of greatest need because so many different types of problems have been covered. This review covers each of the types of problems from the first half of the chapter. Specific section and objective references are provided with each answer to indicate where a student should look for further review.

How Am I Doing? Chapter Test

This test (found at the end of every chapter) provides your students with an excellent opportunity to both practice and review for any test they will take in class. Encourage your students to take this test to see how much of the material they have mastered and then check their answers in the back of the text. Specific section and objective references are provided with each answer to indicate where a student should look for further review.

How Am I Doing? Chapter Test Prep Video CD

If students need to review any of the exercises from the ***How Am I Doing? Chapter Test,*** this video CD found at the back of the text provides worked-out solutions to each of the exercises. Students can simply insert the CD into a computer and watch a math instructor solve each of the Chapter Test exercises in detail. By reviewing these problems, students can study through any points of difficulty and better prepare for an upcoming test or exam.

How Am I Doing? Chapter Test & TestGen

For this new edition of the text, we have provided a new file in each chapter of the *TestGen* program specific to each Chapter Test in the text. The *TestGen* Chapter Test file provides algorithms specific to the problems in the corresponding textbook Chapter Test. This provides a convenient way to create similar tests for practice or assessment purposes.

KEY FEATURES IN THE SIXTH EDITION

Developing Problem-Solving Abilities

We are committed as authors to producing a textbook that emphasizes mathematical reasoning and problem-solving techniques as recommended by AMATYC, NCTM, AMS, NADE, MAA, and other bodies. To this end, the problem sets are built on a wealth of real-life and real-data applications. Unique problems have been developed and incorporated into the exercise sets that help train students in data interpretation, mental mathematics, estimation, geometry and graphing, number sense, critical thinking, and decision making.

Mathematics Blueprint for Problem Solving

The successful Mathematics Blueprint for Problem Solving strengthens problem-solving skills by providing a consistent and interactive outline to help students organize their approach to problem solving. Once students fill in the blueprint, they can refer back to their plan as they do what is needed to solve the problem. Because of its flexibility, this feature can be used with single-step problems, multi-step problems, applications, and nonroutine problems that require problem solving strategies. Students will not need to use the blueprint to solve every problem. It is available for those faced with a problem with which they are not familiar, to alleviate anxiety, to show them where to begin, and to assist them in the steps of reasoning.

Developing Your Study Skills

This highly successful feature has been retained in the new edition. The boxed notes are integrated throughout the text to provide students with techniques for improving their study skills and succeeding in math courses.

Putting Your Skills to Work

This highly successful feature has been revised and expanded in the sixth edition. There are eleven new Putting Your Skills to Work applications in the new edition. These nonroutine application problems challenge students to synthesize the knowledge they have gained and apply it to a totally new area. Each problem is specifically arranged for independent and cooperative learning or group investigation of mathematical problems that pique student interest. Students are given the opportunity to help one another discover mathematical solutions to extended problems. The investigations feature open-ended questions and extrapolation of data to areas beyond what is normally covered in such a course.

Increased Integration and Emphasis on Geometry

Due to the emphasis on geometry on many statewide exams, geometry problems are integrated throughout the text. The new edition contains an increased number of geometry problems. Additionally, examples and exercises that incorporate a principle of geometry are marked with a triangle icon for easy identification.

Graphs, Charts, and Tables

When students encounter mathematics in real-world publications, they often encounter data represented in a graph, chart, or table and are asked to make a reasonable conclusion based on the data presented. This emphasis on graphical interpretation is a continuing trend with today's expanding technology. The number of mathematical problems based on charts, graphs, and tables has been significantly increased in this edition. Students are asked to make simple interpretations, to solve medium-level problems, and to investigate challenging applied problems based on the data shown in a chart, graph, or table.

MASTERING MATHEMATICAL CONCEPTS

Text features that develop the mastery of concepts include the following:

Learning Objectives

Concise learning objectives listed at the beginning of each section allow students to preview the goals of that section.

To Think About

These critical thinking questions may follow examples in the text and appear in the exercise sets. They extend the concept being taught, providing the opportunity for all students to stretch their minds, to look for patterns, and to make conclusions based on their previous experience. The number of these exercises has significantly increased in this edition.

Cumulative Review

Almost every exercise set concludes with a section of cumulative review problems. These problems review topics previously covered, and are designed to assist students in retaining the material. Many additional applied problems have been added to the cumulative review sections.

Calculator Problems

Calculator boxes are placed in the margin of the text to alert students to a scientific or graphing calculator application. In the exercise section, icons are used to indicate problems that are designed for solving with a graphing or scientific calculator.

REVIEWING MATHEMATICAL CONCEPTS

At the end of each chapter we have included problems and tests to provide your students with several different formats to help them review and reinforce the ideas that they have learned. This assists them not only with that specific chapter, but reviews previously covered topics as well.

Chapter Organizers

The concepts and mathematical procedures covered are reviewed at the end of each chapter in a unique chapter organizer. This device has been extremely popular with faculty and students alike. It not only lists concepts and methods, but provides a completely worked-out example for each type of problem. Students find that preparing a similar chapter organizer on their own in higher-level math courses becomes an invaluable way to master the content of a chapter of material.

Chapter Review Problems

These problems are grouped by section as a quick refresher at the end of the chapter. They can also be used by the student as a quiz of the chapter material.

How Am I Doing? Chapter Tests

Found at the end of the chapter, the chapter test is a representative review of the material from that particular chapter that simulates an actual testing format. This provides the students with a gauge to their preparedness for the actual examination.

Cumulative Tests

At the end of each chapter is a cumulative test. One-half of the content of each cumulative test is based on the math skills learned in previous chapters. By completing these tests for each chapter, the students build confidence that they have mastered not only the contents of the chapter but those of previous chapters as well.

RESOURCES FOR THE INSTRUCTOR

Printed Resources

Annotated Instructor's Edition (ISBN: 0-13-148288-2)

- Complete student text
- Answers appear in place on the same text page as exercises
- **Teaching Tips** placed in the margin at key points where students historically need extra help
- Answers to all exercises in the section sets, mid-chapter reviews, chapter reviews, chapter tests, cumulative tests, and practice final

Instructor's Solutions Manual (ISBN: 0-13-148291-2)

- Detailed step-by-step solutions to the even-numbered section exercises
- Solutions to every exercise (odd and even) in the mid-chapter reviews, chapter reviews, chapter tests, cumulative tests, and practice final
- Solution methods reflect those emphasized in the text

Instructor's Resource Manual with Tests (ISBN: 0-13-148290-4)

- New! One *Mini-Lecture* is provided per section. These include key learning objectives, classroom examples, and teaching notes.
- New! One *Skill Builder* is provided per section. These include concept rules, explained examples, and extra problems for students. All answers included.
- New! Two *Activities* per chapter provide short group activities in a convenient ready-to-use handout format. All answers included.
- Twenty *Additional Exercises* are provided per section for added test exercises or worksheets. All answers included.
- *Tests* provide additional suggested testing materials:
  - two *Chapter Pretests* per chapter (1 free response, 1 multiple choice)
  - six *Chapter Tests* per chapter (3 free response, 3 multiple choice)
  - two *Cumulative Tests* per even-numbered chapter (1 free response, 1 multiple choice)
  - two *Final Exams* (1 free response, 1 multiple choice)
  - answers to all items

Media Resources

TestGen with QuizMaster (Windows/Macintosh) (ISBN: 0-13-148294-7)

- Algorithmically driven, text-specific testing program—covers all objectives of the text
- New! Chapter Test file for each chapter provides algorithms specific to exercises in each *How Am I Doing? Chapter Test* from the text
- Edit and add own questions with the built-in question editor, which also allows you to create graphs, import graphics, and insert math notation
- Create a nearly unlimited number of tests and worksheets as well as assorted reports and summaries
- Networkable for administering tests and capturing grades online or on a local area network

CD Lecture Series Videos—Lab Pack (ISBN: 0-13-148293-9)

- Lecture-based instruction for Key Concepts, Examples, and Practice Problems from each text section

- Excellent support for students who want to review classroom lectures when doing homework or studying for a test
- Convenient anytime access to video tutorial support when provided for students as part of the Student Study Pack

New! MyMathLab (instructor)

MyMathLab is an all-in-one, online tutorial, homework, assessment, course management tool with the following features.

- **Powered by CourseCompass™**—Pearson Education's online teaching and learning environment
- **Tutorial powered by *MathXL*®**—our online homework, tutorial, and assessment system
- Rich and flexible set of course materials, **featuring free-response exercises** algorithmically generated for unlimited practice and mastery.
- **The entire textbook online with links to multimedia resources**—video clips, practice exercises, and animations—that are correlated to the textbook examples and exercises.
- **Homework and test managers** to select and assign online exercises correlated directly to the text
- **A personalized Study Plan** generated based on student test results. The Study Plan links directly to unlimited tutorial exercises for the areas students need to study and re-test, so they can practice until they have mastered the skills and concepts.
- **Easy to use tracking** in the *MyMathLab* gradebook of all of the online homework, tests, and tutorial work.
- **Import *TestGen* tests**
- **Online gradebook**—designed specifically for mathematics—automatically tracks students' homework and test results and provides grade control.
- http://www.mymathlab.com

New! MathXL®

MathXL® is a powerful online homework, tutorial, and assessment system. With *MathXL* instructors can:

- Create, edit, and assign online homework and tests using algorithmically generated exercises correlated at the objective level to your textbook.
- Track student work in *MathXL*'s online gradebook.

RESOURCES FOR THE STUDENT

New! Student Study Pack (ISBN: 0-13-171162-8)

Includes the *Student Solutions Manual,* access to the *Prentice Hall Tutor Center,* and the *CD Lecture Series Videos* that accompany the text.

Printed Resources

Student Solutions Manual (ISBN: 0-13-153060-7)

- Solutions to all odd-numbered section exercises
- Solutions to every (even and odd) exercises found in the mid-chapter reviews, chapter reviews, chapter tests, and cumulative reviews
- Solution methods reflect those emphasized in the text
- Ask your bookstore about ordering

MEDIA RESOURCES

New! **Chapter Test Prep Video CD (ISBN: 0-13-153053-4)**

Provides step-by-step video solutions to each problem in each *How Am I Doing? Chapter Test* in the textbook. Packaged at no charge with a new text, inside the back cover.

New! **MyMathLab (student)**

MyMathLab is an all-in-one, online tutorial, homework, assessment, course management tool with the following student features.

- **The entire textbook online with links to multimedia resources**—video clips, practice exercises, and animations—that are correlated to the textbook examples and exercises.
- **Online tutorial, homework, and tests**
- **A personalized Study Plan** generated based on student test results. The Study Plan links directly to unlimited tutorial exercises for the areas students need to study and re-test, so they can practice until they have mastered the skills and concepts.
- http://www.mymathlab.com

New! **MathXL®**

MathXL® is a powerful online homework, tutorial, and assessment system. With *MathXL* students can:

- Take chapter tests and receive a personalized study plan based on their test results.
- See diagnosed weaknesses and link directly to tutorial exercises for the objectives they need to study and retest.
- Access supplemental animations and video clips directly from selected exercises.

New! **MathXL® Tutorials on CD (ISBN: 0-13-153063-1)**

This interactive tutorial CD-ROM provides:

- Algorithmically-generated practice exercises correlated at the objective level.
- Practice exercises accompanied by an example and a guided solution.
- Tutorial video clips within the exercise to help students visualize concepts.
- Easy-to-use tracking of student activity and scores and printed summaries of students' progress.

New! **Interact Math www.interactmath.com**

The power of the *MathXL* text-specific tutorial exercises available for unlimited practice online, without an access code, and without tracking capabilities.

Prentice Hall Tutor Center www.prenhall.com/tutorcenter (ISBN: 0-13-064604-0)

- Tutorial support via phone, fax or email staffed by developmental math faculty.
- Available Sunday—Thursday 5pm EST to midnight—5 days a week, 7 hours a day
- Accessed through a registration number that may be bundled with a new text as part of the Student Study Pack or purchased separately with a used book. Comes automatically within *MyMathLab*.

ACKNOWLEDGMENTS

This book is the product of many years of work and many contributions from faculty and students across the country. We would like to thank the many reviewers and participants in focus groups and special meetings with the authors in preparation of previous editions.

Our deep appreciation to each of the following:

George J. Apostolopoulos, *DeVry Institute of Technology*
Katherine Barringer, *Central Virginia Community College*
Mark Billiris, *St. Petersburg Junior College*
Jamie Blair, *Orange Coast College*
Larry Blevins, *Tyler Junior College*
Connie Buller, *Metropolitan Community College*
Robert Christie, *Miami-Dade Community College*
Nelson Collins, *Joliet Junior College*
Mike Contino, *California State University at Heyward*
Judy Dechene, *Fitchburg State University*
Floyd L. Downs, *Arizona State University*
Robert Dubuc, Jr., *New England Institute of Technology*
Barbara Edwards, *Portland State University*
Janice F. Gahan-Rech, *University of Nebraska at Omaha*
Colin Godfrey, *University of Massachusetts, Boston*
Mary Beth Headlee, *Manatee Community College*
Doug Mace, *Baker College*
Carl Mancuso, *William Paterson College*
James Matovina, *Community College of Southern Nevada*
Janet McLaughlin, *Montclair State College*
Beverly Meyers, *Jefferson College*
Nancy Meyers, *University of Southern Indiana*
Gloria Mills, *Tarrant County Junior College*
Norman Mittman, *Northeastern Illinois University*
Wayne L. Miller, *Lee College*
Sharon L. Morrison, *St. Petersburg Junior College*
Jim Osborn, *Baker College*
Linda Padilla, *Joliet Junior College*
Cathy Panik, *Manatee Community College*
Elizabeth A. Polen, *County College of Morris*
Joel Rappaport, *Miami-Dade Community College*
Jose Rico, *Laredo Community College*
Ronald Ruemmler, *Middlesex County College*
Dennis Runde, *Manatee Community College*
Sally Search, *Tallahassee Community College*
Carolyn Gigi Smith, *Armstrong Atlantic State University*
Lee Ann Spahr, *Durham Technical Community College*
Richard Sturgeon, *University of Southern Maine*
Ara B. Sullenberger, *Tarrant County Community College*
Margie Thrall, *Manatee Community College*

Michael Trappuzanno, *Arizona State University*
Jerry Wisnieski, *Des Moines Community College*

In addition, we want to thank the following individuals for providing splendid insight and suggestions for this new edition.

Carla Ainsworth, *Salt Lake Community College*
Mary Lou Baker, *Columbia State Community College*
Jana Barnard, *Angelo State University*
Linda Beattie, *Western New Mexico University*
Lydia Botsford, *Heald Business College,* Milpitas
Bonnie Brooks, *Sussex County Community College*
David Brown, *Heald Business College,* Vacaville
John Buckley, *Delaware Technical and Community College*
John Close, *Salt Lake Community College*
Gene Coco, *Heald Business College,* Roseville
Kevin Cooper, *National American University*
Gregory Daubenmire, *Las Positas College*
Robert Dubuc, *New England Institute of Technology*
Mahmoud El-Hashash, *Bridgewater State College*
Naomi Gibbs, *Pitt Community College*
Mark Glines, *Salt Lake Community College*
Edna Greenwood, *Tarrant County College, Northwest Campus*
Cynthia Gubitose, *Southern Connecticut State University*
Renu Gupta, *Louisiana State University,* Alexandria
Philip Hammersley, *Ivy Tech State College*
Autumn Hoover, *Angelo State University*
Laura Kaufmann, *Orange Coast College*
Carolyn Krause, *Delaware Technical and Community College*
Euniz Lochte, *Florida Metropolitan University,* Orlando North
Elizabeth Lucas, *North Shore Community College*
Jim Lynn, *Florida Metropolitan University,* Orlando North
Valerie Maley, *Cape Fear Community College*
Mary Marlin, *West Virginia Northern Community College*
Todd Mattson, *DeVry University, DuPage Campus*
Jim McKee, *Florida Metropolitan University,* Tampa
Maria Mendez, *Laredo Community College*
Kathy Morgan, *Coastal Carolina Community College*
Christina Morian, *Lincoln University*
Joe Nagengast, *Florida Career College*
Charlcie Neal, *Clayton College and State University*
Armando Perez, *Laredo Community College*
Larry Pontaski, *Pueblo Community College*
Juan Rivera, *Florida Metropolitan University,* Orlando South
Graciela Rodriguez, *Laredo Community College*
Jeff Simmons, *Ivy Tech State College*
Jed Soifer, *Atlantic Cape Community College*
Gwen Terwilliger, *University of Toledo*

Sharon Testone, *Onondaga Community College*
Georgina Vastola, *Middlesex Community College*
Jonathan Weissman, *Essex County College*
Alice Williamson, *Sussex County Community College*
Mike Wilson, *Florida Metropolitan University,* Tampa
Mary Jane Wolfe, *University of Rio Grande*
Michelle Younker, *Terra Community College*
Peter Zimmer, *West Chester University*

We have been greatly helped by a supportive group of colleagues who not only teach at North Shore Community College but have also provided a number of ideas as well as extensive help on all of our mathematics books. Also, a special word of thanks to Hank Harmeling, Tom Rourke, Wally Hersey, Bob McDonald, Judy Carter, Bob Campbell, Rick Ponticelli, Russ Sullivan, Kathy LeBlanc, Lora Connelly, Sharyn Sharaf, Donna Stefano, and Nancy Tufo. Joan Peabody has done an excellent job of typing various materials for the manuscript and her help is gratefully acknowledged. Sue Ellen Robinson provided new problems, new ideas, and great mental energy. She greatly assisted us with error checking. Her excellent help was much appreciated. A special word of thanks to Richard Semmler, Jenny Crawford, and Ron Salzman for their excellent work in accuracy reviewing page proofs.

Each textbook is a combination of ideas, writing, and revisions from the authors and wise editorial direction and assistance from the editors. We want to thank our Prentice Hall editor, Paul Murphy, for his helpful insight and perspective on each phase of the revision of the textbook. Paul is a man of ideas, wisdom, and energy. He has that rare ability to look at the big picture and consider all the possibilities and then make a wise plan to accomplish the goal in the best possible way. He has found the secret of how to listen to a multitude of ideas and distill them down to a few excellent concepts upon which to improve a textbook. It has been a joy to work with him in the planning, writing, and revising of the new sixth edition of *Beginning Algebra*. Elaine Page, our project manager, provided daily support and encouragement as the book progressed. Elaine is a woman of insight, organization, and helpful suggestions. She has an amazing ability to take hundreds of pages of ideas and condense them into a manageable collection of concrete suggestions. From time to time, as we rolled up our sleeves and went to work on the actual revision and preparation of the manuscript for production, we found that we had much to do and we asked Elaine for help. In every case, she came to our assistance and we accomplished the task together. Tony Palermino, our developmental editor, sifted through mountains of material and offered excellent suggestions for improvement and change.

For the final phases of production of this book, Dawn Nuttall has been our project manager. Dawn is a woman with remarkable perspective and thoughtful analysis. She possesses a wonderful ability to see through problems and find solutions that not only solve the difficulty at hand, but prevent further difficulties from occurring at some later point. When we encountered a wall blocking the way, Dawn always found a clear path to take us around the obstacle. It has been a delight to work with Dawn.

Our mathematics production editor, Lynn Savino Wendel, has been a wonderful help as we finalized the manuscript and checked over the page proofs. Lynn kept things moving on schedule and adjusted tasks in order to make production more efficient. Lynn knows textbook production like the back of her hand and her knowledge proved most helpful throughout the entire process. Special thanks to our art director, Jonathan Boylan, and designer, Susan Anderson-Smith, who coordinated the attractive design and layout of the text and cover for all books in this series.

Nancy Tobey retired from teaching and joined the team as our administrative assistant. Mailing, editing, photocopying, collating, and taping were cheerfully done each day. A special thanks goes to Nancy. We could not have finished the book without you.

Book writing is impossible for us without the loyal support of our families. Our deepest thanks and love to Nancy, Johnny, Melissa, Marcia, Shelley, Rusty, and Abby. Your understanding, your love and help, and your patience have been a source of great encouragement. Finally, we thank God for the strength and energy to write and the opportunity to help others through this textbook.

We have spent more than 33 years teaching mathematics. Each teaching day, we find that our greatest joy is helping students learn. We take a personal interest in ensuring that each student has a good learning experience in taking this course. If you have some personal comments, suggestions, or ideas for future editions of this textbook, please write to us at:

Prof. John Tobey and Prof. Jeffrey Slater
Prentice Hall Publishing
Office of the College Mathematics Editor
Room 300
75 Arlington Street
Boston, MA 02116

or e-mail us at

jtobey@northshore.edu

We wish you success in this course and in your future life!

John Tobey
Jeffrey Slater

Diagnostic Pretest: Beginning Algebra

1. ________
2. ________
3. ________
4. ________
5. ________
6. ________
7. ________
8. ________
9. ________
10. ________
11. ________
12. ________
13. ________
14. ________
15. ________
16. ________
17. ________
18. ________
19. ________
20. ________
21. ________
22. ________
23. ________

Follow the directions for each problem. Simplify each answer.

Chapter 0

1. Add. $3\frac{1}{4} + 2\frac{3}{5}$

2. Multiply. $\left(1\frac{1}{6}\right)\left(2\frac{2}{3}\right)$

3. Divide. $\frac{15}{4} \div \frac{3}{8}$

4. Multiply. $(1.63)(3.05)$

5. Divide. $120 \div 0.0006$

6. Find 7% of 64,000.

Chapter 1

7. Add. $-3 + (-4) + (+12)$

8. Subtract. $-20 - (-23)$

9. Combine. $5x - 6xy - 12x - 8xy$

10. Evaluate. $2x^2 - 3x - 4$ when $x = -3$.

11. Remove the grouping symbols. $2 - 3\{5 + 2[x - 4(3 - x)]\}$

12. Evaluate. $-3(2 - 6)^2 + (-12) \div (-4)$

Chapter 2

In questions 13–16, solve each equation for x.

13. $40 + 2x = 60 - 3x$

14. $7(3x - 1) = 5 + 4(x - 3)$

15. $\frac{2}{3}x - \frac{3}{4} = \frac{1}{6}x + \frac{21}{4}$

16. $\frac{4}{5}(3x + 4) = 20$

17. Solve for p. $A = \frac{1}{2}(3p - 4f)$

18. Solve for x and graph the result. $42 - 18x < 48x - 24$

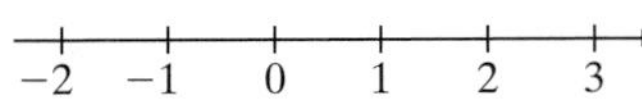

Chapter 3

19. The length of a rectangle is 7 meters longer than the width. The perimeter is 46 meters. Find the dimensions.

20. One side of a triangle is triple the second side. The third side is 3 meters longer than double the second side. Find each side of the triangle if the perimeter of the triangle is 63 meters.

21. Hector has four test scores of 80, 90, 83, and 92. What does he need to score on the fifth test to have an average of 86 on the five tests?

22. Marcia invested $6000 in two accounts. One earned 5% interest, while the other earned 7% interest. After one year she earned $394 in interest. How much did she invest in each account?

23. Melissa has three more dimes than nickels. She has twice as many quarters as nickels. The value of the coins is $4.20. How many of each coin does she have?

24. The drama club put on a play for Thursday, Friday, and Saturday nights. The total attendance for the three nights was 6210. Thursday night had 300 fewer people than Friday night. Saturday night had 510 more people than Friday night. How many people came each night?

Chapter 4

25. Multiply. $(-2xy^2)(-4x^3y^4)$

26. Divide. $\dfrac{36x^5y^6}{-18x^3y^{10}}$

27. Raise to the indicated power. $(-2x^3y^4)^5$

28. Evaluate. $(-3)^{-4}$

29. Multiply. $(3x^2 + 2x - 5)(4x - 1)$

30. Divide. $(x^3 + 6x^2 - x - 30) \div (x - 2)$

Chapter 5

Factor completely.

31. $5x^2 - 5$

32. $x^2 - 12x + 32$

33. $8x^2 - 2x - 3$

34. $3ax - 8b - 6a + 4bx$

Solve for x.

35. $x^3 + 7x^2 + 12x = 0$

36. $16x^2 - 24x + 9 = 0$

Chapter 6

37. Simplify. $\dfrac{x^2 + 3x - 18}{2x - 6}$

38. Multiply. $\dfrac{6x^2 - 14x - 12}{6x + 4} \cdot \dfrac{x + 3}{2x^2 - 2x - 12}$

39. Divide and simplify.

$$\frac{x^2}{x^2 - 4} \div \frac{x^2 - 3x}{x^2 - 5x + 6}$$

40. Add.

$$\frac{3}{x^2 - 7x + 12} + \frac{4}{x^2 - 9x + 20}$$

41. Solve for x.

$$2 - \frac{5}{2x} = \frac{2x}{x + 1}$$

42. Simplify.

$$\frac{3 + \dfrac{1}{x}}{\dfrac{9}{x} + \dfrac{3}{x^2}}$$

24. ______

25. ______

26. ______

27. ______

28. ______

29. ______

30. ______

31. ______

32. ______

33. ______

34. ______

35. ______

36. ______

37. ______

38. ______

39. ______

40. ______

41. ______

42. ______

CHAPTER

0

Have you ever thought about the large lakes that cover the earth? What is the largest lake that you have visited? Some of them are more than 30,000 square miles in area. Turn to page 59 and see if you can solve some mathematical problems involving some of the larger lakes.

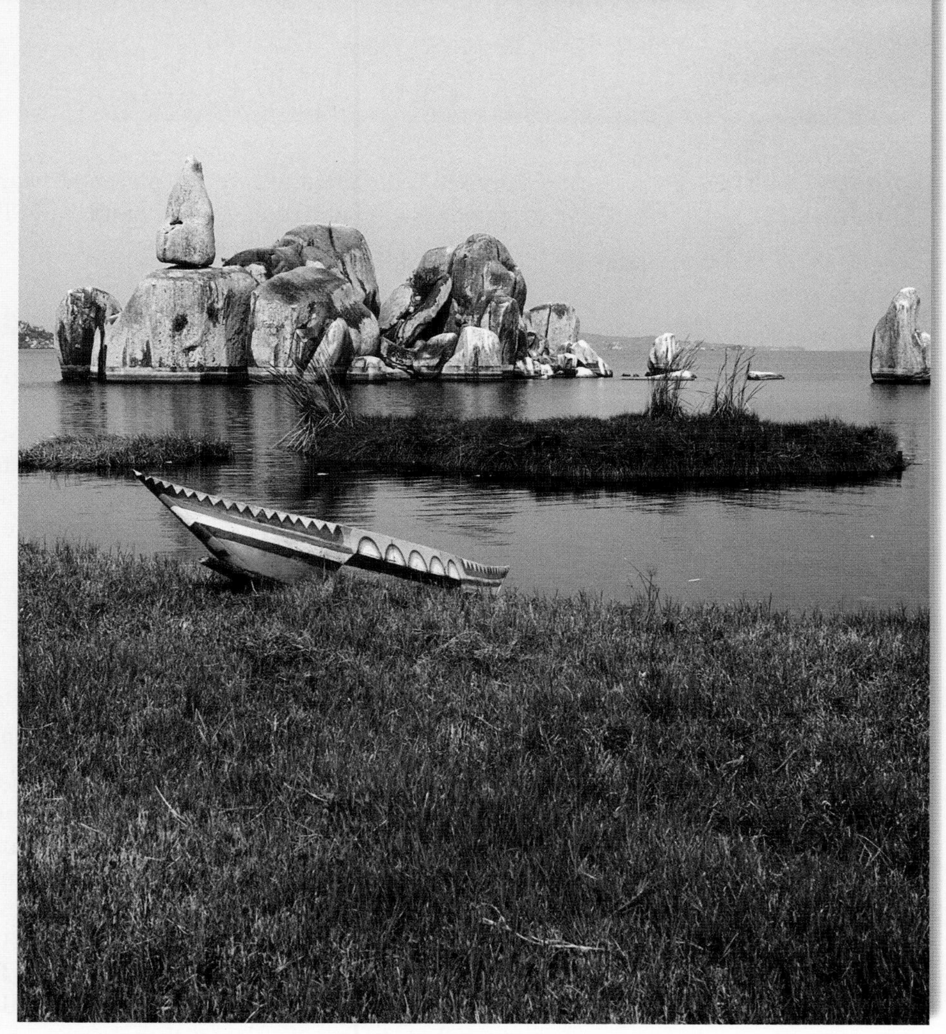

A Brief Review of Arithmetic Skills

0.1 Simplifying Fractions

Student Learning Objectives

After studying this section, you will be able to:

1. **Understand basic mathematical definitions.**
2. **Simplify fractions to lowest terms using prime numbers.**
3. **Convert between improper fractions and mixed numbers.**
4. **Change a fraction to an equivalent fraction with a given denominator.**

Chapter 0 is designed to give you a mental "warm-up." In this chapter you'll be able to step back a bit and tone up your math skills. This brief review of arithmetic will increase your math flexibility and give you a good running start into algebra.

1 Understanding Basic Mathematical Definitions

Whole numbers are the set of numbers 0, 1, 2, 3, 4, 5, 6, 7, ... They are used to describe whole objects, or entire quantities.

Fractions are a set of numbers that are used to describe parts of whole quantities. In the object shown in the figure there are four equal parts. The *three* of the *four* parts that are shaded are represented by the fraction $\frac{3}{4}$. In the fraction $\frac{3}{4}$ the number 3 is called the **numerator** and the number 4, the **denominator.**

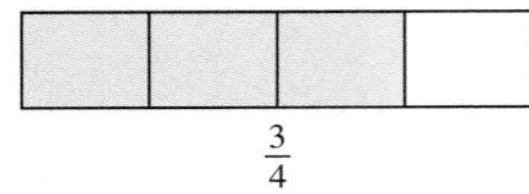

$\frac{3}{4}$

3 ← *Numerator* is on the top
4 ← *Denominator* is on the bottom

The *denominator* of a fraction shows the number of equal parts in the whole and the *numerator* shows the number of these parts being talked about or being used.

Numerals are symbols we use to name numbers. There are many different numerals that can be used to describe the same number. We know that $\frac{1}{2} = \frac{2}{4}$. The fractions $\frac{1}{2}$ and $\frac{2}{4}$ both describe the same number.

Usually, we find it more useful to use fractions that are simplified. A fraction is considered to be in **simplest form** or **reduced form** when the numerator (top) and the denominator (bottom) can both be divided exactly by no number other than 1, and the denominator is greater than 1.

$\frac{1}{2}$ is in simplest form.

 is *not* in simplest form, since the numerator and the denominator can both be divided by 2.

If you get the answer $\frac{2}{4}$ to a problem, you should state it in simplest form, $\frac{1}{2}$. The process of changing $\frac{2}{4}$ to $\frac{1}{2}$ is called **simplifying** or **reducing** the fraction.

2 Simplifying Fractions to Lowest Terms Using Prime Numbers

Natural numbers or **counting numbers** are the set of whole numbers excluding 0. Thus the natural numbers are the numbers 1, 2, 3, 4, 5, 6, ...

When two or more numbers are multiplied, each number that is multiplied is called a **factor.** For example, when we write $3 \times 7 \times 5$, each of the numbers 3, 7, and 5 is called a factor.

Prime numbers are all natural numbers greater than 1 whose only natural number factors are 1 and itself. The number 5 is prime. The only natural number factors of 5 are 5 and 1.

$$5 = 5 \times 1$$

The number 6 is not prime. The natural number factors of 6 are 3 and 2 or 6 and 1.

$$6 = 3 \times 2 \qquad 6 = 6 \times 1$$

The first 15 prime numbers are

2, 3, 5, 7, 11, 13, 17, 19, 23, 29, 31, 37, 41, 43, 47.

Any natural number greater than 1 either is prime or can be written as the product of prime numbers. For example, we can take each of the numbers 12, 30, 14, 19, and 29 and either indicate that they are prime or, if they are not prime, write them as the product of prime numbers. We write as follows:

$12 = 2 \times 2 \times 3$ $\quad 30 = 2 \times 3 \times 5$ $\quad 14 = 2 \times 7$

19 is a prime number. 29 is a prime number.

To reduce a fraction, we use prime numbers to factor the numerator and the denominator. Write each part of the fraction (numerator and denominator) as a product of prime numbers. Note any *factors* that appear in both the *numerator* (top) and *denominator* (bottom) of the fraction. If we divide numerator and denominator by these values we will obtain an equivalent fraction in *simplest form.* When the new fraction is simplified, it is said to be in **lowest terms.** Throughout this text, to *simplify* a fraction will always mean to simplify the fraction to lowest terms.

EXAMPLE 1 Simplify each fraction. **(a)** $\frac{14}{21}$ **(b)** $\frac{15}{35}$ **(c)** $\frac{20}{70}$

Solution

(a) $\frac{14}{21} = \frac{\cancel{7} \times 2}{\cancel{7} \times 3} = \frac{2}{3}$ We factor 14 and factor 21. Then we divide numerator and denominator by 7.

(b) $\frac{15}{35} = \frac{\cancel{5} \times 3}{\cancel{5} \times 7} = \frac{3}{7}$ We factor 15 and factor 35. Then we divide numerator and denominator by 5.

(c) $\frac{20}{70} = \frac{2 \times \cancel{2} \times \cancel{5}}{7 \times \cancel{2} \times \cancel{5}} = \frac{2}{7}$ We factor 20 and factor 70. Then we divide numerator and denominator by both 2 and 5.

Practice Problem 1 Simplify. **(a)** $\frac{10}{16}$ **(b)** $\frac{24}{36}$ **(c)** $\frac{36}{42}$

Sometimes when we simplify a fraction, all the prime factors in the top (numerator) are divided out. When this happens, we must remember that a 1 is left in the numerator.

EXAMPLE 2 Simplify each fraction. **(a)** $\frac{7}{21}$ **(b)** $\frac{15}{105}$

Solution **(a)** $\frac{7}{21} = \frac{\cancel{7} \times 1}{\cancel{7} \times 3} = \frac{1}{3}$ **(b)** $\frac{15}{105} = \frac{\cancel{5} \times \cancel{3} \times 1}{7 \times \cancel{5} \times \cancel{3}} = \frac{1}{7}$

Practice Problem 2 Simplify. **(a)** $\frac{4}{12}$ **(b)** $\frac{25}{125}$ **(c)** $\frac{73}{146}$

***NOTE TO STUDENT:** Fully worked-out solutions to all of the Practice Problems can be found at the back of the text starting at page SP-1*

If all the prime numbers in the bottom (denominator) are divided out, we do not need to leave a 1 in the denominator, since we do not need to express the answer as a fraction. The answer is then a whole number and is not usually expressed as a fraction.

EXAMPLE 3 Simplify each fraction. **(a)** $\frac{35}{7}$ **(b)** $\frac{70}{10}$

Solution **(a)** $\frac{35}{7} = \frac{5 \times \cancel{7}}{\cancel{7} \times 1} = 5$ **(b)** $\frac{70}{10} = \frac{7 \times \cancel{5} \times \cancel{2}}{\cancel{5} \times \cancel{2} \times 1} = 7$

Practice Problem 3 Simplify. **(a)** $\frac{18}{6}$ **(b)** $\frac{146}{73}$ **(c)** $\frac{28}{7}$

Sometimes the fraction we use represents how many of a certain thing are successful. For example, if a baseball player was at bat 30 times and achieved 12 hits, we could say that he had a hit $\frac{12}{30}$ of the time. If we reduce the fraction, we could say he had a hit $\frac{2}{5}$ of the time.

EXAMPLE 4 Cindy got 48 out of 56 questions correct on a test. Write this as a fraction.

Solution Express as a fraction in simplest form the number of correct responses out of the total number of questions on the test.

$$48 \text{ out of } 56 \rightarrow \frac{48}{56} = \frac{6 \times \cancel{8}}{7 \times \cancel{8}} = \frac{6}{7}$$

Cindy answered the questions correctly $\frac{6}{7}$ of the time.

NOTE TO STUDENT: Fully worked-out solutions to all of the Practice Problems can be found at the back of the text starting at page SP-1

Practice Problem 4 The major league pennant winner in 1917 won 56 games out of 154 games played. Express as a fraction in simplest form the number of games won in relation to the number of games played.

The number *one* can be expressed as $1, \frac{1}{1}, \frac{2}{2}, \frac{6}{6}, \frac{8}{8}$, and so on, since

$$1 = \frac{1}{1} = \frac{2}{2} = \frac{6}{6} = \frac{8}{8}.$$

We say that these numerals are *equivalent ways* of writing the number *one* because they all express the same quantity even though they appear to be different.

SIDELIGHT: The Multiplicative Identity

When we simplify fractions, we are actually using the fact that we can multiply any number by 1 without changing the value of that number. (Mathematicians call the number 1 the **multiplicative identity** because it leaves any number it multiplies with the same identical value as before.)

Let's look again at one of the previous examples.

$$\frac{14}{21} = \frac{7 \times 2}{7 \times 3} = \frac{7}{7} \times \frac{2}{3} = 1 \times \frac{2}{3} = \frac{2}{3}$$

So we see that

$$\frac{14}{21} = \frac{2}{3}$$

When we simplify fractions, we are using this property of multiplying by 1.

3 Converting Between Improper Fractions and Mixed Numbers

If the numerator is less than the denominator, the fraction is a **proper fraction**. A proper fraction is used to describe a quantity smaller than a whole.

Fractions can also be used to describe quantities larger than a whole. The following figure shows two bars that are equal in size. Each bar is divided into 5 equal pieces. The first bar is shaded in completely. The second bar has 2 of the 5 pieces shaded in.

The shaded-in region can be represented by $\frac{7}{5}$ since 7 of the pieces (each of which is $\frac{1}{5}$ of a whole box) are shaded. The fraction $\frac{7}{5}$ is called an improper fraction. An **improper fraction** is one in which the numerator is larger than or equal to the denominator.

The shaded-in region can also be represented by 1 whole added to $\frac{2}{5}$ of a whole, or $1 + \frac{2}{5}$. This is written as $1\frac{2}{5}$. The fraction $1\frac{2}{5}$ is called a mixed number. A **mixed number** consists of a whole number added to a proper fraction (the numerator is smaller than the denominator). The addition is understood but not written. When we write $1\frac{2}{5}$, it represents $1 + \frac{2}{5}$. The numbers $1\frac{7}{8}$, $2\frac{3}{4}$, $8\frac{1}{3}$, and $126\frac{1}{10}$ are all mixed numbers. From the preceding figure it seems clear that $\frac{7}{5} = 1\frac{2}{5}$. This suggests that we can change from one form to the other without changing the value of the fraction.

From a picture it is easy to see how to *change improper fractions to mixed numbers*. For example, suppose we start with the fraction $\frac{11}{3}$ and represent it by the following figure (where 11 of the pieces, each of which is $\frac{1}{3}$ of a box, are shaded). We see that $\frac{11}{3} = 3\frac{2}{3}$, since 3 whole boxes and $\frac{2}{3}$ of a box are shaded.

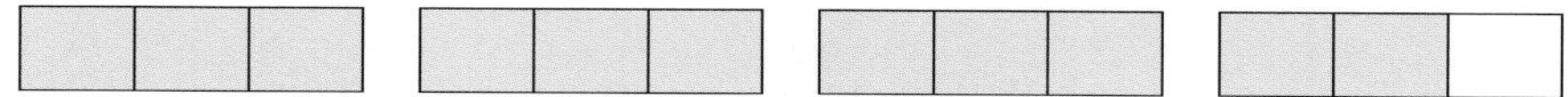

Changing Improper Fractions to Mixed Numbers You can follow the same procedure without a picture. For example, to change $\frac{11}{3}$ to a mixed number, we can do the following:

$$\frac{11}{3} = \frac{3}{3} + \frac{3}{3} + \frac{3}{3} + \frac{2}{3}$$ By the rule for adding fractions (which is discussed in detail in Section 0.2)

$$= 1 + 1 + 1 + \frac{2}{3}$$ Write 1 in place of $\frac{3}{3}$, since $\frac{3}{3} = 1$.

$$= 3 + \frac{2}{3}$$ Write 3 in place of $1 + 1 + 1$.

$$= 3\frac{2}{3}$$ Use the notation for mixed numbers.

Now that you know how to change improper fractions to mixed numbers and why the procedure works, here is a shorter method.

TO CHANGE AN IMPROPER FRACTION TO A MIXED NUMBER

1. Divide the denominator into the numerator.
2. The result is the whole-number part of the mixed number.
3. The remainder from the division will be the numerator of the fraction. The denominator of the fraction remains unchanged.

We can write the fraction as a division statement and divide. The arrows show how to write the mixed number.

$$\frac{7}{5} \qquad 5\overline{)7} \text{ gives quotient } 1,\ 7 - 5 = 2 \text{ Remainder} \quad\rightarrow\quad 1\frac{2}{5}$$

Whole-number part → 1; Remainder → Numerator of fraction (2)

Thus, $\frac{7}{5} = 1\frac{2}{5}$.

$$\frac{11}{3} \qquad 3\overline{)11} \text{ gives quotient } 3,\ 11 - 9 = 2 \text{ Remainder} \quad\rightarrow\quad 3\frac{2}{3}$$

Whole-number part → 3; Remainder → Numerator of fraction (2)

Thus, $\frac{11}{3} = 3\frac{2}{3}$.

Sometimes the remainder is 0. In this case, the improper fraction changes to a whole number.

EXAMPLE 5 Change to a mixed number or to a whole number.

(a) $\frac{7}{4}$ **(b)** $\frac{15}{3}$

Solution

(a) $\frac{7}{4} = 7 \div 4$ $\quad 4\overline{)7}$ gives 1, 4, 3 Remainder

Thus $\frac{7}{4} = 1\frac{3}{4}$

(b) $\frac{15}{3} = 15 \div 3$ $\quad 3\overline{)15}$ gives 5, 15, 0 Remainder

Thus $\frac{15}{3} = 5$

Practice Problem 5 Change to a mixed number or to a whole number.

(a) $\frac{12}{7}$ **(b)** $\frac{20}{5}$

NOTE TO STUDENT: Fully worked-out solutions to all of the Practice Problems can be found at the back of the text starting at page SP-1

Changing Mixed Numbers to Improper Fractions It is not difficult to see how to change mixed numbers to improper fractions. Suppose that you wanted to write $2\frac{2}{3}$ as an improper fraction.

$$2\frac{2}{3} = 2 + \frac{2}{3} \quad \text{The meaning of mixed number notation}$$

$$= 1 + 1 + \frac{2}{3} \quad \text{Since } 1 + 1 = 2$$

$$= \frac{3}{3} + \frac{3}{3} + \frac{2}{3} \quad \text{Since } 1 = \frac{3}{3}$$

When we draw a picture of $\frac{3}{3} + \frac{3}{3} + \frac{2}{3}$, we have this figure:

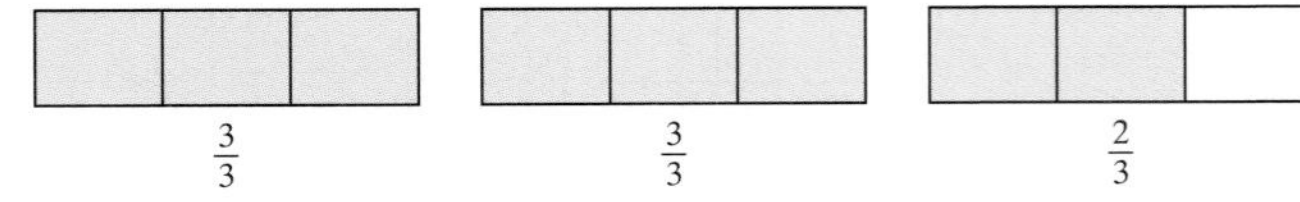

If we count the shaded parts, we see that

$$\frac{3}{3} + \frac{3}{3} + \frac{2}{3} = \frac{8}{3}. \quad \text{Thus} \quad 2\frac{2}{3} = \frac{8}{3}.$$

Now that you have seen how this change can be done, here is a shorter method.

TO CHANGE A MIXED NUMBER TO AN IMPROPER FRACTION

1. Multiply the whole number by the denominator.
2. Add this to the numerator. The result is the new numerator. The denominator does not change.

EXAMPLE 6 Change to an improper fraction.

(a) $3\frac{1}{7}$ **(b)** $5\frac{4}{5}$

Solution

(a) $3\frac{1}{7} = \frac{(3 \times 7) + 1}{7} = \frac{21 + 1}{7} = \frac{22}{7}$

(b) $5\frac{4}{5} = \frac{(5 \times 5) + 4}{5} = \frac{25 + 4}{5} = \frac{29}{5}$

Practice Problem 6 Change to an improper fraction.

(a) $3\frac{2}{5}$ **(b)** $1\frac{3}{7}$ **(c)** $2\frac{6}{11}$ **(d)** $4\frac{2}{3}$

4 Changing a Fraction to an Equivalent Fraction with a Given Denominator

Fractions can be changed to an equivalent fraction with a different denominator by multiplying both numerator and denominator by the same number.

$$\frac{5}{6} = \frac{5}{6} \times 1 = \frac{5}{6} \times \frac{2}{2} = \frac{5 \times 2}{6 \times 2} = \frac{10}{12} \qquad \frac{3}{7} = \frac{3}{7} \times 1 = \frac{3}{7} \times \frac{3}{3} = \frac{3 \times 3}{7 \times 3} = \frac{9}{21}$$

So $\frac{5}{6}$ is equivalent to $\frac{10}{12}$. $\frac{3}{7}$ is equivalent to $\frac{9}{21}$.

We often multiply in this way to obtain an equivalent fraction with a *particular denominator.*

EXAMPLE 7 Find the missing number.

(a) $\frac{3}{5} = \frac{?}{25}$ **(b)** $\frac{3}{7} = \frac{?}{21}$ **(c)** $\frac{2}{9} = \frac{?}{36}$

Solution

(a) $\frac{3}{5} = \frac{?}{25}$ Observe that we need to multiply the denominator by 5 to obtain 25. So we multiply the numerator 3 by 5 also.

$\frac{3 \times 5}{5 \times 5} = \frac{15}{25}$ The desired numerator is 15.

(b) $\frac{3}{7} = \frac{?}{21}$ Observe that $7 \times 3 = 21$. We need to multiply the numerator by 3 to get the new numerator.

$\frac{3 \times 3}{7 \times 3} = \frac{9}{21}$ The desired numerator is 9.

(c) $\frac{2}{9} = \frac{?}{36}$ Observe that $9 \times 4 = 36$. We need to multiply the numerator by 4 to get the new numerator.

$\frac{2 \times 4}{9 \times 4} = \frac{8}{36}$ The desired numerator is 8.

Practice Problem 7 Find the missing number.

(a) $\frac{3}{8} = \frac{?}{24}$ **(b)** $\frac{5}{6} = \frac{?}{30}$ **(c)** $\frac{2}{7} = \frac{?}{56}$

0.1 Exercises

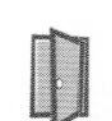

Student Solutions Manual | CD/ Video | PH Math Tutor Center | MathXL®Tutorials on CD | MathXL® | MyMathLab® | Interactmath.com

Verbal and Writing Skills

1. In the fraction $\frac{12}{13}$, what number is the numerator?

2. In the fraction $\frac{13}{17}$, what is the denominator?

3. What is a factor? Give an example.

4. Give some examples of the number 1 written as a fraction.

5. Draw a diagram to illustrate $2\frac{2}{3}$.

6. Draw a diagram to illustrate $3\frac{3}{4}$.

Simplify each fraction.

7. $\frac{18}{24}$ **8.** $\frac{20}{35}$ **9.** $\frac{12}{36}$ **10.** $\frac{12}{48}$ **11.** $\frac{60}{12}$ **12.** $\frac{45}{15}$

Change to a mixed number.

13. $\frac{17}{6}$ **14.** $\frac{19}{5}$ **15.** $\frac{111}{9}$ **16.** $\frac{124}{8}$ **17.** $\frac{38}{7}$ **18.** $\frac{41}{6}$

Change to an improper fraction.

19. $3\frac{1}{5}$ **20.** $2\frac{6}{7}$ **21.** $6\frac{3}{5}$ **22.** $5\frac{3}{8}$ **23.** $\frac{72}{9}$ **24.** $\frac{78}{6}$

Find the missing numerator.

25. $\frac{3}{11} = \frac{?}{44}$ **26.** $\frac{5}{7} = \frac{?}{28}$ **27.** $\frac{3}{5} = \frac{?}{35}$ **28.** $\frac{5}{9} = \frac{?}{45}$ **29.** $\frac{4}{13} = \frac{?}{39}$ **30.** $\frac{13}{17} = \frac{?}{51}$

Applications

Solve.

31. ***Basketball*** Charles Barkley of the Phoenix Suns once scored 1560 points during 68 games played during the season. Express as a mixed number in simplified form how many points he averaged per game.

32. ***Kentucky Derby*** In 2002, 417 horses were nominated to compete in the Kentucky Derby. Only 18 horses were actually chosen to compete in the Derby. What simplified fraction shows what portion of nominated horses actually competed in the Derby?

33. ***Income Tax*** Last year, my parents had a combined income of $64,000. They paid $13,200 in federal income taxes. What simplified fraction shows how much my parents spent on their federal taxes?

34. ***Transfer Students*** The University of California system accepted 14,664 out of 18,330 California Community College students who applied as transfers in the fall of 2003. What simplified fraction shows what portion of applications were accepted?

Trail Mix *The following chart gives the recipe for a trail mix.*

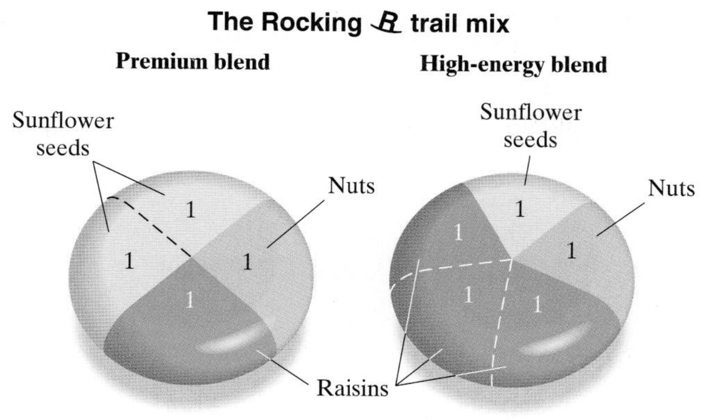

35. What part of the premium blend is nuts?

36. What part of the high-energy blend is raisins?

37. What part of the premium blend is not sunflower seeds?

38. What part of the high-energy blend does not contain nuts?

Baseball *The following chart provides some statistics for the North Andover Knights.*

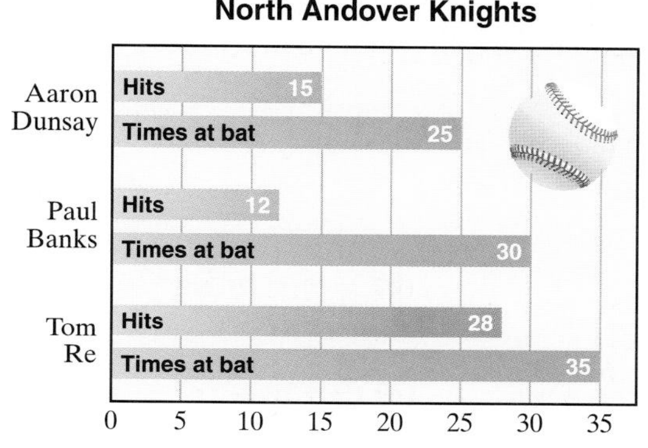

39. Determine how often each player hit the ball based on the number of times at bat. Write each answer as a reduced fraction.

40. Which player was the best hitter?

Fish Catch *The following chart provides some statistics about the fish catch in the United States.*

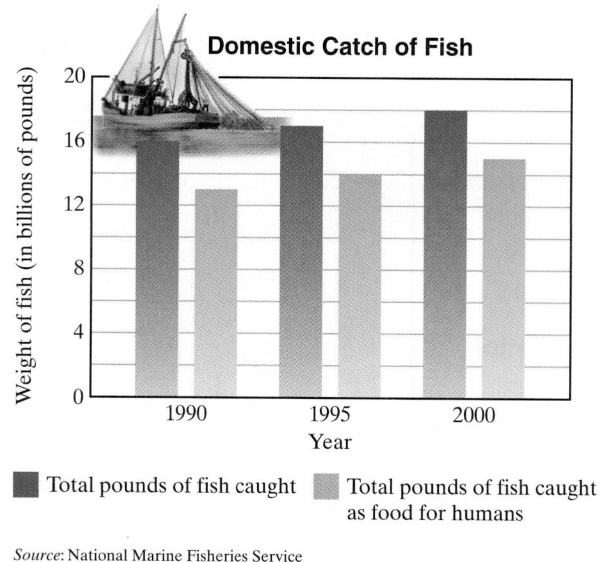

41. What fractional part of the fish catch in 1990 was used as food for humans?

42. What fractional part of the fish catch in 2000 was used as food for humans?

0.2 Adding and Subtracting Fractions

Student Learning Objectives

After studying this section, you will be able to:

1. **Add or subtract fractions with a common denominator.**
2. **Use prime factors to find the least common denominator of two or more fractions.**
3. **Add or subtract fractions with different denominators.**
4. **Add or subtract mixed numbers.**

1 Adding or Subtracting Fractions with a Common Denominator

If fractions have the same denominator, the numerators may be added or subtracted. The denominator remains the same.

TO ADD OR SUBTRACT TWO FRACTIONS WITH A COMMON DENOMINATOR

1. Add or subtract the numerators.
2. Keep the same (common) denominator.
3. Simplify the answer whenever possible.

EXAMPLE 1 Add the fractions. Simplify your answer whenever possible.

(a) $\frac{5}{7} + \frac{1}{7}$ **(b)** $\frac{2}{3} + \frac{1}{3}$ **(c)** $\frac{1}{8} + \frac{3}{8} + \frac{2}{8}$ **(d)** $\frac{3}{5} + \frac{4}{5}$

Solution

(a) $\frac{5}{7} + \frac{1}{7} = \frac{5+1}{7} = \frac{6}{7}$

(b) $\frac{2}{3} + \frac{1}{3} = \frac{2+1}{3} = \frac{3}{3} = 1$

(c) $\frac{1}{8} + \frac{3}{8} + \frac{2}{8} = \frac{1+3+2}{8} = \frac{6}{8} = \frac{3}{4}$

(d) $\frac{3}{5} + \frac{4}{5} = \frac{3+4}{5} = \frac{7}{5} = 1\frac{2}{5}$

Practice Problem 1 Add.

(a) $\frac{3}{6} + \frac{2}{6}$ **(b)** $\frac{3}{11} + \frac{8}{11}$ **(c)** $\frac{1}{8} + \frac{2}{8} + \frac{1}{8}$ **(d)** $\frac{5}{9} + \frac{8}{9}$

EXAMPLE 2 Subtract the fractions. Simplify your answer whenever possible.

(a) $\frac{9}{11} - \frac{2}{11}$ **(b)** $\frac{5}{6} - \frac{1}{6}$

Solution

(a) $\frac{9}{11} - \frac{2}{11} = \frac{9-2}{11} = \frac{7}{11}$

(b) $\frac{5}{6} - \frac{1}{6} = \frac{5-1}{6} = \frac{4}{6} = \frac{2}{3}$

Practice Problem 2 Subtract.

(a) $\frac{11}{13} - \frac{6}{13}$ **(b)** $\frac{8}{9} - \frac{2}{9}$

NOTE TO STUDENT: Fully worked-out solutions to all of the Practice Problems can be found at the back of the text starting at page SP-1

Although adding and subtracting fractions with the same denominator is fairly simple, most problems involve fractions that do not have a common denominator. Fractions and mixed numbers such as halves, fourths, and eighths are often used. To add or subtract such fractions, we begin by finding a common denominator.

Using Prime Factors to Find the Least Common Denominator of Two or More Fractions

Before you can add or subtract fractions, they must have the same denominator. To save work, we select the smallest possible common denominator. This is called the **least common denominator** or LCD (also known as the *lowest common denominator*).

The LCD of two or more fractions is the smallest whole number that is exactly divisible by each denominator of the fractions.

EXAMPLE 3 Find the LCD. $\frac{2}{3}$ and $\frac{1}{4}$

Solution The numbers are small enough to find the LCD by inspection. The LCD is 12, since 12 is exactly divisible by 4 and by 3. There is no smaller number that is exactly divisible by 4 and 3.

Practice Problem 3 Find the LCD. $\frac{1}{8}$ and $\frac{5}{12}$

In some cases, the LCD cannot easily be determined by inspection. If we write each denominator as the product of prime factors, we will be able to find the LCD. We will use (·) to indicate multiplication. For example, $30 = 2 \cdot 3 \cdot 5$. This means $30 = 2 \times 3 \times 5$.

PROCEDURE TO FIND THE LCD USING PRIME FACTORS

1. Write each denominator as the product of prime factors.
2. The LCD is a product containing each different factor.
3. If a factor occurs more than once in any one denominator, the LCD will contain that factor repeated the greatest number of times that it occurs in any one denominator.

EXAMPLE 4 Find the LCD of $\frac{5}{6}$ and $\frac{1}{15}$ by this new procedure.

Solution

$$\begin{aligned} 6 &= 2 \cdot 3 \\ 15 &= \quad\; 3 \cdot 5 \\ &\;\;\downarrow \;\; \downarrow \;\; \downarrow \\ \text{LCD} &= 2 \cdot 3 \cdot 5 \\ \text{LCD} &= 2 \cdot 3 \cdot 5 = 30 \end{aligned}$$

Write each denominator as the product of prime factors.

The LCD is a product containing each different prime factor. The different factors are 2, 3, and 5, and each factor appears at most once in any one denominator.

Practice Problem 4 Use prime factors to find the LCD of $\frac{8}{35}$ and $\frac{6}{15}$.

Great care should be used to determine the LCD in the case of repeated factors.

EXAMPLE 5 Find the LCD of $\frac{4}{27}$ and $\frac{5}{18}$.

Solution

$27 = 3 \cdot 3 \cdot 3$

Write each denominator as the product of prime factors. We observe that the factor 3 occurs three times in the factorization of 27.

$18 = 3 \cdot 3 \cdot 2$

$\text{LCD} = 3 \cdot 3 \cdot 3 \cdot 2$

$\text{LCD} = 3 \cdot 3 \cdot 3 \cdot 2 = 54$

The LCD is a product containing each different factor. The factor 3 *occurred most* in the factorization of 27, where it occurred *three* times. Thus the LCD will be the product of *three* 3's and *one* 2.

NOTE TO STUDENT: Fully worked-out solutions to all of the Practice Problems can be found at the back of the text starting at page SP-1

Practice Problem 5 Find the LCD of $\frac{5}{12}$ and $\frac{7}{30}$.

EXAMPLE 6 Find the LCD of $\frac{5}{12}$, $\frac{1}{15}$, and $\frac{7}{30}$.

Solution

$12 = 2 \cdot 2 \cdot 3$

Write each denominator as the product of prime factors. Notice that the only repeated factor is 2, which occurs twice in the factorization of 12.

$15 = 3 \cdot 5$

$30 = 2 \cdot 3 \cdot 5$

$\text{LCD} = 2 \cdot 2 \cdot 3 \cdot 5$

$\text{LCD} = 2 \cdot 2 \cdot 3 \cdot 5 = 60$

The LCD is the product of each different factor with the factor 2 appearing twice since it occurred twice in one denominator.

Practice Problem 6 Find the LCD of $\frac{2}{27}$, $\frac{1}{18}$, and $\frac{5}{12}$.

3 Adding or Subtracting Fractions with Different Denominators

Before you can add or subtract them, fractions must have the same denominator. Using the LCD will make your work easier. First you must find the LCD. Then change each fraction to a fraction that has the LCD as the denominator. Sometimes one of the fractions will already have the LCD as the denominator. Once all the fractions have the same denominator, you can add or subtract. Be sure to simplify the fraction in your answer if this is possible.

TO ADD OR SUBTRACT FRACTIONS THAT DO NOT HAVE A COMMON DENOMINATOR

1. Find the LCD of the fractions.
2. Change each fraction to an equivalent fraction with the LCD for a denominator.
3. Add or subtract the fractions.
4. Simplify the answer whenever possible.

Let us return to the two fractions of Example 3. We have previously found that the LCD is 12.

EXAMPLE 7 Bob picked $\frac{2}{3}$ of a bushel of apples on Monday and $\frac{1}{4}$ of a bushel of apples on Tuesday. How much did he have in total?

Solution To solve this problem we need to add $\frac{2}{3}$ and $\frac{1}{4}$, but before we can do so, we must change $\frac{2}{3}$ and $\frac{1}{4}$ to fractions with the same denominator. We change each fraction to an equivalent fraction with a common denominator of 12, the LCD.

$$\frac{2}{3} = \frac{?}{12} \qquad \frac{2}{3} \times \frac{4}{4} = \frac{8}{12} \quad \text{so} \quad \frac{2}{3} = \frac{8}{12}$$

$$\frac{1}{4} = \frac{?}{12} \qquad \frac{1}{4} \times \frac{3}{3} = \frac{3}{12} \quad \text{so} \quad \frac{1}{4} = \frac{3}{12}$$

Then we rewrite the problem with common denominators and add.

$$\frac{2}{3} + \frac{1}{4} = \frac{8}{12} + \frac{3}{12} = \frac{8+3}{12} = \frac{11}{12}$$

In total Bob picked $\frac{11}{12}$ of a bushel of apples.

Practice Problem 7 Carol planted corn in $\frac{5}{12}$ of the farm fields at the Old Robinson Farm. Connie planted soybeans in $\frac{1}{8}$ of the farm fields. What fractional part of the farm fields of the Old Robinson Farm was planted in corn or soybeans?

Sometimes one of the denominators is the LCD. In such cases the fraction that has the LCD for the denominator will not need to be changed. If every other denominator divides into the largest denominator, the largest denominator is the LCD.

EXAMPLE 8 Find the LCD and then add. $\frac{3}{5} + \frac{7}{20} + \frac{1}{2}$

Solution We can see by inspection that both 5 and 2 divide exactly into 20. Thus 20 is the LCD. Now add.

$$\frac{3}{5} + \frac{7}{20} + \frac{1}{2}$$

We change $\frac{3}{5}$ and $\frac{1}{2}$ to equivalent fractions with a common denominator of 20, the LCD.

$$\frac{3}{5} = \frac{?}{20} \qquad \frac{3}{5} \times \frac{4}{4} = \frac{12}{20} \quad \text{so} \quad \frac{3}{5} = \frac{12}{20}$$

$$\frac{1}{2} = \frac{?}{20} \qquad \frac{1}{2} \times \frac{10}{10} = \frac{10}{20} \quad \text{so} \quad \frac{1}{2} = \frac{10}{20}$$

Then we rewrite the problem with common denominators and add.

$$\frac{3}{5} + \frac{7}{20} + \frac{1}{2} = \frac{12}{20} + \frac{7}{20} + \frac{10}{20} = \frac{12+7+10}{20} = \frac{29}{20} \quad \text{or} \quad 1\frac{9}{20}$$

Practice Problem 8 Find the LCD and add. $\frac{3}{5} + \frac{4}{25} + \frac{1}{10}$

Now we turn to examples where the selection of the LCD is not so obvious. In Examples 9 through 11 we will use the prime factorization method to find the LCD.

EXAMPLE 9 Add. $\frac{7}{18} + \frac{5}{12}$

Solution First we find the LCD.

$$18 = 3 \cdot 3 \cdot 2$$
$$12 = \quad 3 \cdot 2 \cdot 2$$
$$\text{LCD} = 3 \cdot 3 \cdot 2 \cdot 2 = 9 \cdot 4 = 36$$

Now we change $\frac{7}{18}$ and $\frac{5}{12}$ to equivalent fractions that have the LCD.

$$\frac{7}{18} = \frac{?}{36} \qquad \frac{7}{18} \times \frac{2}{2} = \frac{14}{36}$$
$$\frac{5}{12} = \frac{?}{36} \qquad \frac{5}{12} \times \frac{3}{3} = \frac{15}{36}$$

Now we add the fractions.

$$\frac{7}{18} + \frac{5}{12} = \frac{14}{36} + \frac{15}{36} = \frac{29}{36}$$ This fraction cannot be simplified.

***NOTE TO STUDENT:** Fully worked-out solutions to all of the Practice Problems can be found at the back of the text starting at page SP-1*

Practice Problem 9 Add. $\frac{1}{49} + \frac{3}{14}$

EXAMPLE 10 Subtract. $\frac{25}{48} - \frac{5}{36}$

Solution First we find the LCD.

$$48 = 2 \cdot 2 \cdot 2 \cdot 2 \cdot 3$$
$$36 = \quad 2 \cdot 2 \cdot 3 \cdot 3$$
$$\text{LCD} = 2 \cdot 2 \cdot 2 \cdot 2 \cdot 3 \cdot 3 = 16 \cdot 9 = 144$$

Now we change $\frac{25}{48}$ and $\frac{5}{36}$ to equivalent fractions that have the LCD.

$$\frac{25}{48} = \frac{?}{144} \qquad \frac{25}{48} \times \frac{3}{3} = \frac{75}{144}$$
$$\frac{5}{36} = \frac{?}{144} \qquad \frac{5}{36} \times \frac{4}{4} = \frac{20}{144}$$

Now we subtract the fractions.

$$\frac{25}{48} - \frac{5}{36} = \frac{75}{144} - \frac{20}{144} = \frac{55}{144}$$ This fraction cannot be simplified.

Practice Problem 10 Subtract. $\frac{1}{12} - \frac{1}{30}$

EXAMPLE 11 Combine. $\frac{1}{5} + \frac{1}{6} - \frac{3}{10}$

Solution First we find the LCD.

$$\begin{aligned} 5 &= 5 \\ 6 &= \quad\ 2 \cdot 3 \\ 10 &= 5 \cdot 2 \\ \text{LCD} &= 5 \cdot 2 \cdot 3 = 10 \cdot 3 = 30 \end{aligned}$$

Now we change $\frac{1}{5}$, $\frac{1}{6}$, and $\frac{3}{10}$ to equivalent fractions that have the LCD for a denominator.

$$\frac{1}{5} = \frac{?}{30} \qquad \frac{1}{5} \times \frac{6}{6} = \frac{6}{30}$$

$$\frac{1}{6} = \frac{?}{30} \qquad \frac{1}{6} \times \frac{5}{5} = \frac{5}{30}$$

$$\frac{3}{10} = \frac{?}{30} \qquad \frac{3}{10} \times \frac{3}{3} = \frac{9}{30}$$

Now we combine the three fractions.

$$\frac{1}{5} + \frac{1}{6} - \frac{3}{10} = \frac{6}{30} + \frac{5}{30} - \frac{9}{30} = \frac{2}{30} = \frac{1}{15}$$

Note the important step of simplifying the fraction to obtain the final answer.

Practice Problem 11 Combine. $\frac{2}{3} + \frac{3}{4} - \frac{3}{8}$

Adding or Subtracting Mixed Numbers

If the problem you are adding or subtracting has mixed numbers, change them to improper fractions first and then combine (add or subtract). As a convention in this book, if the original problem contains mixed numbers, express the result as a mixed number rather than as an improper fraction.

EXAMPLE 12 Combine. Simplify your answer whenever possible.

(a) $5\frac{1}{2} + 2\frac{1}{3}$ **(b)** $2\frac{1}{5} - 1\frac{3}{4}$ **(c)** $1\frac{5}{12} + \frac{7}{30}$

Solution

(a) First we change the mixed numbers to improper fractions.

$$5\frac{1}{2} = \frac{5 \times 2 + 1}{2} = \frac{11}{2} \qquad 2\frac{1}{3} = \frac{2 \times 3 + 1}{3} = \frac{7}{3}$$

Next we change each fraction to an equivalent form with a common denominator of 6.

$$\frac{11}{2} = \frac{?}{6} \qquad \frac{11}{2} \times \frac{3}{3} = \frac{33}{6}$$

$$\frac{7}{3} = \frac{?}{6} \qquad \frac{7}{3} \times \frac{2}{2} = \frac{14}{6}$$

Finally, we add the two fractions and change our answer to a mixed number.

$$\frac{33}{6} + \frac{14}{6} = \frac{47}{6} = 7\frac{5}{6}$$

Thus $5\frac{1}{2} + 2\frac{1}{3} = 7\frac{5}{6}$.

(b) First we change the mixed numbers to improper fractions.

$$2\frac{1}{5} = \frac{2 \times 5 + 1}{5} = \frac{11}{5} \qquad 1\frac{3}{4} = \frac{1 \times 4 + 3}{4} = \frac{7}{4}$$

Next we change each fraction to an equivalent form with a common denominator of 20.

$$\frac{11}{5} = \frac{?}{20} \qquad \frac{11}{5} \times \frac{4}{4} = \frac{44}{20}$$

$$\frac{7}{4} = \frac{?}{20} \qquad \frac{7}{4} \times \frac{5}{5} = \frac{35}{20}$$

Now we subtract the two fractions.

$$\frac{44}{20} - \frac{35}{20} = \frac{9}{20}$$

Thus $2\frac{1}{5} - 1\frac{3}{4} = \frac{9}{20}$.

Note: It is not necessary to use these exact steps to add and subtract mixed numbers. If you know another method and can use it to obtain the correct answers, it is all right to continue to use that method throughout this chapter.

(c) Now we add $1\frac{5}{12} + \frac{7}{30}$.

The LCD of 12 and 30 is 60. Why? Change the mixed number to an improper fraction. Then change each fraction to an equivalent form with a common denominator.

$$1\frac{5}{12} = \frac{17}{12} \times \frac{5}{5} = \frac{85}{60} \qquad \frac{7}{30} \times \frac{2}{2} = \frac{14}{60}$$

Then add the fractions, simplify, and write the answer as a mixed number.

$$\frac{85}{60} + \frac{14}{60} = \frac{99}{60} = \frac{33}{20} = 1\frac{13}{20}$$

Thus $1\frac{5}{12} + \frac{7}{30} = 1\frac{13}{20}$.

NOTE TO STUDENT: Fully worked-out solutions to all of the Practice Problems can be found at the back of the text starting at page SP-1

Practice Problem 12 Combine.

(a) $1\frac{2}{3} + 2\frac{4}{5}$ **(b)** $5\frac{1}{4} - 2\frac{2}{3}$

▲ **EXAMPLE 13** Manuel is enclosing a triangular-shaped exercise yard for his new dog. He wants to determine how many feet of fencing he will need. The sides of the yard measure $20\frac{3}{4}$ feet, $15\frac{1}{2}$ feet, and $18\frac{1}{8}$ feet. What is the perimeter of (total distance around) the triangle?

Solution

Understand the problem. Begin by drawing a picture.

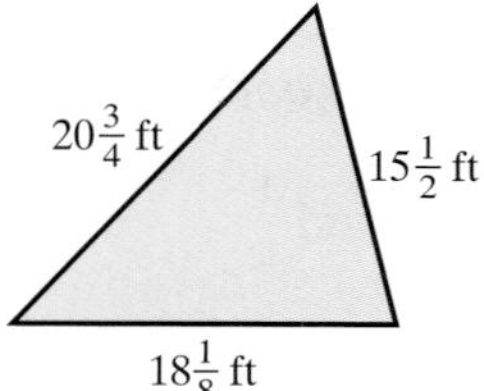

We want to add up the lengths of all three sides of the triangle. This distance around the triangle is called the **perimeter.**

$$20\frac{3}{4} + 15\frac{1}{2} + 18\frac{1}{8} = \frac{83}{4} + \frac{31}{2} + \frac{145}{8}$$
$$= \frac{166}{8} + \frac{124}{8} + \frac{145}{8} = \frac{435}{8} = 54\frac{3}{8} \text{ feet}$$

He will need $54\frac{3}{8}$ feet of fencing.

▲ **Practice Problem 13** Find the perimeter of a rectangle with sides of $4\frac{1}{5}$ cm and $6\frac{1}{2}$ cm. Begin by drawing a picture. Label the picture by including the measure of *each* side.

Developing Your Study Skills

Class Attendance

A student of mathematics needs to get started in the right direction by choosing to attend class every day, beginning with the first day of class. Statistics show that class attendance and good grades go together. Classroom activities are designed to enhance learning and you must be in class to benefit from them. Vital information and explanations that can help you in understanding concepts are given each day. Do not be deceived into thinking that you can just find out from a friend what went on in class. There is no good substitute for firsthand experience. Give yourself a push in the right direction by developing the habit of going to class every day.

Class Participation

People learn mathematics through active participation, not through observation from the sidelines. If you want to do well in this course, be involved in classroom activities. Sit near the front where you can see and hear well and where your focus is on the instruction process and not on the students around you. Ask questions, be ready to contribute toward solutions, and take part in all classroom activities. Your contributions are valuable to the class and to yourself. Class participation requires an investment of yourself in the learning process, which you will find pays huge dividends.

0.2 EXERCISES

Student Solutions Manual | CD/Video | PH Math Tutor Center | MathXL®Tutorials on CD | MathXL® | MyMathLab® | Interactmath.com

Verbal and Writing Skills

1. Explain why the denominator 8 is the least common denominator of $\frac{3}{4}$ and $\frac{5}{8}$.

2. What must you do before you add or subtract fractions that do not have a common denominator?

Find the LCD (least common denominator) of each pair of fractions. Do not combine the fractions; only find the LCD.

3. $\frac{7}{15}$ and $\frac{11}{21}$

4. $\frac{13}{25}$ and $\frac{29}{40}$

5. $\frac{7}{10}$ and $\frac{1}{4}$

6. $\frac{3}{16}$ and $\frac{1}{24}$

7. $\frac{5}{18}$ and $\frac{7}{54}$

8. $\frac{7}{24}$ and $\frac{5}{48}$

9. $\frac{1}{2}, \frac{1}{18}$, and $\frac{13}{30}$

10. $\frac{5}{8}, \frac{3}{14}$, and $\frac{11}{16}$

Combine. Be sure to simplify your answer whenever possible.

11. $\frac{3}{8} + \frac{2}{8}$

12. $\frac{2}{9} + \frac{5}{9}$

13. $\frac{5}{14} - \frac{1}{14}$

14. $\frac{9}{20} - \frac{3}{20}$

15. $\frac{3}{8} + \frac{5}{6}$

16. $\frac{7}{10} + \frac{8}{15}$

17. $\frac{5}{7} - \frac{2}{9}$

18. $\frac{7}{8} - \frac{2}{3}$

19. $\frac{1}{3} + \frac{2}{5}$

20. $\frac{2}{7} + \frac{1}{3}$

21. $\frac{7}{18} + \frac{1}{12}$

22. $\frac{3}{10} + \frac{3}{25}$

23. $\frac{2}{3} + \frac{7}{12} + \frac{1}{4}$

24. $\frac{4}{7} + \frac{7}{9} + \frac{1}{3}$

25. $\frac{5}{36} + \frac{7}{9} - \frac{5}{12}$

26. $\frac{5}{24} + \frac{3}{8} - \frac{1}{3}$

27. $4\frac{1}{3} + 3\frac{2}{5}$

28. $3\frac{1}{8} + 2\frac{1}{6}$

29. $1\frac{5}{24} + \frac{5}{18}$

30. $6\frac{2}{3} + \frac{3}{4}$

31. $7\frac{1}{6} - 2\frac{1}{4}$

32. $7\frac{2}{5} - 3\frac{3}{4}$

33. $8\frac{5}{7} - 2\frac{1}{4}$

34. $7\frac{8}{15} - 2\frac{3}{5}$

35. $2\frac{1}{8} + 3\frac{2}{3}$

36. $3\frac{1}{7} + 4\frac{1}{3}$

37. $11\frac{1}{7} - 6\frac{5}{7}$

38. $17\frac{1}{5} - 10\frac{3}{5}$

39. $2\frac{1}{8} + 6\frac{3}{4}$

40. $3\frac{1}{4} + 4\frac{5}{8}$

Mixed Practice

41. $\frac{7}{9} + \frac{5}{6}$

42. $\frac{7}{15} + \frac{3}{20}$

43. $2\frac{1}{7} + 3\frac{11}{14}$

44. $4\frac{1}{6} + 5\frac{11}{12}$

45. $\frac{16}{21} - \frac{2}{7}$

46. $\frac{15}{24} - \frac{3}{8}$

47. $5\frac{1}{5} - 2\frac{1}{2}$

48. $6\frac{1}{3} - 4\frac{1}{4}$

Applications

49. ***Inline Skating*** Jenny and Laura went inline skating. They skated $3\frac{1}{8}$ miles on Monday, $2\frac{2}{3}$ miles on Tuesday, and $4\frac{1}{2}$ miles on Wednesday. What was their total distance for those three days?

50. ***Marathon Training*** Jomo and Eskinder were training for the New York Marathon. Their coach scheduled them to run $11\frac{1}{2}$ miles Monday, $13\frac{2}{3}$ miles Wednesday, and $21\frac{1}{8}$ miles on Friday, with Tuesday and Thursday reserved for weight training. How many miles did they run this week?

51. ***MTV Video*** Sheryl has $8\frac{1}{2}$ hours this weekend to work on her new video. She estimates that it will take $2\frac{2}{3}$ hours to lip sync the new song and $1\frac{3}{4}$ hours to learn the new dance steps. How much time will she have left over for her MTV interview?

52. ***Aquariums*** Carl bought a 20 gallon aquarium. He put $17\frac{3}{4}$ gallons of water into the aquarium, but it looked too low, so he added $1\frac{1}{4}$ more gallons of water. He then put in the artificial plants and the gravel but now the water was too high, so he siphoned off $2\frac{2}{3}$ gallons of water. How many gallons of water are now in the aquarium?

To Think About

Carpentry *Carpenters use fractions in their work. The picture below is a diagram of a spice cabinet. The symbol ″ means inches. Use the picture to answer exercises 53 and 54.*

53. Before you can determine where the cabinet will fit, you need to calculate the height, *A*, and the width, *B*. Don't forget to include the $\frac{1}{2}$-inch thickness of the wood where needed.

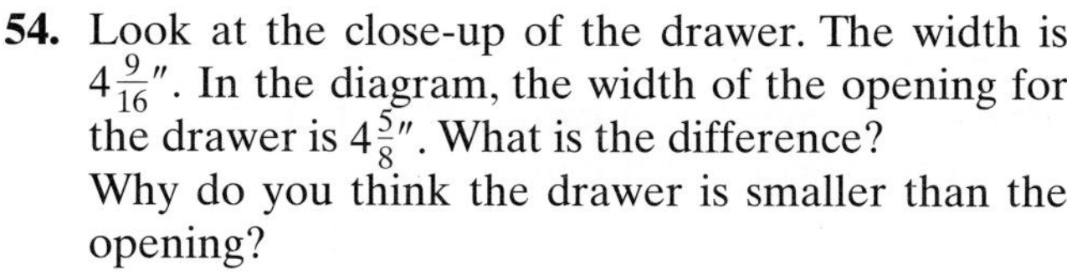

54. Look at the close-up of the drawer. The width is $4\frac{9}{16}$″. In the diagram, the width of the opening for the drawer is $4\frac{5}{8}$″. What is the difference? Why do you think the drawer is smaller than the opening?

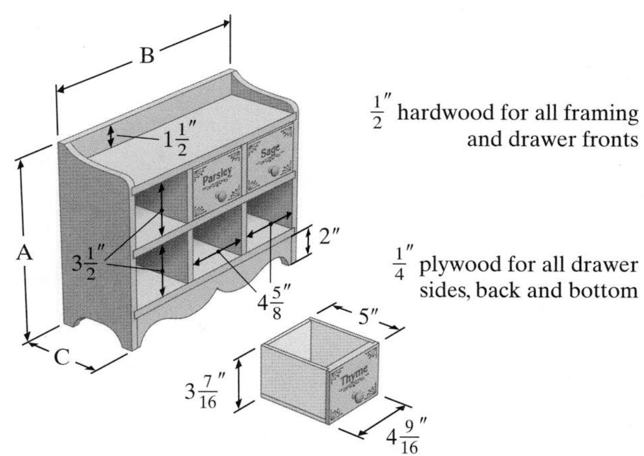

55. ***Putting Green Care*** The Falmouth Country Club maintains the putting greens with a grass height of $\frac{7}{8}$ inch. The grass on the fairways is maintained at $2\frac{1}{2}$ inches. How much must the mower blade be lowered by a person mowing the fairways if that person will be using the same mowing machine on the putting greens?

56. ***Fairway Care*** The director of facilities maintenance at the club discovered that due to slippage in the adjustment lever that the lawn mower actually cuts the grass $\frac{1}{16}$ of an inch too long or too short on some days. What is the maximum height that the fairway grass could be after being mowed with this machine? What is the minimum height that the putting greens could be after being mowed with this machine?

Cumulative Review

57. Simplify. $\frac{36}{44}$

58. Change to an improper fraction. $26\frac{3}{5}$

0.3 Multiplying and Dividing Fractions

Student Learning Objectives

After studying this section, you will be able to:

1. **Multiply fractions, whole numbers, and mixed numbers.**
2. **Divide fractions, whole numbers, and mixed numbers.**

1 Multiplying Fractions, Whole Numbers, and Mixed Numbers

Multiplying Fractions During a recent snowstorm, the runway at Beverly Airport was plowed. However, the plow cleared only $\frac{3}{5}$ of the width and $\frac{2}{7}$ of the length. What fraction of the total runway area was cleared? To answer this question, we need to multiply $\frac{3}{5} \times \frac{2}{7}$.

The answer is that $\frac{6}{35}$ of the total runway area was cleared.

The multiplication rule for fractions states that to multiply two fractions, we multiply the two numerators and multiply the two denominators.

TO MULTIPLY ANY TWO FRACTIONS

1. Multiply the numerators.
2. Multiply the denominators.

EXAMPLE 1 Multiply.

(a) $\frac{3}{5} \times \frac{2}{7}$ **(b)** $\frac{1}{3} \times \frac{5}{4}$ **(c)** $\frac{7}{3} \times \frac{1}{5}$ **(d)** $\frac{6}{5} \times \frac{2}{3}$

Solution

(a) $\frac{3}{5} \times \frac{2}{7} = \frac{3 \cdot 2}{5 \cdot 7} = \frac{6}{35}$ **(b)** $\frac{1}{3} \times \frac{5}{4} = \frac{1 \cdot 5}{3 \cdot 4} = \frac{5}{12}$

(c) $\frac{7}{3} \times \frac{1}{5} = \frac{7 \cdot 1}{3 \cdot 5} = \frac{7}{15}$ **(d)** $\frac{6}{5} \times \frac{2}{3} = \frac{6 \cdot 2}{5 \cdot 3} = \frac{12}{15} = \frac{4}{5}$

Note that we must simplify this fraction.

NOTE TO STUDENT: Fully worked-out solutions to all of the Practice Problems can be found at the back of the text starting at page SP-1

Practice Problem 1 Multiply.

(a) $\frac{2}{7} \times \frac{5}{11}$ **(b)** $\frac{1}{5} \times \frac{7}{10}$ **(c)** $\frac{9}{5} \times \frac{1}{4}$ **(d)** $\frac{8}{9} \times \frac{3}{10}$

It is possible to avoid having to simplify a fraction at the last step. In many cases we can divide by a value that appears as a factor in both a numerator and a denominator. Often it is helpful to write a number as a product of prime factors in order to do this.

EXAMPLE 2 Multiply. **(a)** $\frac{3}{5} \times \frac{5}{7}$ **(b)** $\frac{4}{11} \times \frac{5}{2}$ **(c)** $\frac{15}{8} \times \frac{10}{27}$

Solution **(a)** $\frac{3}{5} \times \frac{5}{7} = \frac{3 \cdot 5}{5 \cdot 7} = \frac{3 \cdot \overset{1}{\cancel{5}}}{7 \cdot \underset{1}{\cancel{5}}} = \frac{3}{7}$ Note that here we divided numerator and denominator by 5.

If we factor each number, we can see the common factors.

(b) $\frac{4}{11} \times \frac{5}{2} = \frac{2 \cdot \overset{1}{\cancel{2}}}{11} \times \frac{5}{\underset{1}{\cancel{2}}} = \frac{10}{11}$ **(c)** $\frac{15}{8} \times \frac{10}{27} = \frac{\overset{1}{\cancel{3}} \cdot 5}{2 \cdot 2 \cdot \underset{1}{\cancel{2}}} \times \frac{5 \cdot \overset{1}{\cancel{2}}}{\underset{1}{\cancel{3}} \cdot 3 \cdot 3} = \frac{25}{36}$

After dividing out common factors, the resulting multiplication problem involves smaller numbers and the answers are in simplified form.

Practice Problem 2 Multiply. **(a)** $\frac{3}{5} \times \frac{4}{3}$ **(b)** $\frac{9}{10} \times \frac{5}{12}$

SIDELIGHT: Dividing Out Common Factors

Why does this method of dividing out a value that appears as a factor in both numerator and denominator work? Let's reexamine one of the examples we have solved previously.

$$\frac{3}{5} \times \frac{5}{7} = \frac{3}{\cancel{5}_1} \times \frac{\cancel{5}^1}{7} = \frac{3}{7}$$

Consider the following steps and reasons.

$\frac{3}{5} \times \frac{5}{7} = \frac{3 \cdot 5}{5 \cdot 7}$ Definition of multiplication of fractions.

$= \frac{5 \cdot 3}{5 \cdot 7}$ Change the order of the factors in the numerator, since $3 \cdot 5 = 5 \cdot 3$. This is called the commutative property of multiplication.

$= \frac{5}{5} \cdot \frac{3}{7}$ Definition of multiplication of fractions.

$= 1 \cdot \frac{3}{7}$ Write 1 in place of $\frac{5}{5}$, since 1 is another name for $\frac{5}{5}$.

$= \frac{3}{7}$ $1 \cdot \frac{3}{7} = \frac{3}{7}$, since any number can be multiplied by 1 without changing the value of the number.

Think about this concept. It is an important one that we will use again when we discuss rational expressions.

Multiplying a Fraction by a Whole Number Whole numbers can be named using fractional notation. 3, $\frac{9}{3}$, $\frac{6}{2}$, and $\frac{3}{1}$ are ways of expressing the number *three*. Therefore,

$$3 = \frac{9}{3} = \frac{6}{2} = \frac{3}{1}.$$

When we multiply a fraction by a whole number, we merely express the whole number as a fraction whose denominator is 1 and follow the multiplication rule for fractions.

EXAMPLE 3 Multiply.

(a) $7 \times \frac{3}{5}$ **(b)** $\frac{3}{16} \times 4$

Solution

(a) $7 \times \frac{3}{5} = \frac{7}{1} \times \frac{3}{5} = \frac{21}{5} = 4\frac{1}{5}$ **(b)** $\frac{3}{16} \times 4 = \frac{3}{16} \times \frac{4}{1} = \frac{3}{4 \cdot \cancel{4}} \times \frac{\cancel{4}}{1} = \frac{3}{4}$

Notice that in (b) we did not use *prime* factors to factor 16. We recognized that $16 = 4 \cdot 4$. This is a more convenient factorization of 16 for this problem. Choose the factorization that works best for each problem. If you cannot decide what is best, factor into primes.

Practice Problem 3 Multiply.

(a) $4 \times \frac{2}{7}$ **(b)** $12 \times \frac{3}{4}$

Multiplying Mixed Numbers When multiplying mixed numbers, we first change them to improper fractions and then follow the multiplication rule for fractions.

$3\frac{1}{3}$ miles

$2\frac{1}{2}$ miles

EXAMPLE 4 How do we find the area of a rectangular field $3\frac{1}{3}$ miles long by $2\frac{1}{2}$ miles wide?

Solution To find the area, we multiply length times width.

$$3\frac{1}{3} \times 2\frac{1}{2} = \frac{10}{3} \times \frac{5}{2} = \frac{\cancel{2} \cdot 5}{3} \times \frac{5}{\cancel{2}} = \frac{25}{3} = 8\frac{1}{3}$$

The area is $8\frac{1}{3}$ square miles.

NOTE TO STUDENT: Fully worked-out solutions to all of the Practice Problems can be found at the back of the text starting at page SP-1

Practice Problem 4 Delbert Robinson had a farm that had a rectangular field that measured $5\frac{3}{5}$ miles long and $3\frac{3}{4}$ miles wide. What was the area of that field?

EXAMPLE 5 Multiply. $2\frac{2}{3} \times \frac{1}{4} \times 6$

Solution $$2\frac{2}{3} \times \frac{1}{4} \times 6 = \frac{8}{3} \times \frac{1}{4} \times \frac{6}{1} = \frac{\cancel{4} \cdot 2}{\cancel{3}} \times \frac{1}{\cancel{4}} \times \frac{2 \cdot \cancel{3}}{1} = \frac{4}{1} = 4$$

Practice Problem 5 Multiply. $3\frac{1}{2} \times \frac{1}{14} \times 4$

2 Dividing Fractions, Whole Numbers, and Mixed Numbers

Dividing Fractions To divide two fractions, we invert the second fraction (that is, the divisor) and then multiply the two fractions.

TO DIVIDE TWO FRACTIONS

1. Invert the second fraction (that is, the divisor).
2. Now multiply the two fractions.

EXAMPLE 6 Divide.

(a) $\frac{1}{3} \div \frac{1}{2}$ **(b)** $\frac{2}{5} \div \frac{3}{10}$ **(c)** $\frac{2}{3} \div \frac{7}{5}$

Solution

(a) $\frac{1}{3} \div \frac{1}{2} = \frac{1}{3} \times \frac{2}{1} = \frac{2}{3}$ Note that we always invert the *second* fraction.

(b) $\frac{2}{5} \div \frac{3}{10} = \frac{2}{5} \times \frac{10}{3} = \frac{2}{\cancel{5}} \times \frac{\cancel{5} \cdot 2}{3} = \frac{4}{3} = 1\frac{1}{3}$ **(c)** $\frac{2}{3} \div \frac{7}{5} = \frac{2}{3} \times \frac{5}{7} = \frac{10}{21}$

Practice Problem 6 Divide. **(a)** $\frac{2}{5} \div \frac{1}{3}$ **(b)** $\frac{12}{13} \div \frac{4}{3}$

Dividing a Fraction and a Whole Number The process of inverting the second fraction and then multiplying the two fractions should be done very carefully when one of the original values is a whole number. Remember, a whole number such as 2 is equivalent to $\frac{2}{1}$.

EXAMPLE 7 Divide.

(a) $\frac{1}{3} \div 2$ **(b)** $5 \div \frac{1}{3}$

Solution

(a) $\frac{1}{3} \div 2 = \frac{1}{3} \div \frac{2}{1} = \frac{1}{3} \times \frac{1}{2} = \frac{1}{6}$

(b) $5 \div \frac{1}{3} = \frac{5}{1} \div \frac{1}{3} = \frac{5}{1} \times \frac{3}{1} = \frac{15}{1} = 15$

Practice Problem 7 Divide.

(a) $\frac{3}{7} \div 6$ **(b)** $8 \div \frac{2}{3}$

SIDELIGHT: Number Sense

Look at the answers to the problems in Example 7. In part (a), you will notice that $\frac{1}{6}$ is less than the original number $\frac{1}{3}$. Does this seem reasonable? Let's see. If $\frac{1}{3}$ is divided by 2, it means that $\frac{1}{3}$ will be divided into two equal parts. We would expect that each part would be less than $\frac{1}{3}$. $\frac{1}{6}$ is a reasonable answer to this division problem.

In part (b), 15 is greater than the original number 5. Does this seem reasonable? Think of what $5 \div \frac{1}{3}$ means. It means that 5 will be divided into thirds. Let's think of an easier problem. What happens when we divide 1 into thirds? We get *three* thirds. We would expect, therefore, that when we divide 5 into thirds, we would get 5×3 or 15 thirds. 15 is a reasonable answer to this division problem.

Complex Fractions

Sometimes division is written in the form of a **complex fraction** with one fraction in the numerator and one fraction in the denominator. It is best to write this in standard division notation first; then complete the problem using the rule for division.

EXAMPLE 8 Divide.

(a) $\dfrac{\frac{3}{7}}{\frac{3}{5}}$ **(b)** $\dfrac{\frac{2}{9}}{\frac{5}{7}}$

Solution

(a) $\dfrac{\frac{3}{7}}{\frac{3}{5}} = \frac{3}{7} \div \frac{3}{5} = \frac{\cancel{3}}{7} \times \frac{5}{\cancel{3}} = \frac{5}{7}$

(b) $\dfrac{\frac{2}{9}}{\frac{5}{7}} = \frac{2}{9} \div \frac{5}{7} = \frac{2}{9} \times \frac{7}{5} = \frac{14}{45}$

Practice Problem 8 Divide.

(a) $\dfrac{\frac{3}{11}}{\frac{5}{7}}$ **(b)** $\dfrac{\frac{12}{5}}{\frac{8}{15}}$

SIDELIGHT: Invert and Multiply

Why does the method of "invert and multiply" work? The division rule really depends on the property that any number can be multiplied by 1 without changing the value of the number. Let's look carefully at an example of division of fractions:

$$\frac{2}{5} \div \frac{3}{7} = \frac{\frac{2}{5}}{\frac{3}{7}}$$ We can write the problem using a complex fraction.

$$= \frac{\frac{2}{5}}{\frac{3}{7}} \times 1$$ We can multiply by 1, since any number can be multiplied by 1 without changing the value of the number.

$$= \frac{\frac{2}{5}}{\frac{3}{7}} \times \frac{\frac{7}{3}}{\frac{7}{3}}$$ We write 1 in the form $\frac{\frac{7}{3}}{\frac{7}{3}}$, since any nonzero number divided by itself equals 1. We choose this value as a multiplier because it will help simplify the denominator.

$$= \frac{\frac{2}{5} \times \frac{7}{3}}{\frac{3}{7} \times \frac{7}{3}}$$ Definition of multiplication of fractions.

$$= \frac{\frac{2}{5} \times \frac{7}{3}}{1}$$ The product in the denominator equals 1.

$$= \frac{2}{5} \times \frac{7}{3}.$$

Thus we have shown that $\frac{2}{5} \div \frac{3}{7}$ is equivalent to $\frac{2}{5} \times \frac{7}{3}$ and have shown some justification for the "invert and multiply rule."

Dividing Mixed Numbers This method for division of fractions can be used with mixed numbers. However, we first must change the mixed numbers to improper fractions and then use the rule for dividing fractions.

EXAMPLE 9 Divide. **(a)** $2\frac{1}{3} \div 3\frac{2}{3}$ **(b)** $\frac{2}{3\frac{1}{2}}$

Solution

(a) $2\frac{1}{3} \div 3\frac{2}{3} = \frac{7}{3} \div \frac{11}{3} = \frac{7}{\cancel{3}} \times \frac{\cancel{3}}{11} = \frac{7}{11}$

(b) $\frac{2}{3\frac{1}{2}} = 2 \div 3\frac{1}{2} = \frac{2}{1} \div \frac{7}{2} = \frac{2}{1} \times \frac{2}{7} = \frac{4}{7}$

Practice Problem 9 Divide.

(a) $1\frac{2}{5} \div 2\frac{1}{3}$ **(b)** $4\frac{2}{3} \div 7$ **(c)** $\frac{1\frac{1}{5}}{1\frac{2}{7}}$

NOTE TO STUDENT: Fully worked-out solutions to all of the Practice Problems can be found at the back of the text starting at page SP-1

EXAMPLE 10 A chemist has 96 fluid ounces of a solution. She pours the solution into test tubes. Each test tube holds $\frac{3}{4}$ fluid ounce. How many test tubes can she fill?

Solution We need to divide the total number of ounces, 96, by the number of ounces in each test tube, $\frac{3}{4}$.

$$96 \div \frac{3}{4} = \frac{96}{1} \div \frac{3}{4} = \frac{96}{1} \times \frac{4}{3} = \frac{\cancel{3} \cdot 32}{1} \times \frac{4}{\cancel{3}} = \frac{128}{1} = 128$$

She will be able to fill 128 test tubes.

Pause for a moment to think about the answer. Does 128 test tubes filled with solution seem like a reasonable answer? Did you perform the correct operation?

Practice Problem 10 A chemist has 64 fluid ounces of a solution. He wishes to fill several jars, each holding $5\frac{1}{3}$ fluid ounces. How many jars can he fill?

Sometimes when solving word problems involving fractions or mixed numbers, it is helpful to solve the problem using simpler numbers first. Once you understand what operation is involved, you can go back and solve using the original numbers in the word problem.

EXAMPLE 11 A car traveled 301 miles on $10\frac{3}{4}$ gallons of gas. How many miles per gallon did it get?

Solution Use simpler numbers: 300 miles on 10 gallons of gas. We want to find out how many miles the car traveled on 1 gallon of gas. You may want to draw a picture.

10 gallons

300 miles

Divide. $300 \div 10 = 30$.

Now use the original numbers given in the problem.

$$301 \div 10\frac{3}{4} = \frac{301}{1} \div \frac{43}{4} = \frac{301}{1} \times \frac{4}{43} = \frac{1204}{43} = 28$$

This is 28 miles to the gallon.

Practice Problem 11 A car can travel $25\frac{1}{2}$ miles on 1 gallon of gas. How many miles can a car travel on $5\frac{1}{4}$ gallons of gas? Check your answer to see if it is reasonable.

Developing Your Study Skills

Why Is Homework Necessary?

Mathematics is a set of skills that you learn by doing, not by watching. Your instructor may make solving a mathematics problem look very easy, but for you to learn the necessary skills, you must practice them over and over again, just as your instructor once had to do. There is no other way. Learning mathematics is like learning to play a musical instrument, to type, or to play a sport. No matter how much you watch someone else do it, how many books you may read on "how to" do it, or how easy it may seem to be, the key to success is to practice on a regular basis. Homework provides this practice.

0.3 Exercises

Student Solutions Manual | CD/Video | PH Math Tutor Center | MathXL®Tutorials on CD | MathXL® | MyMathLab® | Interactmath.com

Verbal and Writing Skills

1. Explain in your own words how to multiply two mixed numbers.

2. Explain in your own words how to divide two proper fractions.

Multiply. Simplify your answer whenever possible.

3. $\frac{36}{7} \times \frac{5}{9}$

4. $\frac{3}{8} \times \frac{24}{5}$

5. $\frac{17}{18} \times \frac{3}{5}$

6. $\frac{21}{22} \times \frac{11}{6}$

7. $\frac{4}{5} \times \frac{3}{10}$

8. $\frac{5}{6} \times \frac{7}{11}$

9. $\frac{24}{25} \times \frac{5}{2}$

10. $\frac{15}{24} \times \frac{8}{9}$

11. $9 \times \frac{2}{5}$

12. $\frac{8}{11} \times 3$

Divide. Simplify your answer whenever possible.

13. $\frac{8}{5} \div \frac{8}{3}$

14. $\frac{13}{9} \div \frac{13}{7}$

15. $\frac{3}{7} \div 3$

16. $\frac{7}{8} \div 4$

17. $10 \div \frac{5}{7}$

18. $18 \div \frac{2}{9}$

19. $\dfrac{\frac{7}{8}}{\frac{3}{4}}$

20. $\dfrac{\frac{5}{6}}{\frac{10}{13}}$

21. $\dfrac{\frac{5}{6}}{\frac{7}{9}}$

22. $\dfrac{\frac{3}{4}}{\frac{11}{12}}$

23. $1\frac{3}{7} \div 6\frac{1}{4}$

24. $4\frac{1}{2} \div 3\frac{3}{8}$

25. $3\frac{1}{3} \div 2\frac{1}{2}$

26. $5\frac{1}{2} \div 3\frac{3}{4}$

27. $\dfrac{\frac{7}{9}}{1\frac{1}{3}}$

28. $\dfrac{\frac{5}{8}}{1\frac{3}{4}}$

29. $\dfrac{\frac{2}{3}}{1\frac{1}{4}}$

30. $\dfrac{\frac{5}{6}}{2\frac{1}{2}}$

Mixed Practice

Perform the proper calculations. Reduce your answer whenever possible.

31. $\frac{6}{5} \times \frac{10}{12}$

32. $\frac{5}{24} \times \frac{18}{15}$

33. $\frac{5}{14} \div \frac{2}{7}$

34. $\frac{5}{6} \div \frac{11}{18}$

35. $10\frac{3}{7} \times 5\frac{1}{4}$

36. $10\frac{2}{9} \div 2\frac{1}{3}$

37. $2\frac{1}{8} \div \frac{1}{4}$

38. $4 \div 1\frac{7}{9}$

39. $6 \times 4\frac{2}{3}$

40. $5\frac{1}{2} \times 10$

41. $2\frac{1}{2} \times \frac{1}{10} \times \frac{3}{4}$

42. $3\frac{1}{3} \times \frac{1}{5} \times \frac{2}{3}$

Applications

43. ***Shirt Manufacturing*** A denim shirt at the Gap requires $2\frac{3}{4}$ yards of material. How many yards would be needed to make 26 shirts?

44. ***Pullover Manufacturing*** A fleece pullover requires $1\frac{5}{8}$ yds of material. How many yards will it take to make 18 pullovers?

45. ***Mountain Biking*** Jennifer rode her mountain bike for $4\frac{1}{5}$ miles after work. Two-thirds of the distance was over a mountain bike trail. How long is the mountain bike trail?

46. ***Cross-Country Racing*** Phil ran a cross-country race that was $3\frac{3}{8}$ miles long. One-third of that race was on a hilly nature preserve trail. How long is the nature preserve trail?

Cumulative Review

In exercises 47 and 48, simplify each fraction.

47. $\frac{116}{124}$

48. $\frac{33}{77}$

0.4 Using Decimals

Student Learning Objectives

After studying this section, you will be able to:

1. **Understand the meaning of decimals.**
2. **Change a fraction to a decimal.**
3. **Change a decimal to a fraction.**
4. **Add and subtract decimals.**
5. **Multiply decimals.**
6. **Divide decimals.**
7. **Multiply or divide a decimal by a multiple of 10.**

1 Understanding the Meaning of Decimals

We can express a part of a whole as a fraction or as a decimal. A **decimal** is another way of writing a fraction whose denominator is 10, 100, 1000, and so on.

$$\frac{3}{10} = 0.3 \qquad \frac{5}{100} = 0.05 \qquad \frac{172}{1000} = 0.172 \qquad \frac{58}{10{,}000} = 0.0058$$

The period in decimal notation is known as the **decimal point.** The number of digits in a number to the right of the decimal point is known as the number of **decimal places** of the number. The place value of decimals is shown in the following chart.

Hundred-thousands	Ten-thousands	Thousands	Hundreds	Tens	ones	← Decimal point	Tenths	Hundredths	Thousandths	Ten-thousandths	Hundred-thousandths
100,000	10,000	1000	100	10	1	.	$\frac{1}{10}$	$\frac{1}{100}$	$\frac{1}{1000}$	$\frac{1}{10{,}000}$	$\frac{1}{100{,}000}$

EXAMPLE 1 Write each of the following decimals as a fraction. State the number of decimal places. Write out in words the way the number would be spoken.

(a) 0.6 **(b)** 0.29 **(c)** 0.527 **(d)** 1.38 **(e)** 0.00007

Solution

Decimal Form	*Fraction Form*	*Number of Decimal Places*	*The Words Used to Describe the Number*
(a) 0.6	$\frac{6}{10}$	one	six-tenths
(b) 0.29	$\frac{29}{100}$	two	twenty-nine hundredths
(c) 0.527	$\frac{527}{1000}$	three	five hundred twenty-seven thousandths
(d) 1.38	$1\frac{38}{100}$	two	one and thirty-eight hundredths
(e) 0.00007	$\frac{7}{100{,}000}$	five	seven hundred-thousandths

Practice Problem 1 Write each decimal as a fraction and in words.

(a) 0.9 **(b)** 0.09 **(c)** 0.731 **(d)** 1.371 **(e)** 0.0005

NOTE TO STUDENT: Fully worked-out solutions to all of the Practice Problems can be found at the back of the text starting at page SP-1

You have seen that a given fraction can be written in several different but equivalent ways. There are also several different equivalent ways of writing the decimal form of fractions. The decimal 0.18 can be written in the following equivalent ways:

$$\text{Fractional form: } \frac{18}{100} = \frac{180}{1000} = \frac{1800}{10{,}000} = \frac{18{,}000}{100{,}000}$$

$$\text{Decimal form: } 0.18 = 0.180 = 0.1800 = 0.18000.$$

Thus we see that *any number of terminal zeros may be added to the right-hand side of a decimal* without changing its value.

$$0.13 = 0.1300 \qquad 0.162 = 0.162000$$

Similarly, *any number of terminal zeros may be removed from the right-hand side of a decimal* without changing its value.

 Changing a Fraction to a Decimal

A fraction can be changed to a decimal by dividing the denominator into the numerator.

EXAMPLE 2 Write each of the following fractions as a decimal.

(a) $\frac{3}{4}$ **(b)** $\frac{21}{20}$ **(c)** $\frac{1}{8}$ **(d)** $\frac{3}{200}$

Solution

(a) $\frac{3}{4} = 0.75$ since

```
   0.75
4)3.00
  28
   20
   20
    0
```

(b) $\frac{21}{20} = 1.05$ since

```
    1.05
20)21.00
   20
    100
    100
      0
```

(c) $\frac{1}{8} = 0.125$ since

```
  0.125
8)1.000
   8
   20
   16
    40
    40
     0
```

(d) $\frac{3}{200} = 0.015$ since

```
     0.015
200)3.000
    200
    1000
    1000
       0
```

Practice Problem 2 Write as decimals.

(a) $\frac{3}{8}$ **(b)** $\frac{7}{200}$ **(c)** $\frac{33}{20}$

Sometimes division yields an infinite repeating decimal. We use three dots to indicate that the pattern continues forever. For example,

$\frac{1}{3} = 0.3333\ldots$

```
  0.333
3)1.000
   9
   10
    9
    10
     9
     1
```

An alternative notation is to place a bar over the repeating digit(s):

$$0.3333\ldots = 0.\overline{3} \qquad 0.575757\ldots = 0.\overline{57}$$

Calculator

Fraction to Decimal

You can use a calculator to change $\frac{3}{5}$ to a decimal. Enter:

3 [÷] 5 [=]

The display should read

[0.6]

Try the following.

(a) $\frac{17}{25}$ **(b)** $\frac{2}{9}$

(c) $\frac{13}{10}$ **(d)** $\frac{15}{19}$

Answers:

(a) 0.68 **(b)** $0.\overline{2}$

(c) 1.3

(d) 0.7894737 (Rounded to seven decimal places.)

EXAMPLE 3 Write each fraction as a decimal.

(a) $\frac{2}{11}$ **(b)** $\frac{5}{6}$

Solution

(a) $\frac{2}{11} = 0.181818\ldots$ or $0.\overline{18}$

$$\begin{array}{r} 0.1818 \\ 11\overline{)2.0000} \\ \underline{11} \\ 90 \\ \underline{88} \\ 20 \\ \underline{11} \\ 90 \\ \underline{88} \\ 2 \end{array}$$

(b) $\frac{5}{6} = 0.8333\ldots$ or $0.8\overline{3}$

$$\begin{array}{r} 0.8333 \\ 6\overline{)5.0000} \\ \underline{48} \\ 20 \\ \underline{18} \\ 20 \\ \underline{18} \\ 20 \\ \underline{18} \\ 2 \end{array}$$

Note that the 8 does not repeat. Only the digit 3 is repeating.

NOTE TO STUDENT: Fully worked-out solutions to all of the Practice Problems can be found at the back of the text starting at page SP-1

Practice Problem 3 Write each fraction as a decimal.

(a) $\frac{1}{6}$ **(b)** $\frac{5}{11}$

Sometimes division must be carried out to many places in order to observe the repeating pattern. This is true in the following example:

$\frac{2}{7} = 0.285714285714285714\ldots$ This can also be written as $\frac{2}{7} = 0.\overline{285714}$.

It can be shown that the denominator determines the maximum number of decimal places that might repeat. So $\frac{2}{7}$ must repeat in the seventh decimal place or sooner.

3 Changing a Decimal to a Fraction

To convert from a decimal to a fraction, merely write the decimal as a fraction with a denominator of 10, 100, 1000, 10,000, and so on, and simplify the result when possible.

EXAMPLE 4 Write each decimal as a fraction.

(a) 0.2 **(b)** 0.35 **(c)** 0.516 **(d)** 0.74 **(e)** 0.138 **(f)** 0.008

Solution

(a) $0.2 = \frac{2}{10} = \frac{1}{5}$ **(b)** $0.35 = \frac{35}{100} = \frac{7}{20}$

(c) $0.516 = \frac{516}{1000} = \frac{129}{250}$ **(d)** $0.74 = \frac{74}{100} = \frac{37}{50}$

(e) $0.138 = \frac{138}{1000} = \frac{69}{500}$ **(f)** $0.008 = \frac{8}{1000} = \frac{1}{125}$

Practice Problem 4 Write each decimal as a fraction and simplify whenever possible.

(a) 0.8 **(b)** 0.88 **(c)** 0.45 **(d)** 0.148 **(e)** 0.612 **(f)** 0.016

All repeating decimals can also be converted to fractional form. In practice, however, repeating decimals are usually rounded to a few places. It will not be necessary, therefore, to learn how to convert $0.\overline{033}$ to $\frac{11}{333}$ for this course.

Adding and Subtracting Decimals

Last week Bob spent \$19.83 on lunches purchased at the cafeteria at work. During this same period, Sally spent \$24.76 on lunches. How much did the two of them spend on lunches last week?

Adding or subtracting decimals is similar to adding and subtracting whole numbers, except that it is necessary to line up decimal points. To perform the operation 19.83 + 24.76, we line up the numbers in column form and add the digits:

$$\begin{array}{r} 19.83 \\ +\ 24.76 \\ \hline 44.59 \end{array}$$

Thus Bob and Sally spent \$44.59 on lunches last week.

ADDITION AND SUBTRACTION OF DECIMALS

1. Write in column form and line up decimal points.
2. Add or subtract the digits.

EXAMPLE 5 Perform the following operations.

(a) 3.6 + 2.3 **(b)** 127.32 − 38.48

(c) 3.1 + 42.36 + 9.034 **(d)** 5.0006 − 3.1248

Solution

(a) $\begin{array}{r} 3.6 \\ +2.3 \\ \hline 5.9 \end{array}$ **(b)** $\begin{array}{r} 127.32 \\ -\ 38.48 \\ \hline 88.84 \end{array}$ **(c)** $\begin{array}{r} 3.1 \\ 42.36 \\ +\ 9.034 \\ \hline 54.494 \end{array}$ **(d)** $\begin{array}{r} 5.0006 \\ -3.1248 \\ \hline 1.8758 \end{array}$

Practice Problem 5 Add or subtract.

(a) 3.12 + 5.08 + 1.42 **(b)** 152.003 − 136.118

(c) 1.1 + 3.16 + 5.123 **(d)** 1.0052 − 0.1234

SIDELIGHT: Adding Zeros to the Right-Hand Side of the Decimal

When we added fractions, we had to have common denominators. Since decimals are really fractions, why can we add them without having common denominators? Actually, we have to have common denominators to add any fractions, whether they are in decimal form or fraction form. However, sometimes the notation does not show this. Let's examine Example 5(c).

Original Problem We are adding the three numbers:

$$\begin{array}{r} 3.1 \\ 42.36 \\ +\ 9.034 \\ \hline 54.494 \end{array} \qquad \begin{array}{l} 3\frac{1}{10} + 42\frac{36}{100} + 9\frac{34}{1000} \\ 3\frac{100}{1000} + 42\frac{360}{1000} + 9\frac{34}{1000} \\ 3.100 + 42.360 + 9.034 \quad \text{This is the new problem.} \end{array}$$

Original Problem	*New Problem*	
3.1	3.100	We notice that the results are the same. The only difference is the notation. We are using the property that any number of zeros may be added to the right-hand side of a decimal without changing its value.
42.36	42.360	
+ 9.034	+ 9.034	
54.494	54.494	

This shows the convenience of adding and subtracting fractions in decimal form. Little work is needed to change the decimals so that they have a common denominator. All that is required is to add zeros to the right-hand side of the decimal (and we usually do not even write out that step except when subtracting).

As long as we line up the decimal points, we can add or subtract any decimal fractions.

In the following example we will find it useful to add zeros to the right-hand side of the decimal.

EXAMPLE 6 Perform the following operations.

(a) $1.0003 + 0.02 + 3.4$ **(b)** $12 - 0.057$

Solution We will add zeros so that each number shows the same number of decimal places.

(a)

$$\begin{array}{r} 1.0003 \\ 0.0200 \\ +\ 3.4000 \\ \hline 4.4203 \end{array}$$

(b)

$$\begin{array}{r} 12.000 \\ -\ 0.057 \\ \hline 11.943 \end{array}$$

NOTE TO STUDENT: Fully worked-out solutions to all of the Practice Problems can be found at the back of the text starting at page SP-1

Practice Problem 6 Perform the following operations.

(a) $0.061 + 5.0008 + 1.3$ **(b)** $18 - 0.126$

5 Multiplying Decimals

MULTIPLICATION OF DECIMALS

To multiply decimals, you first multiply as with whole numbers. To determine the position of the decimal point, you count the total number of decimal places in the two numbers being multiplied. This will determine the number of decimal places that should appear in the answer.

EXAMPLE 7 Multiply. 0.8×0.4

Solution

$$\begin{array}{rl} 0.8 & (\text{one decimal place}) \\ \times 0.4 & (\text{one decimal place}) \\ \hline 0.32 & (\text{two decimal places}) \end{array}$$

Practice Problem 7 Multiply. 0.5×0.3

Note that you will often have to add zeros to the left of the digits obtained in the product so that you obtain the necessary number of decimal places.

EXAMPLE 8 Multiply. 0.123×0.5

Solution

$$\begin{array}{rl} 0.123 & \text{(three decimal places)} \\ \times \quad 0.5 & \text{(one decimal place)} \\ \hline 0.0615 & \text{(four decimal places)} \end{array}$$

Practice Problem 8 Multiply. 0.12×0.4

Here are some examples that involve more decimal places.

EXAMPLE 9 Multiply.

(a) 2.56×0.003 **(b)** 0.0036×0.008

Solution

(a)
$$\begin{array}{rl} 2.56 & \text{(two decimal places)} \\ \times \ 0.003 & \text{(three decimal places)} \\ \hline 0.00768 & \text{(five decimal places)} \end{array}$$

(b)
$$\begin{array}{rl} 0.0036 & \text{(four decimal places)} \\ \times \ 0.008 & \text{(three decimal places)} \\ \hline 0.0000288 & \text{(seven decimal places)} \end{array}$$

Practice Problem 9 Multiply.

(a) 1.23×0.005 **(b)** 0.003×0.00002

SIDELIGHT: Counting the Number of Decimal Places

Why do we count the number of decimal places? The rule really comes from the properties of fractions. If we write the problem in Example 8 in fraction form, we have

$$0.123 \times 0.5 = \frac{123}{1000} \times \frac{5}{10} = \frac{615}{10{,}000} = 0.0615.$$

6 Dividing Decimals

When discussing division of decimals, we frequently refer to the three primary parts of a division problem. Be sure you know the meaning of each term.

The **divisor** is the number you divide into another.
The **dividend** is the number to be divided.
The **quotient** is the result of dividing one number by another.

In the problem $6 \div 2 = 3$ we represent each of these terms as follows:

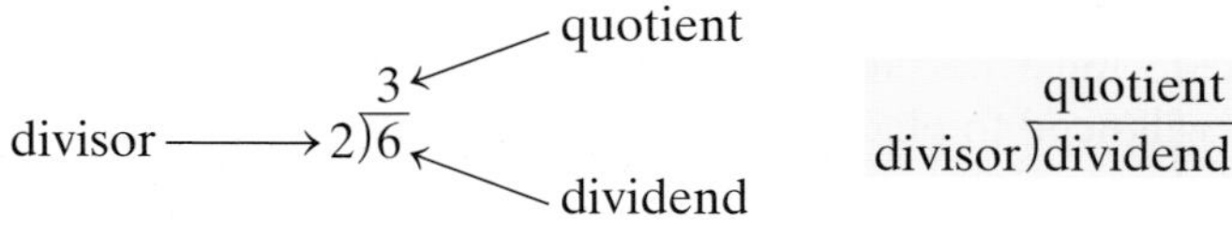

When dividing two decimals, count *the number of decimal places* in the divisor. Then *move the decimal point to the right* that *same number of places* in both *the divisor* and *the dividend.* Mark that position with a caret (‸). Finally, perform the division. Be sure to line up the decimal point in the quotient with the position indicated by the caret in the dividend.

EXAMPLE 10 Four friends went out for lunch. The total bill, including tax, was $32.68. How much did each person pay if they shared the cost equally?

Solution To answer this question, we must calculate $32.68 \div 4$.

```
     8.17
  4)32.68
    32
     6
     4
     28
     28
      0
```

Since there are no decimal places in the divisor, we do not need to move the decimal point. We must be careful, however, to place the decimal point in the quotient directly above the decimal point in the dividend.

Thus $32.68 \div 4 = 8.17$, and each friend paid $8.17.

Practice Problem 10 Sally Keyser purchased 6 boxes of paper for the inkjet printer. The cost was $31.56. There was no tax since she purchased the paper for a charitable organization. How much did she pay for each box of paper?

NOTE TO STUDENT: Fully worked-out solutions to all of the Practice Problems can be found at the back of the text starting at page SP-1

Note that sometimes we will need to place extra zeros in the dividend in order to move the decimal point the required number of places.

EXAMPLE 11 Divide. $16.2 \div 0.027$

Solution

```
               ‸
  0.027)16.200
```

There are **three** decimal places in the divisor, so we move the decimal point **three places** to **the right** in the **divisor** and **dividend** and mark the new position by a caret. Note that we must add two zeros to 16.2 in order to do this.

three decimal places

```
           600.
              ‸
  0.027)16.200
          16 2
           000
```

Now perform the division as with whole numbers. The decimal point in the answer is directly above the caret in the dividend.

Thus $16.2 \div 0.027 = 600$.

Practice Problem 11 Divide. $1800 \div 0.06$

Special care must be taken to line up the digits in the quotient. Note that sometimes we will need to place zeros in the quotient after the decimal point.

EXAMPLE 12 Divide. 0.04288 ÷ 3.2

Solution

$3.2_{\wedge}\overline{)0.0_{\wedge}4288}$

There is **one** decimal place in the divisor, so we move the decimal point **one place** to **the right** in the **divisor** and **dividend** and mark the new position by a caret.

one decimal place

$$\begin{array}{r} 0_{\wedge}0134 \\ 3.2_{\wedge}\overline{)0.0_{\wedge}4288} \\ \underline{32} \\ 108 \\ \underline{96} \\ 128 \\ \underline{128} \\ 0 \end{array}$$

Now perform the division as for whole numbers. The decimal point in the answer is directly above the caret in the dividend. Note the need for the initial zero after the decimal point in the answer.

Thus 0.04288 ÷ 3.2 = 0.0134.

Practice Problem 12 Divide. 0.01764 ÷ 4.9

SIDELIGHT: Dividing Decimals by Another Method

Why does this method of dividing decimals work? Essentially, we are using the steps we used in Section 0.1 to change a fraction to an equivalent fraction by multiplying both the numerator and denominator by the same number. Let's reexamine Example 12.

$0.04288 \div 3.2 = \dfrac{0.04288}{3.2}$ Write the original problem using fraction notation.

$= \dfrac{0.04288 \times 10}{3.2 \times 10}$ Multiply the numerator and denominator by 10. Since this is the same as multiplying by 1, we are not changing the fraction.

$= \dfrac{0.4288}{32}$ Write the result of multiplication by 10.

$= 0.4288 \div 32$ Rewrite the fraction as an equivalent problem with division notation.

Notice that we have obtained a new problem that is the same as the problem in Example 12 when we moved the decimal one place to the right in the divisor and dividend. We see that the reason we can move the decimal point as many places as necessary to the right in divisor and dividend is that this is the same as multiplying the numerator and denominator of a fraction by a power of 10 to obtain an equivalent fraction.

Multiplying and Dividing a Decimal by a Multiple of 10

When multiplying by 10, 100, 1000, and so on, a simple rule may be used to obtain the answer. For every zero in the multiplier, move the decimal point one place to the right.

EXAMPLE 13 Multiply.

(a) 3.24×10 **(b)** 15.6×100 **(c)** 0.0026×1000

Solution

(a) $3.24 \times 10 = 32.4$ One zero—move decimal point one place to the right.

(b) $15.6 \times 100 = 1560$ Two zeros—move decimal point two places to the right.

(c) $0.0026 \times 1000 = 2.6$ Three zeros—move decimal point three places to the right.

Practice Problem 13 Multiply.

(a) 0.0016×100 **(b)** 2.34×1000 **(c)** $56.75 \times 10{,}000$

NOTE TO STUDENT: Fully worked-out solutions to all of the Practice Problems can be found at the back of the text starting at page SP-1

The reverse rule is true for division. When dividing by 10, 100, 1000, 10,000, and so on, move the decimal point one place to the left for every zero in the divisor.

EXAMPLE 14 Divide.

(a) $52.6 \div 10$ **(b)** $0.0038 \div 100$ **(c)** $5936.2 \div 1000$

Solution

(a) $\frac{52.6}{10} = 5.26$ Move one place to the left.

(b) $\frac{0.0038}{100} = 0.000038$ Move two places to the left.

(c) $\frac{5936.2}{1000} = 5.9362$ Move three places to the left.

Practice Problem 14 Divide.

(a) $\frac{5.82}{10}$ **(b)** $123.4 \div 1000$ **(c)** $\frac{0.00614}{10{,}000}$

Developing Your Study Skills

Making a Friend in the Class

Attempt to make a friend in your class. You may find that you enjoy sitting together and drawing support and encouragement from one another. Exchange phone numbers so you can call each other whenever you get stuck in your study. Set up convenient times to study together on a regular basis, to do homework, and to review for exams.

You must not depend on a friend or fellow student to tutor you, do your work for you, or in any way be responsible for your learning. However, you will learn from one another as you seek to master the course. Studying with a friend and comparing notes, methods, and solutions can be very helpful. And it can make learning mathematics a lot more fun!

0.4 EXERCISES

Student Solutions Manual | CD/ Video | PH Math Tutor Center | MathXL®Tutorials on CD | MathXL® | MyMathLab® | Interactmath.com

Verbal and Writing Skills

1. A decimal is another way of writing a fraction whose denominator is ______________.

2. We write 0.42 in words as ______________.

3. When dividing 7432.9 by 1000 we move the decimal point ________ places to the ________.

4. When dividing 96.3 by 10,000 we move the decimal point ________ places to the ________.

Write each fraction as a decimal.

5. $\frac{5}{8}$ **6.** $\frac{6}{25}$ **7.** $\frac{3}{15}$ **8.** $\frac{12}{15}$ **9.** $\frac{7}{11}$ **10.** $\frac{2}{3}$

Write each decimal as a fraction in simplified form.

11. 0.8 **12.** 0.15 **13.** 0.625 **14.** 0.08 **15.** 2.6 **16.** 1.8

Add or subtract.

17. $1.71 + 0.38$ **18.** $3.42 + 0.38$ **19.** $2.5 + 3.42 + 4.9$ **20.** $6.31 + 4.2 + 8.5$

21. $46.03 + 215.1 + 0.078$ **22.** $33.01 + 0.38 + 175.401$ **23.** $147.18 - 15.39$ **24.** $131.43 - 86.95$

Multiply or divide.

25. 7.21×4.2 **26.** 7.12×2.6 **27.** 4.23×0.025 **28.** 3.84×0.0017

29. $169{,}000 \times 0.0013$ **30.** $368{,}000 \times 0.00021$ **31.** $7.9728 \div 3.02$ **32.** $6.519 \div 2.05$

33. $0.5230 \div 0.002$ **34.** $0.031 \div 0.005$ **35.** $0.02056 \div 0.08$ **36.** $0.03222 \div 0.09$

Multiply or divide by moving the decimal point.

37. 3.45×1000 **38.** 1.36×1000 **39.** $0.76 \div 100$ **40.** $175{,}318 \div 1000$

41. $7.36 \times 10{,}000$ **42.** $0.00243 \times 100{,}000$ **43.** $73{,}892 \div 100{,}000$ **44.** $3.52 \div 1000$

Mixed Practice

Perform the indicated calculations.

45. 23.75×0.06

46. 1.824×0.004

47. $1.62 + 2.005 + 8.1007$

48. $1.5 + 3.06 + 4.209$

49. $0.05724 \div 0.027$

50. $77.136 \div 0.003$

51. 0.7683×1000

52. $34.72 \times 10{,}000$

Applications

53. ***Measurement*** In a recent chemistry lab, Jerome needed to change the measured data from inches to centimeters. If there are 2.54 cm in an inch, and the original measurement was 9.5 inches, what is the measured data in cms?

54. ***Hybrid Cars*** Hai Hung bought a hybrid electric-gas–powered car because of its great miles per gallon in the city. The car averages 46.2 miles per gallon in the city, and the tank holds 9.7 gallons of gas. How many miles can Hai travel in the city on a full tank of gas?

55. ***Curtain Material*** Lexi decided that she would need 18.5 yards of material to make curtains. If the material she chose cost $11.50 per yard, what did the material for her curtains cost?

56. ***Turkey Weight*** The Parkins family is going to order a turkey for Thanksgiving dinner from Ray's Turkey Farm. Mrs. Parkins estimates that she will need 12 pounds of meat to serve all her guests. The turkey farm owner claims that each turkey yields about 0.78 of its weight in meat. If Mrs. Parkins buys a 17.3-pound turkey, will there be enough meat for everyone?

57. ***Drinking Water*** The EPA standard for safe drinking water is a maximum of 1.3 milligrams of copper per liter of water. A water testing firm found 6.8 milligrams of copper in a 5-liter sample drawn from Jim and Sharon LeBlanc's house. Is the water safe or not? By how much does the amount of copper exceed or fall short of the maximum allowed?

58. ***Wages*** Harry has a part-time job at Stop and Shop. He earns $8.50 an hour. Last week he worked 19 hours. He had hoped to earn at least $150. Did he reach his goal or not? By how much did he exceed or fall short of his goal?

Cumulative Review

Perform each operation. Simplify all answers.

59. $3\frac{1}{2} \div 5\frac{1}{4}$

60. $\frac{3}{8} \cdot \frac{12}{27}$

61. $\frac{12}{25} + \frac{9}{20}$

62. $1\frac{3}{5} - \frac{1}{2}$

How Am I Doing? Sections 0.1–0.4

How are you doing with your homework assignments in Sections 0.1 to 0.4? Do you feel you have mastered the material so far? Do you understand the concepts you have covered? Before you go further in the textbook, take some time to do each of the following problems.

0.1

In exercises 1 and 2, simplify each fraction.

1. $\frac{15}{55}$

2. $\frac{46}{115}$

3. Write $\frac{15}{4}$ as a mixed number.

4. Change $4\frac{5}{7}$ to an improper fraction.

Find the missing number.

5. $\frac{3}{7} = \frac{?}{14}$

6. $\frac{7}{4} = \frac{?}{20}$

0.2

7. Find the LCD, but do not add. $\frac{3}{8}, \frac{5}{6}$, and $\frac{7}{15}$

Perform the calculation indicated. Write the answer in simplest form.

8. $\frac{3}{7} + \frac{2}{7}$

9. $\frac{5}{14} + \frac{2}{21}$

10. $2\frac{3}{4} + 5\frac{2}{3}$

11. $\frac{17}{18} - \frac{5}{9}$

12. $\frac{6}{7} - \frac{2}{3}$

13. $3\frac{1}{5} - 1\frac{3}{8}$

0.3

Perform the calculations indicated. Write the answer in simplest form.

14. $\frac{25}{7} \times \frac{14}{45}$

15. $2\frac{4}{5} \times 3\frac{3}{4}$

16. $4 \div \frac{8}{7}$

17. $2\frac{1}{3} \div 3\frac{1}{4}$

0.4

Change to a decimal. Use bar notation for repeating decimals.

18. $\frac{7}{8}$

19. $\frac{5}{9}$

20. $\frac{3}{200}$

Perform the calculations indicated.

21. $15.23 + 3.6 + 0.821$

22. 3.28×0.63

23. $3.015 \div 6.7$

24. $12.13 - 9.884$

Now turn to page SA-1 for the answer to each of these problems. Each answer also includes a reference to the objective in which the problem is first taught. If you missed any of these problems, you should stop and review the Examples and Practice Problems in the referenced objective. A little review now will help you master the material in the upcoming sections of the text.

1. ____
2. ____
3. ____
4. ____
5. ____
6. ____
7. ____
8. ____
9. ____
10. ____
11. ____
12. ____
13. ____
14. ____
15. ____
16. ____
17. ____
18. ____
19. ____
20. ____
21. ____
22. ____
23. ____
24. ____

0.5 Using Percent

Student Learning Objectives

After studying this section, you will be able to:

1. **Understand the meaning of percent.**
2. **Change a decimal to a percent.**
3. **Change a percent to a decimal.**
4. **Find the percent of a given number.**
5. **Find the missing percent when given two numbers.**

1 Understanding the Meaning of Percent

A **percent** is a fraction that has a denominator of 100. When you say "sixty-seven percent" or write 67%, you are just expressing the fraction $\frac{67}{100}$ in another way. The word *percent* is a shortened form of the Latin words *per centum,* which means "by the hundred." In everyday use, percent means per one hundred.

Russell Camp owns 100 acres of land in Montana. 49 of the acres are covered with trees. The rest of the land is open fields. We say that 49% of his land is covered with trees.

It is important to see that 49% means 49 parts out of 100 parts. It can also be written as a fraction, $\frac{49}{100}$, or as a decimal 0.49. Understanding the meaning of the notation allows you to change from one form to another. For example,

$$49\% = 49 \text{ out of } 100 \text{ parts} = \frac{49}{100} = 0.49.$$

Similarly, you can express a fraction with denominator 100 as a percent or a decimal.

$$\frac{11}{100} \text{ means 11 parts out of 100 or } 11\%. \qquad \text{So } \frac{11}{100} = 11\% = 0.11.$$

2 Changing a Decimal to a Percent

Now that we understand the concept, we can use some quick procedures to change from decimals to percent, and vice versa.

CHANGING A DECIMAL TO PERCENT

1. Move the decimal point two places to the right.
2. Add the % symbol.

EXAMPLE 1 Change to a percent.

(a) 0.23 **(b)** 0.461 **(c)** 0.4

Solution We move the decimal point two places to the right and add the % symbol.

(a) $0.23 = 23\%$ **(b)** $0.461 = 46.1\%$ **(c)** $0.4 = 0.40 = 40\%$

Practice Problem 1 Change to a percent.

(a) 0.92 **(b)** 0.418 **(c)** 0.7

NOTE TO STUDENT: Fully worked-out solutions to all of the Practice Problems can be found at the back of the text starting at page SP-1

Be sure to follow the same procedure for percents that are less than 1%. Remember, 0.01 is 1%. Thus we would expect 0.001 to be less than 1%. $0.001 = 0.1\%$ or one-tenth (0.1) of a percent.

EXAMPLE 2 Change to a percent.

(a) 0.0364 **(b)** 0.0026 **(c)** 0.0008

Solution We move the decimal point two places to the right and add the % symbol.

(a) 0.0364 = 3.64% **(b)** 0.0026 = 0.26% **(c)** 0.0008 = 0.08%

Practice Problem 2 Change to a percent.

(a) 0.0019 **(b)** 0.0736 **(c)** 0.0003

Be sure to follow the same procedure for percents that are greater than 100%. Remember that 1 is 100%. Thus we would expect 1.5 to be greater than 100%. In fact, 1.5 = 150%.

EXAMPLE 3 Change to a percent.

(a) 1.48 **(b)** 2.938 **(c)** 4.5

Solution We move the decimal point two places to the right and add the percent symbol.

(a) 1.48 = 148% **(b)** 2.938 = 293.8% **(c)** 4.5 = 4.50 = 450%

Practice Problem 3 Change to a percent.

(a) 3.04 **(b)** 5.186 **(c)** 2.1

3 Changing a Percent to a Decimal

In this procedure we move the decimal point to the left and remove the % symbol.

CHANGING A PERCENT TO A DECIMAL

1. Move the decimal point two places to the left.
2. Remove the % symbol.

EXAMPLE 4 Change to a decimal.

(a) 4% **(b)** 3.2% **(c)** 0.6%

Solution First we move the decimal point two places to the left. Then we remove the % symbol.

(a) 4% = 4.% = 0.04
↑
The unwritten decimal point is understood to be here.

(b) 3.2% = 0.032 **(c)** 0.6% = 0.006

Practice Problem 4 Change to a decimal.

(a) 7% **(b)** 9.3% **(c)** 0.2%

Calculator

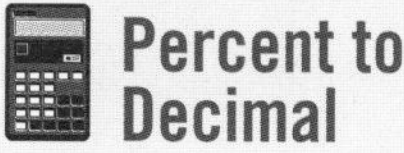

Percent to Decimal

You can use a calculator to change 52% to a decimal. If your calculator has a [%] key, do the following:

Enter: 52 [%]
The display should read:

[0.52]

If your calculator does not have a [%] key, divide the number by 100.
Enter:

52 [÷] 100 [=]

Try the following:

(a) 46% **(b)** 137%
(c) 9.3% **(d)** 6%

Note: The calculator divides by 100 when the percent key is pressed. If you do not have a [%] key, then you can divide by 100 instead.

EXAMPLE 5 Change to a decimal.

(a) 192% **(b)** 254.8% **(c)** 0.027%

Solution First we move the decimal point two places to the left. Then we remove the % symbol.

(a) 192% = 192.% = 1.92

↑

The unwritten decimal point is understood to be here.

(b) 254.8% = 2.548 **(c)** 0.027% = 0.00027

NOTE TO STUDENT: Fully worked-out solutions to all of the Practice Problems can be found at the back of the text starting at page SP-1

Practice Problem 5 Change to a decimal.

(a) 131% **(b)** 301.6% **(c)** 0.04%

4 Finding the Percent of a Given Number

How do we find 60% of 20? Let us relate it to a problem we did in Section 0.2.

Consider the following problem.

$$\begin{array}{ccccc} \text{What} & \text{is} & \frac{3}{5} & \text{of} & 20? \\ \downarrow & \downarrow & \downarrow & \downarrow & \downarrow \\ \boxed{?} & = & \frac{3}{5} & \times & 20 \end{array}$$

$$\boxed{?} = \frac{3}{\cancel{5}} \times \overset{4}{\cancel{20}} = 12 \quad \text{The answer is 12.}$$

Since a percent is really a fraction, a percent problem is solved similarly to the way a fraction problem is solved. Since $\frac{3}{5} = \frac{6}{10} = 60\%$, we could write the problem as

$$\begin{array}{ccccc} \text{What} & \text{is} & 60\% & \text{of} & 20? \\ \downarrow & \downarrow & \downarrow & \downarrow & \downarrow \\ \boxed{?} & = & 60\% & \times & 20 \end{array}$$

$$\boxed{?} = 0.60 \times 20$$

$$\boxed{?} = 12.0 \quad \text{The answer is 12.}$$

Thus we have developed the following rule.

FINDING THE PERCENT OF A NUMBER

To find the percent of a number, change the percent to a decimal and multiply the number by the decimal.

Calculator

Finding the Percent of a Number

You can use a calculator to find 12% of 48.

Enter:

12 [%] [×] 48 [=]

The display should read

[5.76]

If your calculator does not have a [%] key, do the following:

Enter: 0.12 [×] 48 [=]

What is 54% of 450?

EXAMPLE 6 Find.

(a) 10% of 36 **(b)** 2% of 350 **(c)** 182% of 12 **(d)** 0.3% of 42

Solution

(a) 10% of 36 = 0.10 × 36 = 3.6

(b) 2% of 350 = 0.02 × 350 = 7

(c) 182% of 12 = 1.82 × 12 = 21.84

(d) 0.3% of 42 = 0.003 × 42 = 0.126

Practice Problem 6 Find. **(a)** 18% of 50 **(b)** 4% of 64 **(c)** 156% of 35

There are many real-life applications for finding the percent of a number. When you go shopping in a store, you may find sale merchandise marked 35% off. This means that the sale price is 35% off the regular price. That is, 35% of the regular price is subtracted from the regular price to get the sale price.

EXAMPLE 7 A store is having a sale of 35% off the retail price of all sofas. Melissa wants to buy a particular sofa that normally sells for $595.

(a) How much will Melissa save if she buys the sofa on sale?

(b) What will the purchase price be if Melissa buys the sofa on sale?

Solution

(a) To find 35% of $595 we will need to multiply 0.35×595.

$$\begin{array}{r} 595 \\ \times \quad 0.35 \\ \hline 2975 \\ 1785 \\ \hline 208.25 \end{array}$$

Thus Melissa will save $208.25 if she buys the sofa on sale.

(b) The purchase price is the difference between the original price and the amount saved.

$$\begin{array}{r} 595.00 \\ -\ 208.25 \\ \hline 386.75 \end{array}$$

If Melissa buys the sofa on sale, she will pay $386.75.

Practice Problem 7 John received a 4.2% pay raise at work this year. He had previously earned $38,000 per year.

(a) What was the amount of his pay raise in dollars?

(b) What is his new salary?

5 Finding the Missing Percent When Given Two Numbers

Recall that we can write $\frac{3}{4}$ as $\frac{75}{100}$ or 75%. If we were asked the question, "What percent is 3 of 4?" we would say 75%. This gives us a procedure for finding what percent one number is of a second number.

FINDING THE MISSING PERCENT

1. Write a fraction with the two numbers. The number *after* the word "of" is always the denominator, and the other number is the numerator.
2. Simplify the fraction (if possible).
3. Change the fraction to a decimal.
4. Express the decimal as a percent.

EXAMPLE 8 What percent of 24 is 15?

Solution This can be solved quickly as follows.

Step 1 $\frac{15}{24}$ Write the relationship as a fraction. The number after "of" is 24, so 24 is the denominator.

Step 2 $\frac{15}{24} = \frac{5}{8}$ Simplify the fraction (when possible).

Step 3 $= 0.625$ Change the fraction to a decimal.

Step 4 $= 62.5\%$ Change the decimal to percent.

Practice Problem 8 What percent of 148 is 37?

The question in Example 8 can also be written as "15 is what percent of 24?" To answer the question, we begin by writing the relationship as $\frac{15}{24}$. Remember that "of 24" means 24 will be the denominator.

EXAMPLE 9 **(a)** 82 is what percent of 200?

(b) What percent of 16 is 3.8? **(c)** $150 is what percent of $120?

Solution

(a) 82 is what percent of 200?

$\frac{82}{200}$ Write the relationship as a fraction with 200 in the denominator.

$$\frac{82}{200} = \frac{41}{100} = 0.41 = 41\%$$

(b) What percent of 16 is 3.8?

$\frac{3.8}{16}$ Write the relationship as a fraction.

You can divide to change the fraction to a decimal and then change the decimal to a percent.

$$16\overline{)3.8000} = 0.2375 \rightarrow 23.75\%$$

(c) $150 is what percent of $120?

$\frac{150}{120} = \frac{5}{4}$ Reduce the fraction whenever possible to make the division easier.

$$4\overline{)5.00} = 1.25 \rightarrow 125\%$$

Practice Problem 9

(a) What percent of 48 is 24? **(b)** 4 is what percent of 25?

NOTE TO STUDENT: Fully worked-out solutions to all of the Practice Problems can be found at the back of the text starting at page SP-1

Calculator

Finding the Percent Given Two Numbers

You can use a calculator to find a missing percent.
What percent of 95 is 19?

1. Enter as a fraction.
   19 [÷] 95
2. Change to a percent.
   19 [÷] 95 [×] 100 [=]

The display should read [20]

This means 20%.

What percent of 625 is 250?

EXAMPLE 10 Marcia made 29 shots on goal during the last high school field hockey season. She actually scored a goal eight times. What percent of her total shots were goals? Round your answer to the nearest whole percent.

Solution Marcia scored a goal eight times out of 29 tries. We want to know what percent of 29 is 8.

Step 1	$\frac{8}{29}$	Express the relationship as a fraction. The number after the word *of* is 29, so 29 appears in the denominator.
Step 2	$\frac{8}{29} = \frac{8}{29}$	Note that this fraction cannot be reduced.
Step 3	$= 0.2758\ldots$	The decimal equivalent of the fraction has many digits.
Step 4	$= 27.58\ldots\%$	We change the decimal to a percent, which we round to the nearest whole percent.
	$\approx 28\%$	(The $\approx$ symbol means approximately equal to.)

Therefore, Marcia scored a goal approximately 28% of the time she made a shot on goal.

Practice Problem 10 Roberto scored a basket 430 times out of 1256 attempts during his high school basketball career. What percent of the time did he score a basket? Round your answer to the nearest whole percent.

0.5 Exercises

Student Solutions Manual | CD/Video | PH Math Tutor Center | MathXL®Tutorials on CD | MathXL® | MyMathLab® | Interactmath.com

Verbal and Writing Skills

1. When you write 19%, what do you really mean? Describe the meaning in your own words.

2. When you try to solve a problem like "What percent of 80 is 30?" how do you know if you should write the fraction as $\frac{80}{30}$ or as $\frac{30}{80}$?

Change to a percent.

3. 0.28

4. 0.61

5. 0.568

6. 0.089

7. 0.076

8. 0.325

9. 2.39

10. 7.4

Change to a decimal.

11. 3%

12. 66%

13. 0.4%

14. 0.62%

15. 250%

16. 175%

17. 7.4%

18. 87.59%

Find the following.

19. What is 8% of 65?

20. What is 7% of 69?

21. What is 10% of 130?

22. What is 25% of 600?

23. What is 112% of 65?

24. What is 154% of 270?

25. 36 is what percent of 24?

26. 49 is what percent of 28?

27. What percent of 340 is 17?

28. 48 is what percent of 600?

29. 75 is what percent of 30?

30. What percent of 35 is 28?

Applications

31. ***Exam Grades*** Dave took an exam with 80 questions. He had 68 answered correctly. What was his grade for the exam? Write the grade as a percent.

32. ***Soccer*** Ronaldo, the great Brazilian soccer star, made 8 goals out of 21 attempts on goal in the 2002 World Cup Series. What percent of the times that he shoots does Ronaldo make a goal? (Round to the nearest whole percent.)

33. ***Tipping*** Diana and Russ ate a meal costing $32.80 when they went out to dinner. If they want to leave the standard 15% tip for their server, how much will they tip and what will their total bill be?

34. ***CD Failure*** Music CDs have a failure rate of 1.8%. (They skip or get stuck on a song.) If 36,000 CDs were manufactured last week, how many of them were defective?

35. ***Food Budget*** The Gonzalez family has a combined monthly income of $1850. Their food budget is $380/month. What percentage of their monthly income is budgeted for food? (Round your answer to the nearest whole percent.)

36. ***Survey*** In a local college survey, it was discovered that 137 out of 180 students had a grandparent not born in the United States. What percent of the students had a grandparent not born in the United States? (Round your answer to the nearest hundredth of a percent.)

37. ***Gift Returns*** Last Christmas season, the Jones Mill Outlet Store chain calculated that they sold 36,000 gift items. If they assume that there will be a 1.5% return rate after the holidays, how many gifts can they expect to be exchanged?

38. ***Rent*** The total cost of a downtown Boston apartment, including rent, heat, electricity, and water is $3690 per month. Sarah is renting this apartment with four friends. Based on a complicated formula, which takes into account the size of her bedroom and the furniture she brought to the apartment, she must pay 17% of the apartment cost each month. What is her monthly cost?

39. ***Wages*** Jim is earning $12.50 per hour as a cook. He has earned an 8% pay raise this year. What will his raise be, and what will his new hourly rate be?

40. ***On-Time Arrivals*** Eastern Shores charter airline had 2390 flights last year. Of these flights, 560 did not land on time. What percent of the flights landed on time? Round your answer to the nearest whole percent.

41. ***Salary*** Abdul sells computers for a local computer outlet. He gets paid $450 per month plus a commission of 3.8% on all the computer hardware he sells. Last year he sold $780,000 worth of computer hardware. (a) What was his sales commission on the $780,000 worth of hardware he sold? (b) What was his annual salary (that is, his monthly pay and commission combined)?

42. ***Business Travel*** Bruce sells medical supplies on the road. He logged 18,600 miles in his car last year. He declared 65% of his mileage as business travel. (a) How many miles did he travel on business last year? (b) If his company reimburses him 31 cents for each mile traveled, how much should he be paid for travel expenses?

To Think About

43. ***Tipping*** Fred and Nancy Adams go out once a week to a restaurant where their daughter is the chef. They are given a 33% discount on the cost of the meal. They always leave a tip of 20%. Fred thinks the tip should be based on the cost of the meal before the discount. Nancy thinks the tip should be based on the cost of the meal after the discount. If they normally purchase a meal each week that costs $45 for the two of them before the discount and use Nancy's method of calculating the tip, by how much will the tip increase if they switch to Fred's method?

44. ***Tax Deduction*** Dave Bagley traveled 24,500 miles last year. He is a salesperson and 74% of his mileage is for business purposes. He was planning to deduct 31 cents per business mile on his income tax return. However, his accountant told him he can deduct 35 cents per mile. By how much will his deduction increase if he uses the new larger amount?

Cumulative Review

45. ***Checking Account Balance*** Janeen had an opening balance of $45.50 in her checking account this month. She deposited her paycheck of $1189 and a refund check of $33.90. She was charged by the bank $1.50 for ATM fees. Then she made out checks for $98.00, $128.00, $56.89, and $445.88. What will be her final balance at the end of the month?

46. ***Car Loan*** Tally is buying a car and has a bank loan. He has to make 33 more monthly payments of $188.50. How much money will he pay to the bank over the next 33 months?

47. ***Gas Mileage*** Dan took a trip in his Ford Taurus. At the start of the trip his car odometer read 68,459.5 miles. At the end of the trip his car odometer read 69,229.5 miles. He used 35 gallons of gas on the trip. How many miles per gallon did his car achieve?

48. ***Rainfall*** In Hilo, Hawaii, Brad spent three months working in a restaurant for a summer job. In June he observed that 4.6 inches of rain fell. In July the rainfall was 4.5 inches and in August it was 2.9 inches. What was the average monthly rainfall that summer for those three months in Hilo?

0.6 Rounding and Estimating

1 Using Rounding to Estimate

As we begin this section, we will take some time to be sure you understand the idea of rounding a number. You will probably recall the following simple rule from your previous mathematics courses.

ROUNDING A NUMBER

If the first digit to the right of the round-off place is

1. less than 5, we make no change to the digit in the round-off place.
2. 5 or more, we increase the digit in the round-off place by 1.

To illustrate, 4689 rounded to the nearest hundred is 4700. Rounding 233,987 to the nearest ten thousand, we obtain 230,000. We will now use our experience in rounding as we discuss the general area of estimation.

Estimation is the process of finding an approximate answer. It is not designed to provide an exact answer. Estimation will give you a rough idea of what the answer might be. For any given problem, you may choose to estimate in many different ways.

ESTIMATION BY ROUNDING

1. Round each number so that there is one nonzero digit.
2. Perform the calculation with the rounded numbers.

EXAMPLE 1 Find an estimate of the product 5368×2864.

Solution

Step 1 Round 5368 to 5000.

Round 2864 to 3000.

Step 2 Multiply.

$$5000 \times 3000 = 15{,}000{,}000$$

An estimate of the product is 15,000,000.

Practice Problem 1 Find an estimate of the product $128{,}621 \times 378$.

EXAMPLE 2 The four walls of a college classroom are $22\frac{1}{4}$ feet long and $8\frac{3}{4}$ feet high. A painter needs to know the area of these four walls in square feet. Since paints is sold in gallons, an estimate will do. Estimate the area of the four walls.

Solution

Step 1 Round $22\frac{1}{4}$ feet to 20 feet.

Round $8\frac{3}{4}$ feet to 9 feet.

Step 2 Multiply 20×9 to obtain an estimate of the area of one wall.
Multiply $20 \times 9 \times 4$ to obtain an estimate of the area of all four walls.

$$20 \times 9 \times 4 = 720 \text{ square feet}$$

Our estimate for the painter is 720 square feet of wall space.

Student Learning Objective

After studying this section, you will be able to:

1 **Use rounding to estimate.**

NOTE TO STUDENT: Fully worked-out solutions to all of the Practice Problems can be found at the back of the text starting at page SP-1

NOTE TO STUDENT: Fully worked-out solutions to all of the Practice Problems can be found at the back of the text starting at page SP-1

Practice Problem 2 Mr. and Mrs. Ramirez need to carpet two rooms of their house. One room measures $12\frac{1}{2}$ feet by $9\frac{3}{4}$ feet. The other room measures $14\frac{1}{4}$ feet by $18\frac{1}{2}$ feet. Estimate the number of square feet (square footage) in these two rooms.

EXAMPLE 3 Won Lin has a small compact car. He drove 396.8 miles in his car and used 8.4 gallons of gas.

(a) Estimate the number of miles he gets per gallon.

(b) Estimate how much it will cost him for fuel to drive on a cross-country trip of 2764 miles if gasoline usually costs $\$1.59\frac{9}{10}$ per gallon.

Solution

(a) Round 396.8 miles to 400 miles. Round 8.4 gallons to 8 gallons. Now divide.

$$8\overline{)400}\quad = 50$$

Won Lin's car gets about 50 miles per gallon.

(b) We will need to use the information we found in part (a) to determine how many gallons of gasoline Won Lin will use on his trip. Round 2764 miles to 3000 miles and divide 3000 miles by 50 gallons.

$$50\overline{)3000}\quad = 60$$

Won Lin will use about 60 gallons of gas for his cross-country trip.

To estimate the cost, we need to ask ourselves, "What kind of an estimate are we looking for?" It may be sufficient to round $\$1.59\frac{9}{10}$ to \$2.00 and multiply.

$$60 \times \$2.00 = \$120.00$$

Keep in mind that this is a broad estimate. You may want an estimate that will be closer to the exact answer. In that case round $\$1.59\frac{9}{10}$ to \$1.60 and multiply.

$$60 \times \$1.60 = \$96.00$$

CAUTION An estimate is only a rough guess. If we are estimating the cost of something, we may want to round the unit cost to a value that is closer to the actual amount so that our estimate is more accurate. When we estimate costs, it is a good idea to round to a value above the actual unit cost to make sure that we will have enough money for the expenditure. The actual cost to the nearest penny of the cross-country trip in Example 3 is \$93.56.

Practice Problem 3 Roberta drove 422.8 miles in her truck and used 19.3 gallons of gas. Assume that gasoline costs $\$1.69\frac{9}{10}$ per gallon.

(a) Estimate the number of miles she gets per gallon.

(b) Estimate how much it will cost her to drive to Chicago and back, a distance of 3862 miles.

Other words that indicate estimation in word problems are *about* and *approximate.*

EXAMPLE 4 A local manufacturing company releases 1684 pounds of sulfur dioxide per day from its plant. The company operates 294 days per year and has been operating at this level for 32 years. Approximately how many pounds of sulfur dioxide have been released into the air by this company over the last 32 years?

Solution The word *approximately* means we are looking for an estimate. We begin by rounding the given data so that there is only one nonzero digit in each number.

Round 1684 tons to 2000 tons.
Round 294 days to 300 days.
Round 32 years to 30 years.

Now determine the calculation you would perform to find the answer and calculate using the rounded numbers. We multiply the amount released in one day × the number of days in an operating year × years.

$$2000 \times 300 \times 30 = 18{,}000{,}000$$

Thus 18,000,000 tons is an approximation of the sulfur dioxide released by the company during its 32 years of operation.

Practice Problem 4 A space probe is sent from Earth at 43,300 miles per hour toward the planet Pluto, which has an average distance from Earth of 3,580,000,000 miles.

(a) About how many hours will it take for the space probe to travel from Earth to Pluto?
(b) About how many days will it take for the space probe to travel from Earth to Pluto?

EXAMPLE 5 Find an estimate for 2.68% of $54,361.92.

Solution Begin by writing 2.68% as a decimal.

$$2.68\% = 0.0268$$

Next round 0.0268 to the nearest hundredth.

0.0268 is 0.03 rounded to the nearest hundredth.

Finally, round $54,361.92 to $50,000.

Now multiply.

$0.03 \times 50{,}000 = 1500$ Remember that to find a percent of a number you multiply.

Thus we estimate the answer to be $1500.

To get a better estimate of 2.68% of $54,361.92, you may wish to round $54,361.92 to the nearest thousand. Try it and compare this estimate to the previous one. Remember, an estimate is only an approximation. How close you should try to get to the exact answer depends on what you need the estimate for.

Practice Problem 5 Find an estimate for 56.93% of $293,567.12.

0.6 EXERCISES

 Student Solutions Manual
 CD/ Video
 PH Math Tutor Center
 MathXL®Tutorials on CD
 MathXL®
 MyMathLab®
Interactmath.com

In exercises 1–10, follow the principles of estimation to find an approximate value. Round each number so that there is one nonzero digit. Do not find the exact value.

1. 693×307

2. 437×892

3. 2862×5986

4. 4893×6174

5. $14 + 73 + 80 + 21 + 56$

6. $318 + 494 + 613 + 243$

7. $41\overline{)829{,}346}$

8. $16\overline{)5{,}846{,}213}$

9. $\dfrac{2714}{31500}$

10. $\dfrac{53610}{786}$

11. Find 17% of $21,365.85.

12. Find 4.9% of $9321.88.

Applications

In exercises 13–22, determine an estimate of the exact answer. Use estimation by rounding. Do not find the exact value.

▲ **13.** ***Carpeting*** Estimate the cost of new carpeting that costs $22.50 per square yard, if you want to carpet a room that is 18.5 square yards in size.

▲ **14.** ***Garden Design*** Estimate the size of Mr. Brown's garden if it measures $15\frac{2}{3}$ feet by $11\frac{2}{3}$ feet.

15. ***Checkout Sales*** A typical customer at the local Piggly Wiggly supermarket spends approximately $82 at the checkout register. The store keeps four registers open, and each handles 22 customers per hour. Estimate the amount of money the store receives in one hour.

16. ***Weekend Spending Money*** The Westerly Community Credit Union in Rhode Island has found that on Fridays, the average customer withdraws $85 from the ATM for weekend spending money. Each ATM averages 19 customers per hour. There are five machines. Estimate the amount of money withdrawn by customers in one hour.

17. ***Gas Mileage*** Rod's trip from Salt Lake City to his cabin in the mountains was 117.7 miles. If his car used 3.8 gallons of gas for the trip, estimate the number of miles his car gets to the gallon.

18. ***Book Transport*** The Paltrows are transferring their stock of books from one store to another. To save money, they are moving the books themselves. If their car can transport 430 books per trip, and they have 11,900 books to move, estimate the number of trips it will take.

19. ***Revenue*** For fiscal year 2002–2003, Krispy Kreme Donuts had a total revenue of $491,549.00. If there were 279 stores systemwide, estimate the average revenue per store.

20. ***Happy Meals Sales*** The local McDonald's registered $437,690 in sales last month. They know from experience that 18% of their sales are Happy Meals. Estimate the amount of money spent on Happy Meals last month.

21. ***Education Budget*** In the year 2000, it was estimated that 26% of the California state budget of $217,970,000,000 was spent for education. Estimate the amount of money spent on education in California in 2000.

(*Source:* U.S. Census Bureau)

22. ***Operations*** A recent survey of local hospitals by a state medical board estimates that 6.23% of all operations performed in hospitals are unnecessary. If 28,364,122 operations were performed last year, estimate the number of unnecessary operations.

Income and Expenditures *The data for exercises 23–26 was obtained by the U.S. Bureau of Labor Statistics.*

23. In 2002 it was found that the average consumer aged 25 to 34 years had an annual income of \$38,945.89 and spent 14% of his/her income on food. Estimate the annual expenditure for food for a consumer in this age group.

24. In 2002 it was found that the average consumer aged 45 to 54 years had an annual income of \$46,160.56 and spent 31% of his/her income on housing. Estimate the annual expenditure for housing for a consumer in this age group.

25. In 2002 it was found that the average consumer 65 years of age or older had an annual income of \$26,533.67. It was found that this average consumer spent \$3247.54 per year for health care. Estimate the percent of income spent for healthcare for consumers in this group.

26. In 2002 it was found that the average consumer aged 35 to 44 years of age had an annual income of \$45,149.82. It was found that this average consumer spent \$8702.47 per year for transportation. Estimate the percent of income spend for transportation for consumers in this group.

To Think About

27. ***Long Distance Phone Bills*** Laura's boyfriend, James, was transferred to San Diego. He averages 43 long-distance calls to her per month. The average cost of his long-distance calls is \$3.24 per call. A new long-distance telephone company has promised James a 23% reduction in the cost of his phone bills. If that is true, estimate how much he will save in one year.

28. ***Commuting Costs*** Eddie usually drives his car to his job in Denver. His car costs 8 cents per mile to drive. He commutes 22 miles round-trip every day, and drives to work 280 days per year. He can buy an unlimited-use bus pass for one year for \$300. Estimate how much he would save by taking the bus to work.

Cumulative Review

29. What is 0.6% of 350?

30. ***Basketball*** If Samuel plays basketball and scores 9 baskets out of 16 throws, what percent of the time does he score a basket?

31. ***Tipping*** Michael had breakfast at the Agawam Diner. The cost of his breakfast listed on the menu was \$5.85. If he leaves a 15% tip, what will be the total amount he paid for his meal?

32. ***Tire Inspection*** In a recent tire inspection for Ford Explorers, local dealers found that 12% of the treads were defective. For each Explorer that was defective, the dealer offered immediate replacement of all five tires (including the spare). If the local dealers inspected the tires on 450 Explorers, how many new tires did they need?

0.7 Using the Mathematics Blueprint for Problem Solving

Student Learning Objective

After studying this section, you will be able to:

 **Use the Mathematics Blueprint to solve real-life problems.**

1 Using the Mathematics Blueprint to Solve Real-life Problems

When a builder constructs a new home or office building, he or she often has a blueprint. This accurate drawing shows the basic form of the building. It also shows the dimensions of the structure to be built. This blueprint serves as a useful reference throughout the construction process.

Similarly, when solving real-life problems, it is helpful to have a "mathematics blueprint." This is a simple way to organize the information provided in the word problem, in a chart, or in a graph. You can record the facts you need to use. You can determine what it is you are trying to find and how you can go about actually finding it. You can record other information that you think will be helpful as you work through the problem.

As we solve real-life problems, we will use three steps.

Step 1 ***Understand the problem.*** Here we will read through the problem. Draw a picture if it will help, and use the Mathematics Blueprint as a guide to assist us in thinking through the steps needed to solve the problem.

Step 2 ***Solve and state the answer.*** We will use arithmetic or algebraic procedures along with problem-solving strategies to find a solution.

Step 3 ***Check.*** We will use a variety of techniques to see if the answer in step 2 is the solution to the word problem. This will include estimating to see if the answer is reasonable, repeating our calculation, and working backward from the answer to see if we arrive at the original conditions of the problem.

 **EXAMPLE 1** Nancy and John want to install wall-to-wall carpeting in their living room. The floor of the rectangular living room is $11\frac{2}{3}$ feet wide and $19\frac{1}{2}$ feet long. How much will it cost if the carpet is $18.00 per square yard?

Solution

1. ***Understand the problem.*** First, read the problem carefully. Drawing a sketch of the living room may help you see what is required. The carpet will cover the floor of the living room, so we need to find the area. Now we fill in the Mathematics Blueprint.

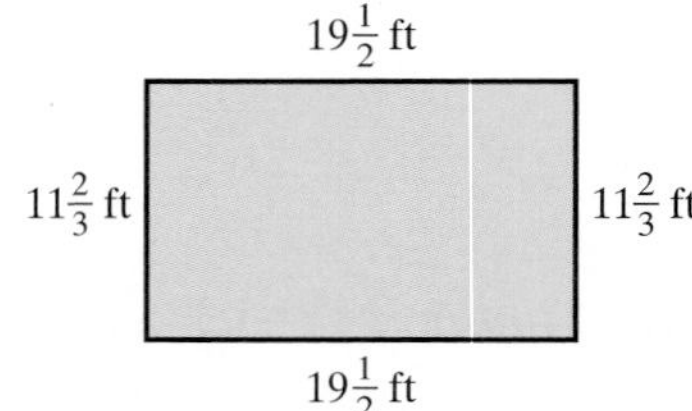

Mathematics Blueprint for Problem Solving

Gather the Facts	What Am I Solving For?	What Must I Calculate?	Key Points to Remember
The living room measures $11\frac{2}{3}$ ft by $19\frac{1}{2}$ ft. The carpet costs $18.00 per square yard.	**(a)** the area of the room in square feet **(b)** the area of the room in square yards **(c)** the cost of the carpet	**(a)** Multiply $11\frac{2}{3}$ ft by $19\frac{1}{2}$ ft to get area in square feet. **(b)** Divide the number of square feet by 9 to get the number of square yards. **(c)** Multiply the number of square yards by $18.00.	There are 9 square feet, 3 feet × 3 feet, in 1 square yard; therefore, we must divide the number of square feet by 9 to obtain square yards.

2. ***Solve and state the answer.***

(a) To find the area of a rectangle, we multiply the length times the width.

$$11\frac{2}{3} \times 19\frac{1}{2} = \frac{35}{3} \times \frac{39}{2}$$
$$= \frac{455}{2} = 227\frac{1}{2} \text{ sq ft}$$

A minimum of $227\frac{1}{2}$ square feet of carpet will be needed. We say a minimum because some carpet may be wasted in cutting. Carpet is sold by the square yard. We will want to know the amount of carpet needed in square yards.

(b) To determine the area in square yards, we divide $227\frac{1}{2}$ by 9. (9 sq ft = 1 sq yd.)

$$227\frac{1}{2} \div 9 = \frac{455}{2} \div \frac{9}{1}$$
$$= \frac{455}{2} \times \frac{1}{9} = \frac{455}{18} = 25\frac{5}{18} \text{ sq yd}$$

A minimum of $25\frac{5}{18}$ square yards of carpet will be needed.

(c) Since the carpet costs $18.00 per square yard, we will multiply the number of square yards needed by $18.00.

$$25\frac{5}{18} \times 18 = \frac{455}{18} \times \frac{18}{1} = \$455$$

The carpet will cost a minimum of $455.00 for this room.

3. ***Check.*** We will estimate to see if our answers are reasonable.

(a) We will estimate by rounding each number to the nearest 10.

$$11\frac{2}{3} \times 19\frac{1}{2} \longrightarrow 10 \times 20 = 200 \text{ sq ft}$$

This is close to our answer of $227\frac{1}{2}$ sq ft. Our answer is reasonable. ✓

(b) We will estimate by rounding to one significant digit.

$$227\frac{1}{2} \div 9 \longrightarrow 200 \div 10 = 20 \text{ sq yd}$$

This is close to our answer of $25\frac{5}{18}$ sq yd. Our answer is reasonable. ✓

(c) We will estimate by rounding each number to the nearest 10.

$$25\frac{5}{18} \times 18 \longrightarrow 30 \times 20 = \$600$$

This is close to our answer of $455. Our answer seems reasonable. ✓

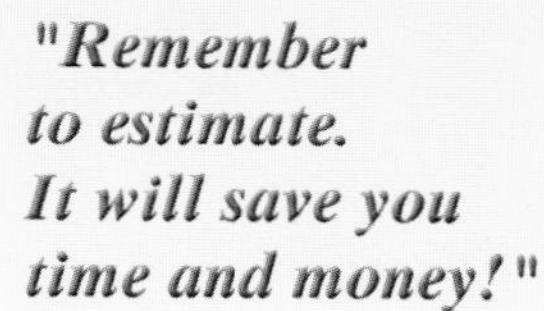

"Remember
to estimate.
It will save you
time and money!"

Practice Problem 1 Jeff went to help Abby pick out wall-to-wall carpet for her new house. Her rectangular living room measures $16\frac{1}{2}$ feet by $10\frac{1}{2}$ feet. How much will it cost to carpet the room if the carpet costs $20 per square yard?

***NOTE TO STUDENT:** Fully worked-out solutions to all of the Practice Problems can be found at the back of the text starting at page SP-1*

Mathematics Blueprint for Problem Solving

Gather the Facts	What Am I Solving For?	What Must I Calculate?	Key Points to Remember

TO THINK ABOUT: Example 1 Follow-Up Assume that the carpet in Example 1 comes in a standard width of 12 feet. How much carpet will be wasted if it is laid out on the living room floor in one strip that is $19\frac{1}{2}$ feet long? How much carpet will be wasted if it is laid in two sections side by side that are each $11\frac{2}{3}$ feet long? Assuming you have to pay for wasted carpet, what is the minimum cost to carpet the room?

EXAMPLE 2 The following chart shows the 2003 sales of Micropower Computer Software for each of the four regions of the United States. Use the chart to answer the following questions (round all answers to the nearest whole percent):

(a) What percent of the sales personnel are assigned to the Northeast?

(b) What percent of the volume of sales is attributed to the Northeast?

(c) What percent of the sales personnel are assigned to the Southeast?

(d) What percent of the volume of sales is attributed to the Southeast?

(e) Which of these two regions of the country has sales personnel that appear to be more effective in terms of the volume of sales?

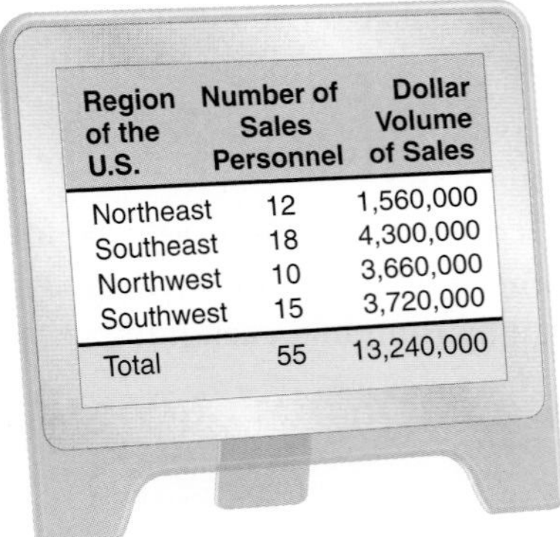

Region of the U.S.	Number of Sales Personnel	Dollar Volume of Sales
Northeast	12	1,560,000
Southeast	18	4,300,000
Northwest	10	3,660,000
Southwest	15	3,720,000
Total	55	13,240,000

Solution

1. ***Understand the problem.*** We will only need to deal with figures from the Northeast region and the Southeast region.

Mathematics Blueprint for Problem Solving

Gather the Facts	What Am I Solving For?	What Must I Calculate?	Key Points to Remember
Personnel: 12 Northeast 18 Southeast 55 total Sales Volume: $1,560,000 NE $4,300,000 SE $13,240,000 Total	**(a)** the percent of the total personnel in the Northeast **(b)** the percent of the total sales in the Northeast **(c)** the percent of the total personnel in the Southeast **(d)** the percent of the total sales in the Southeast **(e)** compare the percentages from the two regions	**(a)** 12 of 55 is what percent? Divide. $12 \div 55$ **(b)** 1,560,000 of 13,240,000 is what percent? $1{,}560{,}000 \div 13{,}240{,}000$ **(c)** $18 \div 55$ **(d)** $4{,}300{,}000 \div 13{,}240{,}000$	We do not need to use the numbers for the Northwest or the Southwest.

2. ***Solve and state the answer.***

(a) $\frac{12}{55} = 0.21818\ldots$

$\approx 22\%$

(b) $\frac{1,560,000}{13,240,000} = \frac{156}{1324} \approx 0.1178$

$\approx 12\%$

(c) $\frac{18}{55} = 0.32727\ldots$

$\approx 33\%$

(d) $\frac{4,300,000}{13,240,000} = \frac{430}{1324} \approx 0.3248$

$\approx 32\%$

(e) We notice that 22% of the sales force in the Northeast made 12% of the sales. The percent of the sales compared to the percent of the sales force is about half (12% of 24% would be half) or 50%. 33% of the sales force in the Southeast made 32% of the sales. The percent of sales compared to the percent of the sales force is close to 100%. We must be cautious here. *If there are no other significant factors,* it would appear that the Southeast sales force is more effective. (There may be other significant factors affecting sales, such as a recession in the Northeast, new and inexperienced sales personnel, or fewer competing companies in the Southeast.)

3. ***Check.*** You may want to use a calculator to check the division in step 2, or you may use estimation.

(a) $\frac{12}{55} \rightarrow \frac{10}{60} \approx 0.17$

$= 17\%$ ✓

(b) $\frac{1,560,000}{13,240,000} \rightarrow \frac{1,600,000}{13,000,000} \approx 0.12$

$= 12\%$ ✓

(c) $\frac{18}{55} \rightarrow \frac{20}{60} \approx 0.33$

$= 33\%$ ✓

(d) $\frac{4,300,000}{13,240,000} \rightarrow \frac{4,300,000}{13,000,000} \approx 0.33$

$= 33\%$ ✓

Practice Problem 2 Using the chart for Example 2, answer the following questions. (Round all answers to the nearest whole percent.)

(a) What percent of the sales personnel are assigned to the Northwest?

(b) What percent of the sales volume is attributed to the Northwest?

(c) What percent of the sales personnel are assigned to the Southwest?

(d) What percent of the sales volume is attributed to the Southwest?

(e) Which of these two regions of the country has sales personnel that appear to be more effective in terms of volume of sales?

NOTE TO STUDENT: Fully worked-out solutions to all of the Practice Problems can be found at the back of the text starting at page SP-1

Mathematics Blueprint for Problem Solving

Gather the Facts	What Am I Solving For?	What Must I Calculate?	Key Points to Remember

TO THINK ABOUT: Example 2 Follow-Up Suppose in 2006 the number of sales personnel (55) increases by 60%. What would the new number of sales personnel be? Suppose in 2006 that the number of sales personnel decreases by 60% from the number of sales personnel in 2003. What would the new number be? Why is this number not 55, since we have increased the number by 60% and then decreased the result by 60%? Explain.

0.7 EXERCISES

Student Solutions Manual | CD/ Video | PH Math Tutor Center | MathXL®Tutorials on CD | MathXL® | MyMathLab® | Interactmath.com

Applications

Use the Mathematics Blueprint for Problem Solving to help you solve each of the following exercises.

▲ **1.** ***Vinyl Flooring*** Jocelyn wants to put new vinyl flooring in her kitchen. The kitchen measures $12\frac{3}{4}$ feet long by $9\frac{1}{2}$ feet wide. If the vinyl flooring she chose costs \$20.00 per square yard, how much will the new flooring cost her? (Round your answer to the nearest cent.)

▲ **2.** ***Decking Costs*** The Carters need to replace the deck floor off their kitchen door. The deck is $11\frac{1}{2}$ feet by $20\frac{1}{2}$ feet. If the new decking costs \$4.50 per square foot, how much will it cost them to replace the deck? (Round your answer to the nearest cent.)

▲ **3.** ***Garden Design*** Jenna White has room for a rectangular garden that can measure as much as $15\frac{1}{2}$ feet wide and $25\frac{2}{3}$ feet long.

(a) She decides the garden should be as large as possible, but wants to fence it off to protect the vegetables from the neighborhood raccoons. How much fencing does she need?

(b) She finds that she can buy a prepackaged 90 feet of fencing for \$155.00 or she can get a cut-to-order length for \$2.10 per foot. Which should she buy? How much money does she save?

▲ **4.** ***Pond Design*** The Lee family is installing a backyard pond for their prize koi. (A koi is a kind of fish bred in Japan. They are noted for their large size and variety of color.)

(a) If the pond measures $11\frac{1}{2}$ feet by 7 feet, and is $3\frac{1}{2}$ feet deep, how much water will it take to fill the pond?

(b) If each cubic foot is 7.5 gallons, how many gallons of water will the pond hold?

(c) If at least 200 gallons of water is recommended for each koi, how many koi can the Lee family place in their pond?

Exercise Training *The following directions are posted on the wall at the gym.*

Beginning exercise training schedule

On day 1, each athlete will begin the morning as follows:

Jog................	$1\frac{1}{2}$ miles
Walk.............	$1\frac{3}{4}$ miles
Rest..............	$2\frac{1}{2}$ minutes
Walk.............	1 mile

5. Betty's athletic trainer told her to follow the beginning exercise training schedule on day 1. On day 2, she is to increase all distances and times by $\frac{1}{3}$ that of day 1. On day 3, she is to increase all distances and times by $\frac{1}{3}$ that of day 2. What will be her training schedule on day 3?

6. Melinda's athletic trainer told her to follow the beginning exercise training schedule on day 1. On day 2, she is to increase all distances and times by $\frac{1}{3}$ that of day 1. On day 3, she is to once again increase all distances and times by $\frac{1}{3}$ that of day 1. What will be her training schedule on day 3?

To Think About

Refer to exercises 5 and 6 in working exercises 7–10.

7. Who will have a more demanding schedule on day 3, Betty or Melinda? Why?

8. If Betty kept up the same type of increase day after day, how many miles would she be jogging on day 5?

9. If Melinda kept up the same type of increase day after day, how many miles would she be jogging on day 7?

10. Which athletic trainer would appear to have the best plan for training athletes if they used this plan for 14 days? Why?

11. ***House Prices*** In 1985, the average selling price of an existing single-family home in Atlanta, Georgia, was $66,200. Between 1985 and 1990, the average price increased by 30%. Between 1990 and 2005 the average price increased again, this time by 15%. What was the median house price in Atlanta in 2005?

12. ***Egg Weight*** Chicken eggs are classified by weight per dozen eggs. Large eggs weigh 24 ounces per dozen and medium eggs weigh 21 ounces per dozen.

(a) If you do not include the shell, which is 12% of the total weight of an egg, how many ounces of eggs do you get from a dozen large eggs? From a dozen medium eggs?

(b) At a local market, large eggs sell for $1.79 a dozen, and medium eggs for $1.39 a dozen. If you do not include the shell, which is a better buy, large or medium eggs?

Family Budgets *For the following problems, use the chart below.*

The Johnson family has created the following budget:

Rent	20%	Clothing	10%
Food	31%	Medical	12%
Utilities	5%	Savings	10%
Entertainment	6%	Miscellaneous	6%

13. The income for this family comes from Mrs. Johnson's annual salary of $50,000.

(a) If 28% of her salary is withheld for various taxes, how much money does the family have available for their budget?

(b) How much of Mrs. Johnson's take home pay is budgeted for food?

14. With one child ready to head off to college, Mrs. Johnson is looking for ways to save money.

(a) She figures out that if they plant a garden this year, the family can save 12% of their food costs. How much will she save in food costs? (This does not account for the cost of planting a garden.) What is the new food budget amount?

(b) What percentage of Mrs. Johnson's budget is the new food amount?

Paycheck Stub *Use the following information from a paycheck stub to solve exercises 15–18.*

TOBEY & SLATER INC. 5000 Stillwell Avenue Queens, NY 10001	Check Number	Payroll Period		Pay Date
		From Date	To Date	
	495885	10-30-04	11-30-04	12-01-04

Name	Social Security No.	I.D. Number	File Number	Rate/Salary	Department	MS	DEP	Res
Fred J. Gilliani	012-34-5678	01	1379	1150.00	0100	M	5	NY

	Current	Year to Date		Current	Year to Date
GROSS	1,150.00	6,670.00	STATE	67.76	388.45
FEDERAL	138.97	781.07	LOCAL	5.18	30.04
FICA	87.98	510.28	DIS-SUI	.00	.00
W-2 GROSS		6,670.00	NET	790.47	4,960.16

Earnings						Special Deductions		
No.	Type	Hours	Rate	Amount	Dept/Job No.	No.	Description	Amount
96	REGULAR			1,150.00	0100	82	Retirement	12.56
						75	Medical	36.28
						56	Union Dues	10.80

Gross pay is the pay an employee receives for his or her services before deductions. Net pay is the pay the employee actually gets to take home. You may round each amount to the nearest whole percent for exercises 15–18.

15. What percent of Fred's gross pay is deducted for federal, state, and local taxes?

16. What percent of Fred's gross pay is deducted for retirement and medical?

17. What percent of Fred's gross pay does he actually get to take home?

18. What percent of Fred's deductions are special deductions?

Developing Your Study Skills

Reading the Textbook

Your homework time each day should begin with the careful reading of the section(s) assigned in your textbook. Usually, much time and effort have gone into the selection of a particular text, and your instructor has decided that this is the book that will help you to become successful in this mathematics class. Textbooks are expensive, but they can be a wise investment if you take advantage of them by reading them.

Reading a mathematics textbook is unlike reading many other types of books that you may find in your literature, history, psychology, or sociology courses. Mathematics texts are technical books that provide you with exercises for practice. Reading a mathematics text requires slow and careful reading of each word, which takes time and effort.

Begin reading your textbook with a paper and pencil in hand. As you come across a new definition or concept, underline it in the text and/or write it down in your notebook. Whenever you encounter an unfamiliar term, look it up and make a note of it. When you come to an example, work through it step-by-step. Be sure to read each word and to follow directions carefully.

Notice the helpful hints that the author provides. They guide you to correct solutions and prevent you from making errors. Take advantage of these pieces of expert advice.

Be sure that you understand what you are reading. Make a note of any of those things that you do not understand and ask your instructor about them. Do not hurry through the material. Learning mathematics takes time.

Putting Your Skills to Work

Bodies of Water: The World's Largest Lakes

Did you know that any body of water surrounded by land is called a lake, even salty bodies of water? Thus, the Caspian Sea in Asia, the Aral Sea in Asia, the Great Salt Lake in the United States, and the Eyre in Australia are all considered lakes. Look at the following information on the largest *freshwater* lakes in the world.

Lake	Location	Area (in 1000 square miles)
Superior	US	31.8
Victoria	Africa	26.6
Huron	United States, Canada	23
Michigan	United States	22.4
Tanganyika	Africa	13.9
Great Bear	Canada	12.3
Lake Baikul	Russia	11.8

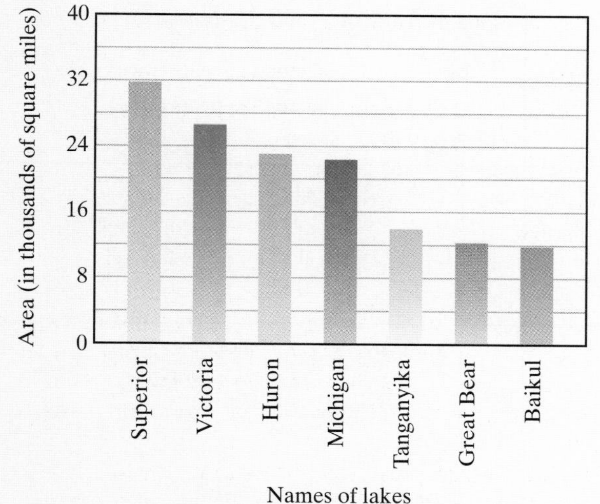

Problems for Individual Investigation and Analysis:

1. How much larger in area is Lake Victoria than Lake Tanganyika?

2. How much larger in area is Lake Superior than Lake Michigan?

Problems for Group Investigation and Cooperative Learning:

3. The smallest Great Lake is Lake Ontario with an area of 7540 sq. mi. About how many times would Lake Ontario fit into Lake Superior?

4. The largest lake in New Hampshire is Lake Winnipesaukee with an area of 72 square miles. About how many times would Lake Winnipesaukee fit into Lake Huron?

Chapter 0 Organizer

Topic	Procedure	Examples
Simplifying fractions, p. 3.	1. Write the **numerator** and **denominator** as a product of prime factors. 2. Use the basic rule of fractions that $$\frac{a \times c}{b \times c} = \frac{a}{b}$$ for any factor that appears in both the numerator and the denominator. 3. Multiply the remaining factors for the numerator and separately for the denominator.	$\frac{15}{25} = \frac{\cancel{5}\cdot 3}{\cancel{5}\cdot 5} = \frac{3}{5}$ $\frac{36}{48} = \frac{\cancel{2}\cdot\cancel{2}\cdot 3\cdot\cancel{3}}{\cancel{2}\cdot\cancel{2}\cdot 2\cdot 2\cdot\cancel{3}} = \frac{3}{4}$ $\frac{26}{39} = \frac{2\cdot\cancel{13}}{3\cdot\cancel{13}} = \frac{2}{3}$
Changing improper fractions to mixed numbers, p. 5.	1. Divide the denominator into the numerator to obtain the whole-number part of the mixed fraction. 2. The remainder from the division will be the numerator of the fraction. 3. The denominator remains unchanged.	$\frac{14}{3} = 4\frac{2}{3}$ since $\begin{array}{r} 4 \\ 3\overline{)14} \\ \underline{12} \\ 2 \end{array}$ $\frac{19}{8} = 2\frac{3}{8}$ since $\begin{array}{r} 2 \\ 8\overline{)19} \\ \underline{16} \\ 3 \end{array}$
Changing mixed numbers to improper fractions, p. 6.	1. Multiply the whole number by the denominator and add the result to the numerator. This will yield the new numerator. 2. The denominator does not change.	$4\frac{5}{6} = \frac{(4 \times 6) + 5}{6} = \frac{24 + 5}{6} = \frac{29}{6}$ $3\frac{1}{7} = \frac{(3 \times 7) + 1}{7} = \frac{21 + 1}{7} = \frac{22}{7}$
Changing fractions to equivalent fractions with a given denominator, p. 7.	1. Divide the original denominator into the new denominator. This result is the value that we use for multiplication. 2. Multiply the numerator and the denominator of the original fraction by that value.	$\frac{4}{7} = \frac{?}{21}$ $\begin{array}{r} 3 \\ 7\overline{)21} \end{array}$ ←Use this to multiply $\frac{4 \times 3}{7 \times 3} = \frac{12}{21}$
Finding the LCD (least common denominator) of two or more fractions, p. 11.	1. Write each denominator as the product of prime factors. 2. The LCD is a product containing each different factor. 3. If a factor occurs more than once in any one denominator, the LCD will contain that factor repeated the greatest number of times that it occurs in any one denominator.	Find the LCD of $\frac{4}{15}$ and $\frac{3}{35}$. $15 = 5\cdot 3$ $35 = 5\cdot 7$ $\text{LCD} = 3\cdot 5\cdot 7 = 105$ Find the LCD of $\frac{11}{18}$ and $\frac{7}{45}$. $18 = 3\cdot 3\cdot 2$ (factor 3 appears twice) $45 = 3\cdot 3\cdot 5$ (factor 3 appears twice) $\text{LCD} = 2\cdot 3\cdot 3\cdot 5 = 90$
Adding and subtracting fractions that do not have a common denominator, p. 12.	1. Find the LCD. 2. Change each fraction to an equivalent fraction with the LCD for a denominator. 3. Add or subtract the fractions and simplify the answer if possible.	$\frac{3}{8} + \frac{1}{3} = \frac{3\cdot 3}{8\cdot 3} + \frac{1\cdot 8}{3\cdot 8} = \frac{9}{24} + \frac{8}{24} = \frac{17}{24}$ $\frac{11}{12} - \frac{1}{4} = \frac{11}{12} - \frac{1\cdot 3}{4\cdot 3} = \frac{11}{12} - \frac{3}{12} = \frac{8}{12} = \frac{2}{3}$
Adding and subtracting mixed numbers, p. 15.	1. Change the mixed numbers to improper fractions. 2. Follow the rules for adding and subtracting fractions. 3. If necessary, change your answer to a mixed number.	$1\frac{2}{3} + 1\frac{3}{4} = \frac{5}{3} + \frac{7}{4} = \frac{5\cdot 4}{3\cdot 4} + \frac{7\cdot 3}{4\cdot 3}$ $= \frac{20}{12} + \frac{21}{12} = \frac{41}{12} = 3\frac{5}{12}$ $2\frac{1}{4} - 1\frac{3}{4} = \frac{9}{4} - \frac{7}{4} = \frac{2}{4} = \frac{1}{2}$
Multiplying fractions, p. 20.	1. If there are no common factors, multiply the numerators. Then multiply the denominators. 2. If possible, write the numerators and denominators as the product of prime factors. Use the basic rule of fractions to divide out any value that appears in both a numerator and a denominator. Multiply the remaining factors in the numerator. Multiply the remaining factors in the denominator.	$\frac{3}{7} \times \frac{2}{13} = \frac{6}{91}$ $\frac{6}{15} \times \frac{35}{91} = \frac{2\cdot\cancel{3}}{\cancel{3}\cdot\cancel{5}} \times \frac{\cancel{5}\cdot\cancel{7}}{\cancel{7}\cdot 13} = \frac{2}{13}$ $3 \times \frac{5}{8} = \frac{3}{1} \times \frac{5}{8} = \frac{15}{8}$ or $1\frac{7}{8}$

Topic	Procedure	Examples
Dividing fractions, p. 22.	**1.** Change the division sign to multiplication. **2.** Invert the second fraction. **3.** Multiply the fractions.	$\frac{4}{7} \div \frac{11}{3} = \frac{4}{7} \times \frac{3}{11} = \frac{12}{77}$ $\frac{5}{9} \div \frac{5}{7} = \frac{\cancel{5}}{9} \times \frac{7}{\cancel{5}} = \frac{7}{9}$
Multiplying and dividing mixed numbers, pp. 21 and 24.	**1.** Change each mixed number to an improper fraction. **2.** Use the rules for multiplying or dividing fractions. **3.** Change your answer to a mixed number.	$2\frac{1}{4} \times 3\frac{3}{5} = \frac{9}{4} \times \frac{18}{5}$ $= \frac{3 \cdot 3}{2 \cdot \cancel{2}} \times \frac{\cancel{2} \cdot 3 \cdot 3}{5} = \frac{81}{10} = 8\frac{1}{10}$ $1\frac{1}{4} \div 1\frac{1}{2} = \frac{5}{4} \div \frac{3}{2} = \frac{5}{2 \cdot \cancel{2}} \times \frac{\cancel{2}}{3} = \frac{5}{6}$
Changing fractional form to decimal form, p. 29.	Divide the denominator into the numerator.	$\frac{5}{8} = 0.625$ since $8\overline{)5.000}$ gives 0.625
Changing decimal form to fractional form, p. 30.	**1.** Write the decimal as a fraction with a denominator of 10, 100, 1000, and so on. **2.** Simplify the fraction, if possible.	$0.37 = \frac{37}{100}$ $\quad 0.375 = \frac{375}{1000} = \frac{3}{8}$
Adding and subtracting decimals, p. 31.	**1.** Carefully line up the decimal points as indicated for addition and subtraction. (Extra zeros may be added to the right-hand side of the decimals if desired.) **2.** Add or subtract the appropriate digits.	Add. $1.236 + 7.825$ 1.236 $+ 7.825$ 9.061 Subtract. $2 - 1.32$ 2.00 $- 1.32$ 0.68
Multiplying decimals, p. 32.	**1.** First multiply the digits. **2.** Count the total number of decimal places in the numbers being multiplied. **3.** This number determines the number of decimal places in the answer.	0.9 (one place) $\times$ 0.7 (one place) 0.63 (two places) 0.009 (three places) $\times$ 0.07 (two places) 0.00063 (five places)
Dividing decimals, p. 33.	**1.** Count the number of decimal places in the divisor. **2.** Move the decimal point to the right the same number of places in both the divisor and dividend. **3.** Mark that position with a caret ($_\wedge$). **4.** Perform the division. Line up the decimal point in the quotient with the position indicated by the caret in the dividend.	Divide. $7.5 \div 0.6$. Move decimal point one place to the right. $0.6_\wedge\overline{)7.5_\wedge0}$ = 12.5 6 15 12 30 30 0 Therefore, $7.5 \div 0.6 = 12.5$
Changing a decimal to a percent, p. 40.	**1.** Move the decimal point two places to the right. **2.** Add the % symbol.	0.46 = 46% 0.002 = 0.2% $\quad$ 1.59 = 159% 0.013 = 1.3% $\quad$ 0.0007 = 0.07%
Changing a percent to a decimal, p. 41.	**1.** Remove the % symbol. **2.** Move the decimal point two places to the left.	49% = 0.49 $\quad$ 180% = 1.8 59.8% = 0.598 $\quad$ 0.13% = 0.0013
Finding a percent of a number, p. 42.	**1.** Convert the percent to a decimal. **2.** Multiply the decimal by the number.	Find 12% of 86. 12% = 0.12 $\quad$ $86 \times 0.12 = 10.32$ Therefore, 12% of 86 = 10.32.
Finding what percent one number is of another number, p. 43.	**1.** Place the number after the word *of* in the denominator. **2.** Place the other number in the numerator. **3.** If possible, simplify the fraction. **4.** Change the fraction to a decimal. **5.** Express the decimal as a percent.	What percent of 8 is 7? $\frac{7}{8} = 0.875 = 87.5\%$ 42 is what percent of 12? $\frac{42}{12} = \frac{7}{2} = 3.5 = 350\%$

Topic	Procedure	Examples
Estimation, p. 47.	**1.** Round each number so that there is one nonzero digit. **2.** Perform the calculation with the rounded numbers.	Estimate the number of square feet in a room that is 22 feet long and 13 feet wide. Assume that the room is rectangular. **1.** We round 22 to 20. We round 13 to 10. **2.** To find the area of a rectangle, we multiply length times width. $20 \times 10 = 200.$ We estimate that there are 200 square feet in the room.
Problem solving, p. 52.	In solving a real-life problem, you may find it helpful to complete the following steps. You will not use all of the steps all of the time. Choose the steps that best fit the conditions of the problem. **1.** ***Understand the problem.*** **(a)** Read the problem carefully. **(b)** Draw a picture if this helps you. **(c)** Use the Mathematics Blueprint for Problem Solving. **2.** ***Solve and state the answer.*** **3.** ***Check.*** **(a)** Estimate to see if your answer is reasonable. **(b)** Repeat your calculation. **(c)** Work backward from your answer. Do you arrive at the original conditions of the problem?	Susan is installing wall-to-wall carpeting in her $10\frac{1}{2}$-ft-by-12-ft bedroom. How much will it cost at \$20 a square yard? **1.** ***Understand the problem.*** We need to find the area of the room in square yards. Then we can find the cost. **2.** ***Solve and state the answer.*** Area: $10\frac{1}{2} \times 12 = \frac{21}{2} \times \frac{12}{1} = 126$ sq ft $126 \div 9 = 14$ sq yd Cost: $14 \times 20 = \$280$ The carpeting will cost \$280. **3.** ***Check.*** Estimate: $10 \times 12 = 120$ sq ft $120 \div 9 = 13\frac{1}{3}$ sq yd $13 \times 20 = \$260$ Our answer is reasonable. ✓

Chapter 0 Review Problems

Section 0.1

In exercises 1–4, simplify.

1. $\frac{36}{48}$ **2.** $\frac{15}{50}$ **3.** $\frac{36}{82}$ **4.** $\frac{18}{30}$

5. Write $4\frac{3}{5}$ as an improper fraction. **6.** Write $\frac{34}{5}$ as a mixed number. **7.** Write $\frac{39}{6}$ as a mixed number.

Change each fraction to an equivalent fraction with the specified denominator.

8. $\frac{5}{8} = \frac{?}{24}$ **9.** $\frac{1}{7} = \frac{?}{35}$ **10.** $\frac{5}{9} = \frac{?}{72}$ **11.** $\frac{2}{5} = \frac{?}{55}$

Section 0.2

Combine.

12. $\frac{3}{5} + \frac{1}{4}$ **13.** $\frac{7}{12} + \frac{5}{8}$ **14.** $\frac{7}{20} - \frac{1}{12}$ **15.** $\frac{7}{10} - \frac{4}{15}$

16. $3\frac{1}{6} + 2\frac{3}{5}$ **17.** $1\frac{1}{4} + 2\frac{7}{10}$ **18.** $6\frac{2}{9} - 3\frac{5}{12}$ **19.** $3\frac{1}{15} - 1\frac{3}{20}$

Section 0.3

Multiply.

20. $6 \times \frac{5}{11}$

21. $2\frac{1}{3} \times 4\frac{1}{2}$

22. $1\frac{1}{8} \times 2\frac{1}{9}$

23. $\frac{4}{7} \times 5$

Divide.

24. $\frac{3}{8} \div 6$

25. $\dfrac{\frac{8}{3}}{\frac{5}{9}}$

26. $\frac{15}{16} \div 6\frac{1}{4}$

27. $2\frac{6}{7} \div \frac{10}{21}$

Section 0.4

Combine.

28. 1.634 + 3.007 + 2.560

29. 24.831 − 17.094

30. 47.251 − 17.69

31. 1.9 + 2.53 + 0.006

Multiply.

32. 0.007 × 5.35

33. 362.341 × 1000

34. 2.6 × 0.03 × 1.02

35. 1.08 × 0.06 × 160

Divide.

36. 0.186 ÷ 100

37. 71.32 ÷ 1000

38. 0.523 ÷ 0.4

39. 1.35 ÷ 0.015

40. 4.186 ÷ 2.3

41. 0.19 ÷ 0.38

42. Write as a decimal: $\frac{3}{8}$.

43. Write as a fraction in simplified form: 0.36.

Section 0.5

In exercises 44–47, write each percentage in decimal form.

44. 1.4%

45. 36.1%

46. 0.02%

47. 125.3%

48. What is 85% of 600?

49. Find 7.2% of 55.

50. 48 is what percent of 75?

51. What percent of 120 is 15?

52. What percent of 1250 is 750?

53. ***Education Level*** In 1997, 80.7% of California residents over the age of 25 reported that they had at least a 4-year high school education. If the population of California over the age of 25 was 20,229,000, how many people reported at least a high school education? (*Source*: U.S. Census Bureau)

54. ***Math Deficiency*** In a given university, 720 of the 960 freshmen had a math deficiency. What percentage of the class had a math deficiency?

Section 0.6

In exercises 55–60, estimate. Do not find an exact value.

55. $234{,}897 \times 1{,}936{,}112$

56. $357 + 923 + 768 + 417$

57. $634{,}318 - 284{,}000$

58. $7\frac{1}{3} + 3\frac{5}{6} + 8\frac{3}{7}$

59. Find 18% of \$56,297.

60. $12{,}482 \div 389$

61. ***Salary*** Estimate Juan's salary for the week if he makes \$7.85 per hour, and worked 32.5 hours.

62. ***Apartment Sharing*** Estimate the monthly cost for each of three roommates who want to share an apartment that costs \$923.50 per month.

Section 0.7

Solve. You may use the Mathematics Blueprint for Problem Solving.

▲ **63.** ***Carpeting*** Mr. and Mrs. Carr are installing wall-to-wall carpeting in a room that measures $12\frac{1}{2}$ ft by $9\frac{2}{3}$ ft. How much will it cost if the carpet is \$26.00 per square yard?

64. ***Population*** The population of Falmouth was 34,000 in 1980 and 36,720 in 2000. What was the percent of increase in population?

Gas Mileage *A six-passenger Piper Cub airplane has a gas tank that holds 240 gallons. Use this information to answer exercises 65 and 66.*

65. When flying at cruising speed, the plane averages $7\frac{2}{3}$ miles per gallon. How far can the plane fly at cruising speed? If the pilot never plans to fly more than 80% of his maximum cruising distance, what is the longest trip he would plan to fly?

66. When flying at maximum speed, the plane averages $6\frac{1}{4}$ miles per gallon. How far can the plane fly at maximum speed? If the pilot never plans to fly more than 70% of his maximum flying distance when flying at full speed, what is the longest trip he would plan to fly at full speed?

▲ **67.** ***Geometry*** What is the volume of a matchbox toy box if it measures: $4'' \text{ long} \times 2\frac{1}{2}'' \text{ long} \times \frac{3}{4}'' \text{ high}$?

▲ **68.** ***Geometry*** Using your results from Exercise 67, if a packing crate measures $16'' \text{ long} \times 12\frac{1}{2}'' \text{ wide} \times 7\frac{1}{2}'' \text{ high}$, how many matchbox toy boxes can be packed inside the crate?

69. ***Sales Commission*** Mike sells sporting goods on an 8% commission. During the first week in July, he sold goods worth \$5785. What was his commission for the week?

70. ***Package Weight*** Sam took to the post office several packages that weighed 0.75 pounds each. The total weight of all the packages was 34.5 pounds. How many packages did he bring to the post office?

71. ***Car Loan*** Dick and Ann Wright purchased a new car. They took out a loan of \$9214.50 to help pay for the car and paid the rest in cash. They paid off the loan with payments of \$225 per month for four years. How much more did they pay back than the amount of the car loan? (This is the amount of interest they were charged for the car loan.)

72. ***Wages*** Frank works as a clerk at Wal-Mart. He is paid \$6.40 an hour for a 40-hour week. For any additional time he gets paid 1.5 times the normal rate. Last week he worked 52 hours. How much did he get paid last week?

How Am I Doing? Chapter 0 Test

Remember to use your Chapter Test Prep Video CD to see the worked-out solutions to the test problems you want to review.

In exercises 1 and 2, simplify.

1. $\frac{16}{18}$

2. $\frac{48}{36}$

3. Write as an improper fraction. $6\frac{3}{7}$

4. Write as a mixed number: $\frac{105}{9}$.

In exercises 5–12, perform the operations indicated. Simplify answers whenever possible.

5. $\frac{2}{3} + \frac{5}{6} + \frac{3}{8}$

6. $1\frac{1}{8} + 3\frac{3}{4}$

7. $3\frac{2}{3} - 2\frac{5}{6}$

8. $\frac{5}{7} \times \frac{28}{15}$

9. $\frac{5}{18} \times \frac{3}{4}$

10. $\frac{7}{4} \div \frac{1}{2}$

11. $2\frac{1}{2} \times 3\frac{1}{4}$

12. $5\frac{3}{8} \div 2\frac{3}{4}$

In exercises 13–18, perform the calculations indicated.

13. $1.6 + 3.24 + 9.8$

14. $7.0046 - 3.0149$

15. 32.8×0.04

16. 0.07385×1000

17. $12.88 \div 0.056$

18. $26{,}325.9 \div 100$

1. ______
2. ______
3. ______
4. ______
5. ______
6. ______
7. ______
8. ______
9. ______
10. ______
11. ______
12. ______
13. ______
14. ______
15. ______
16. ______
17. ______
18. ______

19. ______

20. ______

21. ______

22. ______

23. ______

24. ______

25. ______

26. ______

27. ______

28. ______

29. ______

19. Write as a percent. 0.073

20. Write as a decimal. 196.5%

21. What is 3.5% of 180?

22. What is 2% of 16.8?

23. 39 is what percent of 650?

24. What percent of 460 is 138?

25. A 4-inch stack of computer chips is on the table. Each computer chip is $\frac{2}{9}$ of an inch thick. How many computer chips are in the stack?

In exercises 26–27, estimate. Round each number to one nonzero digit. Then calculate.

26. $52{,}344\overline{)4{,}678{,}987}$

27. 285.36 + 311.85 + 113.6

Solve. You may use the Mathematics Blueprint for Problem Solving.

28. Allison is paid $14,000 per year plus a sales commission of 3% of the value of her sales. Last year she sold $870,000 worth of products. What percent of her total income was her commission?

▲ **29.** Fred and Melinda are laying wall tile in the kitchen. Each tile covers $3\frac{1}{2}$ square inches of space. They plan to cover 210 square inches of wall space. How many tiles will they need?

CHAPTER

1

Do you have any idea how much the use of the Internet has grown in recent years? Do you think it has spread to farmers and fishermen? Do you have any idea how many people use a computer both at home and at work? Turn to the Putting Your Skills to Work on page 125 and see how good your estimates were.

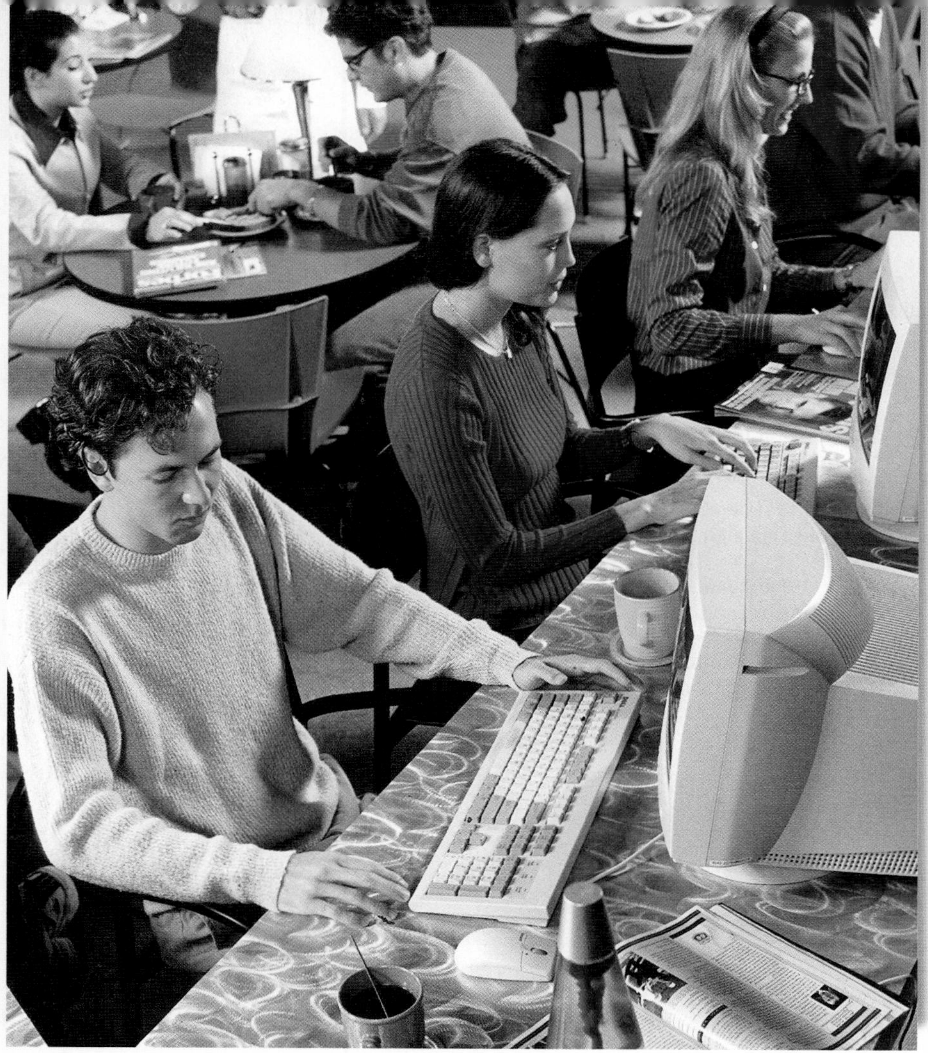

Real Numbers and Variables

1.1 Adding Real Numbers

Student Learning Objectives

After studying this section, you will be able to:

1. **Identify different types of numbers.**
2. **Use real numbers in real-life situations.**
3. **Add real numbers with the same sign.**
4. **Add real numbers with opposite signs.**
5. **Use the addition properties for real numbers.**

1 Identifying Different Types of Numbers

Let's review some of the basic terms we use to talk about numbers.

Whole numbers are numbers such as 0, 1, 2, 3, 4, . . .

Integers are numbers such as . . . , −3, −2, −1, 0, 1, 2, 3, ...

Rational numbers are numbers such as $\frac{3}{2}, \frac{5}{7}, -\frac{3}{8}, -\frac{4}{13}, \frac{6}{1}$, and $-\frac{8}{2}$.

Rational numbers can be written as one integer divided by another integer (as long as the denominator is not zero!). Integers can be written as fractions ($3 = \frac{3}{1}$, for example), so we can see that all integers are rational numbers. Rational numbers can be expressed in decimal form. For example, $\frac{3}{2} = 1.5$, $-\frac{3}{8} = -0.375$, and $\frac{1}{3} = 0.333\ldots$ or $0.\overline{3}$. It is important to note that rational numbers in decimal form are either terminating decimals or repeating decimals.

Irrational numbers are numbers that cannot be expressed as one integer divided by another integer. The numbers π, $\sqrt{2}$, and $\sqrt[3]{7}$ are irrational numbers.

Irrational numbers can be expressed in decimal form. The decimal form of an irrational number is a nonterminating, nonrepeating decimal. For example, $\sqrt{2} = 1.414213\ldots$ can be carried out to an infinite number of decimal places with no repeating pattern of digits

Finally, **real numbers** are all the rational numbers and all the irrational numbers.

EXAMPLE 1 Classify as an integer, a rational number, an irrational number, and/or a real number.

(a) 5 **(b)** $-\frac{1}{3}$ **(c)** 2.85 **(d)** $\sqrt{2}$ **(e)** 0.777 . . .

Solution Make a table. Check off the description of the number that applies.

	Number	Integer	Rational Number	Irrational Number	Real Number
(a)	5	✓	✓		✓
(b)	$-\frac{1}{3}$		✓		✓
(c)	2.85		✓		✓
(d)	$\sqrt{2}$			✓	✓
(e)	0.777 . . .		✓		✓

Practice Problem 1 Classify.

(a) $-\frac{2}{5}$ **(b)** 1.515151 . . . **(c)** −8 **(d)** π

NOTE TO STUDENT: Fully worked-out solutions to all of the Practice Problems can be found at the back of the text starting at page SP-1

Any real number can be pictured on a **number line.**

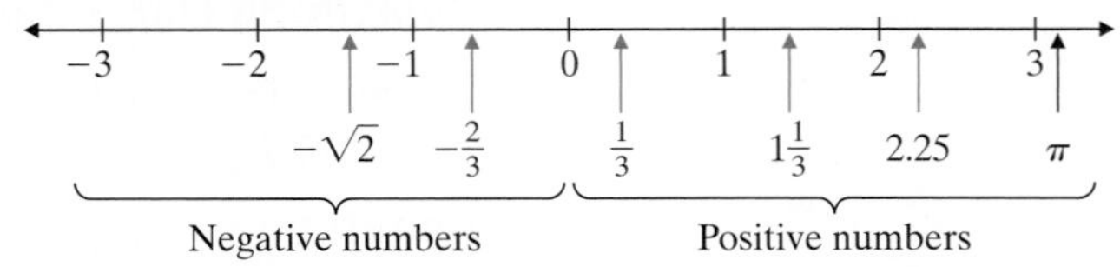

Positive numbers are to the right of 0 on the number line.

Negative numbers are to the left of 0 on the number line.

The **real numbers** include the positive numbers, the negative numbers, and zero.

2 Using Real Numbers in Real-Life Situations

We often encounter practical examples of number lines that include positive and negative rational numbers. For example, we can tell by reading the accompanying thermometer that the temperature is 20° below 0. From the stock market report, we see that the stock opened at 36 and closed at 34.5, and the net change for the day was −1.5.

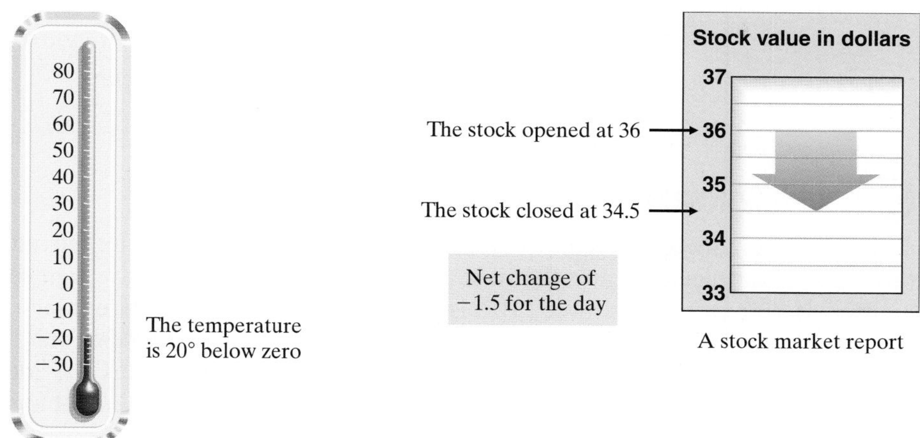

A stock market report

In the following example we use real numbers to represent real-life situations.

EXAMPLE 2 Use a real number to represent each situation.

(a) A temperature of 128.6°F below zero is recorded at Vostok, Antarctica.
(b) The Himalayan peak K2 rises 29,064 feet above sea level.
(c) The Dow gains 10.24 points.
(d) An oil drilling platform extends 328 feet below sea level.

Solution A key word can help you to decide whether a number is positive or negative.

(a) 128.6°F *below* zero is −128.6.
(b) 29,064 feet *above* sea level is +29,064.
(c) A *gain* of 10.24 points is +10.24.
(d) 328 feet *below* sea level is −328.

Practice Problem 2 Use a real number to represent each situation.

(a) A population growth of 1259 **(b)** A depreciation of $763
(c) A wind-chill factor of minus 10

In everyday life we consider positive numbers the opposite of negative numbers. For example, a gain of 3 yards in a football game is the opposite of a loss of 3 yards; a check written for $2.16 on a checking account is the opposite of a deposit of $2.16.

Each positive number has an opposite negative number. Similarly, each negative number has an opposite positive number. **Opposite numbers,** also called **additive inverses,** have the same magnitude but different signs and can be represented on the number line.

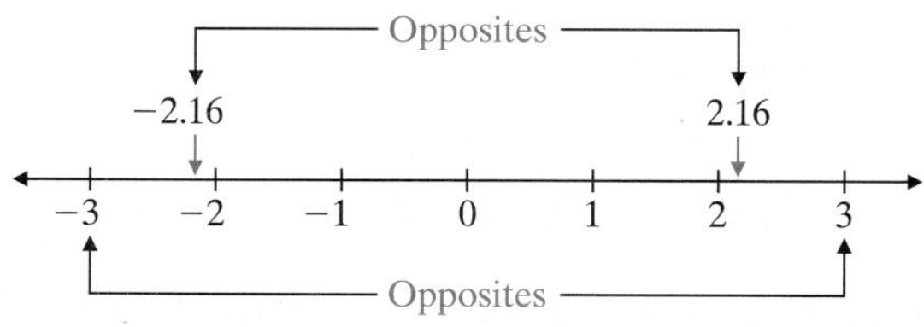

EXAMPLE 3 Find the additive inverse (that is, the opposite).

(a) -7 **(b)** $\frac{1}{4}$

Solution

(a) The opposite of -7 is $+7$. **(b)** The opposite of $\frac{1}{4}$ is $-\frac{1}{4}$.

NOTE TO STUDENT: Fully worked-out solutions to all of the Practice Problems can be found at the back of the text starting at page SP-1

Practice Problem 3 Find the additive inverse (the opposite).

(a) $+\frac{2}{5}$ **(b)** -1.92 **(c)** a loss of 12 yards on a football play

3 Adding Real Numbers with the Same Sign

To use a real number, we need to be clear about its sign. When we write the number three as $+3$, the sign indicates that it is a positive number. The positive sign can be omitted. If someone writes three (3), it is understood that it is a positive three $(+3)$. To write a negative number such as negative three (-3), we must include the sign.

A concept that will help us add and subtract real numbers is the idea of absolute value. The **absolute value** of a number is the distance between that number and zero on the number line. The absolute value of 3 is written $|3|$.

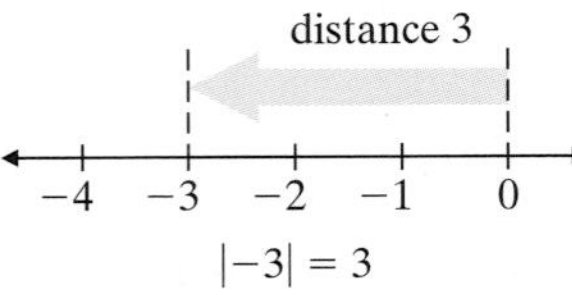

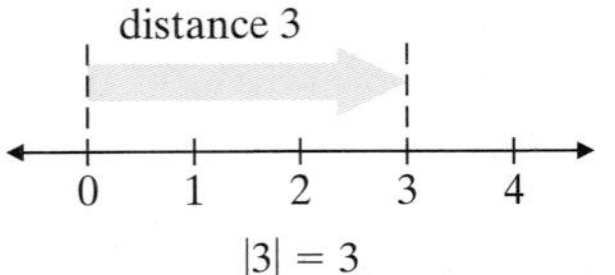

Distance is always a positive number regardless of the direction we travel. This means that the absolute value of any number will be a positive value or zero. We place the symbols | and | around a number to mean the absolute value of the number.

The distance from 0 to 3 is 3, so $|3| = 3$. This is read "the absolute value of 3 is 3."

The distance from 0 to -3 is 3, so $|-3| = 3$. This is read "the absolute value of -3 is 3."

Some other examples are

$$|-22| = 22, \quad |5.6| = 5.6, \quad \text{and} \quad |0| = 0.$$

Thus, the absolute value of a number can be thought of as the magnitude of the number, without regard to its sign.

EXAMPLE 4 Find the absolute value.

(a) $|-4.62|$ **(b)** $\left|\frac{3}{7}\right|$ **(c)** $|0|$

Solution

(a) $|-4.62| = 4.62$ **(b)** $\left|\frac{3}{7}\right| = \frac{3}{7}$ **(c)** $|0| = 0$

Practice Problem 4 Find the absolute value.

(a) $|-7.34|$ **(b)** $\left|\frac{5}{8}\right|$ **(c)** $\left|\frac{0}{2}\right|$

Now let's look at addition of real numbers when the two numbers have the same sign. Suppose that you are keeping track of your checking account at a local bank. When you make a deposit of 5 dollars, you record it as +5. When you write a check for 4 dollars, you record it as −4, as a debit. Consider two situations.

SITUATION 1: Total Deposit You made a deposit of 20 dollars on one day and a deposit of 15 dollars the next day. You want to know the total value of your deposits.

Your record for situation 1.

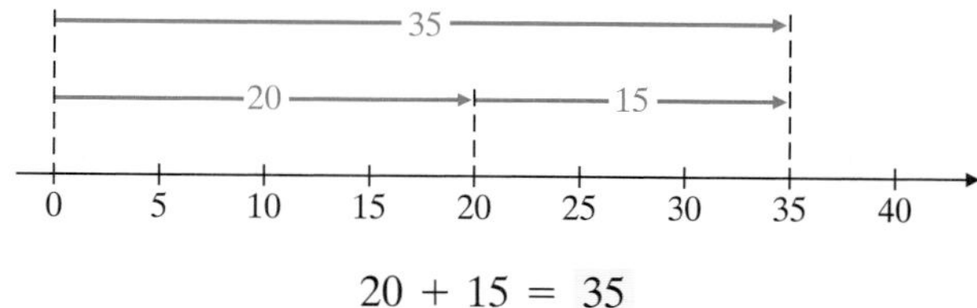

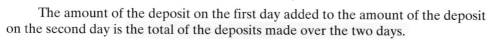

$$20 + 15 = 35$$

The amount of the deposit on the first day added to the amount of the deposit on the second day is the total of the deposits made over the two days.

SITUATION 2: Total Debit You write a check for 25 dollars to pay one bill and two days later write a check for 5 dollars. You want to know the total value of debits to your account for the two checks.

Your record for situation 2.

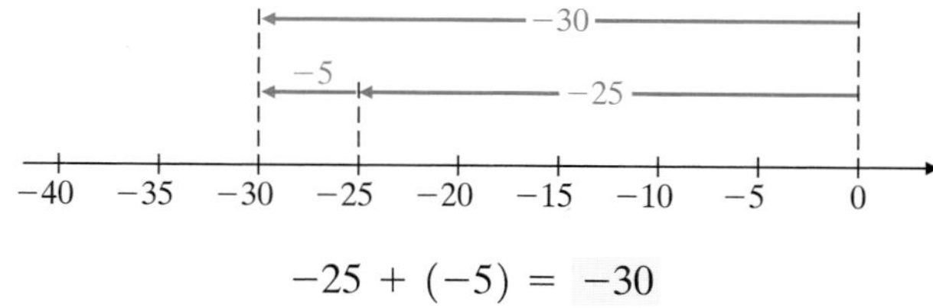

$$-25 + (-5) = -30$$

The value of the first check added to the value of the second check is the total debit to your account.

In each situation we found that we added the absolute value of each number. (That is, we added the numbers without regarding their sign.) The answer always contained the sign that was common to both numbers.

We will now state these results as a formal rule.

ADDITION RULE FOR TWO NUMBERS WITH THE SAME SIGN

To add two numbers with the same sign, add the absolute values of the numbers and use the common sign in the answer.

EXAMPLE 5 Add.

(a) $14 + 16$ **(b)** $-8 + (-7)$

Solution

(a) $14 + 16$ Add the absolute values of the numbers.

$14 + 16 = 30$ Use the common sign in the answer. Here the common sign is the + sign.

$14 + 16 = +30$

(b) $-8 + (-7)$ Add the absolute values of the numbers.

$8 + 7 = 15$ Use the common sign in the answer. Here the common sign is the − sign.

$-8 + (-7) = -15$

Practice Problem 5 Add.

(a) $37 + 19$ **(b)** $-23 + (-35)$

EXAMPLE 6 Add. $\frac{2}{3} + \frac{1}{7}$

Solution

$\frac{2}{3} + \frac{1}{7}$

$\frac{14}{21} + \frac{3}{21}$ Change each fraction to an equivalent fraction with a common denominator of 21.

$\frac{14}{21} + \frac{3}{21} = +\frac{17}{21}$ or $\frac{17}{21}$ Add the absolute values of the numbers. Use the common sign in the answer. Note that if no sign is written, the number is understood to be positive.

NOTE TO STUDENT: Fully worked-out solutions to all of the Practice Problems can be found at the back of the text starting at page SP-1

Practice Problem 6 Add. $-\frac{3}{5} + \left(-\frac{4}{7}\right)$

EXAMPLE 7 Add. $-4.2 + (-3.94)$

Solution

$-4.2 + (-3.94)$

$4.20 + 3.94 = 8.14$ Add the absolute values of the numbers.

$-4.20 + (-3.94) = -8.14$ Use the common sign in the answer.

Practice Problem 7 Add. $-12.7 + (-9.38)$

The rule for adding two numbers with the same signs can be extended to more than two numbers. If we add more than two numbers with the same sign, the answer will have the sign common to all.

EXAMPLE 8 Add. $-7 + (-2) + (-5)$

Solution

$-7 + (-2) + (-5)$ We are adding three real numbers all with the same sign. We begin by adding the first two numbers.

$= -9 + (-5)$ Add $-7 + (-2) = -9$.

$= -14$ Add $-9 + (-5) = -14$.

Of course, this can be shortened by adding the three numbers without regard to sign and then using the common sign for the answer.

Practice Problem 8 Add. $-7 + (-11) + (-33)$

4 Adding Real Numbers with Opposite Signs

What if the signs of the numbers you are adding are different? Let's consider our checking account again to see how such a situation might occur.

SITUATION 3: Net Increase You made a deposit of 30 dollars on one day. On the next day you write a check for 25 dollars. You want to know the result of your two transactions.

Your record for situation 3.

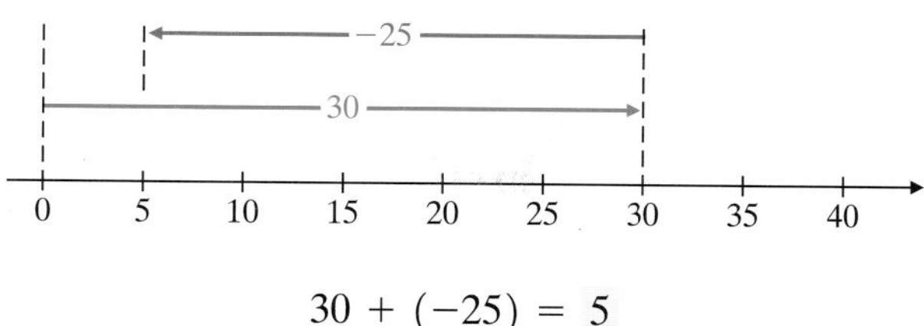

$$30 + (-25) = 5$$

A positive 30 for the deposit added to a negative 25 for the check, which is a debit, gives a net increase of 5 dollars in the account.

SITUATION 4: Net Decrease You made a deposit of 10 dollars on one day. The next day you write a check for 40 dollars. You want to know the result of your two transactions.

Your record for situation 4.

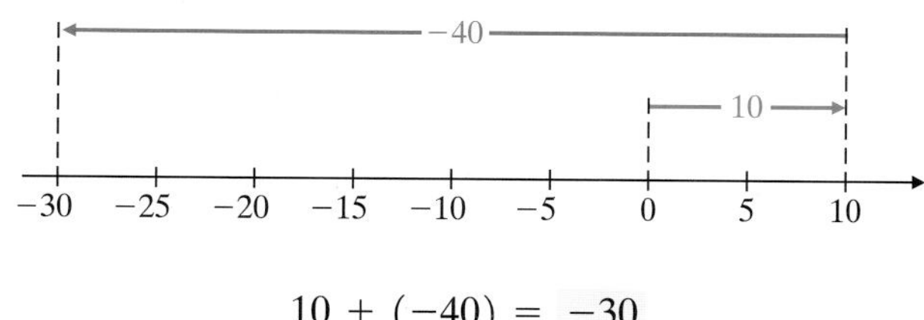

$$10 + (-40) = -30$$

A positive 10 for the deposit added to a negative 40 for the check, which is a debit, gives a net decrease of 30 dollars in the account.

The result is a negative thirty (−30), because the check was larger than the deposit. If you do not have at least 30 dollars in your account at the start of Situation 4, you have overdrawn your account.

What do we observe from situations 3 and 4? In each case, first we found the difference of the absolute values of the two numbers. Then the sign of the result was always the sign of the number with the greater absolute value. Thus, in situation 3, 30 is larger than 25. The sign of 30 is positive. The sign of the answer (5) is positive. In situation 4, 40 is larger than 10. The sign of 40 is negative. The sign of the answer (−30) is negative.

We will now state these results as a formal rule.

ADDITION RULE FOR TWO NUMBERS WITH DIFFERENT SIGNS

1. Find the difference between the larger absolute value and the smaller one.
2. Give the answer the sign of the number having the larger absolute value.

EXAMPLE 9 Add. $8 + (-7)$

Solution

$8 + (-7)$	We are to add two numbers with opposite signs.
$8 - 7 = 1$	Find the difference between the two absolute values, which is 1.
$+8 + (-7) = +1$ or 1	The answer will have the sign of the number with the larger absolute value. That number is +8. Its sign is **positive**, so the answer will be +1.

Practice Problem 9 Add. $-9 + 15$

Calculator

Negative Numbers

To enter a negative number on most scientific calculators, find the key marked [+/−]. To enter the number −2, press the key 2 and then the key +/−. The display should read

[−2]

To find $-32 + (-46)$, enter

32 [+/−] [+] 46 [+/−]

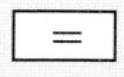

The display should read

[−78]

Try the following.

(a) $-256 + 184$
(b) $94 + (-51)$
(c) $-18 - (-24)$
(d) $-6 + (-10) - (-15)$

Note: The [+/−] key changes the sign of a number from + to − or − to +.

On some calculators the negative sign must be entered first, followed by the number.

Answers:

(a) 72 **(b)** 43
(c) 6 **(d)** −1

Using the Addition Properties for Real Numbers

It is useful to know the following three properties of real numbers.

1. *Addition is commutative.*
   This property states that if two numbers are added, the result is the same no matter which number is written first. The order of the numbers does not affect the result.

$$3 + 6 = 6 + 3 = 9$$
$$-7 + (-8) = (-8) + (-7) = -15$$
$$-15 + 3 = 3 + (-15) = -12$$

2. *Addition of zero to any given number will result in that given number again.*

$$0 + 5 = 5$$
$$-8 + 0 = -8$$

3. *Addition is associative.*
   This property states that if three numbers are added, it does not matter which two numbers are grouped by parentheses and added first.

$$3 + (5 + 7) = (3 + 5) + 7$$
$$3 + (12) = (8) + 7$$
$$15 = 15$$

First combine numbers inside parentheses; then combine the remaining numbers. The results are the same no matter which numbers are grouped first.

We can use these properties along with the rules we have for adding real numbers to add three or more numbers. We go from left to right, adding two numbers at a time.

EXAMPLE 10 Add. $\frac{3}{17} + \left(-\frac{8}{17}\right) + \frac{4}{17}$

Solution

$$-\frac{5}{17} + \frac{4}{17}$$

Add $\frac{3}{17} + \left(-\frac{8}{17}\right) = -\frac{5}{17}$.
The answer is negative since the larger of the two absolute values is negative.

$$= -\frac{1}{17}$$

Add $-\frac{5}{17} + \frac{4}{17} = -\frac{1}{17}$.
The answer is negative since the larger of the two absolute values is negative.

NOTE TO STUDENT: Fully worked-out solutions to all of the Practice Problems can be found at the back of the text starting at page SP-1

Practice Problem 10 Add. $-\frac{5}{12} + \frac{7}{12} + \left(-\frac{11}{12}\right)$

Sometimes the numbers being added have the same signs; sometimes the signs are different. When adding three or more numbers, you may encounter both situations.

EXAMPLE 11 Add. $-1.8 + 1.4 + (-2.6)$

Solution

$$-0.4 + (-2.6)$$

We take the difference of 1.8 and 1.4 and use the sign of the number with the larger absolute value.

$$= -3.0$$

Add $-0.4 + (-2.6) = -3.0$. The signs are the same; we add the absolute values of the numbers and use the common sign.

Practice Problem 11 Add. $-6.3 + (-8.0) + 3.5$

If many real numbers are added, it is often easier to add numbers with like signs in a column format. Remember that addition is commutative; therefore, real numbers can be added *in any order*. You do *not* need to combine the first two numbers as your first step.

EXAMPLE 12 Add. $-8 + 3 + (-5) + (-2) + 6 + 5$

Solution

$$\begin{array}{r} -8 \\ -5 \\ -2 \\ \hline -15 \end{array}$$

All the signs are the same. Add the three negative numbers to obtain -15.

$$\begin{array}{r} +3 \\ +6 \\ +5 \\ \hline +14 \end{array}$$

All the signs are the same Add the three positive numbers to obtain $+14$.

Add the two results.

$$-15 + 14 = -1$$

The answer is negative because the number with the larger absolute value is negative.

Practice Problem 12 Add. $-6 + 5 + (-7) + (-2) + 5 + 3$

A word about notation: The only time we really need to show the sign of a number is when the number is negative—for example, -3. The only time we need to show parentheses when we add real numbers is when we have two different signs preceding a number. For example, $-5 + (-6)$.

EXAMPLE 13 Add.

(a) $2.8 + (-1.3)$ **(b)** $-\frac{2}{5} + \left(-\frac{3}{4}\right)$

Solution

(a) $2.8 + (-1.3) = 1.5$

(b) $-\frac{2}{5} + \left(-\frac{3}{4}\right) = -\frac{8}{20} + \left(-\frac{15}{20}\right) = -\frac{23}{20}$ or $-1\frac{3}{20}$

Practice Problem 13 Add.

(a) $-2.9 + (-5.7)$ **(b)** $\frac{2}{3} + \left(-\frac{1}{4}\right)$

1.1 EXERCISES

Student Solutions Manual

CD/ Video

PH Math Tutor Center

MathXL®Tutorials on CD

MathXL®

MyMathLab®
Interactmath.com

Verbal and Writing Skills

Check off any description of the number that applies.

	Number	Whole Number	Rational Number	Irrational Number	Real Number
1.	23				
2.	$-\frac{4}{5}$				
3.	π				
4.	2.34				
5.	$-6.666\ldots$				

	Number	Whole Number	Rational Number	Irrational Number	Real Number
6.	$-\frac{7}{9}$				
7.	$-2.3434\ldots$				
8.	14				
9.	$\sqrt{2}$				
10.	$3.232232223\ldots$				

Use a real number to represent each situation.

11. Jules Verne wrote a book with the title *20,000 Leagues under the Sea.*

12. The value of the dollar is up \$0.07 with respect to the yen.

13. Ramona lost $37\frac{1}{2}$ pounds on Weight Watchers.

14. The scouts hiked from sea level to the top of a 3642-foot-high mountain.

15. The temperature rises 7°F.

16. Maya lost the game by 12 points.

Find the additive inverse (opposite).

17. 8

18. $-\frac{4}{5}$

19. -2.73

20. 85.4

Find the absolute value.

21. $|-1.3|$

22. $|-5.9|$

23. $\left|\frac{5}{6}\right|$

24. $\left|\frac{7}{12}\right|$

Add.

25. $-6 + (-5)$

26. $-13 + (-3)$

27. $-17 + (-14)$

28. $-12 + (-19)$

29. $-\frac{5}{16} + \frac{9}{16}$

30. $-\frac{2}{9} + \left(\frac{-4}{9}\right)$

31. $-\frac{2}{13} + \left(-\frac{5}{13}\right)$

32. $-\frac{5}{14} + \frac{2}{14}$

33. $-\frac{2}{5} + \frac{3}{7}$

34. $-\frac{2}{7} + \frac{3}{14}$

35. $-1.5 + (-2.3)$

36. $-1.8 + (-1.4)$

37. $0.6 + (-0.2)$

38. $-0.8 + 0.5$

39. $-5.26 + (-8.9)$

40. $-6.48 + (-3.7)$

41. $-8 + 5 + (-3)$

42. $7 + (-8) + (-4)$

43. $-3 + 5 + (-7)$

44. $-9 + 6 + (-12)$

45. $-\frac{4}{5} + \frac{8}{15}$

46. $-\frac{5}{6} + \frac{7}{18}$

47. $-7 + (-9) + 8$

48. $-4 + (-13) + 7$

Mixed Practice

Add.

49. $8 + (-11)$

50. $16 + (-24)$

51. $-83 + 142$

52. $-114 + 186$

53. $-\frac{4}{9} + \frac{5}{6}$

54. $-\frac{3}{5} + \frac{2}{3}$

55. $-\frac{1}{10} + \frac{1}{2}$

56. $-\frac{2}{3} + \left(-\frac{1}{4}\right)$

57. $4.36 + (-3.6)$

58. $4.79 + (-9.1)$

59. $4 + (-8) + 16$

60. $27 + (-11) + (-4)$

61. $34 + (-18) + 11 + (-27)$

62. $-23 + 4 + (-11) + 17$

63. $17.85 + (-2.06) + 0.15$

64. $23.17 + 5.03 + (-11.81)$

Applications

65. ***Profit/Loss*** Holly paid \$47 for a vase at an estate auction. She resold it to an antiques dealer for \$214. What was her profit or loss?

66. ***Temperature*** When we skied at Jackson Hole, Wyoming, yesterday, the temperature at the summit was −12°F. Today when we called the ski report, the temperature had risen 7°F. What is the temperature at the summit today?

67. ***Home Equity Line of Credit*** Ramon borrowed \$2300 from his home equity line of credit to pay off his car loan. He then borrowed another \$1500 to pay to have his kitchen repainted. Represent how much Ramon owed on his home equity line of credit as a real number.

68. ***Time Change*** During the winter, New York City is on Eastern Standard Time (EST). Melbourne, Australia is 15 hours ahead of New York. If it is 11 P.M. in Melbourne, what time is it in New York?

69. ***Football*** On three successive football running plays, Jon gained 9 yards, lost 11 yards, and gained 5 yards. What was his total gain or loss?

70. ***School Fees*** Wanda's financial aid account at school held \$643.85. She withdrew \$185.50 to buy books for the semester. Does she have enough left in her account to pay the \$475.00 registration fee for the next semester? If so, how much extra money does she have? If not, how much is she short?

71. ***Butterfly Population*** The population of a particular butterfly species was 8000. Twenty years later there were 3000 fewer. Today, there are 1500 fewer. Study the graph to the right. What is the new population?

72. ***Credit Card Balance*** Aaron owes \$258 to a credit card company. He makes a purchase of \$32 with the card and then makes a payment of \$150 on the account. How much does he still owe?

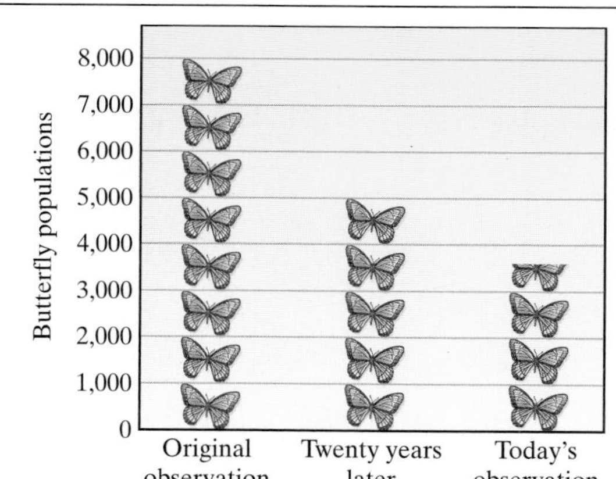

Profit/Loss *During the first five months of 2005 a regional Midwest airline posted profit and loss figures for each month of operation, as shown in the accompanying bar graph.*

73. For the first three months of 2005, what were the total earnings of the airline?

74. For the first five months of 2005, what were the total earnings for the airline?

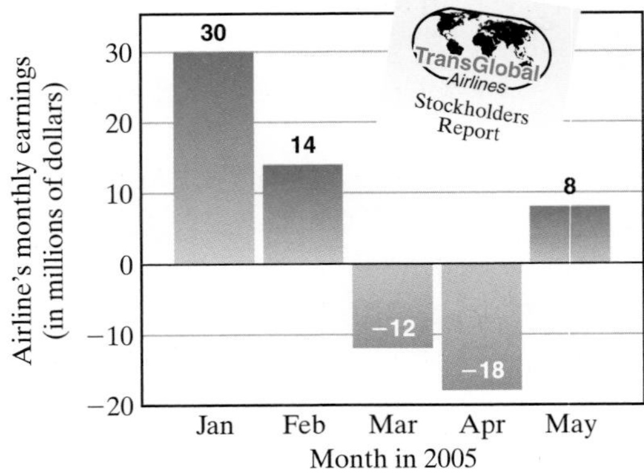

To Think About

75. What number must be added to -13 to get 5?

76. What number must be added to -18 to get 10?

77. ***Football*** Vern rushed for 8 yards to his team's 17-yard line in the last quarter of the home football game. On the next play, the quarterback was sacked and lost 4 yards. On the third down, the pass was incomplete. How many yards must the team make on the next play to make first down?

78. ***Discount Stores*** Filene's Basement Store in Boston is famous for its Automatic Markdown Policy. Each item is dated when it enters the store. If it does not sell after 14 days, the price is reduced by 25%. If it is still there after 21 days, the discount is now 50%. After 28 days, the discount becomes a whopping 75%. If the item has still not sold after 35 days, it is taken from the store and donated to charity. While shopping in Filene's Basement, Heather Bean found two blouses that she liked a lot. The red blouse was originally \$87.99 and had been in the store for 22 days. The blue blouse was originally \$57.99 but had only been in the store for 19 days. Which one was cheaper? Which one was a better value?

Cumulative Review

Perform the indicated calculations.

79. $\frac{3}{7} + \frac{5}{21}$

80. $\left(\frac{2}{5}\right)\left(\frac{20}{27}\right)$

81. $\frac{2}{15} - \frac{1}{20}$

82. $2\frac{1}{2} \div 3\frac{2}{5}$

83. $0.72 + 0.8$

84. $1.63 - 0.98$

85. $(1.63)(0.7)$

86. $0.208 \div 0.8$

1.2 SUBTRACTING REAL NUMBERS

1 Subtracting Real Numbers with Like or Unlike Signs

So far we have developed the rules for adding real numbers. We can use these rules to subtract real numbers. Let's look at a checkbook situation to see how.

SITUATION 5: Subtract a Deposit and Add a Debit You have a balance of 20 dollars in your checking account. The bank calls you and says that a deposit of 5 dollars that belongs to another account was erroneously added to your account. They say they will correct the account balance to 15 dollars. The bank tells you that since they cannot take away the erroneous credit, they will add a debit to your account. You want to keep track of what's happening to your account.

Your record for situation 5.

$$20 - (+5) = 15$$

From your present balance subtract the deposit to give the new balance.

This equation shows what needs to be done to your account. The bank tells you that because the error happened in the past they cannot "take it away." However, they can add to your account a debit of 5 dollars. Here is the equivalent addition.

$$20 + (-5) = 15$$

To your present balance add a debit to give the new balance.

Subtracting a positive 5 has the same effect as adding a negative 5.

Student Learning Objective

After studying this section, you will be able to:

Subtract real numbers with like or unlike signs.

> **SUBTRACTION OF REAL NUMBERS**
>
> To subtract real numbers, add the opposite of the second number (that is, the number you are subtracting) to the first.

The rule tells us to do three things when we subtract real numbers. First, change subtraction to addition. Second, replace the second number by its opposite. Third, add the two numbers using the rules for addition of real numbers.

EXAMPLE 1 Subtract. $6 - (-2)$

Solution

$$6 \quad - \quad (-2)$$

Change subtraction to addition. | Write the opposite of the second number.

$$= 6 \quad + \quad (+2)$$

Add the two real numbers with the same sign.

$$= 8$$

Practice Problem 1 Subtract. $9 - (-3)$

NOTE TO STUDENT: Fully worked-out solutions to all of the Practice Problems can be found at the back of the text starting at page SP-1

EXAMPLE 2 Subtract. $-8 - (-6)$

Solution

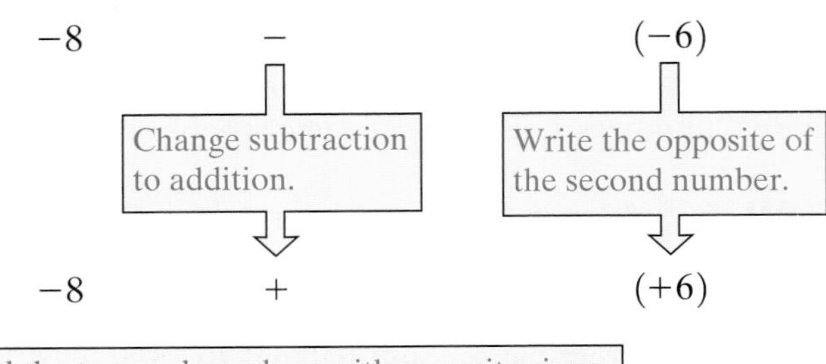

−8 − (−6)
Change subtraction to addition.
Write the opposite of the second number.
= −8 + (+6)

Add the two real numbers with opposite signs.

$= -2$

NOTE TO STUDENT: Fully worked-out solutions to all of the Practice Problems can be found at the back of the text starting at page SP-1

Practice Problem 2 Subtract. $-12 - (-5)$

EXAMPLE 3 Subtract. **(a)** $\frac{3}{7} - \frac{6}{7}$ **(b)** $-\frac{7}{18} - \left(-\frac{1}{9}\right)$

Solution

(a) $\frac{3}{7} - \frac{6}{7} = \frac{3}{7} + \left(-\frac{6}{7}\right)$ Change the subtraction problem to one of adding the opposite of the second number. We note that the problem has two fractions with the same denominator.

$= -\frac{3}{7}$ Add two numbers with different signs.

(b) $-\frac{7}{18} - \left(-\frac{1}{9}\right) = -\frac{7}{18} + \frac{1}{9}$ Change subtracting to adding the opposite.

$= -\frac{7}{18} + \frac{2}{18}$ Change $\frac{1}{9}$ to $\frac{2}{18}$ since LCD $= 18$.

$= -\frac{5}{18}$ Add two numbers with different signs.

Practice Problem 3 Subtract. **(a)** $\frac{5}{9} - \frac{7}{9}$ **(b)** $-\frac{5}{21} - \left(-\frac{3}{7}\right)$

EXAMPLE 4 Subtract. $-5.2 - (-5.2)$

Solution

$-5.2 - (-5.2) = -5.2 + 5.2$ Change the subtraction problem to one of adding the opposite of the second number.

$= 0$ Add two numbers with different signs.

Example 4 illustrates what is sometimes called the **additive inverse property.** When you add two real numbers that are opposites of each other, you will obtain zero. Examples of this are the following:

$$5 + (-5) = 0 \qquad -186 + 186 = 0 \qquad -\frac{1}{8} + \frac{1}{8} = 0.$$

Practice Problem 4 Subtract. $-17.3 - (-17.3)$

EXAMPLE 5 Calculate.

(a) $-8 - 2$ **(b)** $23 - 28$ **(c)** $5 - (-3)$ **(d)** $\frac{1}{4} - 8$

Solution

(a) $-8 - 2 = -8 + (-2)$ Notice that we are subtracting a positive 2. Change to addition.

$= -10$ Add.

In a similar fashion we have

(b) $23 - 28 = 23 + (-28) = -5$

(c) $5 - (-3) = 5 + 3 = 8$

(d) $\frac{1}{4} - 8 = \frac{1}{4} + (-8) = \frac{1}{4} + \left(-\frac{32}{4}\right) = -\frac{31}{4}$

Practice Problem 5 Calculate.

(a) $-21 - 9$ **(b)** $17 - 36$ **(c)** $12 - (-15)$ **(d)** $\frac{3}{5} - 2$

EXAMPLE 6 A satellite is recording radioactive emissions from nuclear waste buried 3 miles below sea level. The satellite orbits the Earth at 98 miles above sea level. How far is the satellite from the nuclear waste?

Solution We want to find the difference between +98 miles and −3 miles. This means we must subtract −3 from 98.

$$98 - (-3) = 98 + 3$$
$$= 101$$

The satellite is 101 miles from the nuclear waste.

Practice Problem 6 A helicopter is directly over a sunken vessel. The helicopter is 350 feet above sea level. The vessel lies 186 feet below sea level. How far is the helicopter from the sunken vessel?

Developing Your Study Skills

Reading the Textbook

Begin reading your textbook with a paper and pencil in hand. As you come across a new definition or concept, underline it in the text and/or write it down in your notebook. Whenever you encounter an unfamiliar term, look it up and make a note of it. When you come to an example, work through it step-by-step. Be sure to read each word and follow directions carefully.

Notice the helpful hints the author provides. They guide you to correct solutions and prevent you from making errors. Take advantage of these pieces of expert advice.

Be sure that you understand what you are reading. Make a note of any of those things that you do not understand and ask your instructor about them. Do not hurry through the material. Learning mathematics takes time.

1.2 Exercises

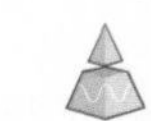

Student Solutions Manual | CD/Video | PH Math Tutor Center | MathXL®Tutorials on CD | MathXL® | MyMathLab® | Interactmath.com

Verbal and Writing Skills

1. Explain in your own words how you would perform the necessary steps to find $-8 - (-3)$.

2. Explain in your own words how you would perform the necessary steps to find $-10 - (-15)$.

Subtract by adding the opposite.

3. $18 - 35$

4. $16 - 48$

5. $15 - 20$

6. $18 - 24$

7. $-14 - (-3)$

8. $-24 - (-7)$

9. $-52 - (-60)$

10. $-48 - (-80)$

11. $0 - (-5)$

12. $0 - (-7)$

13. $-18 - (-18)$

14. $-24 - (-24)$

15. $-11 - (-8)$

16. $-35 - (-10)$

17. $\frac{2}{5} - \frac{4}{5}$

18. $\frac{2}{9} - \frac{7}{9}$

19. $\frac{3}{4} - \left(-\frac{3}{5}\right)$

20. $-\frac{2}{3} - \frac{1}{4}$

21. $-\frac{3}{4} - \frac{5}{6}$

22. $-\frac{7}{10} - \frac{10}{15}$

23. $-0.6 - 0.3$

24. $-0.9 - 0.5$

25. $2.64 - (-1.83)$

26. $-0.03 - 0.06$

Mixed Practice

Calculate.

27. $\frac{3}{5} - 4$

28. $\frac{5}{6} - 3$

29. $-\frac{2}{7} + 6$

30. $-\frac{3}{8} + 5$

31. $34 - 87$

32. $19 - 76$

33. $-25 - 48$

34. $-74 - 11$

35. $2.3 - (-4.8)$

36. $8.4 - (-2.7)$

37. $8 - \left(-\frac{3}{4}\right)$

38. $\frac{2}{3} - (-6)$

39. $\frac{5}{6} - 7$

40. $9 - \frac{2}{3}$

41. $-\frac{3}{10} - \frac{3}{4}$

42. $-\frac{11}{12} - \frac{5}{18}$

43. $-135 - (-126.5)$

44. $-97.6 - (-146)$

45. $\frac{1}{5} - 6$

46. $\frac{2}{7} - (-3)$

47. $5 - (-3.162)$

48. $7 - (-6.183)$

49. $-3 - 2.047$

50. $-1.043 - 4$

51. Subtract -9 from -2.

52. Subtract -12 from 20.

53. Subtract 13 from -35.

One Step Further

Change each subtraction operation to "adding the opposite." Then combine the numbers.

54. $9 + 6 - (-5)$

55. $7 + (-6) - 3$

56. $8 + (-4) - 10$

57. $-10 + 6 - (-15)$

58. $18 - (-15) - 3$

59. $7 + (-42) - 27$

60. $-4.2 - (-3.8) + 1.5$

61. $-6.4 - (-2.7) + 5.3$

62. $-3 - (-12) + 18 + 15 - (-6)$

63. $42 - (-30) - 65 - (-11) + 20$

Applications

64. ***Sea Rescue*** A rescue helicopter is 300 feet above sea level. The captain has located an ailing submarine directly below it that is 126 feet below sea level. How far is the helicopter from the submarine?

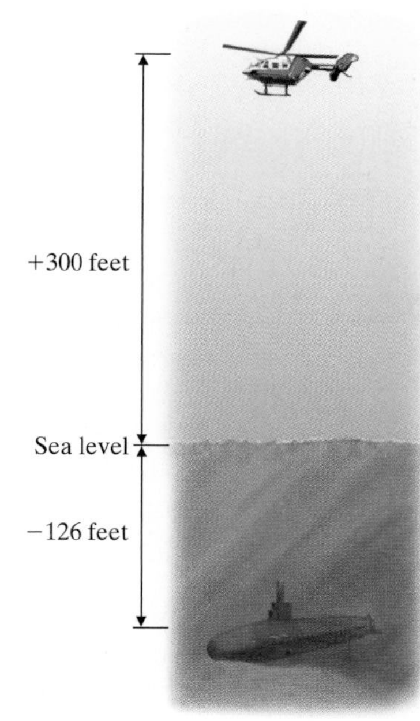

65. ***Checking Account Balance*** Yesterday Jackie had \$112 in her checking account. Today her account reads "balance −\$37." Find the difference in these two amounts.

66. ***Temperature Change*** On June 22, 1943, in Spearfish, South Dakota, the temperature was −4°F at 7:30 A.M. At 7:32 A.M., the temperature was +44.6°F. Find the difference in temperature over those two minutes.

67. ***Elevation Difference*** The highest point in Africa is Mt. Kilimanjaro in Tanzania, which is 5895 meters above sea level. The lowest point in Africa is Lake Assal in Djibouti, which is 156 meters below sea level. What is the difference in elevation between Mt. Kilimanjaro and Lake Assal?

68. ***Federal Taxes*** In 2004, Rachel had \$1815 withheld from her paycheck in federal taxes. When she filed her tax return, she received a \$265 refund. How much did she actually pay in taxes?

Cumulative Review

In exercises 69–73, perform the indicated operations.

69. $-37 + 16$

70. $-37 + (-14)$

71. $-3 + (-6) + (-10)$

72. ***Temperature*** What is the temperature after a rise of 13°C from a start of −21°C?

73. ***Hiking*** Sean and Khalid went hiking in the Blue Ridge Mountains. During their $8\frac{1}{3}$ mile hike, $\frac{4}{5}$ of the distance was covered with snow. How many miles were snow covered?

1.3 Multiplying and Dividing Real Numbers

Student Learning Objectives

After studying this section, you will be able to:

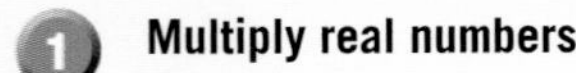

1. **Multiply real numbers.**
2. **Use the multiplication properties for real numbers.**
3. **Divide real numbers.**

1 Multiplying Real Numbers

We are familiar with the meaning of multiplication for positive numbers. For example, $5 \times 90 = 450$ might mean that you receive five weekly checks of 90 dollars each and you gain \$450. Let's look at a situation that corresponds to $5 \times (-90)$. What might that mean?

SITUATION 6: Checking an Account Balance You write a check for five weeks in a row to pay your weekly room rent of 90 dollars. You want to know the total impact on your checking account balance.

Your record for situation 6.

$(+5)$	$\times$	(-90)	$=$	-450
The number of checks you have written	times	negative 90 the value of each check that was a debit to your account,	gives	negative 450 dollars, a net debit to your account.

Note that a multiplication symbol is not needed between the $(+5)$ and the (-90) because the two sets of parentheses indicate multiplication. The multiplication $(5)(-90)$ is the same as repeated addition of five (-90)'s. Note that 5 multiplied by -90 can be written as $5(-90)$ or $(5)(-90)$.

$$(-90) + (-90) + (-90) + (-90) + (-90) = -450$$

This example seems to show that a positive number multiplied by a negative number is negative.

What if the negative number is the one that is written first? If $(5)(-90) = -450$, then $(-90)(5) = -450$ by the commutative property of multiplication. This is an example showing that *when two numbers with opposite signs* (one positive, one negative) *are multiplied, the result is negative.*

But what if both numbers are negative? Consider the following situation.

SITUATION 7: Renting a Room Last year at college you rented a room at 90 dollars per week for 36 weeks, which included two semesters and summer school. This year you will not attend the summer session, so you will be renting the room for only 30 weeks. Thus the number of weekly rental checks will be six less than last year. You are making out your budget for this year. You want to know the financial impact of renting the room for six fewer weeks.

Your record for situation 7.

(-6)	$\times$	(-90)	$=$	540
The difference in the number of checks this year compared to last is -6, which is negative to show a decrease,	times	-90, the value of each check paid out,	gives	$+540$ dollars. The product is positive, because your financial situation will be 540 dollars better this year.

You could check that the answer is positive by calculating the total rental expenses.

	Dollars in rent last year	$(36)(90) =$	3240
(subtract)	Dollars in rent this year	$-(30)(90) =$	-2700
	Extra dollars available this year	$=$	$+540$

This agrees with our previous answer: $(-6)(-90) = +540$.

In this situation it seems reasonable that a negative number times a negative number yields a positive answer. We already know from arithmetic that a positive number times a positive number yields a positive answer. Thus we might see the general rule that *when two numbers with the same sign* (both positive or both negative) *are multiplied, the result is positive.*

We will now state our rule.

MULTIPLICATION OF REAL NUMBERS

To multiply two real numbers with **the same sign,** multiply the absolute values. The sign of the result is **positive.**

To multiply two real numbers with **opposite signs,** multiply the absolute values. The sign of the result is **negative.**

Note that negative 6 times -90 can be written as $-6(-90)$ or $(-6)(-90)$.

EXAMPLE 1 Multiply.

(a) $(3)(6)$ **(b)** $\left(-\frac{5}{7}\right)\left(-\frac{2}{9}\right)$ **(c)** $-4(8)$ **(d)** $\left(\frac{2}{7}\right)(-3)$

Solution

(a) $(3)(6) = 18$

(b) $\left(-\frac{5}{7}\right)\left(-\frac{2}{9}\right) = \frac{10}{63}$

When multiplying two numbers with the same sign, the result is a positive number.

(c) $-4(8) = -32$

(d) $\left(\frac{2}{7}\right)(-3) = \left(\frac{2}{7}\right)\left(-\frac{3}{1}\right) = -\frac{6}{7}$

When multiplying two numbers with opposite signs, the result is a negative number.

Practice Problem 1 Multiply.

(a) $(-6)(-2)$ **(b)** $(7)(9)$ **(c)** $\left(-\frac{3}{5}\right)\left(\frac{2}{7}\right)$ **(d)** $\left(\frac{5}{6}\right)(-7)$

NOTE TO STUDENT: Fully worked-out solutions to all of the Practice Problems can be found at the back of the text starting at page SP-1

To multiply more than two numbers, multiply two numbers at a time.

EXAMPLE 2 Multiply. $(-4)(-3)(-2)$

Solution

$(-4)(-3)(-2) = (+12)(-2)$ We begin by multiplying the first two numbers, (-4) and (-3). The signs are the same. The answer is positive 12.

$= -24$ Now we multiply $(+12)$ and (-2). The signs are different. The answer is negative 24.

Practice Problem 2 Multiply. $(-5)(-2)(-6)$

EXAMPLE 3 Multiply.

(a) $-3(-1.5)$ **(b)** $\left(-\frac{1}{2}\right)(-1)(-4)$ **(c)** $-2(-2)(-2)(-2)$

Solution Multiply two numbers at a time. See if you find a pattern.

(a) $-3(-1.5) = 4.5$ Be sure to place the decimal point in your answer.

(b) $\left(-\frac{1}{2}\right)(-1)(-4) = +\frac{1}{2}(-4) = -2$

(c) $-2(-2)(-2)(-2) = +4(-2)(-2) = -8(-2) = +16$ or 16

What kind of answer would we obtain if we multiplied five negative numbers? If you guessed "negative," you probably see the pattern.

NOTE TO STUDENT: Fully worked-out solutions to all of the Practice Problems can be found at the back of the text starting at page SP-1

Practice Problem 3 Determine the sign of the product. Then multiply to check.

(a) $-2(-3)$ **(b)** $(-1)(-3)(-2)$ **(c)** $-4\left(-\frac{1}{4}\right)(-2)(-6)$

When you multiply two or more real numbers:

1. The result is always **positive** if there are an **even** number of negative signs.
2. The result is always **negative** if there are an **odd** number of negative signs.

2 Using the Multiplication Properties for Real Numbers

For convenience, we will list the properties of multiplication.

1. *Multiplication is commutative.*

   This property states that if two real numbers are multiplied, the order of the numbers does not affect the result. The result is the same no matter which number is written first.

   $$(5)(7) = (7)(5) = 35, \quad \left(\frac{1}{3}\right)\left(\frac{2}{7}\right) = \left(\frac{2}{7}\right)\left(\frac{1}{3}\right) = \frac{2}{21}$$

2. *Multiplication of any real number by zero will result in zero.*

   $$(5)(0) = 0, \quad (-5)(0) = 0, \quad (0)\left(\frac{3}{8}\right) = 0, \quad (0)(0) = 0$$

3. *Multiplication of any real number by 1 will result in that same number.*

   $$(5)(1) = 5, \quad (1)(-7) = -7, \quad (1)\left(-\frac{5}{3}\right) = -\frac{5}{3}$$

4. *Multiplication is associative.*

   This property states that if three real numbers are multiplied, it does not matter which two numbers are grouped by parentheses and multiplied first.

$2 \times (3 \times 4) = (2 \times 3) \times 4$ First multiply the numbers in parentheses. Then multiply the remaining numbers.

$2 \times (12) = (6) \times 4$ The results are the same no matter which numbers are grouped and multiplied first.

$24 = 24$

3 Dividing Real Numbers

What about division? Any division problem can be rewritten as a multiplication problem.

We know that $20 \div 4 = 5$ because $4(5) = 20$.
Similarly, $-20 \div (-4) = 5$ because $-4(5) = -20$.

In both division problems the answer is positive 5. Thus we see that *when you divide two numbers with the same sign* (both positive or both negative), *the answer is positive.* What if the signs are different?

We know that $-20 \div 4 = -5$ because $4(-5) = -20$.
Similarly, $20 \div (-4) = -5$ because $-4(-5) = 20$.

In these two problems the answer is negative 5. So we have reasonable evidence to see that *when you divide two numbers with different signs* (one positive and one negative), *the answer is negative.*

We will now state our rule for division.

DIVISION OF REAL NUMBERS

To divide two real numbers with **the same sign,** divide the absolute values. The sign of the result is **positive.**

To divide two real numbers with **different signs,** divide the absolute values. The sign of the result is **negative.**

EXAMPLE 4 Divide.

(a) $12 \div 4$ **(b)** $(-25) \div (-5)$ **(c)** $\frac{-36}{18}$ **(d)** $\frac{42}{-7}$

Solution

(a) $12 \div 4 = 3$

(b) $(-25) \div (-5) = 5$

When dividing two numbers with the same sign, the result is a positive number.

(c) $\frac{-36}{18} = -2$

(d) $\frac{42}{-7} = -6$

When dividing two numbers with different signs, the result is a negative number.

Practice Problem 4 Divide.

(a) $-36 \div (-2)$ **(b)** $-49 \div 7$ **(c)** $\frac{50}{-10}$ **(d)** $\frac{-39}{13}$

EXAMPLE 5 Divide. **(a)** $-36 \div 0.12$ **(b)** $-2.4 \div (-0.6)$

Solution **(a)** $-36 \div 0.12$ Look at the problem to determine the sign. When dividing two numbers with different signs, the result will be a negative number.

We then divide the absolute values.

$$\begin{array}{r} 3\,00. \\ 0.12_{\wedge}\overline{)36.00_{\wedge}} \\ \underline{36} \\ 00 \end{array}$$

Thus $-36 \div 0.12 = -300$. The answer is a negative number.

(b) $-2.4 \div (-0.6)$ Look at the problem to determine the sign. When dividing two numbers with the same sign, the result will be positive.

We then divide the absolute values.

$$0.6_{\wedge}\overline{)2.4_{\wedge}} = 4. \qquad \underline{2\ 4}$$

Thus $-2.4 \div (-0.6) = 4$. The answer is a positive number.

***NOTE TO STUDENT:** Fully worked-out solutions to all of the Practice Problems can be found at the back of the text starting at page SP-1*

Practice Problem 5 Divide. **(a)** $-12.6 \div (-1.8)$ **(b)** $0.45 \div (-0.9)$

Note that the rules for multiplication and division are the same. When you **multiply** or **divide** two numbers with the **same** sign, you obtain **a positive** number. When you **multiply** or **divide** two numbers with **different** signs, you obtain a **negative** number.

EXAMPLE 6 Divide. $-\frac{12}{5} \div \frac{2}{3}$

Solution

$= \left(-\frac{12}{5}\right)\left(\frac{3}{2}\right)$ Divide two fractions. We invert the second fraction and multiply by the first fraction.

$= \left(-\frac{\cancel{12}^{6}}{5}\right)\left(\frac{3}{\cancel{2}_{1}}\right)$

$= -\frac{18}{5}$ or $-3\frac{3}{5}$ The answer is negative since the two numbers divided have different signs.

Practice Problem 6 Divide. $-\frac{5}{16} \div \left(-\frac{10}{13}\right)$

Note that division can be indicated by the symbol $\div$ or by the fraction bar —. $\frac{2}{3}$ means $2 \div 3$.

EXAMPLE 7 Divide. **(a)** $\dfrac{\frac{7}{8}}{-21}$ **(b)** $\dfrac{-\frac{2}{3}}{-\frac{7}{13}}$

Solution

(a) $\dfrac{\frac{7}{8}}{-21}$

$= \frac{7}{8} \div \left(-\frac{21}{1}\right)$ Change -21 to a fraction. $-21 = -\frac{21}{1}$

$= \frac{\cancel{7}^{1}}{8}\left(-\frac{1}{\cancel{21}_{3}}\right)$ Change the division to multiplication. Cancel where possible.

$= -\frac{1}{24}$ Simplify.

(b) $\dfrac{-\frac{2}{3}}{-\frac{7}{13}} = -\dfrac{2}{3} \div \left(-\dfrac{7}{13}\right) = -\dfrac{2}{3}\left(-\dfrac{13}{7}\right) = \dfrac{26}{21}$ or $1\dfrac{5}{21}$

Practice Problem 7 Divide. **(a)** $\dfrac{-12}{-\frac{4}{5}}$ **(b)** $\dfrac{-\frac{2}{9}}{\frac{8}{13}}$

1. *Division of 0 by any nonzero real number gives 0 as a result.*

$$0 \div 5 = 0, \quad 0 \div \frac{2}{3} = 0, \quad \frac{0}{5.6} = 0, \quad \frac{0}{1000} = 0$$

You can divide zero by 5, $\frac{2}{3}$, 5.6, 1000, or any number (except 0).

2. *Division of any real number by 0 is* **undefined.**

$$7 \div 0 \qquad \frac{64}{0}$$
$$\uparrow \qquad \uparrow$$

Neither of these operations is possible. **Division by zero is undefined.**

You may be wondering why division by zero is undefined. Let us think about it for a minute. We said that $7 \div 0$ is undefined. Suppose there were an answer. Let us call the answer a. So we assume for a minute that $7 \div 0 = a$. Then it would have to follow that $7 = 0(a)$. But this is impossible. Zero times any number is zero. So we see that if there were such a number, it would contradict known mathematical facts. Therefore there is no number a such that $7 \div 0 = a$. Thus we conclude that division by zero is undefined.

When combining two numbers, it is important to be sure you know which rule applies. Think about the concepts in the following chart. See if you agree with each example.

Operation	Two Real Numbers with the Same Sign	Two Real Numbers with Different Signs
Addition	Result may be positive or negative. $9 + 2 = 11$ $-5 + (-6) = -11$	Result may be positive or negative. $-3 + 7 = 4$ $4 + (-12) = -8$
Subtraction	Result may be positive or negative. $15 - 6 = 15 + (-6) = 9$ $-12 - (-3) = -12 + 3 = -9$	Result may be positive or negative. $-12 - 3 = -12 + (-3) = -15$ $5 - (-6) = 5 + 6 = 11$
Multiplication	Result is always positive. $9(3) = 27$ $-8(-5) = 40$	Result is always negative. $-6(12) = -72$ $8(-3) = -24$
Division	Result is always positive. $150 \div 6 = 25$ $-72 \div (-2) = 36$	Result is always negative. $-60 \div 10 = -6$ $30 \div (-6) = -5$

EXAMPLE 8 The Hamilton-Wenham Generals recently analyzed the 48 plays their team made while in the possession of the football during their last game. The following bar graph illustrates the number of plays made in each category. The team statistician prepared the following chart indicating the average number of yards gained or lost during each type of play.

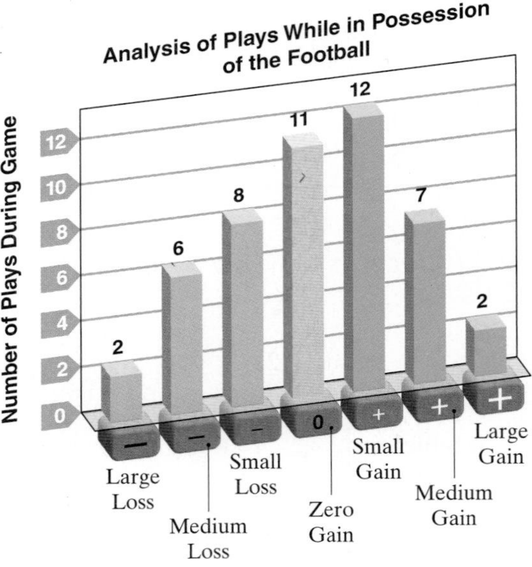

Type of Play	Average Yards Gained or Lost for Play
Large gain	+25
Medium gain	+15
Small gain	+5
Zero gain	0
Small loss	−5
Medium loss	−10
Large loss	−15

(a) How many yards were lost by the Generals in the plays that were considered small losses?

(b) How many yards were gained by the Generals in the plays that were considered small gains?

(c) If the total yards gained in small gains were combined with the total yards lost in small losses, what would be the result?

Solution

(a) We multiply the number of small losses by the average number of total yards lost on each small loss:

$$8(-5) = -40.$$

The team lost approximately 40 yards with plays that were considered small losses.

(b) We multiply the number of small gains by the average number of yards gained on each small gain:

$$12(5) = 60.$$

The team gained approximately 60 yards with plays that were considered small gains.

(c) We combine the results for (a) and (b):

$$-40 + 60 = 20.$$

A total of 20 yards was gained during the plays that were small losses and small gains.

NOTE TO STUDENT: Fully worked-out solutions to all of the Practice Problems can be found at the back of the text starting at page SP-1

Practice Problem 8 Using the information provided in Example 8, answer the following:

(a) How many yards were lost by the Generals in the plays that were considered medium losses?

(b) How many yards were gained by the Generals in the plays that were considered medium gains?

(c) If the total yards gained in medium gains were combined with the total yards lost in medium losses, what would be the result?

1.3 Exercises

Student Solutions Manual | CD/ Video | PH Math Tutor Center | MathXL®Tutorials on CD | MathXL® | MyMathLab® | Interactmath.com

Verbal and Writing Skills

1. Explain in your own words the rule for determining the correct sign when multiplying two real numbers.

2. Explain in your own words the rule for determining the correct sign when multiplying three or more real numbers.

Multiply. Be sure to write your answer in the simplest form.

3. $5(-4)$
4. $8(-2)$
5. $0(-12)$
6. $0(-150)$
7. $16(1.5)$
8. $24(2.5)$
9. $(-1.32)(-0.2)$
10. $(-2.3)(-0.11)$
11. $0.7(-2.5)$
12. $0.6(-3.5)$
13. $\left(\frac{3}{8}\right)(-4)$
14. $(5)\left(-\frac{7}{10}\right)$
15. $\left(-\frac{3}{5}\right)\left(-\frac{15}{11}\right)$
16. $\left(-\frac{4}{9}\right)\left(-\frac{3}{5}\right)$
17. $\left(\frac{12}{13}\right)\left(\frac{-5}{24}\right)$
18. $\left(\frac{14}{17}\right)\left(-\frac{3}{28}\right)$

Divide.

19. $-36 \div (-9)$
20. $0 \div (-15)$
21. $-48 \div (-8)$
22. $-45 \div (9)$
23. $-220 \div (-11)$
24. $240 \div (-15)$
25. $156 \div (-13)$
26. $-0.6 \div 0.3$
27. $-9.1 \div (0.07)$
28. $8.1 \div (-0.03)$
29. $0.54 \div (-0.9)$
30. $-7.2 \div 8$
31. $-6.3 \div 7$
32. $\frac{2}{7} \div \left(-\frac{3}{5}\right)$
33. $\left(-\frac{1}{5}\right) \div \left(\frac{2}{3}\right)$
34. $\left(-\frac{5}{6}\right) \div \left(-\frac{7}{18}\right)$
35. $-\frac{5}{7} \div \left(-\frac{3}{28}\right)$
36. $\left(-\frac{4}{9}\right) \div \left(-\frac{8}{15}\right)$
37. $\left(-\frac{7}{12}\right) \div \left(-\frac{5}{6}\right)$
38. $\frac{12}{-\frac{2}{5}}$
39. $\frac{-6}{-\frac{3}{7}}$
40. $\frac{-\frac{3}{8}}{-\frac{2}{3}}$
41. $\frac{\frac{-2}{3}}{\frac{8}{15}}$
42. $\frac{\frac{5}{12}}{-\frac{7}{24}}$
43. $\frac{-\frac{7}{8}}{-\frac{14}{15}}$

Multiply. You may want to determine the sign of the product before you multiply.

44. $-6(2)(-3)(4)$
45. $-1(-2)(-3)(4)$
46. $-2(-1)(3)(-1)(-4)$
47. $-2(-2)(2)(-1)(-3)$

48. $-3(2)(-4)(0)(-2)$

49. $-3(-2)\left(\frac{1}{3}\right)(-4)(2)$

50. $60(-0.6)(-0.002)(0.5)$

51. $-3(-0.03)(0.001)(-2)$

52. $\left(\frac{3}{8}\right)\left(\frac{1}{2}\right)\left(-\frac{5}{6}\right)$

53. $\left(-\frac{4}{5}\right)\left(-\frac{6}{7}\right)\left(-\frac{1}{3}\right)$

54. $\left(-\frac{1}{2}\right)\left(\frac{4}{5}\right)\left(-\frac{7}{8}\right)\left(-\frac{2}{3}\right)$

55. $\left(-\frac{3}{4}\right)\left(-\frac{7}{15}\right)\left(-\frac{8}{21}\right)\left(-\frac{5}{9}\right)$

Mixed Practice

Take a minute to review the chart before Example 8. Be sure that you can remember the sign rules for each operation. Then do exercises 56–65. Perform the indicated calculations.

56. $-5 - (-2)$

57. $-36 \div (-4)$

58. $-3(-9)$

59. $5 + (-7)$

60. $18 \div (-6)$

61. $8 - (-9)$

62. $-6 + (-3)$

63. $6(-12)$

64. $18 \div (-18)$

65. $-37 \div 37$

Applications

66. ***Stock Trading*** Your favorite stock opened the day's trading at $37.20 per share. When trading closed for the day, your stock was priced at $27.30 per share. If you owned 75 shares, what was your profit or loss that day?

67. ***Equal Contributions*** Ed, Ned, Ted, and Fred went camping. They each contributed an equal share of money towards food. Fred did the shopping. When he returned from the store, he had $17.60 left. How much money did Fred give back to each person?

68. ***Student Loans*** Ramon will pay $6480 on his student loan over the next 3 years. If $180 is automatically deducted from his bank account each month to pay the loan off, how much does he still owe after one year?

69. ***Car Payments*** Keith will pay the Ford dealer a total of $15,768 to be paid off in 48 equal monthly installments. What is his monthly bill?

Football *The Beverly Panthers recently analyzed the 37 plays their team made while in the possession of the football during their last game. The team statistician prepared the following chart indicating the number of plays in each category and the average number of yards gained or lost during each type of play. Use this chart to answer exercises 70–77.*

Type of Play	Number of Plays	Average Yards Gained or Lost per Play
Large gain	1	+25
Medium gain	6	+15
Small gain	4	+5
Zero gain	5	0
Small loss	10	−5
Medium loss	7	−10
Large loss	4	−15

70. How many yards were lost by the Panthers in the plays that were considered small losses?

71. How many yards were gained by the Panthers in the plays that were considered small gains?

72. If the total yards gained in small gains were combined with the total yards lost in small losses, what would be the result?

73. How many yards were lost by the Panthers in the plays that were considered medium losses?

74. How many yards were gained by the Panthers in the plays that were considered medium gains?

75. If the total yards gained in medium gains were combined with the total yards lost in medium losses, what would be the result?

76. The game being studied was lost by the Panthers. The coach said that if two of the large-loss plays had been avoided and the number of small-gain plays had been doubled, they would have won the game. If those actions listed by the coach had happened, how many additional yards would the Panthers have gained? Assume each play would reflect the average yards gained or lost per play.

77. The game being studied was lost by the Panthers. The coach of the opposing team said that they could have scored two more touchdowns against the Panthers if they had caused three more large-loss plays and avoided four medium-gain plays. If those actions had happened, what effect would this have had on total yards gained by the Panthers? Assume each play would reflect the average yards gained or lost per play.

Cumulative Review

78. $-17.4 + 8.31 + 2.40$

79. $-\frac{3}{4} + \left(-\frac{2}{3}\right) + \left(-\frac{5}{12}\right)$

80. $-47 - (-32)$

81. $-37 - 51$

82. ***Sneaker Production*** A sneaker company needs $104\frac{1}{2}$ square yards of white leather, $88\frac{2}{3}$ square yards of neon-yellow leather, and $72\frac{5}{6}$ square yards of neon-red leather to make today's batch of designer sneakers. What is today's required total square yardage of leather?

Developing Your Study Skills

Steps Toward Success in Mathematics

Mathematics is a building process, mastered one step at a time. The foundation of this process consists of a few basic requirements. Those who are successful in mathematics realize the absolute necessity for building a study of mathematics on the firm foundation of these six minimum requirements.

1. Attend class every day.
2. Read the textbook.
3. Take notes in class.
4. Do assigned homework every day.
5. Get help immediately when needed.
6. Review regularly.

1.4 Exponents

Student Learning Objectives

After studying this section, you will be able to:

1. **Write numbers in exponent form.**
2. **Evaluate numerical expressions that contain exponents.**

1 Writing Numbers in Exponent Form

In mathematics, we use exponents as a way to abbreviate repeated multiplication.

Long Notation		Exponent Form
$2 \cdot 2 \cdot 2 \cdot 2 \cdot 2 \cdot 2$	=	2^6

There are two parts to exponent notation: (1) the **base** and (2) the **exponent.** The **base** tells you what number is being multiplied and the **exponent** tells you how many times this number is used as a factor. (A *factor,* you recall, is a number being multiplied.)

$2 \cdot 2 \cdot 2 \cdot 2 \cdot 2 \cdot 2 = 2^6$

The *base* is 2 (the number being multiplied)

The *exponent* is 6 (the number of times 2 is used as a factor)

If the base is a *positive* real number, the exponent appears to the right and slightly above the level of the number as in, for example, 5^6 and 8^3. If the base is a *negative* real number, then parentheses are used around the number and the exponent appears outside the parentheses. For example, $(-2)(-2)(-2) = (-2)^3$.

In algebra, if we do not know the value of a number, we use a letter to represent the unknown number. We call the letter a **variable.** This is quite useful in the case of exponents. Suppose we do not know the value of a number, but we know the number is multiplied by itself several times. We can represent this with a variable base and a whole-number exponent. For example, when we have an unknown number, represented by the variable x, and this number occurs as a factor four times, we have

$$(x)(x)(x)(x) = x^4.$$

Likewise if an unknown number, represented by the variable w, occurs as a factor five times, we have

$$(w)(w)(w)(w)(w) = w^5.$$

EXAMPLE 1 Write in exponent form.

(a) $9(9)(9)$ **(b)** $13(13)(13)(13)$ **(c)** $-7(-7)(-7)(-7)(-7)$

(d) $-4(-4)(-4)(-4)(-4)(-4)$ **(e)** $(x)(x)$ **(f)** $(y)(y)(y)$

Solution

(a) $9(9)(9) = 9^3$ **(b)** $13(13)(13)(13) = 13^4$

(c) The -7 is used as a factor five times. The answer must contain parentheses. Thus $-7(-7)(-7)(-7)(-7) = (-7)^5$.

(d) $-4(-4)(-4)(-4)(-4)(-4) = (-4)^6$

(e) $(x)(x) = x^2$ **(f)** $(y)(y)(y) = y^3$

Practice Problem 1 Write in exponent form.

(a) $6(6)(6)(6)$ **(b)** $-2(-2)(-2)(-2)(-2)$ **(c)** $108(108)(108)$

(d) $-11(-11)(-11)(-11)(-11)(-11)$ **(e)** $(w)(w)(w)$ **(f)** $(z)(z)(z)(z)$

NOTE TO STUDENT: Fully worked-out solutions to all of the Practice Problems can be found at the back of the text starting at page SP-1

If the base has an exponent of 2, we say the base is **squared.**

If the base has an exponent of 3, we say the base is **cubed.**

If the base has an exponent greater than 3, we say the base is raised **to the (exponent)-th power.**

x^2 is read "x squared." y^3 is read "y cubed."

3^6 is read "three to the sixth power" or simply "three to the sixth."

2 Evaluating Numerical Expressions That Contain Exponents

EXAMPLE 2 Evaluate. **(a)** 2^5 **(b)** $2^3 + 4^4$

Solution

(a) $2^5 = (2)(2)(2)(2)(2) = 32$

(b) First we evaluate each power.

$2^3 = 8 \qquad 4^4 = 256$

Then we add. $8 + 256 = 264$

Practice Problem 2 Evaluate. **(a)** 3^5 **(b)** $2^2 + 3^3$

If the base is negative, be especially careful in determining the sign. Notice the following:

$$(-3)^2 = (-3)(-3) = +9 \qquad (-3)^3 = (-3)(-3)(-3) = -27.$$

From Section 1.3 we know that when you multiply two or more real numbers, first you multiply their absolute values.

- The result is positive if there are an even number of negative signs.
- The result is negative if there are an odd number of negative signs.

SIGN RULE FOR EXPONENTS

Suppose that a number is written in exponent form and the base is negative. The result is **positive** if the exponent is **even.** The result is **negative** if the exponent is **odd.**

Be careful how you read expressions with exponents and negative signs.

$(-3)^4$ means $(-3)(-3)(-3)(-3)$ or $+81$.

-3^4 means $-(3)(3)(3)(3)$ or -81.

EXAMPLE 3 Evaluate.

(a) $(-2)^3$ **(b)** $(-4)^6$ **(c)** -3^6 **(d)** $-(5^4)$

Solution

(a) $(-2)^3 = -8$ The answer is negative since the base is negative and the exponent 3 is odd.

(b) $(-4)^6 = +4096$ The answer is positive since the exponent 6 is even.

(c) $-3^6 = -729$ The negative sign is not contained in parentheses. Thus we find 3 raised to the sixth power and then take the negative of that value.

(d) $-(5^4) = -625$ The negative sign is outside the parentheses.

Practice Problem 3 Evaluate.

(a) $(-3)^3$ **(b)** $(-2)^6$ **(c)** -2^4 **(d)** $-(3^6)$

Calculator

Exponents

You can use a calculator to evaluate 3^5. Press the following keys:

3 y^x 5 =

The display should read

243

Try the following.

(a) 4^6 **(b)** $(0.2)^5$

(c) 18^6 **(d)** 3^{12}

Answers:

(a) 4096 **(b)** 0.00032

(c) 34,012,224 **(d)** 531,441

The steps needed to raise a number to a power are slightly different on some calculators.

EXAMPLE 4 Evaluate.

(a) $\left(\frac{1}{2}\right)^4$ **(b)** $(0.2)^4$ **(c)** $\left(\frac{2}{5}\right)^3$

(d) $(3)^3(2)^5$ **(e)** $2^3 - 3^4$

Solution

(a) $\left(\frac{1}{2}\right)^4 = \left(\frac{1}{2}\right)\left(\frac{1}{2}\right)\left(\frac{1}{2}\right)\left(\frac{1}{2}\right) = \frac{1}{16}$

(b) $(0.2)^4 = (0.2)(0.2)(0.2)(0.2) = 0.0016$

(c) $\left(\frac{2}{5}\right)^3 = \left(\frac{2}{5}\right)\left(\frac{2}{5}\right)\left(\frac{2}{5}\right) = \frac{8}{125}$

(d) First we evaluate each power.

$3^3 = 27 \qquad 2^5 = 32$

Then we multiply. $(27)(32) = 864$

(e) $2^3 - 3^4 = 8 - 81 = -73$

***NOTE TO STUDENT:** Fully worked-out solutions to all of the Practice Problems can be found at the back of the text starting at page SP-1*

Practice Problem 4 Evaluate.

(a) $\left(\frac{1}{3}\right)^3$ **(b)** $(0.3)^4$ **(c)** $\left(\frac{3}{2}\right)^4$

(d) $(3)^4(4)^2$ (e) $4^2 - 2^4$

1.4 EXERCISES

Student Solutions Manual | CD/Video | PH Math Tutor Center | MathXL®Tutorials on CD | MathXL® | MyMathLab® | Interactmath.com

Verbal and Writing Skills

1. Explain in your own words how to evaluate 4^4.

2. Explain in your own words how to evaluate 9^2.

3. Explain how you would determine whether $(-5)^3$ is negative or positive.

4. Explain how you would determine whether $(-2)^5$ is negative or positive.

5. Explain the difference between $(-2)^4$ and -2^4. What answers do you obtain when you evaluate the expressions?

6. Explain the difference between $(-3)^4$ and -3^4. What answers do you obtain when you evaluate the expressions?

Write in exponent form.

7. $(5)(5)(5)(5)(5)(5)(5)$ **8.** $(7)(7)(7)(7)(7)$ **9.** $(w)(w)$ **10.** $(z)(z)(z)$

11. $(p)(p)(p)(p)$ **12.** $(x)(x)(x)(x)(x)$ **13.** $(3q)(3q)(3q)$ **14.** $(6x)(6x)(6x)(6x)$

Evaluate.

15. 3^3 **16.** 4^2 **17.** 3^4 **18.** 8^3 **19.** 6^3 **20.** 15^2

21. $(-3)^3$ **22.** $(-2)^3$ **23.** $(-4)^2$ **24.** $(-5)^4$ **25.** -5^2 **26.** -4^2

27. $\left(\frac{1}{4}\right)^2$ **28.** $\left(\frac{1}{2}\right)^3$ **29.** $\left(\frac{2}{5}\right)^3$ **30.** $\left(\frac{2}{3}\right)^4$ **31.** $(1.1)^2$ **32.** $(1.2)^2$

33. $(0.2)^4$ **34.** $(0.7)^3$ **35.** $(-16)^2$ **36.** $(-7)^4$ **37.** -16^2 **38.** -7^4

Evaluate.

39. $5^3 + 6^2$ **40.** $7^2 + 6^3$ **41.** $5^3 - 3^2$ **42.** $4^3 - 2^5$ **43.** $(-3)^3 - (8)^2$

44. $(-2)^3 - (-5)^4$ **45.** $2^5 - (-3)^2$ **46.** $8^2 - (-2)^3$ **47.** $(-4)^3(-3)^2$

48. $(-7)^3(-2)^4$ **49.** $8^2(-2)^3$ **50.** $9^2(-3)^3$ **51.** 4^{12} **52.** 6^{11}

To Think About

53. What number to the third power equals -343?

54. What number to the eighth power equals 256?

Cumulative Review

Evaluate.

55. $(-11) + (-13) + 6 + (-9) + 8$ **56.** $\frac{3}{4} \div \left(-\frac{9}{20}\right)$ **57.** $-17 - (-9)$ **58.** $(-2.1)(-1.2)$

59. Amanda decided to invest her summer job earnings of \$1600 in a bank certificate of deposit, at an annual interest rate of 6% for nine months. How much money did Amanda have at the end of the nine months when her certificate of deposit matured?

1.5 The Order of Operations

Student Learning Objective

After studying this section, you will be able to:

 **Use the order of operations to simplify numerical expressions.**

1 Using the Order of Operations to Simplify Numerical Expressions

It is important to know *when* to do certain operations as well as how to do them. For example, to simplify the expression $2 - 4 \cdot 3$, should we subtract first or multiply first?

Also remember that multiplication can be written several ways. Thus $4 \cdot 3$, 4×3, $4(3)$, and $(4)(3)$ all indicate that we are multiplying 4 times 3.

The following list will assist you. It tells which operations to do first: the correct **order of operations.** You might think of it as a *list of priorities*.

ORDER OF OPERATIONS FOR NUMBERS

Follow this order of operations:

Do first
1. Do all operations inside parentheses.
2. Raise numbers to a power.
3. Multiply and divide numbers from left to right.
4. Add and subtract numbers from left to right.

Do last

Let's return to the problem $2 - 4 \cdot 3$. There are no parentheses or numbers raised to a power, so multiplication comes next. We do that first. Then we subtract since this comes last on our list.

$2 - 4 \cdot 3 = 2 - 12$ Follow the order of operations by first multiplying $4 \cdot 3 = 12$.

$= -10$ Combine $2 - 12 = -10$.

EXAMPLE 1 Evaluate. $8 \div 2 \cdot 3 + 4^2$

Solution

$8 \div 2 \cdot 3 + 4^2 = 8 \div 2 \cdot 3 + 16$ Evaluate $4^2 = 16$ because the highest priority in this problem is raising to a power.

$= 4 \cdot 3 + 16$ Next multiply and divide from left to right. So $8 \div 2 = 4$ and $4 \cdot 3 = 12$.

$= 12 + 16$

$= 28$ Finally, add.

Practice Problem 1 Evaluate. $25 \div 5 \cdot 6 + 2^3$

Note: Multiplication and division have equal priority. We do not do multiplication first. Rather, we work from left to right, doing any multiplication or division that we encounter. Similarly, addition and subtraction have equal priority.

EXAMPLE 2 Evaluate. $(-3)^3 - 2^4$

Solution The highest priority is to raise the expressions to the appropriate powers.

$(-3)^3 - 2^4 = -27 - 16$ In $(-3)^3$ we are cubing the number -3 to obtain -27. Be careful; -2^4 is not $(-2)^4$! Raise 2 to the fourth power and take the negative of the result.

$= -43$ The last step is to add and subtract from left to right.

Practice Problem 2 Evaluate. $(-4)^3 - 2^6$

NOTE TO STUDENT: Fully worked-out solutions to all of the Practice Problems can be found at the back of the text starting at page SP-1

EXAMPLE 3 Evaluate. $2 \cdot (2 - 3)^3 + 6 \div 3 + (8 - 5)^2$

Solution

$2 \cdot (2 - 3)^3 + 6 \div 3 + (8 - 5)^2$ Combine the numbers inside the parentheses.

$= 2 \cdot (-1)^3 + 6 \div 3 + 3^2$

$= 2 \cdot (-1) + 6 \div 3 + 9$ Next, raise to a power. Note that we need parentheses for -1 because of the negative sign, but they are not needed for 3.

$= -2 + 2 + 9$ Next, multiply and divide from left to right.

$= 9$ Finally, add and subtract from left to right.

Practice Problem 3 Evaluate. $6 - (8 - 12)^2 + 8 \div 2$

EXAMPLE 4 Evaluate. $\left(-\frac{1}{5}\right)\left(\frac{1}{2}\right) - \left(\frac{3}{2}\right)^2$

Solution The highest priority is to raise $\frac{3}{2}$ to the second power.

$$\left(\frac{3}{2}\right)^2 = \left(\frac{3}{2}\right)\left(\frac{3}{2}\right) = \frac{9}{4}$$ Next we multiply.

$$\left(-\frac{1}{5}\right)\left(\frac{1}{2}\right) - \left(\frac{3}{2}\right)^2 = \left(-\frac{1}{5}\right)\left(\frac{1}{2}\right) - \frac{9}{4}$$

$$= -\frac{1}{10} - \frac{9}{4}$$

$$= -\frac{1 \cdot 2}{10 \cdot 2} - \frac{9 \cdot 5}{4 \cdot 5}$$ We need to write each fraction as an equivalent fraction with the LCD of 20.

$$= -\frac{2}{20} - \frac{45}{20}$$

$$= -\frac{47}{20}$$ Add.

Practice Problem 4 Evaluate. $\left(-\frac{1}{7}\right)\left(-\frac{14}{5}\right) + \left(-\frac{1}{2}\right) \div \left(\frac{3}{4}\right)$

Calculator

Order of Operations

Use your calculator to evaluate $3 + 4 \cdot 5$.
Enter

3 [+] 4 [×] 5 [=]

If the display is [23], the correct order of operations is built in. If the display is not 23, you will need to modify the way you enter the problem. You should use

4 [×] 5 [+] 3 [=]

Try $6 + 3 \cdot 4 - 8 \div 2$.

Answer:
14

Developing Your Study Skills

Previewing New Material

Part of your study time each day should consist of looking over the sections in your text that are to be covered the following day. You do not necessarily need to study and learn the material on your own, but a survey of the concepts, terminology, diagrams, and examples will help the new ideas seem more familiar as the instructor presents them. You can look for concepts that appear confusing or difficult and be ready to listen carefully for your instructor's explanations. You can be prepared to ask the questions that will increase your understanding. Previewing new material enables you to see what is coming and prepares you to be ready to absorb it.

1.5 Exercises

Student Solutions Manual | CD/ Video | PH Math Tutor Center | MathXL®Tutorials on CD | MathXL® | MyMathLab® | Interactmath.com

Verbal and Writing Skills

Game Points *You have lost a game of UNO and are counting the points left in your hand. You announce that you have three fours and six fives.*

1. Write this as a number expression.

2. How many points have you in your hand?

3. What answer would you get for the number expression if you simplified it by
(a) performing the operations from left to right?
(b) following the order of operations?

4. Which procedure in exercise 3 gives the correct number of total points?

Evaluate.

5. $(2 - 5)^2 \div 3 \times 4$

6. $(3 - 7)^2 \div 2 \times 5$

7. $2(3 - 5 + 6) + 5$

8. $3(9 - 2 + 3) + 7$

9. $8 - 2^3 \cdot 5 + 3$

10. $6 - 3^2 \cdot 6 + 4$

11. $4 + 42 \div 3 \cdot 2 - 8$

12. $7 + 36 \div 12 \cdot 3 - 14$

13. $3 \cdot 5 + 7 \cdot 3 - 5 \cdot 3$

14. $2 \cdot 6 + 5 \cdot 3 - 7 \cdot 4$

15. $8 - 5(2)^3 \div (-8)$

16. $11 - 3(4)^2 \div (-6)$

17. $3(5 - 7)^2 - 6(3)$

18. $-2(3 - 6)^2 - (-2)$

19. $5 \cdot 6 - (3 - 5)^2 + 8 \cdot 2$

20. $(-3)^2 \cdot 6 \div 9 + 4 \cdot 2$

21. $\frac{1}{2} \div \frac{2}{3} + 6 \cdot \frac{1}{4}$

22. $\frac{5}{6} \div \frac{2}{3} - 6 \cdot \left(\frac{1}{2}\right)^2$

23. $0.8 + 0.3(0.6 - 0.2)^2$

24. $0.05 + 1.4 - (0.5 - 0.7)^3$

25. $\frac{3}{4}\left(-\frac{2}{5}\right) - \left(-\frac{3}{5}\right)$

26. $-\frac{2}{3}\left(\frac{3}{5}\right) + \frac{5}{7} \div \frac{5}{3}$

Mixed Practice

27. $(3 - 7)^2 \div 8 + 3$

28. $\left(\frac{3}{5}\right)\left(\frac{5}{6}\right) - \frac{3}{4} \div 6$

29. $\left(\frac{3}{4}\right)^2(-16) + \frac{4}{5} \div \frac{-8}{25}$

30. $\left(2\frac{4}{7}\right) \div \left(-1\frac{1}{5}\right)$

31. $-6.3 - (-2.7)(1.1) + (3.3)^2$

32. $4.35 + 8.06 \div (-2.6) - (2.1)^2$

33. $\left(\frac{1}{2}\right)^3 + \frac{1}{4} - \left(\frac{1}{6} - \frac{1}{12}\right) - \frac{2}{3} \cdot \left(\frac{1}{4}\right)^2$

34. $(2.4 \cdot 1.2)^2 - 1.6 \cdot 2.2 \div 4.0 - 3.6$

Applications

Tiger Woods just completed a round of golf, and created the following scoring table based on his score per hole, compared to par:

Score on a Hole	Number of Times the Score Occurred
Eagle (−2)	3
Birdie (−1)	9
Par (0)	5
Bogey (+1)	1

35. Write his score as the sum of eagles, birdies, pars, and bogeys.

36. What was his final score for the round, when compared to par?

37. What answer do you get if you do the arithmetic left to right?

38. Explain why the answers in #36 and #37 do not match.

Cumulative Review

Simplify.

39. $(0.5)^3$

40. $-\frac{3}{4} - \frac{5}{6}$

41. -1^{20}

42. $3\frac{3}{5} \div 6\frac{1}{4}$

43. ***Health Drink*** An Olympic weight lifter has been told by his trainer to increase his daily consumption of protein by 15 grams. The trainer suggested a health drink that provides 2 grams of protein for every 6 ounces consumed. How many ounces of this health drink would the weight lifter need to consume daily to reach his goal of 15 additional grams per day?

44. $(0.76)\ (0.9)$

45. $0.324 \div 0.6$

How Am I Doing? Sections 1.1–1.5

1. ______
2. ______
3. ______
4. ______
5. ______
6. ______
7. ______
8. ______
9. ______
10. ______
11. ______
12. ______
13. ______
14. ______
15. ______
16. ______
17. ______
18. ______
19. ______
20. ______
21. ______
22. ______

How are you doing with your homework assignments in Sections 1.1 to 1.5? Do you feel you have mastered the material so far? Do you understand the concepts you have covered? Before you go further in the textbook, take some time to do each of the following problems.

Simplify each of the following. If the answer is a fraction, be sure to leave it in reduced form.

1.1

1. $3 + (-12)$

2. $-\frac{5}{6} + \left(-\frac{7}{8}\right)$

3. $0.34 + 0.9$

4. $-14 + 3 + (-2.5) + 6.4$

1.2

5. $-23 - (-34)$

6. $-\frac{4}{5} - \frac{1}{3}$

7. $4.5 - (-7.8)$

8. $-4 - (-5) + 9$

1.3

9. $(-3)(-8)(2)(-2)$

10. $\left(-\frac{6}{11}\right)\left(-\frac{5}{3}\right)$

11. $-0.072 \div 0.08$

12. $\frac{5}{8} \div \left(-\frac{17}{16}\right)$

1.4

Evaluate.

13. $(0.7)^3$

14. $(-4)^4$

15. -2^8

16. $\left(\frac{2}{3}\right)^3$

17. $5^3 + (-2)^4$

1.5

18. $12 \div 6(2) + 3$

19. $15 + 3 - 2 + (-6)$

20. $(9 - 13)^2 + 15 \div (-3)$

21. $-0.12 \div 0.6 + (-3)(1.2) - (-0.5)$

22. $\left(\frac{3}{4}\right)\left(-\frac{2}{5}\right) + \left(-\frac{1}{2}\right)\left(\frac{4}{5}\right) + \left(\frac{1}{2}\right)^2$

Now turn to page SA-3 for the answer to each of these problems. Each answer also includes a reference to the objective in which the problem is first taught. If you missed any of these problems, you should stop and review the Examples and Practice Problems in the referenced objective. A little review now will help you master the material in the upcoming sections of the text.

1.6 Using the Distributive Property to Simplify Algebraic Expressions

Using the Distributive Property to Simplify Algebraic Expressions

As we learned previously, we use letters called *variables* to represent unknown numbers. If a number is multiplied by a variable we do not need any symbol between the number and variable. Thus, to indicate $(2)(x)$, we write $2x$. To indicate $3 \cdot y$, we write $3y$. If one variable is multiplied by another variable, we place the variables next to each other. Thus, $(a)(b)$ is written ab. We use exponent form if an unknown number (a variable) is used several times as a factor. Thus, $x \cdot x \cdot x = x^3$. Similarly, $(y)(y)(y)(y) = y^4$.

In algebra, we need to be familiar with several definitions. We will use them throughout the remainder of this book. Take some time to think through how each of these definitions is used.

An **algebraic expression** is a quantity that contains numbers and variables, such as $a + b$, $2x - 3$, and $5ab^2$. In this chapter we will be learning rules about adding and multiplying algebraic expressions. A **term** is a number, a variable, or a product of numbers and variables. 17, x, $5xy$, and $22xy^3$ are all examples of terms. We will refer to terms when we discuss the distributive property.

An important property of algebra is the **distributive property.** We can state it in an equation as follows:

DISTRIBUTIVE PROPERTY

For all real numbers a, b, and c,

$$a(b + c) = ab + ac.$$

A numerical example shows that it does seem reasonable.

$$5(3 + 6) = 5(3) + 5(6)$$
$$5(9) = 15 + 30$$
$$45 = 45$$

We can use the distributive property to multiply any term by the sum of two or more terms. In Section 1.4, we defined the word *factor*. Two or more algebraic expressions that are multiplied are called **factors.** Consider the following examples of multiplying algebraic expressions.

EXAMPLE 1 Multiply. **(a)** $5(a + b)$ **(b)** $-3(3x + 2y)$

Solution

(a) $5(a + b) = 5a + 5b$ — Multiply the factor $(a + b)$ by the factor 5.

(b) $-3(3x + 2y) = -3(3x) + (-3)(2y)$ — Multiply the factor $(3x + 2y)$ by the factor (-3).

$= -9x - 6y$

Practice Problem 1 Multiply. **(a)** $3(x + 2y)$ **(b)** $-a(a - 3b)$

If the parentheses are preceded by a negative sign, we consider this to be the product of (-1) and the expression inside the parentheses.

Student Learning Objective

After studying this section, you will be able to:

Use the distributive property to simplify algebraic expressions.

***NOTE TO STUDENT:** Fully worked-out solutions to all of the Practice Problems can be found at the back of the text starting at page SP-1*

EXAMPLE 2 Multiply. $-(a - 2b)$

Solution

$$-(a - 2b) = (-1)(a - 2b) = (-1)(a) + (-1)(-2b) = -a + 2b$$

NOTE TO STUDENT: Fully worked-out solutions to all of the Practice Problems can be found at the back of the text starting at page SP-1

Practice Problem 2 Multiply. $-(-3x + y)$

In general, we see that in all these examples we have multiplied each term of the expression in the parentheses by the expression in front of the parentheses.

EXAMPLE 3 Multiply. **(a)** $\frac{2}{3}(x^2 - 6x + 8)$ **(b)** $1.4(a^2 + 2.5a + 1.8)$

Solution

(a)
$$\begin{aligned}\frac{2}{3}(x^2 - 6x + 8) &= \left(\frac{2}{3}\right)(1x^2) + \left(\frac{2}{3}\right)(-6x) + \left(\frac{2}{3}\right)(8)\\ &= \frac{2}{3}x^2 + (-4x) + \frac{16}{3}\\ &= \frac{2}{3}x^2 - 4x + \frac{16}{3}\end{aligned}$$

(b)
$$\begin{aligned}1.4(a^2 + 2.5a + 1.8) &= 1.4(1a^2) + (1.4)(2.5a) + (1.4)(1.8)\\ &= 1.4a^2 + 3.5a + 2.52\end{aligned}$$

Practice Problem 3 Multiply.

(a) $\frac{3}{5}(a^2 - 5a + 25)$ **(b)** $2.5(x^2 - 3.5x + 1.2)$

There are times we multiply a variable by itself and use exponent notation. For example, $(x)(x) = x^2$ and $(x)(x)(x) = x^3$. In other cases there will be numbers and variables multiplied at the same time.

We will see problems like $(2x)(x) = (2)(x)(x) = 2x^2$. Some expressions will involve multiplication of more than one variable. We will see problems like $(3x)(xy) = (3)(x)(x)(y) = 3x^2y$. There will be times when we use the distributive property and all of these methods will be used. For example,

$$\begin{aligned}2x(x - 3y + 2) &= 2x(x) + (2x)(-3y) + (2x)(2)\\ &= 2x^2 + (-6)(xy) + 4(x)\\ &= 2x^2 - 6xy + 4x.\end{aligned}$$

We will discuss this type of multiplication of variables with exponents in more detail in Section 4.1. At that point we will expand these examples and other similar examples to develop the general rule for multiplication $(x^a)(x^b) = x^{a+b}$.

EXAMPLE 4 Multiply. $-2x(3x + y - 4)$

Solution

$$\begin{aligned}-2x(3x + y - 4) &= -2(x)(3)(x) + (-2)(x)(y) + (-2)(x)(-4)\\ &= -2(3)(x)(x) + (-2)(xy) + (-2)(-4)(x)\\ &= -6x^2 - 2xy + 8x\end{aligned}$$

Practice Problem 4 Multiply. $-4x(x - 2y + 3)$

The distributive property can also be presented with the a on the right.

$$(b + c)a = ba + ca$$

The a is "distributed" over the b and c inside the parentheses.

EXAMPLE 5 Multiply. $(2x^2 - x)(-3)$

Solution

$$\begin{aligned}(2x^2 - x)(-3) &= 2x^2(-3) + (-x)(-3) \\ &= -6x^2 + 3x\end{aligned}$$

Practice Problem 5 Multiply.

$$(3x^2 - 2x)(-4)$$

▲ **EXAMPLE 6** A farmer has a rectangular field that is 300 feet wide. One portion of the field is $2x$ feet long. The other portion of the field is $3y$ feet long. Use the distributive property to find an expression for the area of this field.

Solution First we draw a picture of a field that is 300 feet wide and $2x + 3y$ feet long.

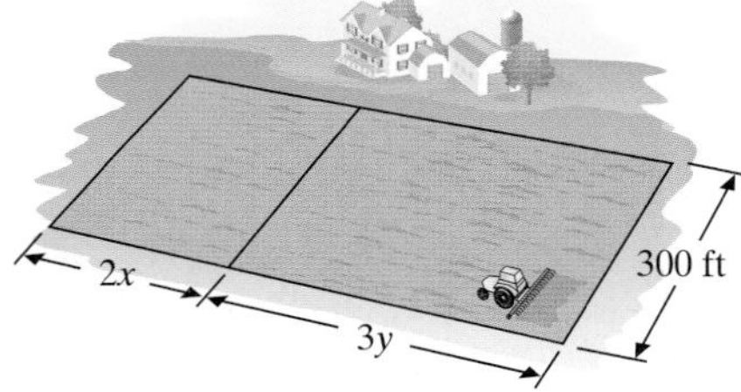

To find the area of the field, we multiply the width times the length.

$$300(2x + 3y) = 300(2x) + 300(3y) = 600x + 900y$$

Thus the area of the field in square feet is $600x + 900y$.

▲ **Practice Problem 6** A farmer has a rectangular field that is 400 feet wide. One portion of the field is $6x$ feet long. The other portion of the field is $9y$ feet long. Use the distributive property to find an expression for the area of this field.

Developing Your Study Skills

How to Do Homework

As you begin your homework assignments, read the directions carefully. You need to understand what is being asked for. Concentrate on each exercise, taking time to solve it accurately. Rushing through your work usually causes errors. Check your answers with those given in the back of the textbook. If your answer is incorrect, check to see that you are doing the right exercise. Redo the exercise, watching for little errors. If it is still wrong, check with a friend. Perhaps the two of you can figure it out.

1.6 Exercises

     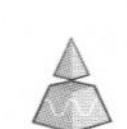

Student Solutions Manual | CD/ Video | PH Math Tutor Center | MathXL®Tutorials on CD | MathXL® | MyMathLab® | Interactmath.com

Verbal and Writing Skills

In exercises 1 and 2, complete each sentence by filling in the blank.

1. A ___________ is a symbol used to represent an unknown number.

2. When we write an expression with numbers and variables such as $7x$, it indicates that we are _______________ 7 by x.

3. Explain in your own words how we multiply a problem like $(4x)(x)$.

4. Explain why you think the property $a(b + c) = ab + ac$ is called the distributive property. What does distribute mean?

5. Does the following distributive property work? $a(b - c) = ab - ac$ Why or why not? Give an example.

6. Susan tried to use the distributive property and wrote

$$-5(x + 3y - 2) = -5x - 15y - 10.$$

What did she do wrong?

Multiply. Use the distributive property.

7. $3(x - 2y)$

8. $4(3x - y)$

9. $-2(4a - 3b)$

10. $-3(2a - 5b)$

11. $3(3x + y)$

12. $2(4x + y)$

13. $5(-2a - 3b)$

14. $6(-4a - 2b)$

15. $-(x - 3y)$

16. $-(-4x + y)$

17. $-9(9x - 5y + 8)$

18. $-5(3x + 9 - 7y)$

19. $2(-5x + y - 6)$

20. $3(2x - 6y - 5)$

21. $\frac{5}{6}(12x^2 - 24x + 18)$

22. $\frac{2}{3}(-27a^4 + 9a^2 - 21)$

23. $\frac{x}{5}(x + 10y - 4)$ $\left(\text{Hint: } \frac{x}{5} = \frac{1}{5}x\right)$

24. $\frac{y}{3}(3y - 4x - 6)$ $\left(\text{Hint: } \frac{y}{3} = \frac{1}{3}y\right)$

25. $5x(x + 2y + z)$

26. $3a(2a + b - c)$

27. $(2x - 3)(-2)$

28. $(5x + 1)(-4)$

29. $(6x + y - 1)(3x)$

30. $(3x - 3y + 4)(2x)$

Mixed Practice

Multiply. Use the distributive property.

31. $(3x + 2y - 1)(-xy)$

32. $(4a - 2b - 1)(-ab)$

33. $(2x + 3y - 2)3xy$

34. $(-2x + y - 3)4xy$

35. $2.3(4.1x^2 - 2.3x + 0.4)$

36. $3.1(2.5x^2 - 3.1x + 0.7)$

37. $-0.3x(-1.2x^2 - 0.3x + 0.5)$

38. $-0.9q(2.1q - 0.2r - 0.8s)$

39. $0.5x(0.6x + 0.8y - 5)$

Applications

▲ **40.** ***Geometry*** Blaine Johnson has a rectangular field that is 700 feet wide. One portion of the field is $12x$ feet long. The other portion of the field is $8y$ feet long. Use the distributive property to find an expression for the area of this field.

▲ **41.** ***Geometry*** Kathy DesMaris has a rectangular field that is 800 feet wide. One portion of the field is $5x$ feet long. The other portion of the field is $14y$ feet long. Use the distributive property to find an expression for the area of this field.

▲ **42.** ***Mural Painting*** Marc Adler was in charge of painting a mural on the side of the school gym. The gym was 85 feet long. If the distance from the floor to a banner rail is $3x$ feet and it is $2y$ feet from the banner rail to the ceiling, what was the area that the mural had to cover?

43. ***Cell Phone Sales*** The price of a cell phone was $2x$. A manager's special reduced the price by \$5.00. If the store sold $4y$ cell phones, use the distributive property to find the value of the cell phones sold.

To Think About

▲ **44.** ***Athletic Field*** The athletic field at Baxford College is $3x$ feet wide. It used to be 1500 feet long. However, due to the construction of a new dormitory, the field length was decreased by $4y$ feet. Use the distributive property to find an expression for the area of the new field after construction of the dormitory.

▲ **45.** ***Airport Runway*** The Beverly Airport runway is $4x$ feet wide. The airport was supposed to have a 3000-foot-long runway. However, some of the land was wetland, so a runway could not be built on all of it. Therefore, the length of the runway was decreased by $2y$ feet. Use the distributive property to find an expression for the area of the final runway.

Cumulative Review

In exercises 46–48, evaluate.

46. $-18 + (-20) + 36 + (-14)$

47. $(-2)^6$

48. $-27 - (-41)$

49. $25 \div 5(2) + (-6)$

50. $(12 - 10)^2 + (-3)(-2)$

51. ***Soccer Practice*** The San Rafael Junior Soccer League would practice 365 days per year if it could. Last year because of the weather, the players could practice only 205 days. What percent of the days last year could players practice? (Round to the nearest whole percent.)

52. ***Soccer Practice*** The coach of the team in exercise 51 predicts that this year the team will be able to practice 60% of the year. How many more days of practice will be possible this year than were possible last year?

1.7 Combining Like Terms

Student Learning Objectives

After studying this section, you will be able to:

 **Identify like terms.**

 **Combine like terms.**

1 Identifying Like Terms

We can add or subtract quantities that are *like quantities*. This is called **combining** like quantities.

5 inches + 6 inches = 11 inches
20 square inches − 16 square inches = 4 square inches

However, we cannot combine things that are not the same.

16 square inches − 4 inches (Cannot be done!)

Similarly, in algebra we can **combine like terms.** This means to add or subtract like terms. Remember, we cannot combine terms that are not the same. Recall that a *term* is a number, a variable, or a product of numbers and variables. **Like terms** are terms that have identical variables and exponents. In other words, like terms must have exactly the same letter parts.

EXAMPLE 1 List the like terms of each expression.

(a) $5x - 2y + 6x$ **(b)** $2x^2 - 3x - 5x^2 - 8x$

Solution

(a) $5x$ and $6x$ are like terms. These are the only like terms.

(b) $2x^2$ and $-5x^2$ are like terms.

$-3x$ and $-8x$ are like terms.

Note that x^2 and x are not like terms.

NOTE TO STUDENT: Fully worked-out solutions to all of the Practice Problems can be found at the back of the text starting at page SP-1

Practice Problem 1 List the like terms of each expression.

(a) $5a + 2b + 8a - 4b$ **(b)** $x^2 + y^2 + 3x - 7y^2$

Do you really understand what a term is? A term is a number, a variable, or a product of numbers and variables. Terms are the parts of an algebraic expression separated by plus or minus signs. The sign in front of the term is considered part of the term.

2 Combining Like Terms

It is important to know how to combine like terms. Since

4 inches + 5 inches = 9 inches,

we would expect in algebra that $4x + 5x = 9x$.

Why is this true? Let's take a look at the distributive property.

Like terms may be added or subtracted by using the distributive property:

$$ab + ac = a(b + c) \quad \text{and} \quad ba + ca = (b + c)a.$$

For example,

$$-7x + 9x = (-7 + 9)x = 2x$$
$$5x^2 + 12x^2 = (5 + 12)x^2 = 17x^2.$$

EXAMPLE 2 Combine like terms.

(a) $-4x^2 + 8x^2$ **(b)** $5x + 3x + 2x$

Solution

(a) Notice that each term contains the factor x^2. Using the distributive property, we have

$$-4x^2 + 8x^2 = (-4 + 8)x^2 = 4x^2.$$

(b) Note that each term contains the factor x. Using the distributive property, we have

$$5x + 3x + 2x = (5 + 3 + 2)x = 10x.$$

Practice Problem 2 Combine like terms.

(a) $16y^3 + 9y^3$ **(b)** $5a + 7a + 4a$

In this section, the direction *simplify* means to remove parentheses and/or combine like terms.

EXAMPLE 3 Simplify. $5a^2 - 2a^2 + 6a^2$

Solution

$$5a^2 - 2a^2 + 6a^2 = (5 - 2 + 6)a^2 = 9a^2$$

Practice Problem 3 Simplify. $-8y^2 - 9y^2 + 4y^2$

After doing a few problems, you will find that it is not necessary to write out the step of using the distributive property. We will omit this step for the remaining examples in this section.

EXAMPLE 4 Simplify.

(a) $5.6a + 2b + 7.3a - 6b$ **(b)** $3x^2y - 2xy^2 + 6x^2y$

(c) $2a^2b + 3ab^2 - 6a^2b^2 - 8ab$

Solution

(a) $5.6a + 2b + 7.3a - 6b = 12.9a - 4b$ We combine the a terms and the b terms separately.

(b) $3x^2y - 2xy^2 + 6x^2y = 9x^2y - 2xy^2$ **Note:** x^2y and xy^2 are not like terms because of different powers.

(c) $2a^2b + 3ab^2 - 6a^2b^2 - 8ab$ These terms cannot be combined; there are no like terms in this expression.

Practice Problem 4 Simplify.

(a) $1.3x + 3a - 9.6x + 2a$ **(b)** $5ab - 2ab^2 - 3a^2b + 6ab$

(c) $7x^2y - 2xy^2 - 3x^2y - 4xy^2 + 5x^2y$

The two skills in this section that a student must practice are identifying like terms and correctly adding and subtracting like terms. If a problem involves many terms, you may find it helpful to rearrange the terms so that like terms are together.

EXAMPLE 5 Simplify. $3a - 2b + 5a^2 + 6a - 8b - 12a^2$

Solution There are three pairs of like terms.

$$\underbrace{3a + 6a}_{a \text{ terms}} \underbrace{- 2b - 8b}_{b \text{ terms}} \underbrace{+ 5a^2 - 12a^2}_{a^2 \text{ terms}}$$ You can rearrange the terms so that like terms are together, making it easier to combine them.

$= 9a - 10b - 7a^2$ Combine like terms.

Because of the commutative property, the order of terms in an answer to this problem is not significant. These three terms can be rearranged in a different order. $-10b + 9a - 7a^2$ and $-7a^2 + 9a - 10b$ are also correct. However, we usually write polynomials in order of descending exponents. $-7a^2 + 9a - 10b$ would be the preferred way to write the answer.

***NOTE TO STUDENT:** Fully worked-out solutions to all of the Practice Problems can be found at the back of the text starting at page SP-1*

Practice Problem 5 Simplify. $5xy - 2x^2y + 6xy^2 - xy - 3xy^2 - 7x^2y$

Use extra care with fractional values.

EXAMPLE 6 Simplify. $\frac{3}{4}x^2 - 5y - \frac{1}{8}x^2 + \frac{1}{3}y$

Solution We need a least common denominator for the x^2 terms, which is 8. Change $\frac{3}{4}$ to eighths by multiplying the numerator and denominator by 2.

$$\frac{3}{4}x^2 - \frac{1}{8}x^2 = \frac{3 \cdot 2}{4 \cdot 2}x^2 - \frac{1}{8}x^2 = \frac{6}{8}x^2 - \frac{1}{8}x^2 = \frac{5}{8}x^2$$

The least common denominator for the y terms is 3. Change 5 to thirds.

$$-\frac{5}{1}y + \frac{1}{3}y = \frac{-5 \cdot 3}{1 \cdot 3}y + \frac{1}{3}y = \frac{-15}{3}y + \frac{1}{3}y = -\frac{14}{3}y$$

Thus, our solution is $\frac{5}{8}x^2 - \frac{14}{3}y$.

Practice Problem 6 Simplify. $\frac{1}{7}a^2 - \frac{5}{12}b + 2a^2 - \frac{1}{3}b$

EXAMPLE 7 Simplify. $6(2x + 3xy) - 8x(3 - 4y)$

Solution First remove the parentheses; then combine like terms.

$6(2x + 3xy) - 8x(3 - 4y) = 12x + 18xy - 24x + 32xy$ Use the distributive property.

$= -12x + 50xy$ Combine like terms.

Practice Problem 7 Simplify. $5a(2 - 3b) - 4(6a + 2ab)$

1.7 Exercises

    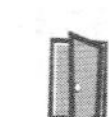 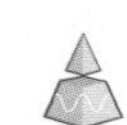

Student Solutions Manual | CD/ Video | PH Math Tutor Center | MathXL®Tutorials on CD | MathXL® | MyMathLab® | Interactmath.com

Verbal and Writing Skills

1. Explain in your own words the mathematical meaning of the word *term*.

2. Explain in your own words the mathematical meaning of the phrase *like terms*.

3. Explain which terms are like terms in the expression $5x - 7y - 8x$.

4. Explain which terms are like terms in the expression $12a - 3b - 9a$.

5. Explain which terms are like terms in the expression $7xy - 9x^2y - 15xy^2 - 14xy$.

6. Explain which terms are like terms in the expression $-3a^2b - 12ab + 5ab^2 + 9ab$.

Combine like terms.

7. $-14b^2 - 11b^2$

8. $-17x^5 + 3x^5$

9. $10x^4 + 8x^4 + 7x^2$

10. $3a^3 - 6a^2 + 5a^3$

11. $3x + 2y - 8x - 7y$

12. $4a - 3b - 2a - 8b$

13. $1.3x - 2.6y + 5.8x - 0.9y$

14. $3.1a - 0.2b - 0.8a + 5.3b$

15. $1.6x - 2.8y - 3.6x - 5.9y$

16. $1.9x - 2.4b - 3.8x - 8.2b$

17. $3p - 4q + 2p + 3 + 5q - 21$

18. $6x - 5y - 3y + 7 - 11x - 5$

19. $2ab + 5bc - 6ac - 2ab$

20. $7ab - 3bc - 12ac + 8ab$

21. $2x^2 - 3x - 5 - 7x + 8 - x^2$

22. $5x + 7 - 6x^2 + 6 - 11x + 4x^2$

23. $2y^2 - 8y + 9 - 12y^2 - 8y + 3$

24. $3y^2 + 9y - 12 - 4y^2 - 6y + 2$

25. $\frac{1}{3}x - \frac{2}{3}y - \frac{2}{5}x + \frac{4}{7}y$

26. $\frac{2}{5}s - \frac{3}{8}t - \frac{4}{15}s - \frac{5}{12}t$

27. $\frac{3}{4}a^2 - \frac{1}{3}b - \frac{1}{5}a^2 - \frac{1}{2}b$

28. $\frac{2}{5}y - \frac{3}{4}x^2 - \frac{1}{3}y + \frac{7}{8}x^2$

29. $ab - 7a - 9ab + 4a - 6b$

30. $ab + 3a - 4ab + 2a - 8b$

Simplify. Use the distributive property to remove parentheses; then combine like terms.

31. $5(2a - b) - 3(5b - 6a)$

32. $8(3x - 2y) + 4(3y - 5x)$

33. $-3b(5a - 3b) + 4(-3ab - 5b^2)$

34. $2x(x - 3y) - 4(-3x^2 - 2xy)$

35. $-3(x^2 + 3y) + 5(-6y - x^2)$

36. $-3(7xy - 11y^2) - 2y(-2x + 3y)$

37. $4(2 - x) - 3(-5 - 12x)$

38. $7(3 - x) - 6(8 - 13x)$

To Think About

▲ **39.** ***Fencing in a Pool*** Mr. Jimenez has a pool behind his house that needs to be fenced in. The backyard is an odd quadrilateral shape. The four sides are $3a$, $2b$, $4a$, and $7b$ in length. How much fencing (the length of the perimeter) would he need to enclose the pool?

▲ **40.** ***Framing a Masterpiece*** The new Degas masterpiece purchased by the Museum of Fine Arts in Boston needs to be reframed. If the rectangular picture measures $6x - 3$ wide by $8x - 7$ high, what is the perimeter of the painting?

▲ **41.** ***Geometry*** A triangle has sides of length $2a$ centimeters, $7b$ centimeters, and $5a + 3$ centimeters. What is the perimeter of the triangle?

▲ **42.** ***Geometry*** A rectangle has sides of length $7x - 2$ meters and $3x + 4$ meters. What is the perimeter of the rectangle?

▲ **43.** ***Geometry*** A square has a side of length $9x - 2$ inches. Each side is shortened by 3 inches. What is the perimeter of the new smaller square?

▲ **44.** ***Geometry*** A triangle has sides of length $4a - 5$ feet, $3a + 8$ feet, and $9a + 2$ feet. Each side is doubled in length. What is the perimeter of the new enlarged triangle?

Cumulative Review

Evaluate.

45. $-\frac{1}{3} - \left(-\frac{1}{5}\right)$

46. $\left(-\frac{5}{3}\right)\left(\frac{1}{2}\right)$

47. $\frac{4}{5} + \left(-\frac{1}{25}\right) + \left(-\frac{3}{10}\right)$

48. $\left(\frac{5}{7}\right) \div \left(-\frac{14}{3}\right)$

49. ***Serving Size*** A 2-quart container of orange juice produces 9.5 average servings. The container holds approximately 1.9 liters of orange juice. How many liters are in one serving?

1.8 Using Substitution to Evaluate Algebraic Expressions and Formulas

1 Evaluating an Algebraic Expression for a Specified Value

You will use the order of operations to **evaluate** variable expressions. Suppose we are asked to evaluate

$$6 + 3x \text{ for } x = -4.$$

In general, x represents some unknown number. Here we are told x has the value -4. We can replace x with -4. Use parentheses around -4. Note that we always put replacement values in parentheses.

$$6 + 3(-4) = 6 + (-12) = -6$$

When we replace a variable by a particular value, we say we have **substituted** the value for the variable. We then evaluate the expression (that is, find a value for it).

EXAMPLE 1 Evaluate $\frac{2}{3}x - 5$ for $x = -6$.

Solution

$\frac{2}{3}x - 5 = \frac{2}{3}(-6) - 5$ Substitute $x = -6$. Be sure to enclose the -6 in parentheses.

$= -4 - 5$ Multiply $\left(\frac{2}{3}\right)\left(-\frac{6}{1}\right) = -4$.

$= -9$ Combine.

Practice Problem 1 Evaluate $4 - \frac{1}{2}x$ for $x = -8$.

Compare parts (a) and (b) in the next example. The two parts illustrate that you must be careful what value you raise to a power. *Note:* In part (b) we will need parentheses within parentheses. To avoid confusion, we use brackets [ ] to represent the outside parentheses.

EXAMPLE 2 **(a)** Evaluate $2x^2$ for $x = -3$.

(b) Evaluate $(2x)^2$ for $x = -3$.

Solution

(a) Here the value x is squared.

$2x^2 = 2(-3)^2$

$= 2(9)$ First square -3.

$= 18$ Then multiply.

(b) Here the value $(2x)$ is squared.

$(2x)^2 = [(2)(-3)]^2$

$= (-6)^2$ First multiply the numbers inside the parentheses.

$= 36$ Then square -6.

Practice Problem 2 Evaluate for $x = -3$. **(a)** $4x^2$ **(b)** $(4x)^2$

Carefully study the solutions to Example 2(a) and Example 2(b). You will find that taking the time to see *how* and *why* they are different is a good investment of study time.

Student Learning Objectives

After studying this section, you will be able to:

1. **Evaluate an algebraic expression for a specified value.**
2. **Evaluate a formula by substituting values.**

NOTE TO STUDENT: Fully worked-out solutions to all of the Practice Problems can be found at the back of the text starting at page SP-1

EXAMPLE 3 Evaluate $x^2 + 3x$ for $x = -4$.

Solution

$$
\begin{aligned}
x^2 + 3x &= (-4)^2 + 3(-4) && \text{Replace } x \text{ by } -4 \text{ in the original expression.}\\
&= 16 + (3)(-4) && \text{Raise to a power.}\\
&= 16 - 12 && \text{Multiply.}\\
&= 4 && \text{Finally, add.}
\end{aligned}
$$

Practice Problem 3 Evaluate $2x^2 - 3x$ for $x = -2$.

 Evaluating a Formula by Substituting Values

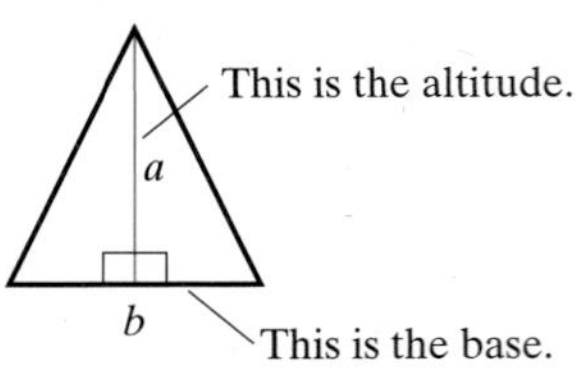

We can *evaluate a formula* by substituting values for the variables. For example, the area of a triangle can be found using the formula $A = \frac{1}{2}ab$, where b is the length of the base of the triangle and a is the altitude of the triangle (see figure). If we know values for a and b, we can substitute those values into the formula to find the area. The units for area are *square units*.

Because some of the examples and exercises in this section involve geometry, it may be helpful to review this topic.

However, before we proceed to do any examples, it may be helpful to review a little geometry. The following information is very important. If you have forgotten some of this material (or if you have never learned it), please take the time to learn it completely now. Throughout the entire book we will be using this information in solving applied problems.

Perimeter is the distance around a plane figure. Perimeter is measured in linear units (inches, feet, centimeters, miles). **Area** is a measure of the amount of surface in a region. Area is measured in square units (square inches, square feet, square centimeters).

In our sketches we will show angles of 90° by using a small square (⌞⌟). This indicates that the two lines are at right angles. All angles that measure 90° are called **right angles.** An **altitude** is perpendicular to the base of a figure. That is, the altitude forms right angles with the base. The small corner square in a sketch helps us identify the altitude of the figure.

The following box provides a handy guide to some facts and formulas you will need to know. Use it as a reference when solving word problems involving geometric figures.

GEOMETRIC FORMULAS: TWO-DIMENSIONAL FIGURES

A **parallelogram** is a four-sided figure with opposite sides parallel. In a parallelogram, opposite sides are equal and opposite angles are equal.

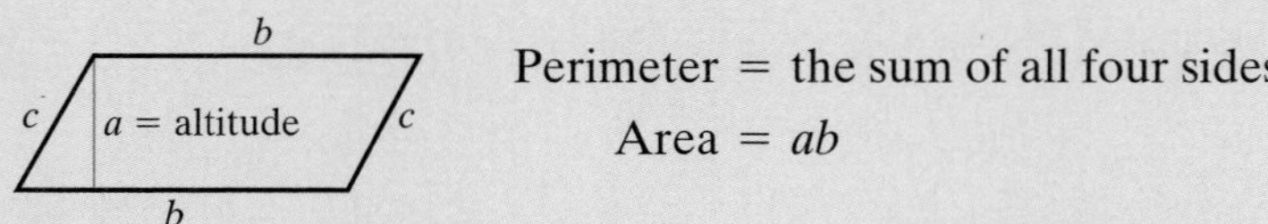

A **rectangle** is a parallelogram with all interior angles measuring 90°.

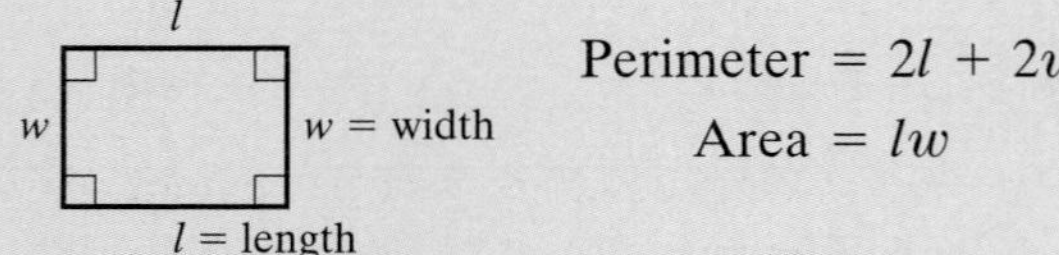

A **square** is a rectangle with all four sides equal.

s = side

Perimeter $= 4s$

Area $= s^2$

A **trapezoid** is a four-sided figure with two sides parallel. The parallel sides are called the *bases* of the trapezoid.

b_1 = base one, b_2 = base two, a = altitude, d, e

Perimeter $=$ the sum of all four sides

Area $= \frac{1}{2}a(b_1 + b_2)$

A **triangle** is a closed plane figure with three sides.

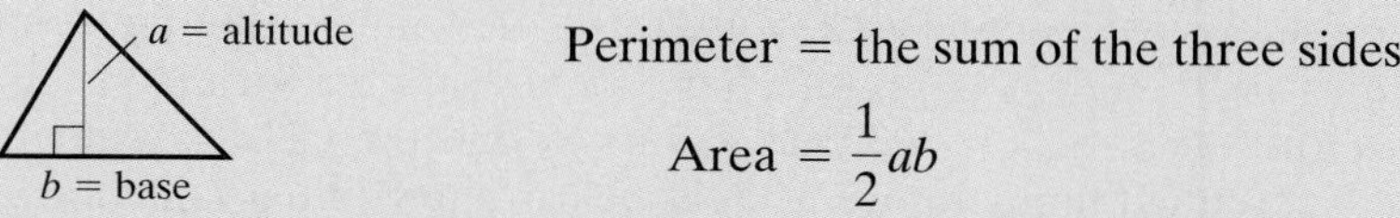

Perimeter $=$ the sum of the three sides

Area $= \frac{1}{2}ab$

A **circle** is a plane curve consisting of all points at an equal distance from a given point called the center.

Circumference is the distance around a circle.

r = radius

d = diameter $= 2r$

Circumference $= 2\pi r$

Area $= \pi r^2$

π (the number *pi*) is a constant associated with circles. It is an irrational number that is approximately 3.141592654. We usually use 3.14 as a sufficiently accurate approximation. Thus we write $\pi \approx 3.14$ for most of our calculations involving π.

EXAMPLE 4 Find the area of a triangle with a base of 16 centimeters (cm) and a height of 12 centimeters (cm).

Solution Use the formula $A = \frac{1}{2}ab$.

Substitute 12 centimeters for a and 16 centimeters for b.

$$A = \frac{1}{2}(12 \text{ centimeters})(16 \text{ centimeters})$$

$$= \frac{1}{2}(12)(16)(\text{cm})(\text{cm}) \quad \text{If you take } \tfrac{1}{2} \text{ of 12 first, it will make your calculation easier.}$$

$$= (6)(16)(\text{cm})^2 = 96 \text{ square centimeters}$$

The area of the triangle is 96 square centimeters.

Practice Problem 4 Find the area of a triangle with an altitude of 3 meters and a base of 7 meters.

NOTE TO STUDENT: Fully worked-out solutions to all of the Practice Problems can be found at the back of the text starting at page SP-1

The area of a circle is given by

$$A = \pi r^2.$$

We will use 3.14 as an approximation for the *irrational number* π.

EXAMPLE 5 Find the area of a circle if the radius is 2 inches.

Solution

$A = \pi r^2 \approx (3.14)(2 \text{ inches})^2$ Write the formula and substitute the given values for the letters.

$= (3.14)(4)(\text{in.})^2$ Raise to a power. Then multiply.

$= 12.56$ square inches

Practice Problem 5 Find the area of a circle if the radius is 3 meters.

The formula $C = \frac{5}{9}(F - 32)$ allows us to find the Celsius temperature if we know the Fahrenheit temperature. That is, we can substitute a value for F in degrees Fahrenheit into the formula to obtain a temperature C in degrees Celsius.

EXAMPLE 6 What is the Celsius temperature when the Fahrenheit temperature is $F = -22°$?

Solution Use the formula.

$C = \frac{5}{9}(F - 32)$

$= \frac{5}{9}((-22) - 32)$ Substitute -22 for F in the formula.

$= \frac{5}{9}(-54)$ Combine the numbers inside the parentheses.

$= (5)(-6)$ Simplify.

$= -30$ Multiply.

The temperature is $-30°$ Celsius.

NOTE TO STUDENT: Fully worked-out solutions to all of the Practice Problems can be found at the back of the text starting at page SP-1

Practice Problem 6 What is the Celsius temperature when the Fahrenheit temperature is $F = 68°$? Use the formula $C = \frac{5}{9}(F - 32)$.

When driving in Canada or Mexico, we must observe speed limits posted in kilometers per hour. A formula that converts r (miles per hour) to k (kilometers per hour) is $k \approx 1.61r$. Note that this is an approximation.

EXAMPLE 7 You are driving on a highway in Mexico. It has a posted maximum speed of 100 kilometers per hour. You are driving at 61 miles per hour. Are you exceeding the speed limit?

Solution Use the formula.

$$\begin{aligned} k &\approx 1.61r \\ &= (1.61)(61) && \text{Replace } r \text{ by 61.} \\ &= 98.21 && \text{Multiply the numbers.} \end{aligned}$$

You are driving at approximately 98 kilometers per hour. You are not exceeding the speed limit.

Practice Problem 7 You are driving behind a heavily loaded truck on a Canadian highway. The highway has a posted minimum speed of 65 kilometers per hour. When you travel at exactly the same speed as the truck ahead of you, you observe that the speedometer reads 35 miles per hour. Assuming that your speedometer is accurate, determine whether the truck is violating the minimum speed law.

Developing Your Study Skills

Problems with Accuracy

Strive for accuracy. Mistakes are often made as a result of human error rather than from lack of understanding. Such mistakes are frustrating. A simple arithmetic or sign error can lead to an incorrect answer.

These five steps will help you cut down on errors.

1. Work carefully and take your time. Do not rush through a problem just to get it done.
2. Concentrate on one problem at a time. Sometimes problems become mechanical, and your mind begins to wander. You can become careless and make a mistake.
3. Check your problem. Be sure that you copied it correctly from the book.
4. Check your computations from step to step. Check the solution in the problem. Does it work? Does it make sense?
5. Keep practicing new skills. Remember the old saying, "Practice makes perfect." An increase in practice results in an increase in accuracy. Many errors are due simply to lack of practice.

There is no magic formula for eliminating all errors, but these five steps will be a tremendous help in reducing them.

1.8 EXERCISES

Student Solutions Manual | CD/Video | PH Math Tutor Center | MathXL®Tutorials on CD | MathXL® | MyMathLab® | Interactmath.com

Evaluate.

1. $-2x + 1$ for $x = 3$

2. $-4x - 2$ for $x = 5$

3. $\frac{2}{3}x - 5$ for $x = -9$

4. $\frac{3}{4}x + 8$ for $x = -8$

5. $5x + 10$ for $x = \frac{1}{2}$

6. $7x + 20$ for $x = -\frac{1}{2}$

7. $2 - 4x$ for $x = 7$

8. $3 - 5x$ for $x = 8$

9. $3.5 - 2x$ for $x = 2.4$

10. $6.3 - 3x$ for $x = 2.3$

11. $9x + 13$ for $x = -\frac{3}{4}$

12. $5x + 7$ for $x = -\frac{2}{3}$

13. $x^2 - 3x$ for $x = -2$

14. $x^2 + 3x$ for $x = 4$

15. $3x^2$ for $x = -1$

16. $4x^2$ for $x = -1$

17. $-3x^3$ for $x = 2$

18. $-7x^2$ for $x = 5$

19. $-5x^2$ for $x = -2$

20. $-2x^2$ for $x = -3$

21. $2x^2 + 3x$ for $x = -3$

22. $18 + 3x^2$ for $x = -3$

23. $(2x)^2 + x$ for $x = 3$

24. $2 - x^2$ for $x = -2$

25. $2 - (-x)^2$ for $x = -2$

26. $2x - 3x^2$ for $x = -4$

27. $7x + (2x)^2$ for $x = -3$

28. $5x + (3x)^2$ for $x = -2$

29. $3x^2 - 5x$ for $x = -3$

30. $7 - 2x^2$ for $x = -4$

31. $x^2 - 7x + 3$ for $x = 3$

32. $4x^2 - 3x + 9$ for $x = 2$

33. $\frac{1}{2}x^2 - 3x + 9$ for $x = -4$

34. $\frac{1}{3}x^2 + 2x - 5$ for $x = -3$

35. $x^2 - 2y + 3y^2$ for $x = -3$ and $y = 4$

36. $2x^2 - 3xy + 2y$ for $x = 4$ and $y = -1$

37. $a^3 + 2abc - 3c^2$ for $a = 5, b = 9$, and $c = -1$

38. $a^2 - 2ab + 2c^2$ for $a = 3, b = 2$, and $c = -4$

39. $\frac{a^2 + ab}{3b}$ for $a = -1$ and $b = -2$

40. $\frac{x^2 - 2xy}{2y}$ for $x = -2$ and $y = -3$

Applications

▲ **41.** ***Geometry*** A sign is made in the shape of a parallelogram. The base measures 22 feet. The altitude measures 16 feet. What is the area of the sign?

▲ **42.** ***Geometry*** A field is shaped like a parallelogram. The base measures 92 feet. The altitude measures 54 feet. What is the area of the field?

▲ **43.** ***TV Parts*** A square support unit in a television is made with a side measuring 3 centimeters. A new model being designed for next year will have a larger square with a side measuring 3.2 centimeters. By how much will the area of the square be increased?

▲ **44.** ***Computer Chips*** A square computer chip for last year's computer had a side measuring 23 millimeters. This year the computer chip has been reduced in size. The new square chip has a side of 20 millimeters. By how much has the area of the chip decreased?

▲ **45.** ***Carpentry*** A carpenter cut out a small trapezoid as a wooden support for the front step. It has an altitude of 4 inches. One base of the trapezoid measures 9 inches and the other base measures 7 inches. What is the area of this support?

▲ **46.** ***Signal Tower*** The Comcast signal tower has a small trapezoid frame on the top of the tower. The frame has an altitude of 9 inches. One base of the trapezoid is 20 inches and the other base measures 17 inches. What is the area of this small trapezoidal frame?

▲ **47.** ***Geometry*** Bradley Palmer State Park has a triangular piece of land on the border. The altitude of the triangle is 400 feet. The base of the triangle is 280 feet. What is the area of this piece of land?

▲ **48.** ***Roofing*** The ceiling in the Madisons' house has a leak. The roofer exposed a triangular region that needs to be sealed and then reroofed. The region has an altitude of 14 feet. The base of the region is 19 feet. What is the area of the region that needs to be reroofed?

▲ **49.** ***Geometry*** The radius of a circular opening of a chemistry flask is 4 cm. What is the area of the opening?

▲ **50.** ***Geometry*** An ancient outdoor sundial has a radius of 5 meters. What is its area?

Temperature *For exercises 51 and 52, use the formula* $C = \frac{5}{9}(F - 32)$ *to find the Celsius temperature.*

51. Dry ice is solid carbon dioxide. Dry ice does not melt, it goes directly from the solid state to the gaseous state. Dry ice changes from a solid to a gas at $-109.3°$F. What is this temperature in C?

52. Ivana was an exchange student from Russia, attending school in Montgomery, Alabama. Her host family told her to take a jacket to school because the temperature was not supposed to rise above 50°. Since Ivana was used to temperatures in Celsius, this made no sense at all, for 50°C is incredibly warm. The host family realized they needed to change the temperature into Celsius for Ivana. What was the temperature in Celsius?

Solve.

▲ 53. ***Sail Dimensions*** Find the total cost of making a triangular sail that has a base dimension of 12 feet and a height of 20 feet if the price for making the sail is $19.50 per square foot.

▲ 54. ***Window Coating*** A semicircular window of radius 15 inches is to be laminated with a sunblock coating that costs $0.85 per square inch to apply. What is the total cost of coating the window, to the nearest cent? (Use $\pi \approx 3.14$.)

55. ***Temperature Tolerance*** Some new computers can be exposed to extreme temperatures (as high as 60°C and as low as −50°C). What is the temperature range in Fahrenheit that these computers can be exposed to? (Use the formula $F = \frac{9}{5}C + 32$.)

56. ***Temperature Tolerance*** To deal with extreme temperatures while doing research at the South Pole, scientists have developed accommodations that can comfortably withstand an outside temperature of −60°C with no wind blowing, or −30°C with wind gusts of up to 50 miles per hour. What is the corresponding Fahrenheit temperature range? (Use the formula $F = \frac{9}{5}C + 32$.)

57. ***Sea Level*** Bruce becomes exhausted while on a bicycle trip in Canada. He reads on the map that his present elevation is 2.3 kilometers above sea level. How many miles to the nearest tenth above sea level is he? Why is he so tired? Use the formula $r = 0.62k$ where r is the number of miles and k is the number of kilometers.

58. ***Bicycle Travel*** While biking down the Pacific coast of Mexico, you see on the map that it is 20 kilometers to the nearest town. Approximately how many miles is it to the nearest town? Use the formula $r = 0.62k$ where r is the number of miles and k is the number of kilometers.

Cumulative Review

In exercises 59–60, simplify.

59. $(-2)^4 - 4 \div 2 - (-2)$

60. $3(x - 2y) - (x^2 - y) - (x - y)$

61. ***CD Recording*** A 93-minute-long recordable compact disc is used to record 15 songs. Express in decimal form the average number of minutes available per song.

62. ***Homework Grading*** The economics class lecture session had 214 students. If there were 4 teaching assistants to grade homework, approximately how many homework papers were given to each teaching assistant? (Give in decimal form; then round to the nearest whole number.)

1.9 Grouping Symbols

Simplifying Algebraic Expressions by Removing Grouping Symbols

Many expressions in algebra use **grouping symbols** such as parentheses, brackets, and braces. Sometimes expressions are inside other expressions. Because it can be confusing to have more than one set of parentheses, brackets and braces are also used. How do we know what to do first when we see an expression like $2[5 - 4(a + b)]$?

To simplify the expression, we start with the innermost grouping symbols. Here is a set of parentheses. We first use the distributive law to multiply.

$$2[5 - 4(a + b)] = 2[5 - 4a - 4b]$$

We use the distributive law again.

$$= 10 - 8a - 8b$$

There are no like terms, so this is our final answer.

Notice that we started with two sets of grouping symbols, but our final answer has none. So we can say we *removed* the grouping symbols. Of course, we didn't just take them away; we used the distributive law and the rules for real numbers to simplify as much as possible. Although simplifying expressions like this involves many steps, we sometimes say "remove parentheses" as a shorthand direction. Sometimes we say "simplify."

Remember to remove the innermost parentheses first. Keep working from the inside out.

Student Learning Objective

After studying this section, you will be able to:

Simplify algebraic expressions by removing grouping symbols.

EXAMPLE 1 Simplify. $3[6 - 2(x + y)]$

Solution We want to remove the innermost parentheses first. Therefore, we first use the distributive property to simplify $-2(x + y)$.

$$3[6 - 2(x + y)] = 3[6 - 2x - 2y] \quad \text{Use the distributive property.}$$

$$= 18 - 6x - 6y \quad \text{Use the distributive property again.}$$

Practice Problem 1 Simplify. $5[4x - 3(y - 2)]$

NOTE TO STUDENT: Fully worked-out solutions to all of the Practice Problems can be found at the back of the text starting at page SP-1

You recall that a negative sign in front of parentheses is equivalent to having a coefficient of negative 1. You can write the -1 and then multiply by -1 using the distributive property.

$$-(x + 2y) = -1(x + 2y) = -x - 2y$$

Notice that this has the effect of removing the parentheses. Each term in the result now has its sign changed.

Similarly, a positive sign in front of parentheses can be viewed as multiplication by $+1$.

$$+(5x - 6y) = +1(5x - 6y) = 5x - 6y$$

If a grouping symbol has a positive or negative sign in front, we mentally multiply by $+1$ or -1, respectively.

Fraction bars are also considered grouping symbols. Later in this book we will encounter problems where our first step will be to simplify expressions above and below fraction bars. This type of operation will have some similarities to the operation of removing parentheses.

EXAMPLE 2 Simplify. $-2\,[3a - (b + 2c) + (d - 3e)]$

Solution

$= -2\,[3a - b - 2c + d - 3e\,]$ Remove the two innermost sets of parentheses. Since one is not inside the other, we remove both sets at once.

$= -6a + 2b + 4c - 2d + 6e$ Now we remove the brackets by multiplying each term by -2.

NOTE TO STUDENT: Fully worked-out solutions to all of the Practice Problems can be found at the back of the text starting at page SP-1

Practice Problem 2 Simplify. $-3\,[2a - (3b - c) + 4a]$

EXAMPLE 3 Simplify. $2\,[3x - (y + w)] - 3\,[2x + 2(3y - 2w)]$

Solution

$= 2\,[3x - y - w] - 3\,[2x + 6y - 4w]$ In each set of brackets, remove the inner parentheses.

$= 6x - 2y - 2w - 6x - 18y + 12w$ Remove each set of brackets by multiplying by the appropriate number.

$= -20y + 10w$ or $10w - 20y$ Combine like terms. (Note that $6x - 6x = 0x = 0$.)

Practice Problem 3 Simplify. $3\,[4x - 2\,(1 - x)] - [3x + (x - 2)]$

You can always simplify problems with many sets of grouping symbols by the method shown. Essentially, you just keep removing one level of grouping symbols at each step. Finally, at the end you add up the like terms if possible.

Sometimes it is possible to combine like terms at each step.

EXAMPLE 4 Simplify. $-3\,\{7x - 2\,[x - (2x - 1)]\}$

Solution

$= -3\,\{7x - 2\,[x - 2x + 1]\}$ Remove the inner parentheses by multiplying each term within the parentheses by -1.

$= -3\,\{7x - 2\,[-x + 1]\}$ Combine like terms by combining $+x - 2x$.

$= -3\,\{7x + 2x - 2\}$ Remove the brackets by multiplying each term within them by -2.

$= -3\,\{9x - 2\}$ Combine the x-terms.

$= -27x + 6$ Remove the braces by multiplying each term by -3.

Practice Problem 4 Simplify. $-2\,\{5x - 3x\,[2x - (x^2 - 4x)]\}$

Developing Your Study Skills

The Night Before Your Exam

With adequate preparation, you can spend the night before an exam pulling together the final details.

1. Look over each section to be covered in the exam. Review the steps needed to solve each type of problem.
2. Review your list of terms, rules, and formulas that you are expected to know for the exam.
3. Take the Practice Test at the end of the chapter just as though you were taking the actual exam. Do not look in your text or get help in any way. Time yourself so that you know how long it takes you to complete the test.
4. Check the Practice Test. Redo the problems you missed.
5. Be sure you have ready the necessary supplies for taking your exam.

1.9 EXERCISES

Student Solutions Manual

CD/ Video

PH Math Tutor Center

MathXL®Tutorials on CD

MathXL®

MyMathLab®

Interactmath.cor

Verbal and Writing Skills

1. Rewrite the expression $-3x - 2y$ using a negative sign and parentheses.

2. Rewrite the expression $-x + 5y$ using a negative sign and parentheses.

3. To simplify expressions with grouping symbols, we use the ____________ property.

4. When an expression contains many grouping symbols, remove the ____________ parentheses first.

Simplify. Remove grouping symbols and combine like terms.

5. $6x - 3(x - 2y)$

6. $-4x - 2(y - 3x)$

7. $2(a + 3b) - 3(b - a)$

8. $4(x - y) - 2(3x + y)$

9. $-3(x + 3y) + 2(2x + y)$

10. $-4(a + 2b) + 5(2b - a)$

11. $2x[4x^2 - 2(x - 3)]$

12. $4y[-3y^2 + 2(4 - y)]$

13. $2[5(x + y) - 2(3x - 4y)]$

14. $-3[2(3a + b) - 5(a - 2b)]$

15. $2(x - 2y) - [3 - 2(x - y)]$

16. $3(x + 2y) - [4 - 2(x + y)]$

17. $5[3a - 2a(3a + 6b) + 6a^2]$

18. $3[x - y(3x + y) + y^2]$

19. $6a(2a^2 - 3a - 4) - a(a - 2)$

20. $7b(3b^2 - 2b - 5) - 2b(4 - b)$

21. $3a^2 - 4[2b - 3b(b + 2)]$

22. $2b^2 - 3[5b + 2b(2 - b)]$

23. $6b - \{5a - 2[a + (b - 2a)]\}$

24. $2a - \{6b - 4[a - (b - 3a)]\}$

25. $3\{3b^2 + 2[5b - (2 - b)]\}$

26. $2\{3x^2 + 4[2x - (3 - x)]\}$

27. $-4\{3a^2 - 2[4a^2 - (b + a^2)]\}$

28. $-2\{x^2 - 3[x - (x - 2x^2)]\}$

To Think About

29. ***Robot Success*** The job of a four-wheeled robot called Nomad, built by the Robotics Institute at Carnegie Mellon University, is to find samples of meteorites in Antarctica. If Nomad is successful in finding meteorites 2.5% of the time, out of four tries per day for six years, estimate the number of successful and unsuccessful meteorite search attempts. Round to the nearest whole number.

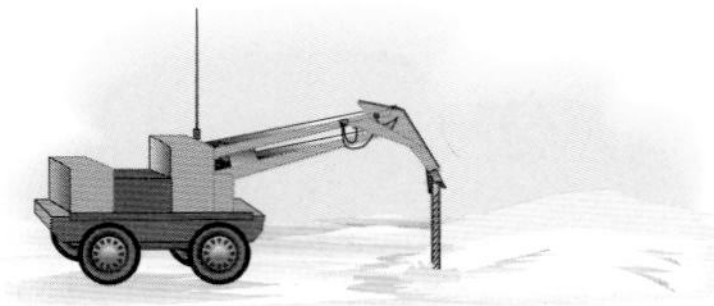

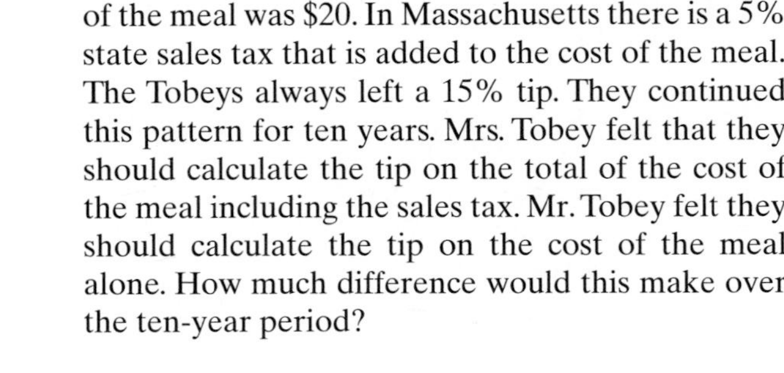

30. ***Tipping*** Grandma and Grandpa Tobey had a tradition of eating out once a week. The average cost of the meal was \$20. In Massachusetts there is a 5% state sales tax that is added to the cost of the meal. The Tobeys always left a 15% tip. They continued this pattern for ten years. Mrs. Tobey felt that they should calculate the tip on the total of the cost of the meal including the sales tax. Mr. Tobey felt they should calculate the tip on the cost of the meal alone. How much difference would this make over the ten-year period?

Cumulative Review

31. ***Temperature*** Use $F = 1.8C + 32$ to find the Fahrenheit temperature equivalent to 36.4° Celsius.

▲ **32.** ***Geometry*** Use 3.14 as an approximation for π to compute the area covered by a circular irrigation system with radial arm of length 380 feet. $A = \pi r^2$.

▲ **33.** ***Marble Flooring*** The base of an office building is in the shape of a trapezoid. The altitude of the trapezoid is 400 feet. The bases of the trapezoid are 700 feet and 800 feet, respectively. What is the area of the base of the office building? If the base has a marble floor that cost \$55 per square foot, what was the cost of the marble floor?

▲ **34.** ***Signal Paint*** The Global Media Tower has a triangular signal tester at the top of the tower. The altitude of the triangle is 3.5 feet and the base is 6.5 feet. What is the area of the triangular signal tester? If the signal tester is coated with a special metallic surface paint that costs \$122 per square foot, what was the cost of the amount of paint needed to coat one side of the triangle?

35. ***Dog Weight*** An average Great Dane weighs between 120 and 150 pounds. Express the range of weight for a Great Dane in kilograms. Use the formula $k = 2.205p$ (where k = kilograms, p = pounds).

36. ***Dog Weight*** An average Miniature Pinscher weighs between 9 and 14 pounds. Express the range of weight for a Miniature Pinscher in kilograms. Use the formula $k = 2.205p$ (where k = kilograms, p = pounds.)

Putting Your Skills to Work

Looking at Computer Usage

NTIA and the Economics and Statistics Administration have published *A Nation Online: How Americans Are Expanding Their Use of the Internet.* This report is based on the September 2001 U.S. Census Bureau's Current Population Survey—a survey of approximately 57,000 households and more than 137,000 individuals across the United States. As such, the data in this study are among the most broad-based and reliable data sets that have been gathered on Internet, broadband, and computer connectivity.

Computer use is expanding ever quicker both at work and at home. Look at the following information gathered for this government report.

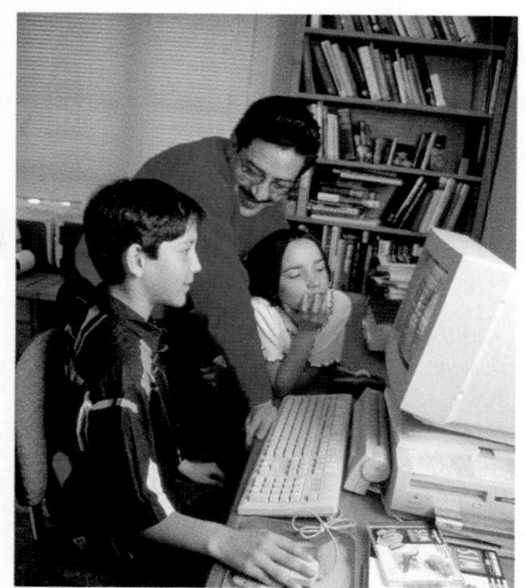

Computer Use at Work by Occupation (2001)

	Employed		Uses computer at main job		Main computer uses (by percent)			
Occupation	Total (in 1000s)	Percent Women	Total (in 1000s)	Percent of employed	E-mail	Word processing	Spreadsheet database	Calendar, schedule
TOTAL	**115,065**	**46.3**	**65,190**	**56.7**	**41.7**	**38.6**	**35.9**	**30.4**
Professional Managerial	39,412	50.2	31,723	80.5	66.8	63.2	56.5	48.8
Support Staff	31,482	62.9	22,205	70.5	49.2	45.5	43.1	34.7
Precision Production	13,083	8.4	4,152	31.7	19.0	14.8	16.6	14.6
Service	13,678	61.6	3,478	25.4	13.9	14.3	11.8	12.3
Laborers	14,504	24.3	3,006	20.7	9.2	7.6	8.7	7.0
Farming, forestry, fishing	2,905	20.3	625	21.5	14.6	13.0	13.2	9.2

Source: Statistical Abstract of the United States, 2002

Problems for Individual Investigation and Analysis

1. The data shows that 66.8% of computer using professionals use e-mail on a regular basis. How many professionals in the United States use e-mail at their main job?
2. How many more professionals than support staff use computers at their main job?
3. The NTIA estimates that 77% of Americans who use computers at home also use computers at work. How many American do you estimate used computers at home as of September 2001?
4. If computer use grows by 17.5% per year, how many people would you expect used computers at work in 2002, the year after this survey?

Problems for Group Investigation and Cooperative Learning

A number of business professionals feel that the number of people using computers at work in the future can be predicted in the near future by the formula

$$N = 65{,}190{,}000 + 4{,}500{,}000x,$$

where N is the number of people using computers at work and x is the number of years since 2001. For example, in the year 2003 the value of x would be 2. In the year 2004 the value of x would be 3.

5. Use this formula to estimate the number of people who will use computers at work in the year 2007.
6. Use this formula to estimate the number of people who will use computers at work in the year 2010.

Chapter 1 Organizer

Topic	Procedure	Examples
Absolute value, p. 70.	The absolute value of a number is the distance between that number and zero on the number line. The absolute value of any number will be positive or zero.	$\lvert 3\rvert = 3$ $\lvert -2\rvert = 2$ $\lvert 0\rvert = 0$ $\left\lvert -\frac{5}{6}\right\rvert = \frac{5}{6}$ $\lvert -1.38\rvert = 1.38$
Adding real numbers with the same sign, p. 71.	If the signs are the same, add the absolute values of the numbers. Use the common sign in the answer.	$-3 + (-7) = -10$
Adding real numbers with opposite signs, p. 73.	If the signs are different: **1.** Find the difference between the larger and the smaller absolute value. **2.** Give the answer the sign of the number having the larger absolute value.	$(-7) + 13 = 6$ $7 + (-13) = -6$
Adding several real numbers, p. 74.	When adding several real numbers, separate them into two groups by sign. Find the sum of all the positive numbers and the sum of all the negative numbers. Combine these two subtotals by the method described above.	$-7 + 6 + 8 + (-11) + (-13) + 22$ $\begin{array}{rr} -7 & +6 \\ -11 & +8 \\ \underline{-13} & \underline{+22} \\ -31 & +36 \end{array}$ $-31 + 36 = 5$ The answer is positive since 36 is positive.
Subtracting real numbers, p. 79.	Change the sign of the second number (the number you are subtracting) and then add.	$-3 - (-13) = -3 + (+13) = 10$
Multiplying and dividing real numbers, p. 85 and p. 87.	**1.** If the two numbers have the same sign, multiply (or divide) the absolute values. The result is positive. **2.** If the two numbers have different signs, multiply (or divide) the absolute values. The result is negative.	$-5(-3) = +15$ $-36 \div (-4) = +9$ $28 \div (-7) = -4$ $-6(3) = -18$
Exponent form, p. 94.	The base tells you what number is being multiplied. The exponent tells you how many times this number is used as a factor.	$2^5 = 2 \cdot 2 \cdot 2 \cdot 2 \cdot 2 = 32$ $4^3 = 4 \cdot 4 \cdot 4 = 64$ $(-3)^4 = (-3)(-3)(-3)(-3) = 81$
Raising a negative number to a power, p. 95.	When the base is negative, the result is positive for even exponents, and negative for odd exponents.	$(-3)^3 = -27$ but $(-2)^4 = 16$
Order of operations, p. 98.	Remember the proper order of operations: **1.** Perform operations inside parentheses. **2.** Raise to powers. **3.** Multiply and divide from left to right. **4.** Add and subtract from left to right.	$3(5 + 4)^2 - 2^2 \cdot 3 \div (9 - 2^3)$ $= 3 \cdot 9^2 - 4 \cdot 3 \div (9 - 8)$ $= 3 \cdot 81 - 12 \div 1$ $= 243 - 12 = 231$
Removing parentheses, p. 103.	Use the distributive property to remove parentheses. $a(b + c) = ab + ac$	$3(5x + 2) = 15x + 6$ $-4(x - 3y) = -4x + 12y$

Topic	Procedure	Examples
Combining like terms, p. 108.	Combine terms that have identical letters and exponents.	$7x^2 - 3x + 4y + 2x^2 - 8x - 9y = 9x^2 - 11x - 5y$
Substituting into variable expressions, p. 113.	**1.** Replace each letter by the numerical value given for it. **2.** Follow the order of operations in evaluating the expression.	Evaluate $2x^3 + 3xy + 4y^2$ for $x = -3$ and $y = 2$. $2(-3)^3 + 3(-3)(2) + 4(2)^2$ $= 2(-27) + 3(-3)(2) + 4(4)$ $= -54 - 18 + 16$ $= -56$
Using formulas, p. 115.	**1.** Replace the variables in the formula by the given values. **2.** Evaluate the expression. **3.** Label units carefully.	Find the area of a circle with radius 4 feet. Use $A = \pi r^2$, with π as approximately 3.14. $A = (3.14)(4\text{ feet})^2$ $= (3.14)(16\text{ feet}^2)$ $= 50.24\text{ feet}^2$ The area of the circle is approximately 50.24 square feet.
Removing grouping symbols, p. 121.	**1.** Remove innermost grouping symbols first. **2.** Then remove remaining innermost grouping symbols. **3.** Continue until all grouping symbols are removed. **4.** Combine like terms.	$5\{3x - 2[4 + 3(x - 1)]\}$ $= 5\{3x - 2[4 + 3x - 3]\}$ $= 5\{3x - 8 - 6x + 6\}$ $= 15x - 40 - 30x + 30$ $= -15x - 10$

Chapter 1 Review Problems

Section 1.1

Add.

1. $-6 + (-2)$

2. $-12 + 7.8$

3. $5 + (-2) + (-12)$

4. $3.7 + (-1.8)$

5. $\frac{1}{2} + \left(-\frac{5}{6}\right)$

6. $-\frac{3}{11} + \left(-\frac{1}{22}\right)$

7. $\frac{3}{4} + \left(-\frac{1}{12}\right) + \left(-\frac{1}{2}\right)$

8. $-\frac{4}{15} + \frac{12}{5} + \left(-\frac{2}{3}\right)$

Section 1.2

Add or subtract.

9. $5 - (-3)$

10. $-2 - (-15)$

11. $-30 - (+3)$

12. $8 - (-1.2)$

13. $-\frac{7}{8} + \left(-\frac{3}{4}\right)$

14. $-\frac{3}{14} + \frac{5}{7}$

15. $-20.8 - 1.9$

16. $-151 - (-63)$

Section 1.3

17. $87 \div (-29)$

18. $-5(-6) + 4(-3)$

19. $\dfrac{-24}{-\frac{3}{4}}$

20. $-\frac{1}{2} \div \left(\frac{3}{4}\right)$

21. $\frac{5}{7} \div \left(-\frac{5}{25}\right)$

22. $-6(3)(4)$

23. $-1(-2)(-3)(-5)$

24. $(-5)\left(-\frac{1}{2}\right)(4)(-3)$

Mixed Practice

Sections 1.1–1.3

Perform the operations indicated. Simplify all answers.

25. $-5 + (-2) - (-3)$

26. $6 - (-4) + (-2) + 8$

27. $-16 + (-13)$

28. $-11 - (-12)$

29. $-\frac{4}{3} + \frac{2}{3} + \frac{1}{6}$

30. $-\frac{6}{7} + \frac{1}{2} + \left(-\frac{3}{14}\right)$

31. $-3(-2)(-5)$

32. $-6 + (-2) - (-3)$

33. $3.5(-2.6)$

34. $-5.4 \div (-6)$

35. $5 - (-3.5) + 1.6$

36. $-8 + 2 - (-4.8)$

37. $17 + 3.4 + (-16) + (-2.5)$

38. $37 + (-44) + 12.5 + (-6.8)$

Solve.

39. ***Football*** The Dallas Cowboys football team had three plays in which they lost 8 yards each time. What was the total yardage lost?

40. ***Temperature Change*** The low temperature in Anchorage, Alaska, last night was −34°F. During the day the temperature rose 12°F. What was the temperature during the day?

41. ***Elevation Levels*** A mountain peak is 6895 feet above sea level. A location in Death Valley is 468 feet below sea level. What is the difference in height between these two locations?

42. ***Stock Prices*** During January 2000, IBM stock rose $1\frac{1}{2}$ points on Monday, dropped $3\frac{1}{4}$ points on Tuesday, rose 2 points on Wednesday, and dropped $2\frac{1}{2}$ points on Thursday. What was the total gain or loss on the value of the stock over this four-day period?

Section 1.4

Evaluate.

43. $(-3)^5$

44. $(-2)^7$

45. $(-5)^4$

46. $\left(\frac{2}{3}\right)^3$

47. -9^2

48. $(0.6)^2$

49. $\left(\frac{5}{6}\right)^2$

50. $\left(\frac{3}{4}\right)^3$

Section 1.5

Simplify using the order of operations.

51. $5(-4) + 3(-2)^3$

52. $20 - (-10) - (-6) + (-5) - 1$

53. $(7 - 9)^3 + -6(-2) + (-3)$

Section 1.6

Use the distributive property to multiply.

54. $5(3x - 7y)$

55. $2x(3x - 7y + 4)$

56. $-(7x^2 - 3x + 11)$

57. $(2xy + x - y)(-3y)$

Section 1.7

Combine like terms.

58. $3a^2b - 2bc + 6bc^2 - 8a^2b - 6bc^2 + 5bc$

59. $9x + 11y - 12x - 15y$

60. $4x^2 - 13x + 7 - 9x^2 - 22x - 16$

61. $-x + \frac{1}{2} + 14x^2 - 7x - 1 - 4x^2$

Section 1.8

Evaluate for the given value of the variable.

62. $7x - 6$ for $x = -7$

63. $7 - \frac{3}{4}x$ for $x = 8$

64. $x^2 + 3x - 4$ for $x = -3$

65. $-3x^2 - 4x + 5$ for $x = 2$

66. $-3x^3 - 4x^2 + 2x + 6$ for $x = -2$

67. $vt - \frac{1}{2}at^2$ for $v = 24, t = 2$, and $a = 32$

68. $\frac{nRT}{V}$ for $n = 16, R = -2, T = 4$, and $V = -20$

Solve.

69. ***Simple Interest*** Find the simple interest on a loan of \$6000 at an annual interest rate of 18% per year for $\frac{3}{4}$ of a year. Use $I = prt$, where p = principal, r = rate per year, and t = time in years.

70. ***Temperature*** Find the Fahrenheit temperature if a radio announcer in Mexico City says that the high temperature today was 30°C. Use the formula

$$F = \frac{9C + 160}{5}.$$

▲ 71. ***Sign Painting*** How much will it cost to paint a circular sign with a radius of 15 meters if the painter charges \$3 per square meter? Use $A = \pi r^2$, where π is approximately 3.14.

72. ***Profit*** Find the daily profit P at a furniture factory if the initial cost of setting up the factory C = \$1200, rent R = \$300, and sales of furniture S = \$56. Use the profit formula $P = 180S - R - C$.

▲ 73. ***Parking Lot Sealer*** A parking lot is in the shape of a trapezoid. The altitude of the trapezoid is 200 feet, and the bases of the trapezoid are 300 feet and 700 feet. What is the area of the parking lot? If the parking lot had a sealer applied that costs \$2 per square foot, what was the cost of the amount of sealer needed for the entire parking lot?

▲ 74. ***Signal Paint*** The Green Mountain Telephone Company has a triangular signal tester at the top of a communications tower. The altitude of the triangle is 3.8 feet and the base is 5.5 feet. What is the area of the triangular signal tester? If the signal tester is painted with a special metallic surface paint that costs \$66 per square foot, what was the cost of the amount of paint needed to paint one side of the triangle?

Section 1.9

Simplify.

75. $5x - 7(x - 6)$

76. $3(x - 2) - 4(5x + 3)$

77. $2[3 - (4 - 5x)]$

78. $-3x[x + 3(x - 7)]$

79. $2xy^3 - 6x^3y - 4x^2y^2 + 3(xy^3 - 2x^2y - 3x^2y^2)$

80. $-5(x + 2y - 7) + 3x(2 - 5y)$

81. $2\{x - 3(y - 2) + 4[x - 2(y + 3)]\}$

82. $-5\{2a - b[5a - b(3 + 2a)]\}$

83. $-3\{2x - [x - 3y(x - 2y)]\}$

84. $2\{3x + 2[x + 2y(x - 4)]\}$

Mixed Practice

Simplify the following.

85. $-6.3 + 4$

86. $4 + (-8) + 12$

87. $-\frac{2}{3} - \frac{4}{5}$

88. $-\frac{7}{8} - \left(-\frac{3}{4}\right)$

89. $3 - (-4) + (-8)$

90. $-1.1 - (-0.2) + 0.4$

91. $\left(-\frac{3}{5}\right)\left(-2\frac{1}{2}\right)$

92. $(-4.2) \div (-0.7)$

93. $-14.4 \div (-0.06)$

94. $(-8.2)(3.1)$

95. ***Jeopardy*** A Jeopardy quiz show contestant began the second round (Double Jeopardy) with \$400. She buzzed in on the first two questions, answering a \$1000 question correctly, but then giving the incorrect answer to a \$800 question. What was her score?

Simplify the following.

96. $(-0.3)^4$

97. -0.5^4

98. $9(5) - 5(2)^3 + 5$

99. $3.8x - 0.2y - 8.7x + 4.3y$

100. *Evaluate.* $\frac{2p + q}{3q}$ for $p = -2$ and $q = 3$

101. *Evaluate.* $\frac{4s - 7t}{s}$ for $s = -3$ and $t = -2$

102. ***Dog Body Temperature*** The normal body temperature of a dog is 38.6°C. Your dog has a temperature of 101.1°F. Does your dog have a fever? Use the formula $F = \frac{9}{5}C + 32$ to convert normal temperature in Fahrenheit.

103. $-7(x - 3y^2 + 4) + 3y(4 - 6y)$

104. $-2\{6x - 3[7y - 2y(3 - x)]\}$

How Am I Doing? Chapter 1 Test

Remember to use your Chapter Test Prep Video CD to see the worked-out solutions to the test problems you want to review

Simplify.

1. $-2.5 + 6.3 + (-4.1)$

2. $-5 - (-7)$

3. $\left(-\frac{2}{3}\right)(7)$

4. $-5(-2)(7)(-1)$

5. $-12 \div (-3)$

6. $-1.8 \div (0.6)$

7. $(-4)^3$

8. $(1.6)^2$

9. $\left(\frac{2}{3}\right)^4$

10. $(0.2)^2 - (2.1)(-3) + 0.46$

11. $3(4 - 6)^3 + 12 \div (-4) + 2$

12. $-5x(x + 2y - 7)$

13. $-2ab^2(-3a - 2b + 7ab)$

14. $6ab - \frac{1}{2}a^2b + \frac{3}{2}ab + \frac{5}{2}a^2b$

15. $2.3x^2y - 8.1xy^2 + 3.4xy^2 - 4.1x^2y$

16. $3(2 - a) - 4(-6 - 2a)$

17. $5(3x - 2y) - (x + 6y)$

1. ______
2. ______
3. ______
4. ______
5. ______
6. ______
7. ______
8. ______
9. ______
10. ______
11. ______
12. ______
13. ______
14. ______
15. ______
16. ______
17. ______

18. ______

In questions 18–20, evaluate for the value of the variable indicated.

18. $x^3 - 3x^2y + 2y - 5$ for $x = 3$ and $y = -4$

19. ______

19. $3x^2 - 7x - 11$ for $x = -3$

20. $2a - 3b$ for $a = \frac{1}{3}$ and $b = -\frac{1}{2}$

20. ______

21. If you are traveling 60 miles per hour on a highway in Canada, how fast are you traveling in kilometers per hour? (Use $k = 1.61r$, where r = rate in miles per hour and k = rate in kilometers per hour.)

21. ______

▲ **22.** A field is in the shape of a trapezoid. The altitude of the trapezoid is 120 feet and the bases of the trapezoid are 180 feet and 200 feet. What is the area of the field?

22. ______

▲ **23.** Jeff Slater's garage has a triangular roof support beam. The support beam is covered with a sheet of plywood. The altitude of the triangular region is 6.8 feet and the base is 8.5 feet. If the triangular piece of plywood was painted with paint that cost $0.80 per square foot, what was the cost of the amount of paint needed to coat one side of the triangle?

23. ______

▲ **24.** You wish to apply blacktop sealer to your driveway, but do not know how much to buy. If your rectangular driveway measures 60 feet long by 10 feet wide, and a can of blacktop sealer claims to cover 200 square feet, how many cans should you buy?

24. ______

25. ______

Simplify.

25. $3[x - 2y(x + 2y) - 3y^2]$

26. ______

26. $-3\{a + b[3a - b(1 - a)]\}$

CHAPTER

2

People who own sport fishing boats and charter them out for fishing are often concerned with the cost of fuel. Many outboard boats are equipped with either one or two motors. Having two motors increases realibility and generates a higher speed. However, the added fuel cost may present a problem. Can you analyze exactly how much more fuel will be used if a boat is equipped with two outboard motors instead of one? Turn to the Putting Your Skills to Work on page 183 to find out.

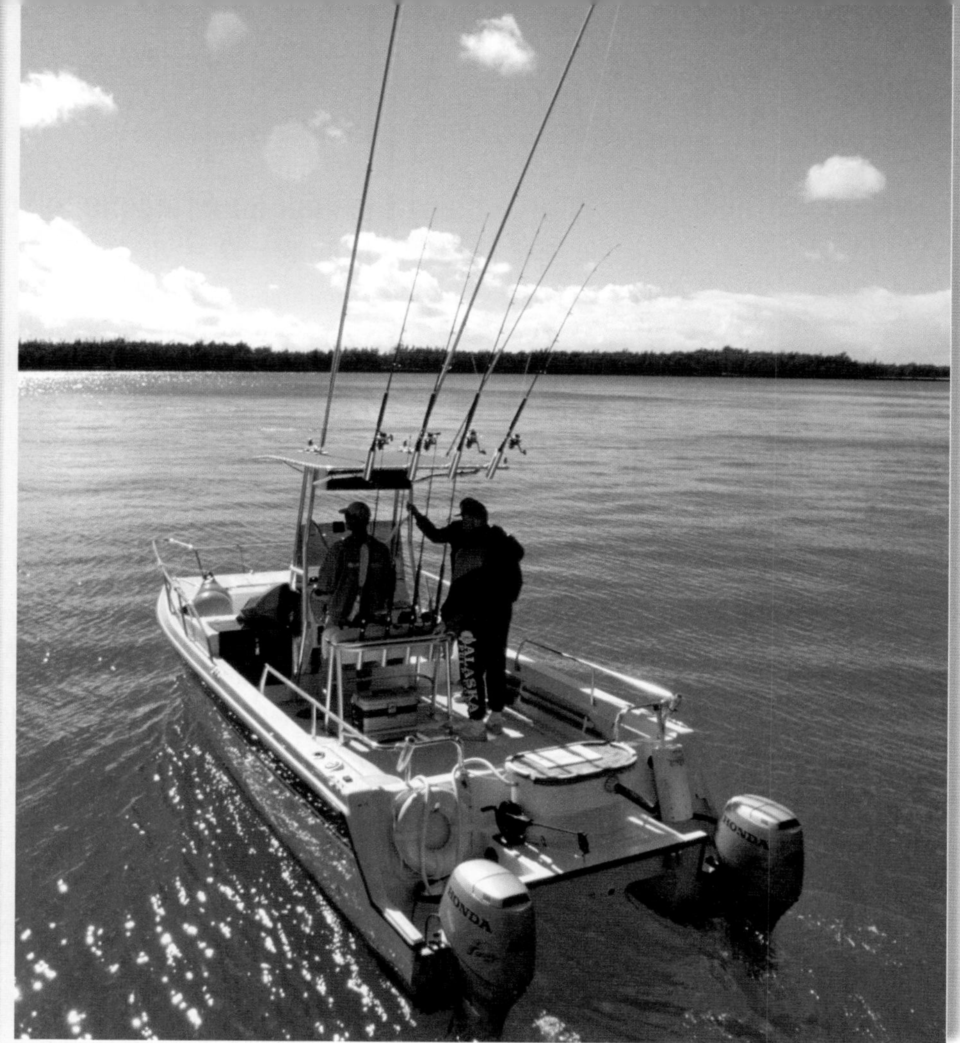

Equations and Inequalities

2.1 The Addition Principle of Equality

Student Learning Objective

After studying this section, you will be able to:

Use the addition principle to solve equations of the form $x + b = c$.

Using the Addition Principle to Solve Equations of the Form $x + b = c$

When we use an equal sign (=), we are indicating that two expressions are equal in value. Such a statement is called an **equation.** For example, $x + 5 = 23$ is an equation. A **solution** of an equation is a number that when substituted for the variable makes the equation true. Thus 18 is a solution of $x + 5 = 23$ because $18 + 5 = 23$. Equations that have exactly the same solutions are called **equivalent equations.** By following certain procedures, we can often transform an equation to a simpler equivalent one that has the form $x =$ some number. Then this number is a solution of the equation. The process of finding all solutions of an equation is called **solving the equation.**

One of the first procedures used in solving equations has an application in our everyday world. Suppose that we place a 10-kilogram box on one side of a seesaw and a 10-kilogram stone on the other side. If the center of the box is the same distance from the balance point as the center of the stone, we would expect the seesaw to balance. The box and the stone do not look the same, but their weights are equal. If we add a 2-kilogram lead weight to the center of weight of each object at the same time, the seesaw should still balance. The weights are still equal.

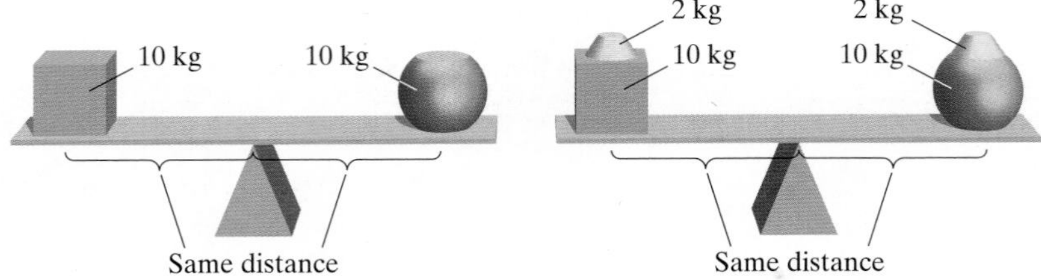

There is a similar principle in mathematics. We can state it in words as follows.

THE ADDITION PRINCIPLE

If the same number is added to both sides of an equation, the results on both sides are equal in value.

We can restate it in symbols this way.

For real numbers a, b, and c, if $a = b$, then $a + c = b + c$.

Here is an example. If $3 = \frac{6}{2}$, then $3 + 5 = \frac{6}{2} + 5$.

Since we added the same amount, 5, to both sides, the sides remain equal to each other.

$$3 + 5 = \frac{6}{2} + 5$$

$$8 = \frac{6}{2} + \frac{10}{2}$$

$$8 = \frac{16}{2}$$

$$8 = 8$$

We can use the addition principle to solve certain equations.

EXAMPLE 1 Solve for x. $x + 16 = 20$

Solution $x + 16 + (-16) = 20 + (-16)$ Use the addition principle to add -16 to both sides.

$x + 0 = 4$ Simplify.

$x = 4$ The value of x is 4.

We have just found a solution of the equation. A **solution** is a value for the variable that makes the equation true. We then say that the value 4 in our example **satisfies** the equation. We can easily verify that 4 is a solution by substituting this value into the original equation. This step is called **checking** the solution.

Check.

$$x + 16 = 20$$
$$4 + 16 \stackrel{?}{=} 20$$
$$20 = 20 \checkmark$$

When the same value appears on both sides of the equal sign, we call the equation an **identity.** Because the two sides of the equation in our check have the same value, we know that the original equation has been solved correctly. We have found a solution, and since no other number makes the equation true, it is the only solution.

Practice Problem 1 Solve for x and check your solution. $x + 14 = 23$ 

NOTE TO STUDENT: Fully worked-out solutions to all of the Practice Problems can be found at the back of the text starting at page SP-1

Notice that when you are trying to solve these types of equations, you must add a particular number to both sides of the equation. What is the number to choose? Look at the number that is on the same side of the equation with x, that is, the number added to x. Then think of the number that is **opposite in sign.** This is called the **additive inverse** of the number. The additive inverse of 16 is -16. The additive inverse of -3 is 3. The number to add to both sides of the equation is precisely this additive inverse.

It does not matter which side of the equation contains the variable. The x-term may be on the right or left. In the next example the x-term will be on the right.

EXAMPLE 2 Solve for x. $14 = x - 3$

Solution $14 + 3 = x - 3 + 3$ Notice that -3 is being added to x in the original equation. Add 3 to both sides, since 3 is the additive inverse of -3. This will eliminate the -3 on the right and isolate x.

$17 = x + 0$ Simplify.

$17 = x$ The value of x is 17.

Check. $14 = x - 3$

$14 \stackrel{?}{=} 17 - 3$ Replace x by 17.

$14 = 14 \checkmark$ Simplify. It checks. The solution is 17.

Practice Problem 2 Solve for x and check your solution. $17 = x - 5$

Before you add a number to both sides, you should always simplify the equation. The following example shows how combining numbers by addition—separately, on both sides of the equation—simplifies the equation.

EXAMPLE 3 Solve for x. $1.5 + 0.2 = 0.3 + x + 0.2$

Solution

$1.7 = x + 0.5$	Simplify by adding.
$1.7 + (-0.5) = x + 0.5 + (-0.5)$	Add the value -0.5 to both sides, since -0.5 is the additive inverse of 0.5.
$1.2 = x$	Simplify. The value of x is 1.2.

Check.

$1.5 + 0.2 = 0.3 + x + 0.2$	
$1.5 + 0.2 \stackrel{?}{=} 0.3 + 1.2 + 0.2$	Replace x by 1.2 in the original equation.
$1.7 = 1.7$ ✓	It checks.

Practice Problem 3 Solve for x and check your solution. $0.5 - 1.2 = x - 0.3$

In Example 3 we added -0.5 to each side. You could subtract 0.5 from each side and get the same result. In Chapter 1 we discussed how subtracting a 0.5 is the same as adding a negative 0.5. Do you see why?

Just as it is possible to add the same number to both sides of an equation, it is also possible to subtract the same number from both sides of an equation. This is so because any subtraction problem can be rewritten as an addition problem. For example, $17 - 5 = 17 + (-5)$. Thus the addition principle tells us that we can subtract the same number from both sides of the equation.

We can determine whether a value is the solution to an equation by following the same steps used to check an answer. Substitute the value to be tested for the variable in the original equation. We will obtain an identity if the value is the solution.

EXAMPLE 4 Is 10 the solution to the equation $-15 + 2 = x - 3$? If it is not, find the solution.

Solution We substitute 10 for x in the equation and see if we obtain an identity.

$-15 + 2 = x - 3$	
$-15 + 2 \stackrel{?}{=} 10 - 3$	
$-13 \neq 7$	The values are not equal. The statement is not an identity.

Thus, 10 is not the solution. Now we take the original equation and solve to find the solution.

$-15 + 2 = x - 3$	
$-13 = x - 3$	Simplify by adding.
$-13 + 3 = x - 3 + 3$	Add 3 to both sides. 3 is the additive inverse of -3.
$-10 = x$	

Check to see if -10 is the solution. The value 10 was incorrect because of a sign error. We must be especially careful to write the correct sign for each number when solving equations.

Practice Problem 4 Is -2 the solution to the equation $x + 8 = -22 + 6$? If it is not, find the solution.

***NOTE TO STUDENT:** Fully worked-out solutions to all of the Practice Problems can be found at the back of the text starting at page SP-1*

EXAMPLE 5 Find the value of x that satisfies the equation

$$\frac{1}{5} + x = -\frac{1}{10} + \frac{1}{2}.$$

Solution To be combined, the fractions must have common denominators. The least common denominator (LCD) of the fractions is 10.

$$\frac{1 \cdot 2}{5 \cdot 2} + x = -\frac{1}{10} + \frac{1 \cdot 5}{2 \cdot 5}$$ Change each fraction to an equivalent fraction with a denominator of 10.

$$\frac{2}{10} + x = -\frac{1}{10} + \frac{5}{10}$$ This is an equivalent equation.

$$\frac{2}{10} + x = \frac{4}{10}$$ Simplify by adding.

$$\frac{2}{10} + \left(-\frac{2}{10}\right) + x = \frac{4}{10} + \left(-\frac{2}{10}\right)$$ Add the additive inverse of $\frac{2}{10}$ to each side. You could also say that you are subtracting $\frac{2}{10}$ from each side.

$$x = \frac{2}{10}$$ Add the fractions.

$$x = \frac{1}{5}$$ Simplify the answer.

Check. We substitute $\frac{1}{5}$ for x in the original equation and see if we obtain an identity.

$$\frac{1}{5} + x = -\frac{1}{10} + \frac{1}{2}$$

$$\frac{1}{5} + \frac{1}{5} \stackrel{?}{=} -\frac{1}{10} + \frac{1}{2}$$ Substitute $\frac{1}{5}$ for x.

$$\frac{2}{5} \stackrel{?}{=} -\frac{1}{10} + \frac{5}{10}$$

$$\frac{2}{5} \stackrel{?}{=} \frac{4}{10}$$

$$\frac{2}{5} = \frac{2}{5} \checkmark$$ It checks.

Practice Problem 5 Find the value of x that satisfies the equation

$$\frac{1}{20} - \frac{1}{2} = x + \frac{3}{5}.$$

Developing Your Study Skills

Why Study Mathematics?

In our present-day, technological world, it is easy to see mathematics at work. Many vocational and professional areas—such as the fields of business, statistics, economics, psychology, finance, computer science, chemistry, physics, engineering, electronics, nuclear energy, banking, quality control, and teaching—require a certain level of expertise in mathematics. Those who want to work in these fields must be able to function at a given mathematical level. Those who cannot will not make it. So if your field of study requires you to take higher-level mathematics courses, be sure to master the topics of this course. Then you will be ready for the next one.

2.1 Exercises

Student Solutions Manual | CD/ Video | PH Math Tutor Center | MathXL®Tutorials on CD | MathXL® | MyMathLab® | Interactmath.com

Verbal and Writing Skills

In exercises 1–3, fill in the blank with the appropriate word.

1. When we use the ________ sign, we indicate two expressions are ________ in value.

2. If the ________________ is added to both sides of an equation, the results on each side are equal in value.

3. The ____________ of an equation is a value of the variable that makes the equation true.

4. What is the additive inverse of -20?

5. Why do we add the additive inverse of a to each side of $x + a = b$ to solve for x?

6. What is the additive inverse of a?

Solve for x. Check your answers.

7. $x + 11 = 15$

8. $x + 12 = 18$

9. $17 = 5 + x$

10. $23 = x + 16$

11. $x - 3 = 14$

12. $x - 11 = 5$

13. $0 = x + 5$

14. $0 = x - 7$

15. $x - 6 = -19$

16. $x - 11 = -13$

17. $-12 + x = 50$

18. $-18 + x = 48$

19. $3 + 5 = x - 7$

20. $8 - 2 = x + 5$

21. $32 - 17 = x - 6$

22. $27 - 12 = x - 9$

23. $4 + 8 + x = 6 + 6$

24. $18 - 6 + x = 15 - 3$

25. $8 - 23 + 7 = 1 + x - 2$

26. $3 - 17 + 8 = 8 + x - 3$

27. $-12 + x - 3 = 15 - 18 + 9$

28. $-19 + x - 7 = 20 - 42 + 10$

In exercises 29–36, determine whether the given solution is correct. If it is not, find the solution.

29. Is $x = 5$ the solution to $-7 + x = 2$?

30. Is $x = 7$ the solution to $-13 + x = 4$?

31. Is -3 a solution to $-18 - 2 = x - 7$?

32. Is -5 a solution to $-16 + 5 = x - 6$?

33. Is -33 the solution to $x - 23 = -56$?

34. Is -8 the solution to $-39 = x - 47$?

35. Is 35 the solution to $15 - 3 + 20 = x - 3$?

36. Is -12 the solution to $x + 8 = 12 - 19 + 3$?

Find the value of x that satisfies each equation.

37. $2.5 + x = 0.7$

38. $4.2 + x = 1.3$

39. $2.7 + x - 1.4 = 3.8$

40. $4.3 + x - 2.6 = 3.4$

41. $x - \frac{1}{4} = \frac{3}{4}$

42. $x + \frac{1}{3} = \frac{2}{3}$

43. $\frac{2}{3} + x = \frac{1}{6} + \frac{1}{4}$

44. $\frac{2}{5} + x = \frac{1}{2} - \frac{3}{10}$

Mixed Practice

Solve for x.

45. $3 + x = -12 + 8$

46. $12 + x = -7 + 20$

47. $5\frac{1}{6} + x = 8$

48. $7\frac{1}{8} = -20 + x$

49. $\frac{5}{12} - \frac{5}{6} = x - \frac{3}{2}$

50. $\frac{4}{15} - \frac{3}{5} = x - \frac{4}{3}$

51. $1.6 + 4x - 3.2 = -2x + 5.6 + 5x$

52. $0.7 + 3x - 4.2 = 9x + 3.6 - 7x$

53. $x + 0.7513 = 2.2419$

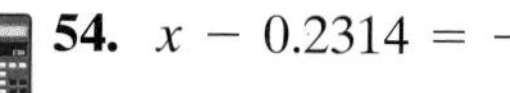

54. $x - 0.2314 = -4.0144$

Cumulative Review

Simplify by adding like terms.

55. $x + 3y - 5x - 7y + 2x$

56. $y^2 + y - 12 - 3y^2 - 5y + 16$

57. ***Quality Control*** The Perception Toy Company wishes to cut costs and decides that improving quality control will help. It can do this by reducing the amount of rejected frisbees to 3%. In a recent week, a quality control inspector found that 8 out of 413 frisbees were rejected. Did they meet Perception's goal?

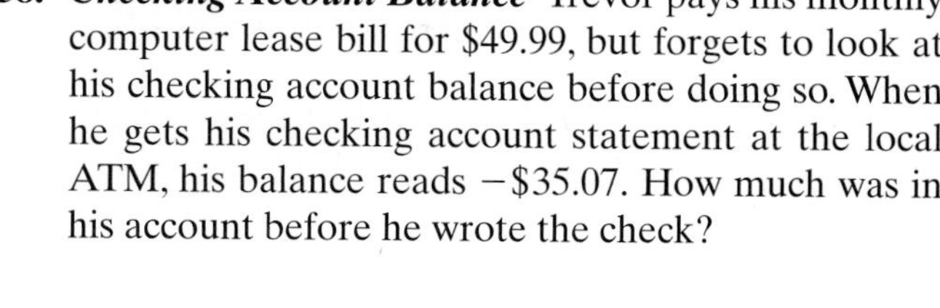

58. ***Checking Account Balance*** Trevor pays his monthly computer lease bill for \$49.99, but forgets to look at his checking account balance before doing so. When he gets his checking account statement at the local ATM, his balance reads −\$35.07. How much was in his account before he wrote the check?

59. ***Radar Picture*** A 90-meter-wide radar picture is taken of a swamp in northern Australia. The radar detects a rock outcrop that is 90 feet above sea level, and a vein of opal (a semiprecious stone) 27 feet below sea level. How far is the top of the rock from the location of the opal?

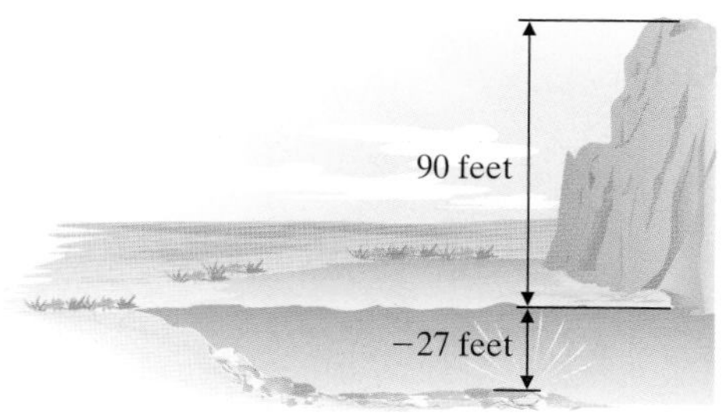

2.2 The Multiplication Principle of Equality

Student Learning Objectives

After studying this section, you will be able to:

1. **Solve equations of the form $\frac{1}{a}x = b$.**
2. **Solve equations of the form $ax = b$.**

1 Solving Equations of the Form $\frac{1}{a}x = b$

The addition principle allows us to add the same number to both sides of an equation. What would happen if we multiplied each side of an equation by the same number? For example, what would happen if we multiplied each side of an equation by 3?

To answer this question, let's return to our simple example of the box and the stone on a balanced seesaw. If we triple the weight on each side (that is, multiply the weight on each side by 3), the seesaw should still balance. The weight values of both sides remain equal.

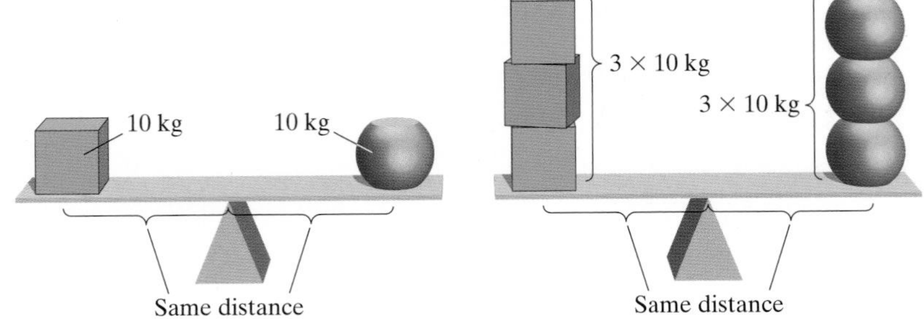

In words we can state this principle thus.

MULTIPLICATION PRINCIPLE

If both sides of an equation are multiplied by the same nonzero number, the results on both sides are equal in value.

In symbols we can restate the multiplication principle this way.

For real numbers a, b, and c with $c \neq 0$, if $a = b$, then $ca = cb$.

It is important that we say $c \neq 0$. We will explore this idea in the To Think About exercises.

Let us look at an equation where it would be helpful to multiply each side by 3.

EXAMPLE 1 Solve for x. $\frac{1}{3}x = -15$

Solution We know that $(3)\left(\frac{1}{3}\right) = 1$. We will multiply each side of the equation by 3 because we want to isolate the variable x.

$$3\left(\frac{1}{3}x\right) = 3(-15)$$ Multiply each side of the equation by 3 since $(3)\left(\frac{1}{3}\right) = 1$.

$$\left(\frac{3}{1}\right)\left(\frac{1}{3}\right)(x) = -45$$

$$1x = -45$$ Simplify.

$$x = -45$$ The solution is -45.

Check. $$\frac{1}{3}(-45) \stackrel{?}{=} -15$$ Substitute -45 for x in the original equation.

$$-15 = -15 \checkmark$$ It checks.

Practice Problem 1 Solve for x. $\frac{1}{8}x = -2$

NOTE TO STUDENT: Fully worked-out solutions to all of the Practice Problems can be found at the back of the text starting at page SP-1

Note that $\frac{1}{5}x$ can be written as $\frac{x}{5}$. To solve the equation $\frac{x}{5} = 3$, we could multiply each side of the equation by 5. Try it. Then check your solution.

2 Solving Equations of the Form $ax = b$

We can see that using the multiplication principle to multiply each side of an equation by $\frac{1}{2}$ is the same as dividing each side of the equation by 2. Thus, it would seem that the multiplication principle would allow us to divide each side of the equation by any nonzero real number. Is there a real-life example of this idea?

Let's return to our simple example of the box and the stone on a balanced seesaw. Suppose that we were to cut the two objects in half (so that the amount of weight of each was divided by 2). We then return the objects to the same places on the seesaw. The seesaw would still balance. The weight values of both sides remain equal.

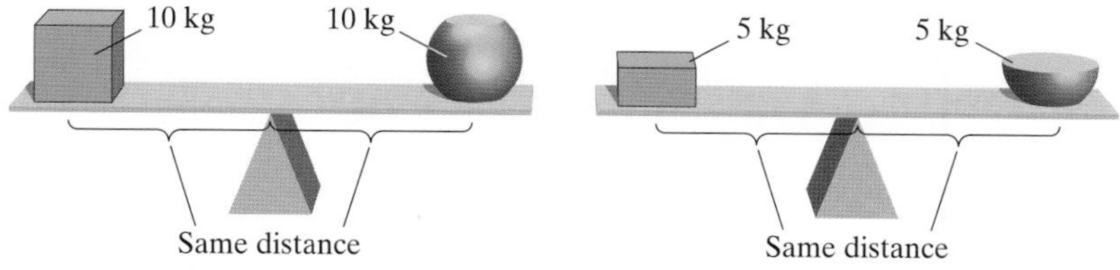

In words we can state this principle thus.

DIVISION PRINCIPLE

If both sides of an equation are divided by the same nonzero number, the results on both sides are equal in value.

Note: We put a restriction on the number by which we are dividing. We cannot divide by zero. We say that expressions like $\frac{2}{0}$ are not defined. Thus we restrict our divisor to *nonzero* numbers. We can restate the division principle this way.

For real numbers a, b, and c where $c \neq 0$, if $a = b$, then $\frac{a}{c} = \frac{b}{c}$.

EXAMPLE 2 Solve for x. $5x = 125$

Solution

$$\frac{5x}{5} = \frac{125}{5} \quad \text{Divide both sides by 5.}$$

$$x = 25 \quad \text{Simplify. The solution is 25.}$$

Check.

$$5x = 125$$

$$5(25) \stackrel{?}{=} 125 \quad \text{Replace } x \text{ by 25.}$$

$$125 = 125 \checkmark \quad \text{It checks.}$$

Practice Problem 2 Solve for x. $9x = 72$

For equations of the form $ax = b$ (a number multiplied by x equals another number), we solve the equation by choosing to divide both sides by a particular number. What is the number to choose? We look at the side of the equation that contains x. We notice the number that is multiplied by x. We divide by that number.

The division principle tells us that we can still have a true equation provided that we divide by that number *on both sides* of the equation.

The solution to an equation may be a proper fraction or an improper fraction.

EXAMPLE 3 Solve for x. $4x = 38$

Solution

$$\frac{4x}{4} = \frac{38}{4} \quad \text{Divide both sides by 4.}$$

$$x = \frac{19}{2} \quad \text{Simplify. The solution is } \tfrac{19}{2}.$$

If you leave the solution as a fraction, it will be easier to check that solution in the original equation.

Check.

$$4x = 38$$

$$\overset{2}{\cancel{4}}\left(\frac{19}{\cancel{2}}\right) \stackrel{?}{=} 38 \quad \text{Replace } x \text{ by } \tfrac{19}{2}.$$

$$38 = 38 \checkmark \quad \text{It checks.}$$

NOTE TO STUDENT: Fully worked-out solutions to all of the Practice Problems can be found at the back of the text starting at page SP-1

Practice Problem 3 Solve for x. $6x = 50$

In Examples 2 and 3 we *divided by the number multiplied by x*. This procedure is followed regardless of whether the sign of that number is positive or negative. In equations of the form $ax = b$ the **coefficient** of x is a. A coefficient is a multiplier.

EXAMPLE 4 Solve for x. $-3x = 48$

Solution

$$\frac{-3x}{-3} = \frac{48}{-3} \quad \text{Divide both sides by } -3.$$

$$x = -16 \quad \text{The solution is } -16.$$

Check. Can you check this solution?

Practice Problem 4 Solve for x. $-27x = 54$

The coefficient of x may be 1 or -1. You may have to rewrite the equation so that the coefficient of 1 or -1 is obvious. With practice you may be able to recognize the coefficient without actually rewriting the equation.

EXAMPLE 5 Solve for x. $-x = -24$.

Solution

$$-1x = -24 \quad \text{Rewrite the equation. } -1x \text{ is the same as } -x. \text{ Now the coefficient of } -1 \text{ is obvious.}$$

$$\frac{-1x}{-1} = \frac{-24}{-1} \quad \text{Divide both sides by } -1.$$

$$x = 24 \quad \text{The solution is 24.}$$

Check. Can you check this solution?

Practice Problem 5 Solve for x. $-x = 36$

The variable can be on either side of the equation. The equation $-78 = -3x$ can be solved in exactly the same way as $-3x = -78$.

EXAMPLE 6 Solve for x. $-78 = -3x$

Solution

$$\frac{-78}{-3} = \frac{-3x}{-3}$$ Divide both sides by -3.

$$26 = x$$ The solution is 26.

Check.

$$-78 = -3x$$

$$-78 \stackrel{?}{=} -3(26)$$ Replace x by 26.

$$-78 = -78 \checkmark$$ It checks.

Practice Problem 6 Solve for x. $-51 = -6x$

There is a mathematical concept that unites what we have learned in this section. The concept uses the idea of a multiplicative inverse. For any nonzero number a, the **multiplicative inverse** of a is $\frac{1}{a}$. Likewise, for any nonzero number a, the multiplicative inverse of $\frac{1}{a}$ is a. So to solve an equation of the form $ax = b$, we say that we need to multiply each side by the multiplicative inverse of a. Thus to solve $5x = 45$, we would multiply each side of the equation by the multiplicative inverse of 5, which is $\frac{1}{5}$. In similar fashion, if we wanted to solve the equation $\left(\frac{1}{6}\right)x = 4$, we would multiply each side of the equation by the multiplicative inverse of $\frac{1}{6}$, which is 6. In general, all the problems we have covered so far in this section can be solved by multiplying both sides of the equation by the multiplicative inverse of the coefficient of x.

EXAMPLE 7 Solve for x. $31.2 = 6.0x - 0.8x$

Solution

$$31.2 = 6.0x - 0.8x$$ There are like terms on the right side.

$$31.2 = 5.2x$$ Collect like terms.

$$\frac{31.2}{5.2} = \frac{5.2x}{5.2}$$ Divide both sides by 5.2 (which is the same as multiplying both sides by the multiplicative inverse of 5.2).

$$6 = x$$ The solution is 6.

Note: Be sure to place the decimal point in the quotient directly above the caret ($_\wedge$) when performing the division.

$$\begin{array}{r} 6. \\ 5.2_\wedge\overline{)31.2_\wedge} \\ \underline{31.2} \\ 0 \end{array}$$

Check. The check is up to you.

Practice Problem 7 Solve for x. $16.2 = 5.2x - 3.4x$

Developing Your Study Skills

Getting Help

Getting the right kind of help at the right time can be a key ingredient in being successful in mathematics. When you have gone to class on a regular basis, taken careful notes, methodically read your textbook, and diligently done your homework—all of which means making every effort possible to learn the mathematics—you may find that you are still having difficulty. If this is the case, then you need to seek help. Make an appointment with your instructor to find out what help is available to you. The instructor, tutoring services, a mathematics lab, videotapes, and computer software may be among the resources you can draw on.

Once you discover the resources available in your school, you need to take advantage of them. Do not put it off, or you will find yourself getting behind. You cannot afford that. When studying mathematics, you must keep up with your work.

2.2 Exercises

Student Solutions Manual | CD/ Video | PH Math Tutor Center | MathXL®Tutorials on CD | MathXL® | MyMathLab® | Interactmath.com

Verbal and Writing Skills

1. To solve the equation $6x = -24$, divide each side of the equation by ______.

2. To solve the equation $-7x = 56$, divide each side of the equation by ______.

3. To solve the equation $\frac{1}{7}x = -2$, multiply each side of the equation by ______.

4. To solve the equation $\frac{1}{9}x = 5$, multiply each side of the equation by ______.

Solve for x. Be sure to reduce your answer. Check your solution.

5. $\frac{1}{9}x = 4$

6. $\frac{1}{7}x = 6$

7. $\frac{1}{3}x = -9$

8. $\frac{1}{4}x = -20$

9. $\frac{x}{5} = 16$

10. $\frac{x}{10} = 8$

11. $-3 = \frac{x}{5}$

12. $\frac{x}{3} = -12$

13. $13x = 52$

14. $15x = 60$

15. $56 = 7x$

16. $46 = 2x$

17. $-16 = 6x$

18. $-35 = 21x$

19. $1.5x = 75$

20. $2x = 0.36$

21. $-15 = -x$

22. $32 = -x$

23. $-112 = 16x$

24. $-108 = -18x$

25. $0.4x = 0.08$

26. $2.1x = 0.3$

27. $-3.9x = -15.6$

28. $-4.7x = -14.1$

Determine whether the given solution is correct. If it is not, find the correct solution.

29. Is 7 the solution for $-3x = 21$?

30. Is 8 the solution for $5x = -40$?

31. Is -6 the solution for $-11x = 66$?

32. Is -20 the solution for $-x = 20$?

Mixed Practice

Find the value of the variable that satisfies the equation.

33. $7y = -0.21$

34. $-3y = 0.42$

35. $-56 = -21t$

36. $34 = -51q$

37. $4.6y = -3.22$

38. $-2.8y = -3.08$

39. $4x + 3x = 21$

40. $5x + 4x = 36$

41. $2x - 7x = 20$

42. $3x - 9x = 18$

43. $-6x - 3x = -7$

44. $y - 11y = 7$

45. $12 - 19 = -7x$

46. $36 - 22 = -2x$

47. $6x = -18 + 36$

48. $11x = -20 + 42$

49. $\frac{2}{3}x = 18$

50. $\frac{3}{5}x = 39$

51. $3.6172x = -19.026472$

52. $-4.0518x = 14.505444$

To Think About

53. We have said that if $a = b$ and $c \neq 0$, then $ac = bc$. Why is it important that $c \neq 0$? What would happen if we tried to solve an equation by multiplying both sides by zero?

54. We have said that if $a = b$ and $c \neq 0$ then $\frac{a}{c} = \frac{b}{c}$. Why is it important that $c \neq 0$? What would happen if we tried to solve an equation by dividing both sides by zero?

Cumulative Review

Evaluate using the correct order of operations. (Be careful to avoid sign errors.)

55. $(-6)(-8) + (-3)(2)$

56. $(-3)^3 + (-20) \div 2$

57. $5 + (2 - 6)^2$

58. ***Discount Merchandise*** An off-price clothing store chain specializes in last year's merchandise. Their contact in Hong Kong has purchased 12,000 famous designer men's sport coats for the stores. When the shipment is unloaded, 800 sport coats have no left sleeve. What percent of the shipment is acceptable?

59. ***Investments*** In January, Keiko invested \$600 in a certain stock. In February, the stock gained \$82.00. In March, the stock lost \$47.00. In April, the stock gained \$103.00. In May, the stock lost \$106.00. What was Keiko's stock holding worth after the May loss?

60. ***Whale Calf Population*** In 1995, the humpback whale calf population at Stellwagen Bank, near Gloucester, Massachusetts, was estimated at 12 calves. The population grew by 21 calves in 1996, 18 calves in 1997, and 51 calves in 1998. In 1999, the number of whale calves decreased by 4, and in 2000 it increased by 6. What was the whale calf population at the end of 2000?

61. ***Earthquakes*** In an average year, worldwide, there are 20 earthquakes of magnitude 7 on the Richter scale. If next year is predicted to be an exceptional year, and the number of earthquakes of magnitude 7 is expected to increase by 35%, about how many earthquakes of magnitude 7 can be expected? (Round off to the nearest whole number.)

2.3 Using the Addition and Multiplication Principles Together

Student Learning Objectives

After studying this section, you will be able to:

1. **Solve equations of the form $ax + b = c$.**
2. **Solve equations with the variable on both sides of the equation.**
3. **Solve equations with parentheses.**

NOTE TO STUDENT: Fully worked-out solutions to all of the Practice Problems can be found at the back of the text starting at page SP-1

1 Solving Equations of the Form $ax + b = c$

Jenny Crawford scored several goals in field hockey during April. Her teammates scored three more than five times the number she scored. Together the team scored 18 goals in April. How many did Jenny score? To solve this problem, we need to solve the equation $5x + 3 = 18$.

To solve an equation of the form $ax + b = c$, we must use both the addition principle and the multiplication principle.

EXAMPLE 1 Solve for x to determine how many goals Jenny scored and check your solution.

$$5x + 3 = 18$$

Solution We first want to isolate the variable term.

$5x + 3 + (-3) = 18 + (-3)$	Use the addition principle to add -3 to both sides.
$5x = 15$	Simplify.
$\frac{5x}{5} = \frac{15}{5}$	Use the division principle to divide both sides by 5.
$x = 3$	The solution is 3. Thus Jenny scored 3 goals.

Check.

$$5(3) + 3 \stackrel{?}{=} 18$$
$$15 + 3 \stackrel{?}{=} 18$$
$$18 = 18 \checkmark \quad \text{It checks.}$$

Practice Problem 1 Solve for x and check your solution. $9x + 2 = 38$

2 Solving Equations with the Variable on Both Sides of the Equation

In some cases the variable appears on both sides of the equation. We would like to rewrite the equation so that all the terms containing the variable appear on one side. To do this, we apply the addition principle to the variable term.

EXAMPLE 2 Solve for x. $9x = 6x + 15$

Solution

$9x + (-6x) = 6x + (-6x) + 15$	Add $-6x$ to both sides. Notice $6x + (-6x)$ eliminates the variable on the right side.
$3x = 15$	Combine like terms.
$\frac{3x}{3} = \frac{15}{3}$	Divide both sides by 3.
$x = 5$	The solution is 5.

Check. The check is left to the student.

Practice Problem 2 Solve for x. $13x = 2x - 66$

In many problems the variable terms and constant terms appear on both sides of the equations. You will want to get all the variable terms on one side and all the constant terms on the other side.

EXAMPLE 3 Solve for x and check your solution. $9x + 3 = 7x - 2$.

Solution First we want to isolate the variable term.

$9x + (-7x) + 3 = 7x + (-7x) - 2$ Add $-7x$ to both sides of the equation.

$2x + 3 = -2$ Combine like terms.

$2x + 3 + (-3) = -2 + (-3)$ Add -3 to both sides.

$2x = -5$ Simplify.

$\frac{2x}{2} = \frac{-5}{2}$ Divide both sides by 2.

$x = -\frac{5}{2}$ The solution is $-\frac{5}{2}$.

Check. $9x + 3 = 7x - 2$

$9\left(-\frac{5}{2}\right) + 3 \stackrel{?}{=} 7\left(-\frac{5}{2}\right) - 2$ Replace x by $-\frac{5}{2}$.

$-\frac{45}{2} + 3 \stackrel{?}{=} -\frac{35}{2} - 2$ Simplify.

$-\frac{45}{2} + \frac{6}{2} \stackrel{?}{=} -\frac{35}{2} - \frac{4}{2}$ Change to equivalent fractions with a common denominator.

$-\frac{39}{2} = -\frac{39}{2}$ ✓ It checks. The solution is $-\frac{5}{2}$.

Practice Problem 3 Solve for x and check your solution. $3x + 2 = 5x + 2$

In our next example we will study equations that need simplifying before any other steps are taken. Where it is possible, you should first collect like terms on one or both sides of the equation. The variable terms can be collected on the right side or the left side. In this example we will collect all the x-terms on the right side.

EXAMPLE 4 Solve for x. $5x + 26 - 6 = 9x + 12x$

Solution

$5x + 20 = 21x$ Combine like terms.

$5x + (-5x) + 20 = 21x + (-5x)$ Add $-5x$ to both sides.

$20 = 16x$ Combine like terms.

$\frac{20}{16} = \frac{16x}{16}$ Divide both sides by 16.

$\frac{5}{4} = x$ Don't forget to reduce the resulting fraction.

Check. The check is left to the student.

Practice Problem 4 Solve for z. $-z + 8 - z = 3z + 10 - 3$

Do you really need all these steps? No. As you become more proficient you will be able to combine or eliminate some of these steps. However, it is best to write each step in its entirety until you are consistently obtaining the correct solution. It is much better to show every step than to take a lot of shortcuts and possibly obtain a wrong answer. This is a section of the algebra course where working neatly and accurately will help you—both now and as you progress through the course.

3 Solving Equations with Parentheses

The equations that you just solved are simpler versions of equations that we will now discuss. These equations contain parentheses. If the parentheses are first removed, the problems then become just like those encountered previously. We use the distributive property to remove the parentheses.

EXAMPLE 5 Solve for x and check your solution.

$$4(x + 1) - 3(x - 3) = 25$$

Solution $4(x + 1) - 3(x - 3) = 25$

$4x + 4 - 3x + 9 = 25$ — Multiply by 4 and -3 to remove parentheses. Be careful of the signs. Remember that $(-3)(-3) = 9$.

After removing the parentheses, it is important to collect like terms on each side of the equation. Do this before going on to isolate the variable.

$x + 13 = 25$ — Collect like terms.

$x + 13 - 13 = 25 - 13$ — Add -13 to both sides to isolate the variable.

$x = 12$ — The solution is 12.

Check. $4(12 + 1) - 3(12 - 3) \stackrel{?}{=} 25$ — Replace x by 12.

$4(13) - 3(9) \stackrel{?}{=} 25$ — Combine numbers inside parentheses.

$52 - 27 \stackrel{?}{=} 25$ — Multiply.

$25 = 25$ ✓ — Simplify. It checks.

***NOTE TO STUDENT:** Fully worked-out solutions to all of the Practice Problems can be found at the back of the text starting at page SP-1*

Practice Problem 5 Solve for x and check your solution.

$$4x - (x + 3) = 12 - 3(x - 2)$$

EXAMPLE 6 Solve for x. $3(-x - 7) = -2(2x + 5)$

Solution $-3x - 21 = -4x - 10$ — Remove parentheses. Watch the signs carefully.

$-3x + 4x - 21 = -4x + 4x - 10$ — Add $4x$ to both sides.

$x - 21 = -10$ — Simplify.

$x - 21 + 21 = -10 + 21$ — Add 21 to both sides.

$x = 11$ — The solution is 11.

Check. The check is left to the student.

Practice Problem 6 Solve for x. $4(-2x - 3) = -5(x - 2) + 2$

In problems that involve decimals, great care should be taken. In some steps you will be multiplying decimal quantities, and in other steps you will be adding them.

EXAMPLE 7 Solve for x. $0.3(1.2x - 3.6) = 4.2x - 16.44$

Solution

$$0.36x - 1.08 = 4.2x - 16.44$$ Remove parentheses.

$$0.36x - 0.36x - 1.08 = 4.2x - 0.36x - 16.44$$ Subtract $0.36x$ from both sides.

$$-1.08 = 3.84x - 16.44$$ Collect like terms.

$$-1.08 + 16.44 = 3.84x - 16.44 + 16.44$$ Add 16.44 to both sides.

$$15.36 = 3.84x$$ Simplify.

$$\frac{15.36}{3.84} = \frac{3.84x}{3.84}$$ Divide both sides by 3.84.

$$4 = x$$ The solution is 4.

Check. The check is left to the student.

Practice Problem 7 Solve for x. $0.3x - 2(x + 0.1) = 0.4(x - 3) - 1.1$

EXAMPLE 8 Solve for z and check. $2(3z - 5) + 2 = 4z - 3(2z + 8)$

Solution

$$6z - 10 + 2 = 4z - 6z - 24$$ Remove parentheses.

$$6z - 8 = -2z - 24$$ Collect like terms.

$$6z - 8 + 2z = -2z + 2z - 24$$ Add $2z$ to each side.

$$8z - 8 = -24$$ Simplify.

$$8z - 8 + 8 = -24 + 8$$ Add 8 to each side.

$$8z = -16$$ Simplify.

$$\frac{8z}{8} = \frac{-16}{8}$$ Divide each side by 8.

$$z = -2$$ Simplify. The solution is -2.

Check.

$$2[3(-2) - 5] + 2 \stackrel{?}{=} 4(-2) - 3[2(-2) + 8]$$ Replace z by -2.

$$2[-6 - 5] + 2 \stackrel{?}{=} -8 - 3[-4 + 8]$$ Multiply.

$$2[-11] + 2 \stackrel{?}{=} -8 - 3[4]$$ Simplify.

$$-22 + 2 \stackrel{?}{=} -8 - 12$$

$$-20 = -20 \checkmark$$ It checks.

Practice Problem 8 Solve for z and check.

$$5(2z - 1) + 7 = 7z - 4(z + 3)$$

2.3 Exercises

Student Solutions Manual | CD/Video | PH Math Tutor Center | MathXL®Tutorials on CD | MathXL® | MyMathLab® | Interactmath.com

Find the value of the variable that satisfies the equation in exercises 1–22. Check your solution. Answers that are not integers may be left in fractional form or decimal form.

1. $4x + 13 = 21$

2. $7x + 4 = 53$

3. $4x - 11 = 13$

4. $5x - 11 = 39$

5. $7x - 18 = -46$

6. $6x - 23 = -71$

7. $-4x + 17 = -35$

8. $-6x + 25 = -83$

9. $2x + 3.2 = 9.4$

10. $4x + 4.6 = 9.2$

11. $\frac{1}{5}x - 2 = 6$

12. $\frac{1}{3}x - 7 = 4$

13. $\frac{1}{3}x + 5 = -4$

14. $\frac{1}{8}x - 3 = -9$

15. $8x = 48 + 2x$

16. $5x = 22 + 3x$

17. $-6x = -27 + 3x$

18. $-7x = -26 + 6x$

19. $63 - x = 8x$

20. $56 - 3x = 5x$

21. $54 - 2x = -8x$

22. $72 - 4x = -12x$

23. Is 2 the solution for $2y + 3y = 12 - y$?

24. Is 4 the solution for $5y + 2 = 6y - 6 + y$?

25. Is 11 a solution for $7x + 6 - 3x = 2x - 5 + x$?

26. Is -12 a solution for $9x + 2 - 5x = -8 + 5x - 2$?

Solve for the variable. You may move the variable terms to the right or to the left.

27. $14 - 2x = -5x + 11$

28. $8 - 3x = 7x + 8$

29. $x - 6 = 8 - x$

30. $-x + 12 = -4 + x$

31. $0.8y - 0.4 = 0.9 - 0.5y$

32. $0.7y - 0.5 = 1.1 - 0.1y$

33. $5x - 9 = 3x + 23$

34. $9x - 5 = 7x + 43$

To Think About

First collect like terms on each side of the equation. Then solve for y by getting all the y-terms on the left. Then solve for y by getting all the y-terms on the right. Which approach is better?

35. $-3 + 10y + 6 = 15 + 12y - 18$

36. $7y + 21 - 5y = 5y - 7 + y$

Remove the parentheses and solve for the variable. Check your solution. Answers that are not integers may be left in fractional form or decimal form.

37. $5(x + 3) = 35$

38. $6(x + 2) = 42$

39. $6(3x + 2) - 8 = -2$

40. $4(2x + 1) - 7 = 6 - 5$

41. $7x - 3(5 - x) = 10$

42. $8x - 2(4 - x) = 14$

43. $0.5x - 0.3(2 - x) = 4.6$

44. $0.4x - 0.2(3 - x) = 1.8$

45. $5(x - 3) + 5 = 3(x + 2)$

46. $3(x - 2) + 2 = 2(x - 4)$

47. $-2(x + 3) + 4 = 3(x + 4) + 2$

48. $-3(x + 5) + 2 = 4(x + 6) - 9$

49. $-3(y - 3y) + 4 = -4(3y - y) + 6 + 13y$

50. $2(4x - x) + 6 = 2(2x + x) + 8 - x$

Mixed Practice

Solve for the variable.

51. $5.7x + 3 = 4.2x - 3$

52. $4x - 3.1 = 5.3 - 3x$

53. $5z + 7 - 2z = 32 - 2z$

54. $8 - 7z + 2z = 20 + 5z$

55. $-0.3a + 1.4 = -1.2 - 0.7a$

56. $-0.7b + 1.6 = -1.7 - 1.5b$

57. $6x + 8 - 3x = 11 - 12x - 13$

58. $4 - 7x - 13 = 8x - 3 - 5x$

59. $-3.5x + 1.3 = -2.7x + 1.5$

60. $2.8x - 0.9 = 5.2x - 3.3$

61. $5(4 + x) = 3(3x - 1) - 9$

62. $6(3x - 1) = 4(2x + 5) - 6$

63. $4x + 3.2 - 1.9x = 0.3x - 4.9$

64. $3x + 2 - 1.7x = 0.6x + 31.4$

65. $3(x + 4) - 5(3x - 2) = 8$

66. $3(2z - 4) - 4(z + 5) = 6$

Solve for x. Round your answer to the nearest hundredth.

67. $1.63x - 9.23 = 5.71x + 8.04$

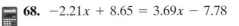

68. $-2.21x + 8.65 = 3.69x - 7.78$

Cumulative Review

Simplify.

69. $2x(3x - y) + 4(2x^2 - 3xy)$

70. $2\{x - 3[4 + 2(3 + x)]\}$

71. ***Investments*** On March 30, 2000, Nancy owned three different stocks: Coca Cola, General Motors and Alcoa. Her portfolio contained the following:

4.0 shares of Coca Cola stock valued at $\$52\frac{1}{8}$,
3.2 shares of General Motors stock valued at $\$81\frac{7}{8}$, and
5.2 shares of Alcoa stock valued at $\$71\frac{7}{8}$.

Find the market value of Nancy's stock holdings on March 30, 2000. (*Note*: In 2000 stock quotes were given in fractional form. Now decimals are used.)

72. ***Employee Discount*** Bea works for a large department store and obtains a 10% discount on anything she buys from the store. One item Bea wishes to purchase costs \$140 and is on sale at a 25% discount.

(a) What is the price if Bea has a total discount of 35%? (Disregard sales tax.)

(b) What is the price if Bea has a 10% discount on the 25% discount price? (Disregard sales tax.)

2.4 Solving Equations with Fractions

Solving Equations with Fractions

Equations with fractions can be rather difficult to solve. This difficulty is simply due to the extra care we usually have to use when computing with fractions. The actual equation-solving procedures are the same, with fractions or without. To avoid unnecessary work, we transform the given equation with fractions to an equivalent equation that does not contain fractions. How do we do this? We multiply each side of the equation by the least common denominator of all the fractions contained in the equation. We then use the distributive property so that the LCD is multiplied by each term of the equation.

Student Learning Objective

After studying this section, you will be able to:

1 Solve equations with fractions.

EXAMPLE 1 Solve for x. $\frac{1}{4}x - \frac{2}{3} = \frac{5}{12}x$

Solution First we find that the LCD = 12.

$$12\left(\frac{1}{4}x - \frac{2}{3}\right) = 12\left(\frac{5}{12}x\right) \quad \text{Multiply each side by 12.}$$

$$\left(\frac{12}{1}\right)\left(\frac{1}{4}\right)(x) - \left(\frac{12}{1}\right)\left(\frac{2}{3}\right) = \left(\frac{12}{1}\right)\left(\frac{5}{12}\right)(x) \quad \text{Use the distributive property.}$$

$$3x - 8 = 5x \quad \text{Simplify.}$$

$$3x + (-3x) - 8 = 5x + (-3x) \quad \text{Add } -3x \text{ to each side.}$$

$$-8 = 2x \quad \text{Simplify.}$$

$$\frac{-8}{2} = \frac{2x}{2} \quad \text{Divide each side by 2.}$$

$$-4 = x \quad \text{Simplify.}$$

Check.

$$\frac{1}{4}(-4) - \frac{2}{3} \stackrel{?}{=} \frac{5}{12}(-4)$$

$$-1 - \frac{2}{3} \stackrel{?}{=} -\frac{5}{3}$$

$$-\frac{3}{3} - \frac{2}{3} \stackrel{?}{=} -\frac{5}{3}$$

$$-\frac{5}{3} = -\frac{5}{3} \ \checkmark \quad \text{It checks.}$$

Practice Problem 1 Solve for x. $\frac{3}{8}x - \frac{3}{2} = \frac{1}{4}x$

***NOTE TO STUDENT:** Fully worked-out solutions to all of the Practice Problems can be found at the back of the text starting at page SP-1*

In Example 1 we multiplied each side of the equation by the LCD. However, most students prefer to go immediately to the second step and multiply each term by the LCD. This avoids having to write out a separate step using the distributive property.

EXAMPLE 2 Solve for x and check your solution. $\frac{x}{3} + 3 = \frac{x}{5} - \frac{1}{3}$

Solution

$$15\left(\frac{x}{3}\right) + 15(3) = 15\left(\frac{x}{5}\right) - 15\left(\frac{1}{3}\right)$$ The LCD is 15. Use the multiplication principle to multiply each term by 15.

$5x + 45 = 3x - 5$ Simplify.

$5x - 3x + 45 = 3x - 3x - 5$ Add $-3x$ to both sides.

$2x + 45 = -5$ Combine like terms.

$2x + 45 - 45 = -5 - 45$ Add -45 to both sides.

$2x = -50$ Simplify.

$\frac{2x}{2} = \frac{-50}{2}$ Divide both sides by 2.

$x = -25$ The solution is -25.

Check.

$$\frac{-25}{3} + 3 \stackrel{?}{=} \frac{-25}{5} - \frac{1}{3}$$

$$-\frac{25}{3} + \frac{9}{3} \stackrel{?}{=} -\frac{5}{1} - \frac{1}{3}$$

$$-\frac{16}{3} \stackrel{?}{=} -\frac{15}{3} - \frac{1}{3}$$

$$-\frac{16}{3} = -\frac{16}{3} \checkmark$$

Practice Problem 2 Solve for x and check your solution.

$\frac{5x}{4} - 1 = \frac{3x}{4} + \frac{1}{2}$

NOTE TO STUDENT: Fully worked-out solutions to all of the Practice Problems can be found at the back of the text starting at page SP-1

EXAMPLE 3 Solve for x. $\frac{x + 5}{7} = \frac{x}{4} + \frac{1}{2}$

Solution

$$\frac{x}{7} + \frac{5}{7} = \frac{x}{4} + \frac{1}{2}$$ First we rewrite the left side as two fractions. This is actually multiplying $\frac{1}{7}(x + 5) = \frac{x}{7} + \frac{5}{7}$.

$$28\left(\frac{x}{7}\right) + 28\left(\frac{5}{7}\right) = 28\left(\frac{x}{4}\right) + 28\left(\frac{1}{2}\right)$$ We observe that the LCD is 28, so we multiply each term by 28.

$4x + 20 = 7x + 14$ Simplify.

$4x - 4x + 20 = 7x - 4x + 14$ Add $-4x$ to both sides.

$20 = 3x + 14$ Combine like terms.

$20 - 14 = 3x + 14 - 14$ Add -14 to both sides.

$6 = 3x$ Combine like terms.

$\frac{6}{3} = \frac{3x}{3}$ Divide both sides by 3.

$2 = x$ The solution is 2.

Check. The check is left to the student.

Practice Problem 3 Solve for x $\frac{x + 6}{9} = \frac{x}{6} + \frac{1}{2}$

If a problem contains both parentheses and fractions, it is best to remove the parentheses first. Many students find it is helpful to have a written procedure to follow in solving these more involved equations.

PROCEDURE TO SOLVE EQUATIONS

1. Remove any parentheses.
2. If fractions exist, multiply all terms on both sides by the least common denominator of all the fractions.
3. Combine like terms if possible.
4. Add or subtract terms on both sides of the equation to get all terms with the variable on one side of the equation.
5. Add or subtract a constant value on both sides of the equation to get all terms not containing the variable on the other side of the equation.
6. Divide both sides of the equation by the coefficient of the variable.
7. Simplify the solution (if possible).
8. Check your solution.

Let's use each step in solving the next example.

EXAMPLE 4 Solve for x and check your solution.

$$\frac{1}{3}(x-2)=\frac{1}{5}(x+4)+2$$

Solution

Step 1	$\frac{x}{3}-\frac{2}{3}=\frac{x}{5}+\frac{4}{5}+2$	Remove parentheses.
Step 2	$15\left(\frac{x}{3}\right)-15\left(\frac{2}{3}\right)=15\left(\frac{x}{5}\right)+15\left(\frac{4}{5}\right)+15(2)$	Multiply by the LCD, 15.
	$5x-10=3x+12+30$	Simplify.
Step 3	$5x-10=3x+42$	Combine like terms on each side.
Step 4	$5x-3x-10=3x-3x+42$	Add $-3x$ to both sides.
	$2x-10=42$	Simplify.
Step 5	$2x-10+10=42+10$	Add 10 to both sides.
	$2x=52$	Simplify.
Step 6	$\frac{2x}{2}=\frac{52}{2}$	Divide both sides by 2.
Step 7	$x=26$	Simplify the solution.
Step 8 *Check.*	$\frac{1}{3}(26-2)\stackrel{?}{=}\frac{1}{5}(26+4)+2$	Replace x by 26.
	$\frac{1}{3}(24)\stackrel{?}{=}\frac{1}{5}(30)+2$	Combine values within parentheses.
	$8\stackrel{?}{=}6+2$	Simplify.
	$8=8$ ✓	The solution is 26.

***NOTE TO STUDENT:** Fully worked-out solutions to all of the Practice Problems can be found at the back of the text starting at page SP-1*

Practice Problem 4 Solve for x and check your solution.

$$\frac{1}{3}(x - 2) = \frac{1}{4}(x + 5) - \frac{5}{3}$$

Remember that not every step will be needed in each problem. You can combine some steps as well, *as long as you are consistently obtaining the correct solution.* However, you are encouraged to write out every step as a way of helping you to avoid careless errors.

It is important to remember that when we write decimals these numbers are really fractions written in a special way. Thus, $0.3 = \frac{3}{10}$ and $0.07 = \frac{7}{100}$. It is possible to take an equation containing decimals and to multiply each term by the appropriate value to obtain integer coefficients.

EXAMPLE 5 Solve for x. $0.2\,(1 - 8x) + 1.1 = -5\,(0.4x - 0.3)$

Solution

$0.2 - 1.6x + 1.1 = -2.0x + 1.5$	Remove parentheses.
$10(0.2) - 10(1.6x) + 10(1.1) = 10(-2.0x) + 10(1.5)$	Multiply each term by 10.
$2 - 16x + 11 = -20x + 15$	Multiplying by 10 moves the decimal point one place to the right.
$-16x + 13 = -20x + 15$	Simplify.
$-16x + 20x + 13 = -20x + 20x + 15$	Add $20x$ to each side.
$4x + 13 = 15$	Simplify.
$4x + 13 + (-13) = 15 + (-13)$	Add -13 to each side.
$4x = 2$	Simplify.
$\frac{4x}{4} = \frac{2}{4}$	Divide each side by 4.
$x = \frac{1}{2}$ or 0.5	Simplify.

Check.

$$0.2[1 - 8(0.5)] + 1.1 \stackrel{?}{=} -5[0.4(0.5) - 0.3]$$
$$0.2[1 - 4] + 1.1 \stackrel{?}{=} -5[0.2 - 0.3]$$
$$0.2[-3] + 1.1 \stackrel{?}{=} -5[-0.1]$$
$$-0.6 + 1.1 \stackrel{?}{=} 0.5$$
$$0.5 = 0.5 \quad ✓$$

Practice Problem 5 Solve for x. $2.8 = 0.3\,(x - 2) + 2\,(0.1x - 0.3)$

TO THINK ABOUT: Does Every Equation Have One Solution? Actually, no. There are some rare cases where an equation has no solution at all. Suppose we try to solve the equation

$$5(x + 3) = 2x - 8 + 3x.$$

If we remove the parentheses and collect like terms we have

$$5x + 15 = 5x - 8.$$

If we add $-5x$ to each side, we obtain

$$15 = -8.$$

Clearly this is impossible. There is no value of x for which these two numbers are equal. We would say this equation has **no solution.**

One additional surprise may happen. An equation may have an infinite number of solutions. Suppose we try to solve the equation

$$9x - 8x - 7 = 3 + x - 10.$$

If we combine like terms on each side, we have the equation

$$x - 7 = x - 7.$$

If we add $-x$ to each side, we obtain

$$-7 = -7.$$

Now this statement is always true, no matter what the value of x. We would say this equation has **an infinite number of solutions.**

In the To Think About exercises in this section, we will encounter some equations that have no solution or an infinite number of solutions.

Developing Your Study Skills

Taking Notes in Class

An important part of studying mathematics is taking notes. To take meaningful notes, you must be an active listener. Keep your mind on what the instructor is saying, and be ready with questions whenever you do not understand something.

If you have previewed the lesson material, you will be prepared to take good notes. The important concepts will seem somewhat familiar. If you frantically try to write all that the instructor says or copy all the examples done in class, you may find your notes nearly worthless when you are home alone. Write down *important* ideas and examples as the instructor lectures, making sure that you are listening and following the logic. Include any helpful hints or suggestions that your instructor gives you or refers to in your text.

2.4 EXERCISES

Student Solutions Manual | CD/Video | PH Math Tutor Center | MathXL®Tutorials on CD | MathXL® | MyMathLab® | Interactmath.com

In exercises 1–16, solve for the variable and check your answer. Noninteger answers may be left in fractional form or decimal form.

1. $\frac{1}{2}x + \frac{2}{3} = \frac{1}{6}$

2. $\frac{1}{3} + \frac{5}{12}x = \frac{3}{4}$

3. $\frac{2}{3}x = \frac{1}{15}x + \frac{3}{5}$

4. $\frac{5}{21}x = \frac{2}{3}x - \frac{1}{7}$

5. $\frac{x}{2} + \frac{x}{5} = \frac{7}{10}$

6. $\frac{x}{5} - \frac{x}{3} = \frac{8}{15}$

7. $20 - \frac{1}{3}x = \frac{1}{2}x$

8. $15 - \frac{1}{2}x = \frac{1}{4}x$

9. $2 + \frac{y}{2} = \frac{3y}{4} - 3$

10. $\frac{x}{3} - 1 = -\frac{1}{2} - x$

11. $\frac{x - 3}{5} = 1 - \frac{x}{3}$

12. $\frac{y - 5}{4} = 1 - \frac{y}{5}$

13. $\frac{x + 3}{4} = \frac{x}{2} + \frac{1}{6}$

14. $\frac{x + 5}{6} = \frac{x}{2} + \frac{3}{4}$

15. $0.6x + 5.9 = 3.8$

16. $1.2x - 2.2 = 5.6$

17. Is 4 a solution to $\frac{1}{2}(y - 2) + 2 = \frac{3}{8}(3y - 4)$?

18. Is 2 a solution to $\frac{1}{5}(y + 2) = \frac{1}{10}y + \frac{3}{5}$?

19. Is $\frac{5}{8}$ a solution to $\frac{1}{2}\left(y - \frac{1}{5}\right) = \frac{1}{5}(y + 2)$?

20. Is $\frac{13}{3}$ a solution to $\frac{y}{2} - \frac{7}{9} = \frac{y}{6} + \frac{2}{3}$?

Remove parentheses first. Then collect like terms. Solve for the variable. Noninteger answers may be left in fractional form or decimal form.

21. $\frac{3}{4}(3x + 1) = 2(3 - 2x) + 1$

22. $\frac{1}{4}(3x + 1) = 2(2x - 4) - 8$

23. $2(x - 2) = \frac{2}{5}(3x + 1) + 2$

24. $2(x - 4) = \frac{5}{6}(x + 6) - 6$

25. $0.3x - 0.2(3 - 5x) = -0.5(x - 6)$

26. $0.3(x - 2) + 0.4x = -0.2(x - 6)$

27. $-5(0.2x + 0.1) - 0.6 = 1.9$

28. $0.3x + 1.7 = 0.2x - 0.4(5x + 1)$

Mixed Practice

Solve. Noninteger answers may be left in fractional form or decimal form.

29. $\frac{1}{3}(y + 2) = 3y - 5(y - 2)$

30. $\frac{1}{4}(y + 6) = 2y - 3(y - 3)$

31. $\frac{1 + 2x}{5} + \frac{4 - x}{3} = \frac{1}{15}$

32. $\frac{1 + 3x}{2} + \frac{2 - x}{3} = \frac{5}{6}$

33. $\frac{1}{5}(x + 3) = 2x - 3(2 - x) - 3$

34. $\frac{2}{3}(x + 4) = 6 - \frac{1}{4}(3x - 2) - 1$

35. $\frac{1}{3}(x - 2) = 3x - 2(x - 1) + \frac{16}{3}$

36. $\frac{3}{4}(x - 2) + \frac{3}{5} = \frac{1}{5}(x + 1)$

37. $\frac{4}{5}x - \frac{2}{3} = \frac{3x + 1}{2}$

38. $\frac{4}{7}x + \frac{1}{3} = \frac{3x - 2}{14}$

39. $0.2(x + 3) = 4(0.5x - 0.03)$

40. $0.6(x + 0.1) = 2(0.4x - 0.2)$

To Think About

Solve. Be careful to examine your work to see if the equation may have no solution or an infinite number of solutions.

41. $-1 + 5(x - 2) = 12x + 3 - 7x$

42. $x + 3x - 2 + 3x = -11 + 7(x + 2)$

43. $9(x + 3) - 6 = 24 - 2x - 3 + 11x$

44. $7(x + 4) - 10 = 3x + 20 + 4x - 2$

45. $7x + 6 = 2(3x - 1) + 8$

46. $9x + 10 = 5(4x - 1) + 15$

47. $3(4x + 1) - 2x = 2(5x - 3)$

48. $5(-3 + 4x) = 4(2x + 4) + 12x$

Cumulative Review

49. Add. $\frac{3}{7} + 1\frac{5}{10}$

50. Subtract. $3\frac{1}{5} - 2\frac{1}{4}$

51. Multiply: $\left(-3\frac{1}{4}\right)\left(5\frac{1}{3}\right) =$

52. Divide. $5\frac{1}{2} \div 1\frac{1}{4}$

53. ***Falcon Population*** In 1975 there were 40 nesting pairs of the American peregrine falcon nesting in the United States and Canada. Between 1975 and 1985, the peregrine falcon population increased by 20 percent. Between 1985 and 2000, the population increased by 450 percent. How many pairs of peregrine falcons were thriving in 2000? (Source: U.S. Department of the Interior.)

54. ***Auditorium Seating*** The seating area of an auditorium is shaped like a trapezoid, with front and back sides parallel. The front of the auditorium measures 88 feet across, the back of the auditorium measures 150 feet across, and the auditorium is 200 feet from front to back. If each seat requires a space that is 2.5 feet wide by 3 feet deep, how many seats will the auditorium hold? (This will only be an approximation because of the angled side walls. Round off to the nearest whole number.)

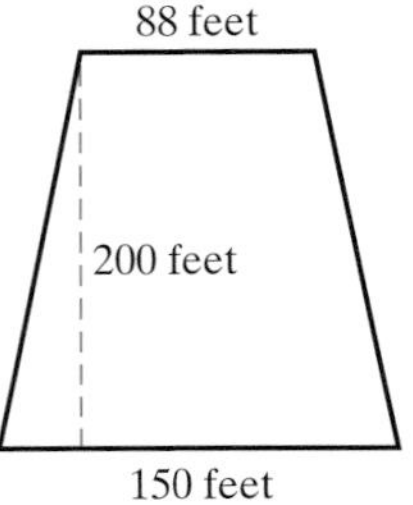

▲ 55. ***Vent Grill*** The Newbury Elementary School needs a new air vent drilled into the wall of the maintenance room. The circular hole that is necessary will have a radius of 6 inches. The stainless steel grill that will cover the vent costs \$2 per square inch. How much will the vent cost? Use $\pi \approx 3.14$.

▲ 56. ***Sail Material*** Tom Rourke needs to replace the sail on his sailboat. It is in the shape of a triangle with an altitude of 9 feet and a base of 8 feet. The material to make the sail costs \$3 per square foot. How much will the material cost to make a new sail for the boat?

How Am I Doing? Sections 2.1–2.4

How are you doing with your homework assignments in Sections 2.1 to 2.4? Do you feel you have mastered the material so far? Do you understand the concepts you have covered? Before you go further in the textbook, take some time to do each of the following problems.

Solve for x. If the solution is not an integer, you may express your answer as a fraction or as a decimal.

2.1

1. $5 - 8 + x = -12$

2. $3.6 + x = -7.3$

2.2

3. $-45 = -5x$

4. $12x - 6x = -48$

2.3

5. $-1.2x + 3.5 = 2.7$

6. $9x - 3 = -17x + 4$

7. $14x + 2(7 - 2x) = 20$

8. $0.5(1.2x - 3.4) = -1.4x + 5.8$

9. $3(x + 6) = -2(4x - 1) + x$

2.4

10. $\frac{x}{5} + \frac{x}{4} = \frac{2}{5}$

11. $\frac{1}{4}(x + 3) = 4x - 2(x - 3)$

12. $\frac{1}{2}(x - 1) + 2 = 3(2x - 1)$

13. $\frac{1}{7}(7x - 14) - 2 = \frac{1}{3}(x - 2)$

14. $0.2\,(x - 3) = 4\,(0.2x - 0.1)$

Now turn to page SA-6 for the answer to each of these problems. Each answer also includes a reference to the objective in which the problem is first taught. If you missed any of these problems, you should stop and review the Examples and Practice Problems in the referenced objective. A little review now will help you master the material in the upcoming sections of the text.

1. __________

2. __________

3. __________

4. __________

5. __________

6. __________

7. __________

8. __________

9. __________

10. __________

11. __________

12. __________

13. __________

14. __________

2.5 FORMULAS

Student Learning Objective

After studying this section, you will be able to:

 **Solve a formula for a specified variable.**

1 Solving a Formula for a Specified Variable

Formulas are equations with one or more variables that are used to describe real-life situations. The formula describes the relationship that exists among the variables. For example, in the formula $d = rt$, distance (d) is equal to the rate of speed (r) multiplied by the time (t). We can use this formula to find distance if we know the rate and time. Sometimes, however, we are given the distance and the rate, and we are asked to find the time.

EXAMPLE 1 American Airlines recently scheduled a non-stop flight in a new Boeing 777 jet from Chicago to London. The approximate air distance traveled on the flight was 3975 miles. The average speed of the aircraft on the trip was 530 miles per hour. How many hours did it take the Boeing 777 to fly this trip? (*Source:* www.aa.com)

Solution

$d = rt$ Use the distance formula.

$3975 = 530t$ Substitute the known values for the variables.

$\dfrac{3975}{530} = \dfrac{530t}{530}$ Divide both sides of the equation by 530 to solve for t.

$7.5 = t$ Simplify.

It took the Boeing 777 about 7.5 hours to fly this trip from Chicago to London.

NOTE TO STUDENT: Fully worked-out solutions to all of the Practice Problems can be found at the back of the text starting at page SP-1

Practice Problem 1 The airlines are planning a nonstop flight from Chicago to Prague. This distance is approximately 4565 miles and the time of the flight is 8.3 hours. Find the average rate of speed for the flight.

If we have many problems that ask us to find the time given the distance and rate, it may be worthwhile to rewrite the formula in terms of time.

EXAMPLE 2 Solve for t. $d = rt$

Solution

$\dfrac{d}{r} = \dfrac{rt}{r}$ We want to isolate t. Therefore we divide both sides of the equation by the coefficient of t, which is r.

$\dfrac{d}{r} = t$ We have solved for the variable indicated.

Practice Problem 2 Einstein's equation relating energy E to mass m and the speed of light c is $E = mc^2$. Solve it for m.

A straight line can be described by an equation of the form $Ax + By = C$ where A, B, and C are real numbers and A and B are not both zero. We will study this in later chapters. Often it is useful to solve such an equation for the variable y in order to make graphing the equation easier.

EXAMPLE 3 Solve for y. $3x - 2y = 6$

Solution

$-2y = 6 - 3x$ We want to isolate the term containing y, so we subtract $3x$ from both sides.

$\frac{-2y}{-2} = \frac{6 - 3x}{-2}$ Divide both sides by the coefficient of y.

$y = \frac{6}{-2} + \frac{-3x}{-2}$ Rewrite the fraction on the right side as two fractions.

$y = \frac{3}{2}x - 3$ Simplify and reorder the terms on the right.

This is known as the slope–intercept form of the equation of a line.

Practice Problem 3 Solve for y. $8 - 2y + 3x = 0$

Our procedure for solving an equation can be rewritten to give us a procedure for solving a formula for a specified variable.

PROCEDURE TO SOLVE A FORMULA FOR A SPECIFIED VARIABLE

1. Remove any parentheses.
2. If fractions exist, multiply all terms on both sides by the LCD of all the fractions.
3. Combine like terms on each side if possible.
4. Add or subtract terms on both sides of the equation to get all terms with the desired variable on one side of the equation.
5. Add or subtract the appropriate quantities to get all terms that do *not* have the desired variable on the other side of the equation.
6. Divide both sides of the equation by the coefficient of the desired variable.
7. Simplify if possible.

▲ **EXAMPLE 4** A trapezoid is a four-sided figure with two parallel sides. If the parallel sides are a and b and the altitude is h, the area is given by

$$A = \frac{h}{2}(a + b).$$

In some houses, two of the sides of the roof are in the shape of a trapezoid. Solve this equation for a.

Solution $A = \frac{h}{2}(a + b)$

$A = \frac{ha}{2} + \frac{hb}{2}$ Remove the parentheses.

$2(A) = 2\left(\frac{ha}{2}\right) + 2\left(\frac{hb}{2}\right)$ Multiply all terms by the LCD of 2.

$2A = ha + hb$ Simplify.

$$2A - hb = ha$$ We want to isolate the term containing a. Therefore, we subtract hb from both sides.

$$\frac{2A - hb}{h} = \frac{ha}{h}$$ Divide both sides by h (the coefficient of a).

$$\frac{2A - hb}{h} = a$$ The solution is obtained.

Note: Although the solution is in simple form, it could be written in an alternative way. Since

$$\frac{2A - hb}{h} = \frac{2A}{h} - \frac{hb}{h} = \frac{2A}{h} - b,$$

we could also have written $\frac{2A}{h} - b = a$.

NOTE TO STUDENT: Fully worked-out solutions to all of the Practice Problems can be found at the back of the text starting at page SP-1

Practice Problem 4 The relationship between the circumference C of a circle and the circle's diameter d is described by the equation $C = \pi d$. Solve it for d.

Developing Your Study Skills

Keep Trying

You may be one of those students who have had much difficulty with mathematics in the past and who are sure that you cannot do well in this course. Perhaps you are thinking, "I have never been any good at mathematics," or "I have always hated mathematics," or "Math always scares me," or "I have not had any math for so long that I have forgotten it all." You may have even picked up the label "math anxiety" and attached it to yourself. That is most unfortunate, and it is time for you to reprogram your thinking. Replace those negative thoughts with more positive ones. You need to say things like, "I will give this math class my best shot," or "I can learn mathematics if I work at it," or "I will try to do better than I have done in previous math classes." You will be pleasantly surprised at the difference a positive attitude makes!

We live in a highly technical world, and you cannot afford to give up on the study of mathematics. Dropping mathematics may prevent you from entering certain career fields that you may find interesting. You may not have to take math courses as high-level as calculus, but such courses as intermediate algebra, finite math, college algebra, and trigonometry may be necessary. Learning mathematics can open new doors for you.

Learning mathematics is a process that takes time and effort. You will find that regular study and daily practice are necessary to strengthen your skills and to help you to grow academically. This process will lead you toward success in mathematics. Then, as you become more successful, your confidence in your ability to do mathematics will grow.

2.5 Exercises

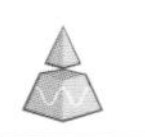

Student Solutions Manual | CD/ Video | PH Math Tutor Center | MathXL®Tutorials on CD | MathXL® | MyMathLab® | Interactmath.com

Verbal and Writing Skills

1. ***Temperature*** The formula for calculating the temperature in degrees Fahrenheit when you know the temperature in degrees Celsius is $F = \frac{9}{5}C + 32$. Explain in your own words how you would solve this equation for C.

▲ 2. ***Geometry*** The formula for finding the area of a trapezoid with an altitude of 9 meters and bases of b meters and c meters is given by the equation $A = \frac{9}{2}(b + c)$. Explain in your own words how you would solve this equation for b.

Applications

▲ 3. ***Geometry*** The formula for the area of a triangle is $A = \frac{1}{2}ab$, where b is the *base* of the triangle and a is the *altitude* of the triangle.

(a) Use this formula to find the base of a triangle that has an area of 60 square meters and an altitude of 12 meters.

(b) Use this formula to find the altitude of a triangle that has an area of 88 square meters and a base of 11 meters.

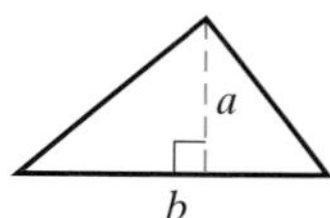

4. ***Simple Interest*** The formula for calculating simple interest is $I = Prt$, where P is the *principal* (amount of money invested), r is the *rate* at which the money is invested, and t is the *time.*

(a) Use this formula to find how long it would take to earn \$720 in interest on an investment of \$3000 at the rate of 6%.

(b) Use this formula to find the rate of interest if \$5000 earns \$400 interest in 2 years.

(c) Use this formula to find the amount of money invested if the interest earned was \$120 and the rate of interest was 5% over 3 years.

5. The equation $4x + 3y = 18$ describes a line and is written in standard form.

(a) Solve for the variable y.

(b) Use this result to find y with $x = -3$.

6. The equation $5y - 3x = 15$ describes a line and is written in standard form.

(a) Solve for the variable x.

(b) Use this result to find x with $y = -6$.

In each formula or equation, solve for the variable indicated.

Area of a triangle

▲ 7. $A = \frac{1}{2}bh$ Solve for b.

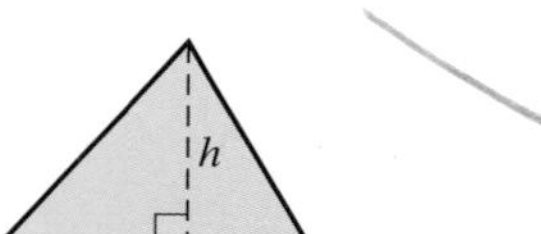

▲ 8. $A = \frac{1}{2}bh$ Solve for h.

Simple interest formula

9. $I = Prt$ Solve for P.

10. $I = Prt$ Solve for r.

Slope–intercept form of a line

11. $y = mx + b$ Solve for m.

12. $y = mx + b$ Solve for b.

Standard form of a line

13. $8x - 12y = 24$. Solve for y.

14. $3y - 5x = 9$. Solve for y.

Slope–intercept form of a line

15. $y = -\frac{2}{3}x + 4$. Solve for x.

16. $y = \frac{3}{8}x - 9$. Solve for x.

Standard form of a line

17. $ax + by = c$ Solve for y.

18. $ax + by = c$ Solve for x.

Area of a circle

▲ **19.** $A = \pi r^2$ Solve for r^2.

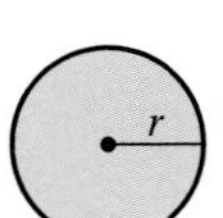

Surface area of a sphere

▲ **20.** $s = 4\pi r^2$ Solve for r^2.

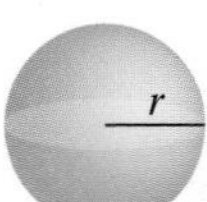

Distance of a falling object

21. $S = \frac{1}{2}gt^2$ Solve for g.

22. $S = \frac{1}{2}gt^2$ Solve for t^2.

Simple interest formula

23. $A = P(1 + rt)$ Solve for t.

Area of a trapezoid

▲ **24.** $A = \frac{1}{2}a(b_1 + b_2)$ Solve for b_1.

Surface area of a right circular cylinder

▲ **25.** $S = 2\pi rh + 2\pi r^2$ Solve for h.

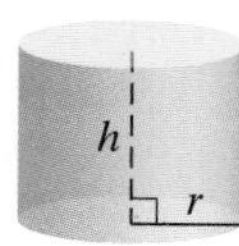

26. $H = 5as + 10a^2$ Solve for s.

Volume of a right circular cylinder

▲ **27.** $V = \pi r^2 h$ Solve for h.

▲ **28.** $V = \pi r^2 h$ Solve for r^2.

Volume of a rectangular prism

▲ **29.** $V = LWH$ Solve for L.

▲ **30.** $V = LWH$ Solve for H.

Volume of a cone

▲ **31.** $V = \frac{1}{3}\pi r^2 h$ Solve for r^2.

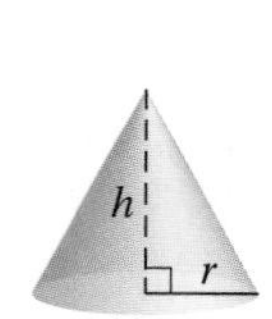

▲ **32.** $V = \frac{1}{3}\pi r^2 h$ Solve for h.

Perimeter of a rectangle

▲ **33.** $P = 2L + 2W$ Solve for W.

Finding the nth term of an arithmetic sequence

34. $N = F + d(n - 1)$. Solve for n.

Pythagorean theorem

▲ **35.** $c^2 = a^2 + b^2$ Solve for a^2.

▲ **36.** $c^2 = a^2 + b^2$ Solve for b^2.

Temperature conversion formulas

37. $F = \frac{9}{5}C + 32$ Solve for C.

38. $C = \frac{5}{9}(F - 32)$ Solve for F.

Ohm's law

39. $P = \dfrac{E^2}{R}$. Solve for R.

Density formula (density, mass, and volume)

40. $d = \dfrac{m}{v}$. Solve for v.

Area of a sector of a circle

▲ **41.** $A = \dfrac{\pi r^2 S}{360}$ Solve for S.

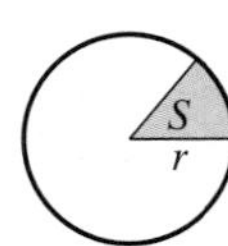

▲ **42.** $A = \dfrac{\pi r^2 S}{360}$ Solve for r^2.

Applications

▲ **43.** ***Geometry*** Use the result you obtained in exercise 33 to solve the following problem. A farmer has a rectangular field with a perimeter of 5.8 miles and a length of 2.1 miles. Find the width of the field.

44. Use the result you obtained in exercise 34 to solve the following problem. If you are given an arithmetic sequence where the first term (F) is 6, the difference (d) is 3, and nth term (N) is 24, what number term (n) is it?

▲ **45.** ***Geometry*** Use the result you obtained in exercise 29 to solve the following problem. The foundation of a house is in the shape of a rectangular solid. The volume held by the foundation is 5940 cubic feet. The height of the foundation is 9 feet and the width is 22 feet. What is the length of the foundation?

▲ **46.** ***Geometry*** Use the result you obtained in exercise 30 to solve the following problem. The fish tank at the Mandarin Danvers Restaurant is in the shape of a rectangular solid. The volume held by the tank is 3024 cubic inches. The length of the tank is 18 inches while the width of the tank is 14 inches. What is the height of the tank?

47. ***Tourism*** The number of foreign visitors measured in thousands (V) admitted to the United States for a pleasure trip for any given year can be predicted by the equation $V = 1100x + 7050$, where x is the number of years since 1985. For example, if $x = 20$ (this would be the year 2005), the predicted number of visitors in thousands would be $1100(20) + 7050 = 29{,}050$. Thus we would predict that in 2005, a total of 29,050,000 visitors came to the United States for a pleasure trip. (Source: U.S. Immigration and Naturalization Service.)

(a) Solve this equation for x.

(b) Use the result of your answer in (a) to find the year in which the number of visitors will be predicted to be 25,750,000. (*Hint:* Let $V = 25{,}750$ in your answer for (a).)

48. ***Tourism*** The number of foreign visitors from Europe measured in thousands (E) admitted to the United States from Europe for a pleasure trip for any given year can be predicted by the equation $E = 480x + 2400$, where x is the number of years since 1985. For example, if $x = 25$ (this would be the year 2010), the predicted number of visitors in thousands would be $480(25) + 2400 = 14{,}400$. Thus we would predict that in 2010, a total of 14,400,000 visitors from Europe came to the United States for a pleasure trip. (*Source:* U.S. Immigration and Naturalization Service.)

(a) Solve this equation for x.

(b) Use the result of your answer in (a) to find the year in which the number of visitors from Europe will be predicted to be 11,520,000. (*Hint:* Let $E = 11{,}520$ in your answer for (a).)

To Think About

▲ **49.** In the formula $A = \frac{1}{2}ab$, if b doubles, what is the effect on A?

▲ **50.** In the formula $A = \frac{1}{2}ab$, if both a and b double, what is the effect on A?

▲ **51.** In $A = \pi r^2$, if r doubles, what is the effect on A?

▲ **52.** In $A = \pi r^2$, if r is halved, what is the effect on A?

Cumulative Review

53. Find 12% of 260.

54. What is 0.2% of 48?

55. ***Corral Fencing*** Greg Boyd recently replaced 500 feet of corral fencing. He estimated that he replaced 40% of the total amount of fencing aroung the corral. How much fencing was around the corral?

56. ***Stereo Defects*** A major auto company received a shipment of car stereos. Four stereos out of 160 are defective. What percent of the shipment is defective?

57. ***Electronic Games*** A very popular handheld electronic game requires $3\frac{1}{4}$ square feet of a certain type of durable plastic in the manufacturing process. How many square feet of durable plastic does this company need to make 12,000 handheld games?

58. ***Spotlight Rental*** The Superstar Lighting Company rents out giant spotlights that shine up in the sky to mark the location of special events, such as the opening of a movie, a major sports play-off game, or a huge sales event at an auto dealership. A giant spotlight was used for $4\frac{1}{3}$ hours on Saturday, $2\frac{3}{4}$ hours on Tuesday, and $3\frac{1}{2}$ hours on Wednesday. What was the total number of hours that the spotlight was in use?

2.6 Writing and Graphing Inequalities

Student Learning Objectives

After studying this section, you will be able to:

1. **Interpret inequality statements.**
2. **Graph an inequality on a number line.**
3. **Translate English phrases into algebraic statements**

1 Interpreting Inequality Statements

We frequently speak of one value being greater than or less than another value. We say that "5 is less than 7" or "9 is greater than 4." These relationships are called **inequalities.** We can write inequalities in mathematics by using symbols. We use the symbol $<$ to represent the words "**is less than.**" We use the symbol $>$ to represent the words "**is greater than.**"

Statement in Words	Statement in Algebra
5 is less than 7.	$5 < 7$
9 is greater than 4.	$9 > 4$

Note: "5 is less than 7" and "7 is greater than 5" have the same meaning. Similarly, $5 < 7$ and $7 > 5$ have the same meaning. They represent two equivalent ways of describing the same relationship between the two numbers 5 and 7.

We can better understand the concept of inequality if we examine a number line.

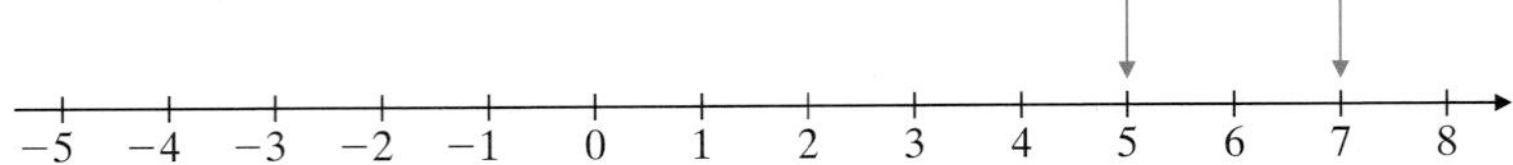

We say that one number is greater than another if it is to the right of the other on the number line. Thus $7 > 5$, since 7 is to the right of 5.

What about negative numbers? We can say "-1 is greater than -3" and write it in symbols as $-1 > -3$ because we know that -1 lies to the right of -3 on the number line.

EXAMPLE 1 In each statement, replace the question mark with the symbol $<$ or $>$.

(a) $3 ? -1$ **(b)** $-2 ? 1$ **(c)** $-3 ? -4$ **(d)** $0 ? 3$ **(e)** $-3 ? 0$

Solution

(a) $3 > -1$ Use $>$, since 3 is to the right of -1 on the number line.

(b) $-2 < 1$ Use $<$, since -2 is to the left of 1. (Or equivalently, we could say that 1 is to the right of -2.)

(c) $-3 > -4$ Note that -3 is to the right of -4.

(d) $0 < 3$

(e) $-3 < 0$

***NOTE TO STUDENT:** Fully worked-out solutions to all of the Practice Problems can be found at the back of the text starting at page SP-1*

Practice Problem 1 In each statement, replace the question mark with the symbol $<$ or $>$.

(a) $7 ? 2$ **(b)** $-3 ? -4$ **(c)** $-1 ? 2$ **(d)** $-8 ? -5$ **(e)** $0 ? -2$ **(f)** $\frac{2}{5} ? \frac{3}{8}$

2 Graphing an Inequality on a Number Line

Sometimes we will use an inequality to express the relationship between a variable and a number. $x > 3$ means that x could have the value of *any number* greater than 3.

Any number that makes an inequality true is called a **solution** of the inequality. The set of all numbers that make the inequality true is called the **solution set.** A picture that represents all of the solutions of an inequality is called a **graph** of the inequality. The inequality $x > 3$ can be graphed on the number line as follows:

Case 1

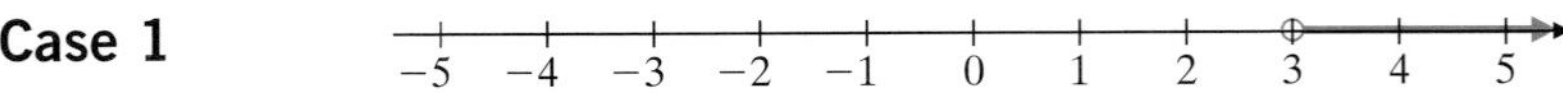

Note that all of the points to the right of 3 are shaded. The open circle at 3 indicates that we do not include the point for the number 3.

Similarly, we can graph $x < -2$ as follows:

Case 2

Note that all of the points to the left of -2 are shaded.

Sometimes a variable will be either greater than or equal to a certain number. In the statement "x is greater than or equal to 3," we are implying that x could have the value of 3 or any number greater than 3. We write this as $x \geq 3$. We graph it as follows:

Case 3

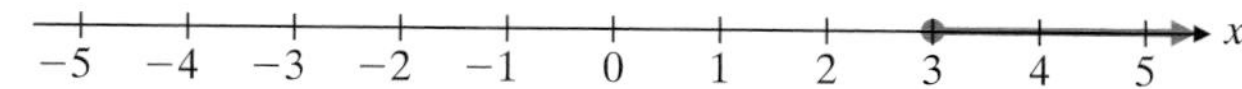

Note that the closed circle at 3 indicates that we *do* include the point for the number 3.

Similarly, we can graph $x \leq -2$ as follows:

Case 4

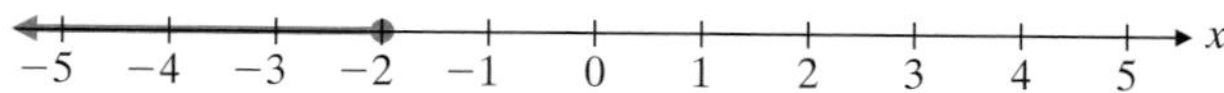

Note: Be careful you do not confuse ○⟶ with ●⟶. It is important to decide if you need an open circle or a closed one. Case 1 and Case 2 use open circles. Case 3 and Case 4 use closed circles.

EXAMPLE 2 State each mathematical relationship in words and then graph it.

(a) $x < -2$ **(b)** $-3 < x$ **(c)** $x \geq -2$ **(d)** $x \leq -6$

Solution

(a) We state that "x is less than -2."

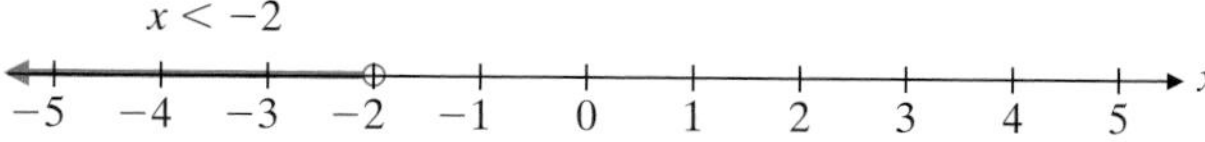

(b) We can state that "-3 is less than x" or, equivalently, that "x is greater than -3." Be sure you see that $-3 < x$ is equivalent to $x > -3$. Although both statements are correct, we *usually write the variable first* in a simple inequality containing a variable and a numerical value.

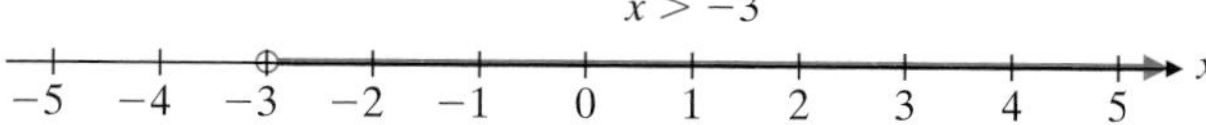

(c) We state that "x is greater than or equal to -2."

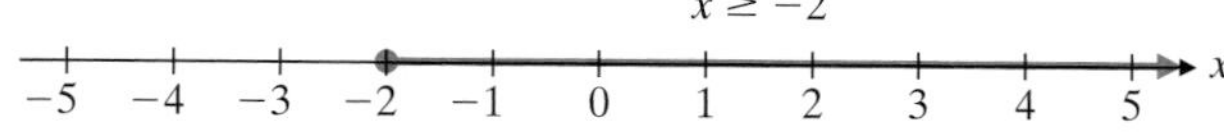

(d) We state that "x is less than or equal to -6."

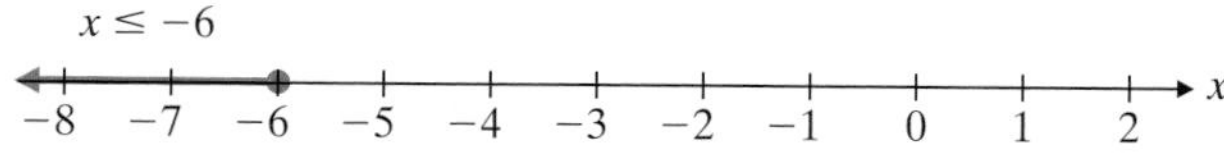

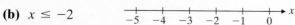

Practice Problem 2 State each mathematical relationship in words and then graph it on a number line in the margin.

(a) $x > 5$

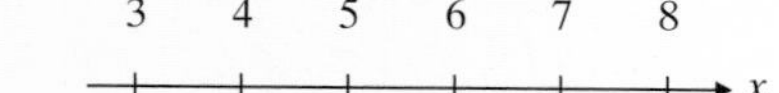

(b) $x \leq -2$

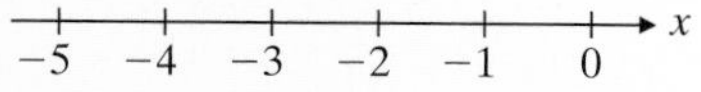

(c) $3 > x$

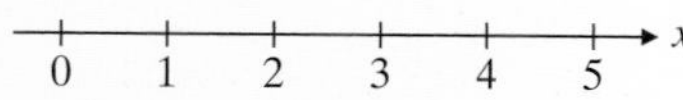

(d) $x \geq -\frac{3}{2}$

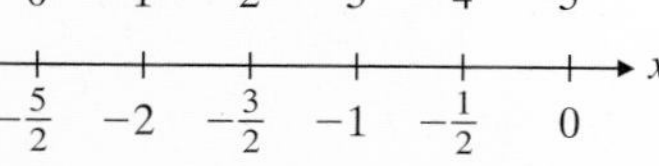

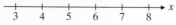

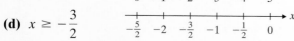

Translating English Phrases into Algebraic Statements

We can translate many everyday situations into algebraic statements with an unknown value and an inequality symbol. This is the first step in solving word problems using inequalities.

EXAMPLE 3 Translate each English statement into an algebraic statement.

(a) The police on the scene said that the car was traveling more than 80 miles per hour. (Use the variable s for speed.)

(b) The owner of the trucking company said that the payload of a truck must never exceed 4500 pounds. (Use the variable p for payload.)

Solution

(a) Since the speed must be greater than 80, we have $s > 80$.

(b) If the payload of the truck can never exceed 4500 pounds, then the payload must be always less than or equal to 4500 pounds. Thus we write $p \leq 4500$.

Practice Problem 3 Translate each English statement into an inequality.

(a) During the drying cycle, the temperature inside the clothes dryer must never exceed 180 degrees Fahrenheit. (Use the variable t for temperature.)

(b) The bank loan officer said that the total consumer debt incurred by Wally and Mary must be less than $15,000 if they want to qualify for a mortgage to buy their first home. (Use the variable d for debt.)

NOTE TO STUDENT: Fully worked-out solutions to all of the Practice Problems can be found at the back of the text starting at page SP-1

Developing Your Study Skills

Getting Organized for an Exam

Studying adequately for an exam requires careful preparation. Begin early so that you will be able to spread your review over several days. Even though you may still be learning new material at this time, you can be reviewing concepts previously learned in the chapter. Giving yourself plenty of time for review will take the pressure off. You need this time to process what you have learned and to tie concepts together.

Adequate preparation enables you to feel confident and to think clearly with less tension and anxiety.

2.6 Exercises

Student Solutions Manual | CD/Video | PH Math Tutor Center | MathXL®Tutorials on CD | MathXL® | MyMathLab® | Interactmath.com

Verbal and Writing Skills

1. Is the statement $5 > -6$ equivalent to the statement $-6 < 5$? Why?

2. Is the statement $-8 < -3$ equivalent to the statement $-3 > -8$? Why?

Replace the ? by < or >.

3. $9 ? -3$

4. $-2 ? 5$

5. $-4 ? -2$

6. $-3 ? -6$

7. $\frac{3}{5} ? \frac{4}{7}$

8. $\frac{4}{6} ? \frac{7}{9}$

9. $-4.2 ? 3.5$

10. $-2.6 ? 7.5$

11. $-\frac{13}{3} ? -4$

12. $-3 ? -\frac{15}{4}$

13. $-\frac{5}{8} ? -\frac{3}{5}$

14. $-\frac{2}{3} ? -\frac{3}{4}$

Which is greater?

15. $\frac{123}{4986}$ or 0.0247?

16. $\frac{997}{6384}$ or 0.15613?

Graph each inequality on the number line.

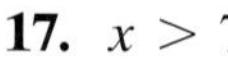

17. $x > 7$

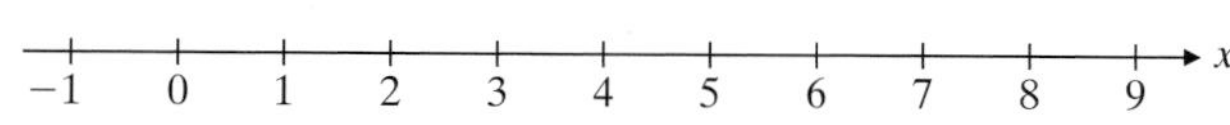

18. $x < 1$

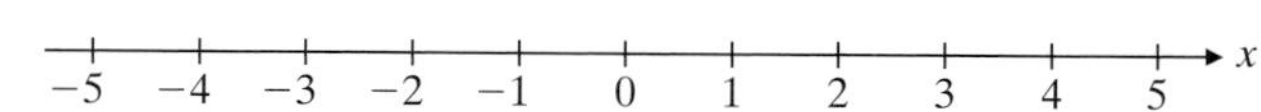

19. $x \geq -6$

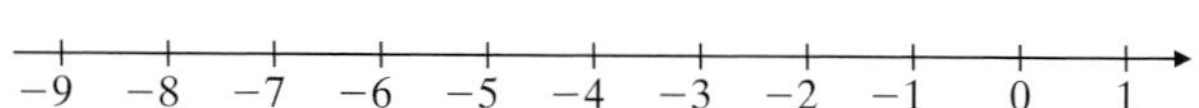

20. $x \leq -2$

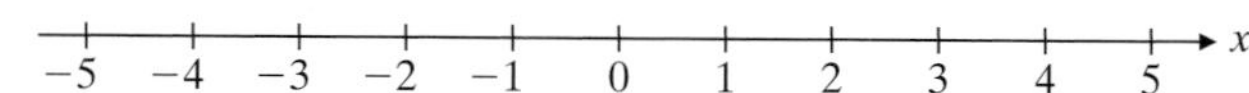

21. $x > \frac{3}{4}$

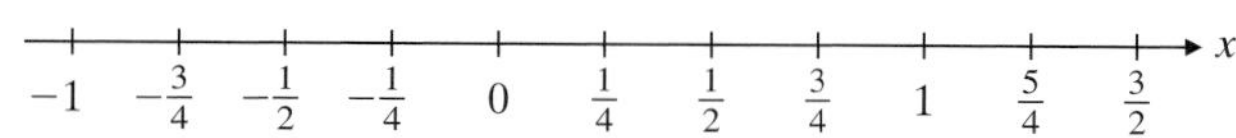

22. $x \geq -\frac{5}{2}$

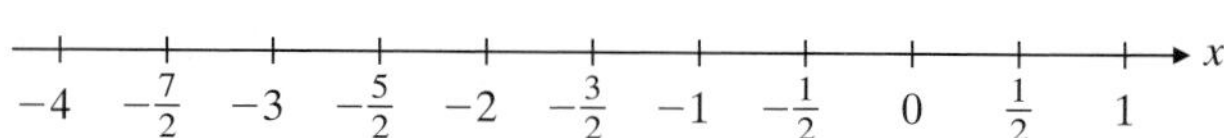

23. $x \leq -5.3$

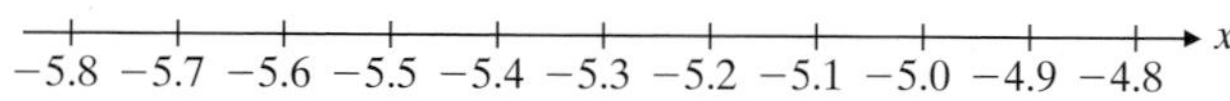

24. $x > -3.5$

−4.1 −4.0 −3.9 −3.8 −3.7 −3.6 −3.5 −3.4 −3.3 −3.2 −3.1 x

25. $25 < x$

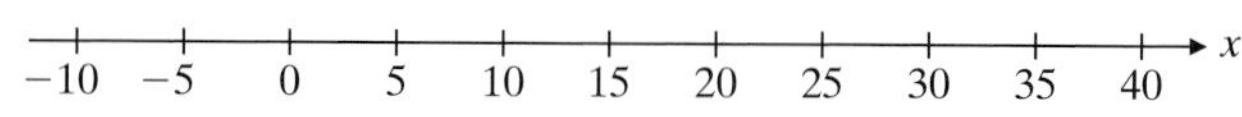

26. $35 \geq x$

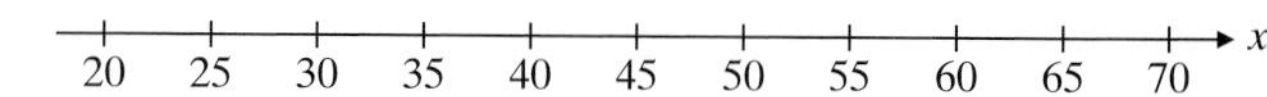

Translate each graph to an inequality using the variable x.

27.

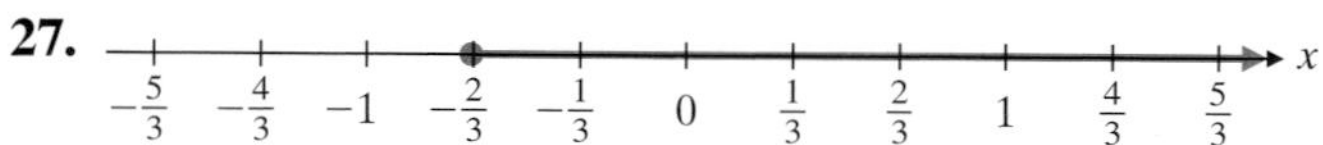

28.

−5 −4.5 −4 −3.5 −3 −2.5 −2 −1.5 −1 −0.5 0 x

29. −25 −24 −23 −22 −21 −20 −19 −18 −17 −16 −15 x

30.

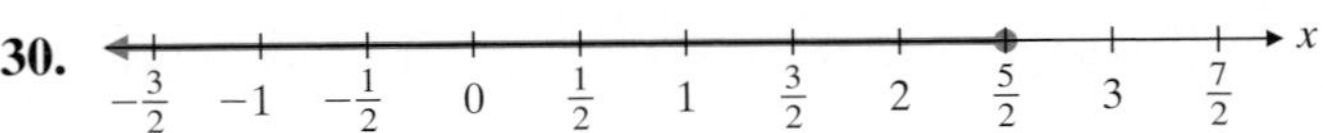

31. 2.2 2.3 2.4 2.5 2.6 2.7 2.8 2.9 3.0 3.1 3.2 x

32.

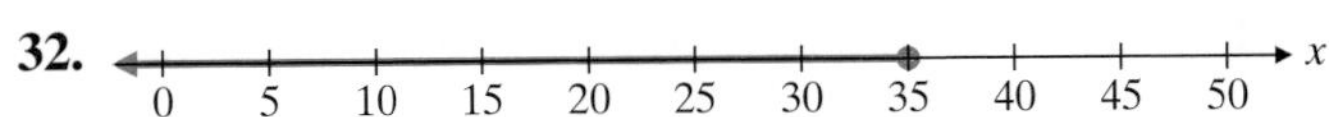

Translate each English statement into an inequality.

33. ***Weight Category*** To box in the heavyweight category, your weight must be greater than 175 pounds. (Use the variable W for weight.)

34. ***Cloud Formation*** Cirrus clouds form more than 16,500 feet above the earth's surface. (Use the variable C for distance above the earth.)

35. ***Full-Time Work*** The number of hours for a full-time position at this company cannot be less than 37 in order to receive full-time benefits. (Use the variable h for hours.)

36. ***Nurses on Duty*** The number of nurses on duty on the floor can never exceed 6. (Use the variable n for the number of nurses.)

37. ***Height Limit*** In order for you to be allowed to ride the roller coaster at the theme park, your height must be at least 48 inches. (Use h for height.)

38. ***College Credits*** In order for you to avoid paying extra tuition for a semester, the number of credits you are taking must not exceed 18. (Use C for credits.)

To Think About

39. Suppose that the variable x must satisfy *all* of these conditions.

$$x \le 2, \quad x > -3, \quad x < \frac{5}{2}, \quad x \ge -\frac{5}{2}$$

Graph on a number line the region that satisfies all of the conditions.

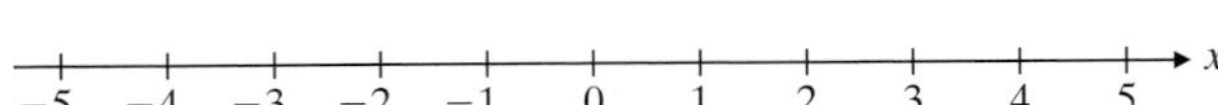

40. Suppose that the variable x must satisfy *all* of these conditions.

$$x < 4, \quad x > -4, \quad x \le \frac{7}{2}, \quad x \ge -\frac{9}{2}$$

Graph on a number line the region that satisfies all of the conditions.

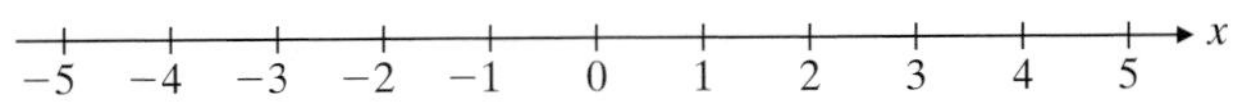

Cumulative Review

41. Find 16% of 38.

42. 18 is what percent of 120?

43. ***Percent Accepted*** For the most coveted graduate study positions, only 16 out of 800 students are accepted. What percent are accepted?

44. Write the fraction $\frac{3}{8}$ as a percent.

45. ***Dry Cleaning*** The Apex Dry Cleaners raised the cost of dry cleaning a sports coat from \$8 to \$10. If the same percent of increase applies to all other dry cleaning also, what will the new price for dry cleaning a men's suit be if the old price was \$12?

46. ***Radar Picture*** A radar picture is taken of a portion of the Amazon rain forest. The radar detects that a cliff is 414 feet above sea level and that a giant tree trunk is directly below it in a body of water. The tree trunk is 81 feet below sea level. How far is the top of the cliff from the tree trunk?

2.7 Solving Inequalities

 Solving and Graphing Inequalities on a Number Line

As stated in Section 2.6, the possible values that make an inequality true are called its **solutions.** Thus, when we **solve an inequality,** we are finding *all* the values that make it true. To solve an inequality, we simplify it to the point where we can clearly see all possible values for the variable. We've solved equations by adding, subtracting, multiplying by, and dividing by a particular value on both sides of the equation. Here we perform similar operations with inequalities with one important exception. We'll show some examples so that you can see how these operations can be used with inequalities just as with equations.

We will first examine the pattern that occurs when we perform these operations *with a positive value* on both sides of an inequality.

Student Learning Objective

After studying this section, you will be able to:

 **Solve and graph inequalities on a number line.**

EXAMPLE 1

Original Inequality	Operations with a Positive Number	New Inequality
$4 < 6$	Add 2 to both sides.	$6 < 8$
	Subtract 2 from both sides.	$2 < 4$
	Multiply both sides by 2.	$8 < 12$
	Divide both sides by 2.	$2 < 3$

Notice that the inequality symbol remains the same when these operations are performed.

Practice Problem 1 Perform the given operation and write a new inequality.

(a) $9 > 6$ Add 4 to each side.
(b) $-2 < 5$ Subtract 3 from both sides.
(c) $1 > -3$ Multiply both sides by 2.
(d) $10 < 15$ Divide both sides by 5.

NOTE TO STUDENT: Fully worked-out solutions to all of the Practice Problems can be found at the back of the text starting at page SP-1

Now let us examine what happens when we perform these operations *with a negative value.*

Original Inequality	Operations with a Negative Number	New Inequality
$4 < 6$	Add -2 to both sides.	$2 < 4$
	Subtract -2 from both sides.	$6 < 8$
	Multiply both sides by -2.	$-8 ? -12$
	Divide both sides by -2.	$-2 ? -3$

What happens to the inequality sign when we multiply both sides by a negative number? Since -8 is to the right of -12 on the number line, we know that the new inequality should be $-8 > -12$ if we want the statement to remain true. Notice how we reverse the direction of the inequality from $<$ (less than) to $>$ (greater than). Thus we have the following.

$$4 < 6 \longrightarrow \text{Multiply both sides by } -2. \longrightarrow -8 > -12$$

The same thing happens when we divide by a negative number. The inequality is reversed from $<$ to $>$. We know this since -2 is to the right of -3 on the number line.

$$4 < 6 \longrightarrow \text{Divide both sides by } -2. \longrightarrow -2 > -3$$

EXAMPLE 2

Original Inequality				New Inequality
(a) $-2 < -1$	$\longrightarrow$	Multiply both sides by -3.	$\longrightarrow$	$6 > 3$
(b) $0 > -4$	$\longrightarrow$	Divide both sides by -2.	$\longrightarrow$	$0 < 2$
(c) $8 \geq 4$	$\longrightarrow$	Divide both sides by -4.	$\longrightarrow$	$-2 \leq -1$

Notice that we perform the arithmetic with signed numbers just as we always do. But the new inequality signs reversed (from those of the original inequalities). *Whenever both sides of an inequality are multiplied or divided by a negative quantity, the direction of the inequality is reversed.*

NOTE TO STUDENT: Fully worked-out solutions to all of the Practice Problems can be found at the back of the text starting at page SP-1

Practice Problem 2

(a) $7 > 2$ Multiply each side by -2.
(b) $-3 < -1$ Multiply each side by -1.
(c) $-10 \geq -20$ Divide each side by -10.
(d) $-15 \leq -5$ Divide each side by -5.

PROCEDURE FOR SOLVING INEQUALITIES

You may use the same procedures to solve inequalities that you did to solve equations *except* that the direction of an inequality is *reversed* if you *multiply* or *divide* both sides *by a negative number.*

It may be helpful to think over quickly what we have discussed here. The inequalities remain the same when we add a number to both sides or subtract a number from both sides of the equation. The inequalities remain the same when we multiply both sides by a positive number or divide both sides by a positive number.

RULES WHEN INEQUALITIES REMAIN THE SAME

For all real numbers a, b, and c:

1. If $a > b$, then $a + c > b + c$.
2. If $a > b$, then $a - c > b - c$.
3. If $a > b$ and c is a **positive number** $(c > 0)$, then $ac > bc$.
4. If $a > b$ and c is a **positive number** $(c > 0)$, then $\frac{a}{c} > \frac{b}{c}$.

If we multiply both sides of an inequality by a negative number or if we divide both sides of an inequality by a negative number, then the inequality is reversed.

RULES WHEN INEQUALITIES ARE REVERSED

For all real numbers a, b, and c:

1. If $a > b$, and c is a **negative number** $(c < 0)$, then $ac < bc$.
2. If $a > b$, and c is a **negative number** $(c < 0)$, then $\frac{a}{c} < \frac{b}{c}$.

The pattern is fairly simple. We could also make similar rule boxes for the cases where $a \geq b$, $a < b$, and $a \leq b$, but they are really not necessary. We simply remember that the inequality is reversed when we multiply or divide by a negative number. Otherwise the inequality remains unchanged.

EXAMPLE 3 Solve and graph $3x + 7 \geq 13$.

Solution

$3x + 7 - 7 \geq 13 - 7$ Subtract 7 from both sides.

$3x \geq 6$ Simplify.

$\dfrac{3x}{3} \geq \dfrac{6}{3}$ Divide both sides by 3.

$x \geq 2$ Simplify. Note that the direction of the inequality is not changed, since we have divided by a positive number.

The graph is as follows:

Practice Problem 3 Solve and graph $8x - 2 < 3$.

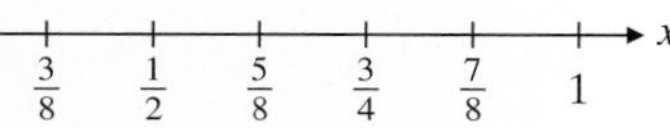

EXAMPLE 4 Solve and graph $5 - 3x > 7$.

Solution

$5 - 5 - 3x > 7 - 5$ Subtract 5 from both sides.

$-3x > 2$ Simplify.

$\dfrac{-3x}{-3} < \dfrac{2}{-3}$ Divide by -3 and **reverse the inequality** since you are dividing by a negative number.

$x < -\dfrac{2}{3}$ Note the direction of the inequality.

The graph is as follows:

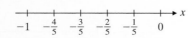

Practice Problem 4 Solve and graph $4 - 5x > 7$.

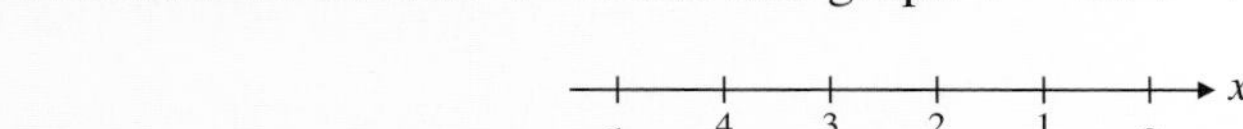

Just like equations, some inequalities contain parentheses and fractions. The initial steps to solve these inequalities will be the same as those used to solve equations with parentheses and fractions. When the variable appears on both sides of the inequality, it is advisable to collect the x-terms on the left side of the inequality symbol.

EXAMPLE 5 Solve and graph $-\dfrac{13x}{2} \leq \dfrac{x}{2} - \dfrac{15}{8}$.

Solution

$8\left(\dfrac{-13x}{2}\right) \leq 8\left(\dfrac{x}{2}\right) - 8\left(\dfrac{15}{8}\right)$ Multiply all terms by LCD $= 8$. We do **not** reverse the direction of the inequality symbol since we are multiplying by a positive number.

$-52x \leq 4x - 15$ Simplify.

$-52x - 4x \leq 4x - 15 - 4x$ Subtract $4x$ from both sides.

$-56x \leq -15$ Combine like terms.

$$\frac{-56x}{-56} \geq \frac{-15}{-56}$$

Divide both sides by -56. We **reverse** the direction of the inequality when we divide both sides by a negative number.

$$x \geq \frac{15}{56}$$

The graph is as follows:

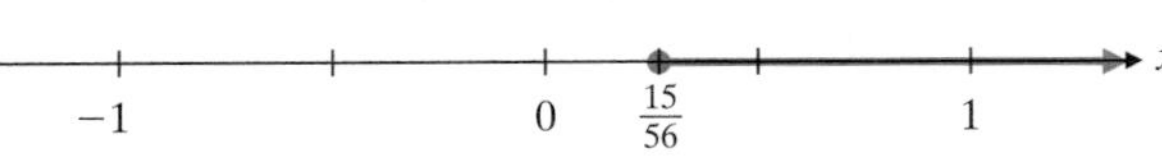

Practice Problem 5 Solve and graph $\frac{1}{2}x + 3 < \frac{2}{3}x$.

16 17 18 19 20 21 x

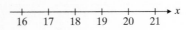

NOTE TO STUDENT: Fully worked-out solutions to all of the Practice Problems can be found at the back of the text starting at page SP-1

EXAMPLE 6 Solve and graph $\frac{1}{3}(3 - 2x) \leq -4(x + 1)$.

Solution

$1 - \frac{2x}{3} \leq -4x - 4$ Remove parentheses.

$3(1) - 3\left(\frac{2x}{3}\right) \leq 3(-4x) - 3(4)$ Multiply all terms by LCD = 3.

$3 - 2x \leq -12x - 12$ Simplify.

$3 - 2x + 12x \leq -12x + 12x - 12$ Add $12x$ to both sides.

$3 + 10x \leq -12$ Combine like terms.

$3 - 3 + 10x \leq -12 - 3$ Subtract 3 from both sides.

$10x \leq -15$ Simplify.

$$\frac{10x}{10} \leq \frac{-15}{10}$$

Divide both sides by 10. Since we are dividing by a **positive** number, the inequality is **not** reversed.

$$x \leq -\frac{3}{2}$$

The graph is as follows:

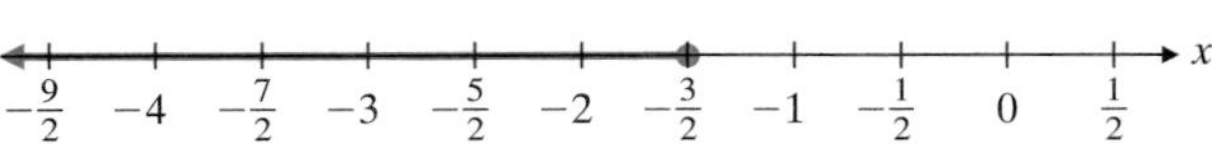

Practice Problem 6 Solve and graph $\frac{1}{2}(3 - x) \leq 2x + 5$.

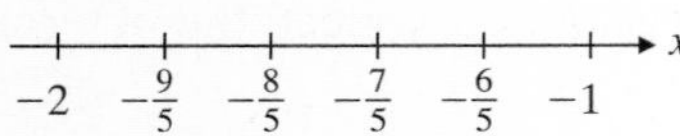

CAUTION The most common error students make in solving inequalities is forgetting to reverse the direction of the inequality symbol when multiplying or dividing both sides of the inequality by a negative number.

Normally when solve inequalities you solve for x by putting the variables on the left side. If you solve by placing the variables on the right side, you will end up with statements like $3 > x$. This is equivalent to $x < 3$. It is wise to express your answer with the variable on the left side.

EXAMPLE 7 A hospital director has determined that the costs of operating one floor of the hospital for an eight-hour shift must never exceed \$2370. An expression for the cost of operating one floor of the hospital is $130n + 1200$, where n is the number of nurses. This expression is based on an estimate of \$1200 in fixed costs and a cost of \$130 per nurse for an eight-hour shift. Solve the inequality $130n + 1200 \leq 2370$ to determine the number of nurses that may be on duty on this floor during an eight-hour shift if the director's cost control measure is to be followed.

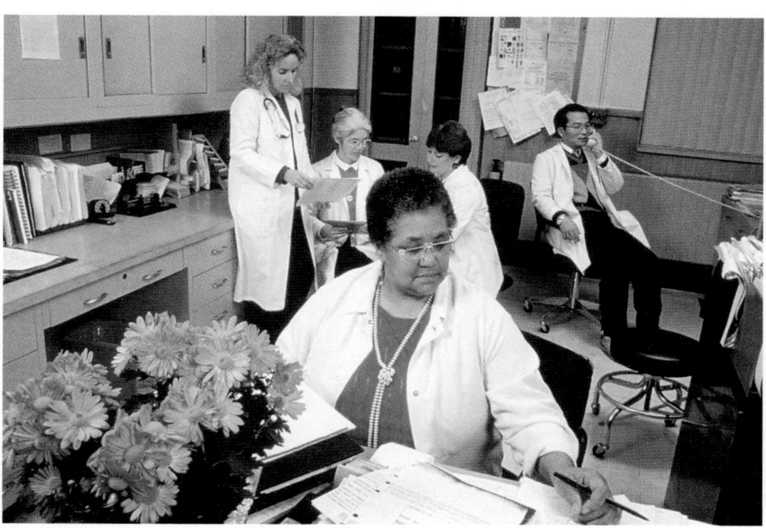

Solution

$$130n + 1200 \leq 2370 \qquad \text{The inequality we must solve.}$$

$$130n + 1200 - 1200 \leq 2370 - 1200 \qquad \text{Subtract 1200 from each side.}$$

$$130n \leq 1170 \qquad \text{Simplify.}$$

$$\frac{130n}{130} \leq \frac{1170}{130} \qquad \text{Divide each side by 130.}$$

$$n \leq 9$$

The number of nurses on duty on this floor during an eight-hour shift must always be less than or equal to nine.

Practice Problem 7 The company president of Staywell, Inc., wants the monthly profits never to be less than \$2,500,000. He has determined that an expression for monthly profit for the company is $2000n - 700{,}000$. In the expression, n is the number of exercise machines manufactured each month. The profit on each machine is \$2000, and the $-\$700{,}000$ in the expression represents the fixed costs of running the manufacturing division.

Solve the inequality $2000n - 700{,}000 \geq 2{,}500{,}000$ to find how many machines must be made and sold each month to satisfy these financial goals.

2.7 Exercises

Student Solutions Manual

CD/ Video

PH Math Tutor Center

MathXL®Tutorials on CD
MathXL®

MyMathLab®

Interactmath.com

Solve and graph the result.

1. $x + 7 \leq 4$

−5 −4 −3 −2 −1 0 1 2 3 4 5 x

2. $x - 5 < -3$

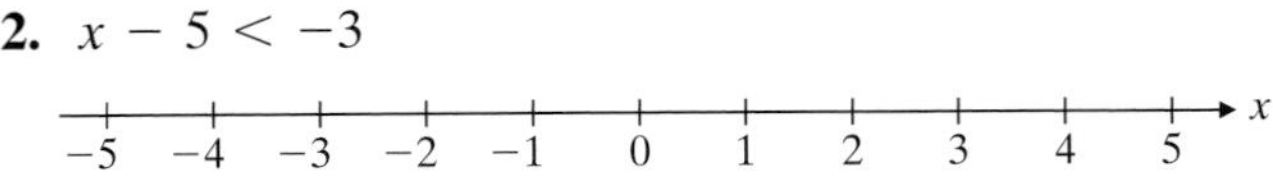

3. $5x \leq 25$

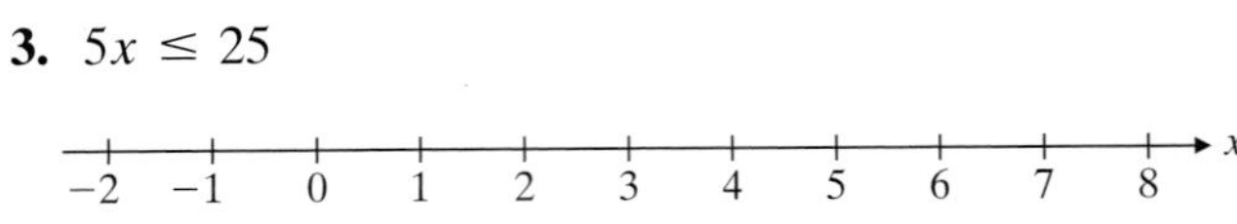

4. $7x \geq -35$

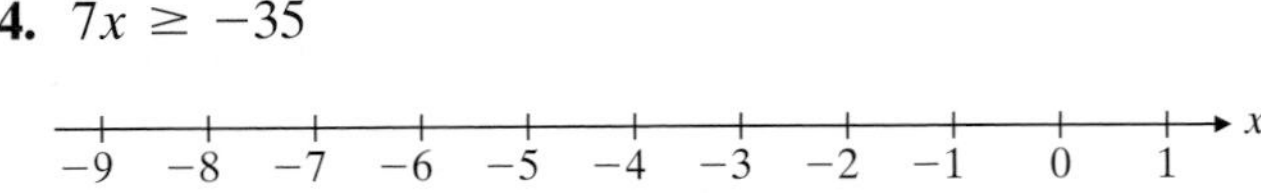

5. $-2x < 18$

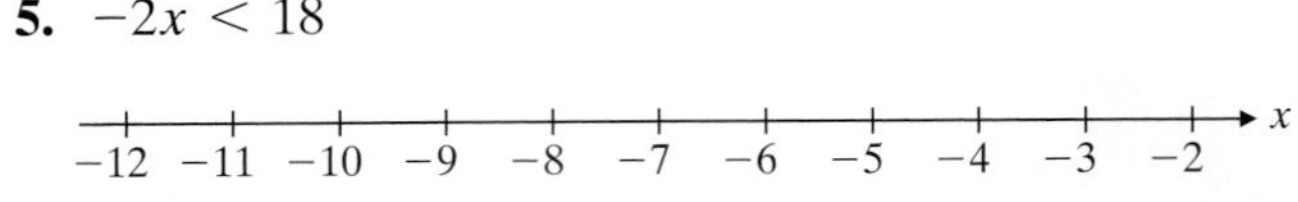

6. $-6x > 24$

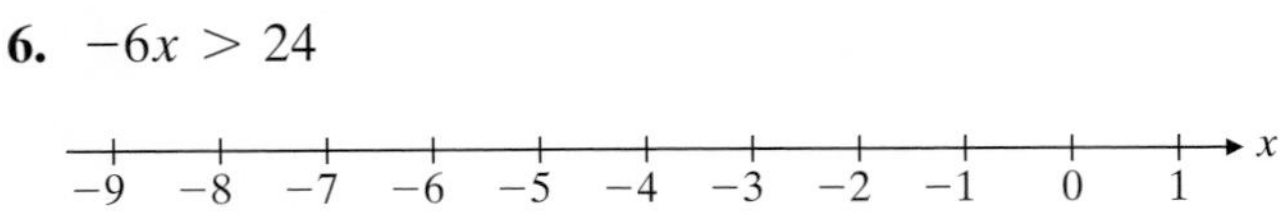

7. $\frac{1}{2}x \geq 4$

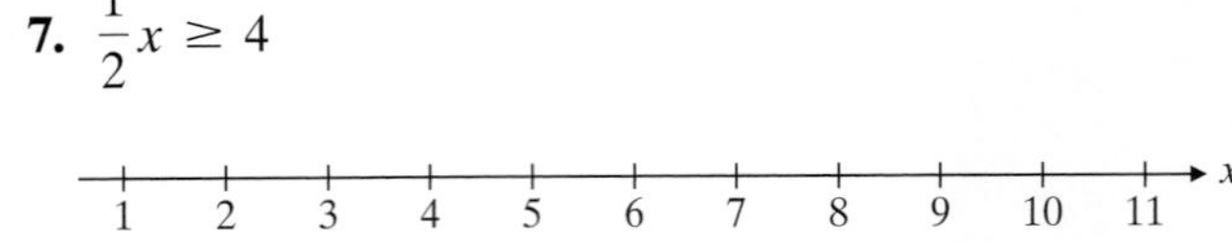

8. $\frac{1}{3}x \leq 2$

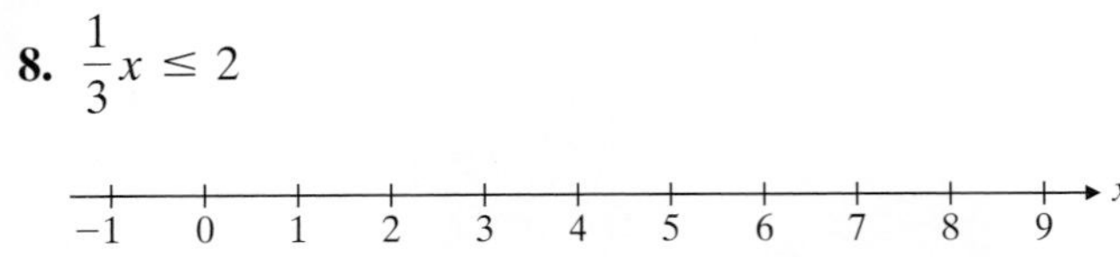

9. $-\frac{1}{4}x > 3$

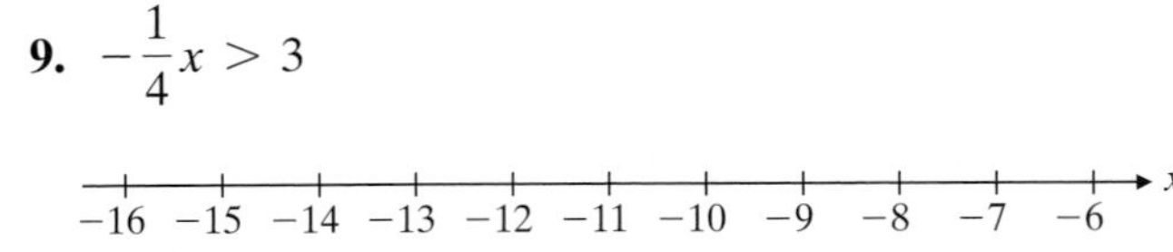

10. $-\frac{1}{5}x < 10$

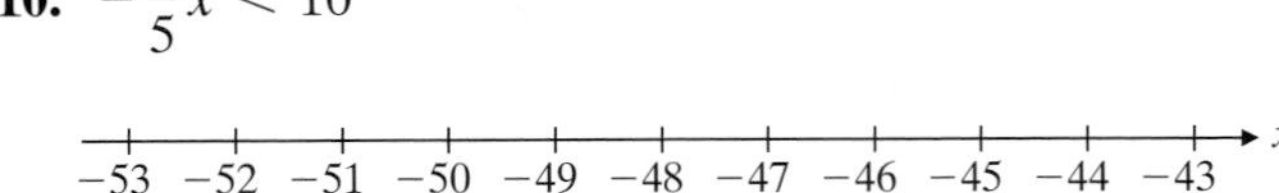

11. $2x - 3 < 4$

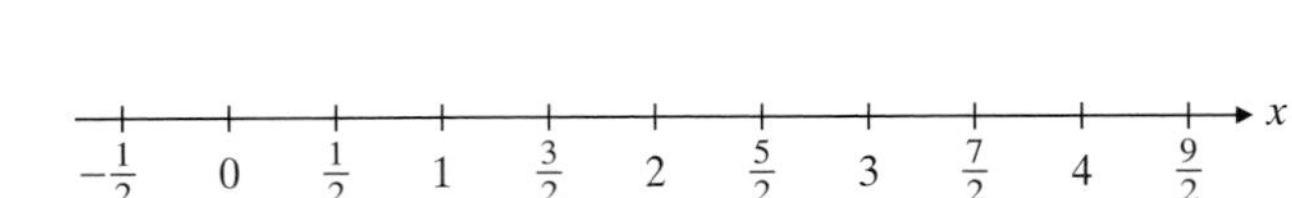

12. $4x - 6 \geq -8$

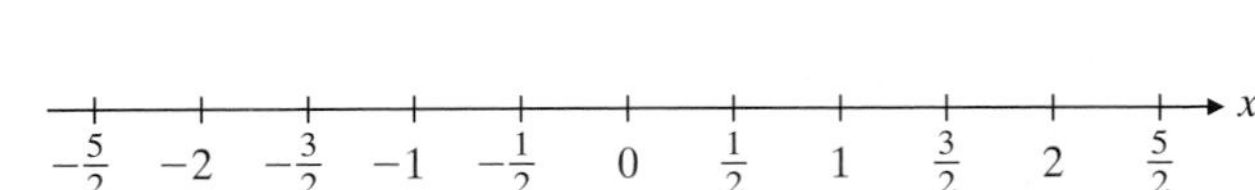

13. $5 - 2x \leq 9$

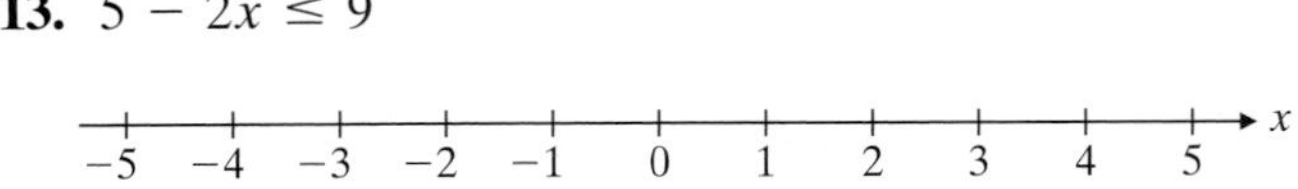

14. $3 - 3x > 12$

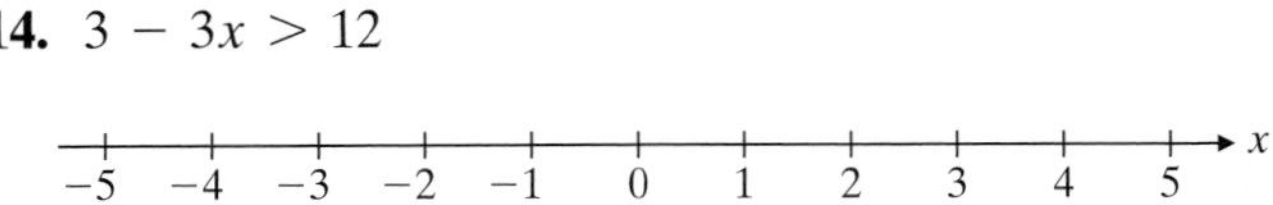

15. $-4 + 5x < -3x + 8$

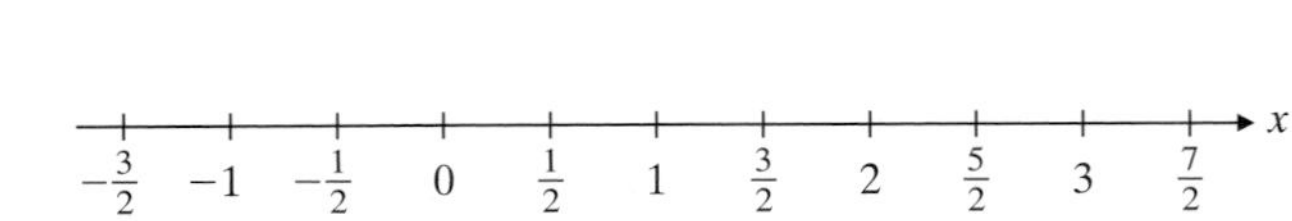

16. $-6 - 4x < 1 - 6x$

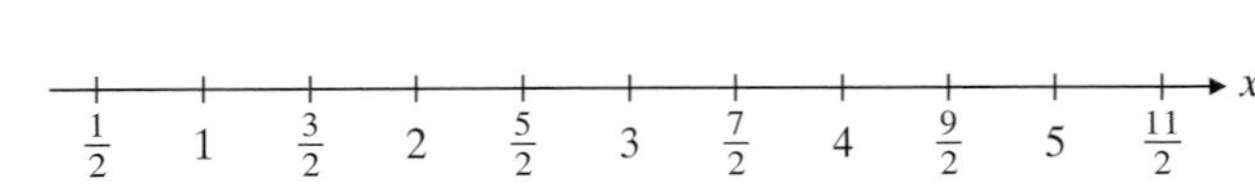

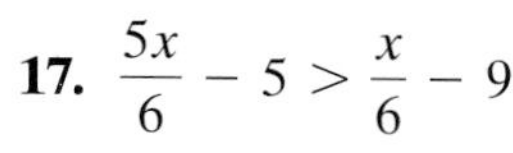

17. $\frac{5x}{6} - 5 > \frac{x}{6} - 9$

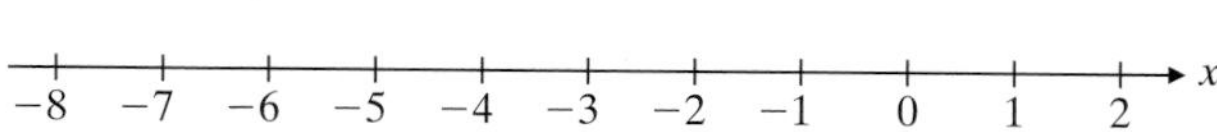

18. $\frac{x}{4} - 2 < \frac{3x}{4} + 5$

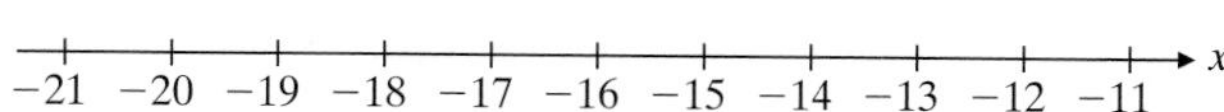

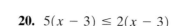

19. $2(3x + 4) > 3(x + 3)$

20. $5(x - 3) \leq 2(x - 3)$

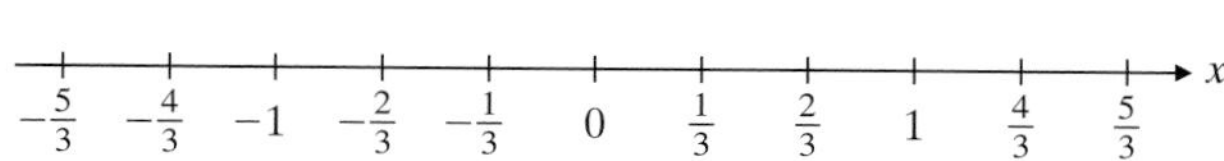

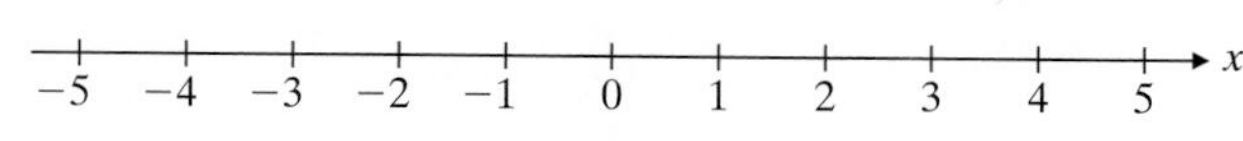

Verbal and Writing Skills

21. Add -2 to both sides of the inequality $5 > 3$. What is the result? Why is the direction of the inequality not reversed?

22. Divide -3 into both sides of the inequality $-21 > -29$. What is the result? Why is the direction of the inequality reversed?

Mixed Practice

Solve. Collect the variable terms on the left side of the inequality.

23. $3x + 8 < 7x - 4$

24. $7x + 3 > 9x - 5$

25. $6x - 2 \geq 4x + 6$

26. $5x - 5 \leq 2x + 10$

27. $0.3(x - 1) < 0.1x - 0.5$

28. $0.2(3 - x) + 0.1 > 0.1(x - 2)$

29. $3 + 5(2 - x) \geq -3(x + 5)$

30. $7 - 2(x - 4) \leq 7(x - 3)$

31. $\frac{x + 6}{7} - \frac{6}{14} > \frac{x + 3}{2}$

32. $\frac{3x + 5}{4} + \frac{7}{12} > -\frac{x}{6}$

33. $\frac{1}{6} - \frac{1}{2}(3x + 2) < \frac{1}{3}\left(x - \frac{1}{2}\right)$

34. $\frac{2}{3}(2x - 5) + 3 \geq \frac{1}{4}(3x + 1) - 5$

Applications

35. ***Course Average*** To pass a course with a B grade, a student must have an average of 80 or greater. A student's grades on three tests are 75, 83, and 86. Solve the inequality $\frac{75 + 83 + 86 + x}{4} \geq 80$ to find what score the student must get on the next test to get a B average or better.

36. ***Payment Options*** Sharon sells very expensive European sports cars. She may choose to receive \$10,000.00 or 8% of her sales as payment for her work. Solve the inequality $0.08x > 10{,}000$ to find how much she needs to sell to make the 8% offer a better deal.

37. ***Elephant Weight*** The average African elephant weighs 268 pounds at birth. During the first three weeks of life the baby elephant will usually gain about 4 pounds per day. Assuming that growth rate, solve the inequality $268 + 4x \geq 300$ to find how many days it will be until a baby elephant weighs at least 300 pounds.

38. ***Car Loan*** Rennie is buying a used car that costs \$4500. The deal called for a \$600 down payment, and payments of \$260 monthly. He wants to know whether he can pay off the car within a year. Solve the inequality $600 + 260x \geq 4500$ to find out the minimum number of months it will take to pay off the car.

Cumulative Review

▲ 39. ***Tennis Court Fence*** A rectangular tennis court measures 36 feet wide and 78 feet long. Robert is building a fence to surround the tennis court. He wants the fence to be 4 feet from each side of the court. How many feet of fence will he need?

▲ 40. ***Photo Enlargement*** Jemma has job with the school newspaper. She has taken a picture with the dimensions 3" high by 5" wide. The editor likes the picture, but the available space is 30% wider and 20% higher than the picture Jemma took. What dimensions must Jemma enlarge the picture to?

▲ 41. ***Basketball Poster*** Melinda is making a poster for her college basketball team. On the poster she is placing a life-sized picture of a basketball. When inflated properly, a basketball has a diameter of 9 inches. What is the area of the basketball on her poster? Use $\pi \approx 3.14$. Round your answer to the nearest tenth.

▲ 42. ***Seating Area*** The seats of an outdoor amphitheater are arranged in the shape of a trapezoid. The altitude of the trapezoid is 120 feet. The bases of the trapezoid are 90 feet and 170 feet. What is the area of this seating area?

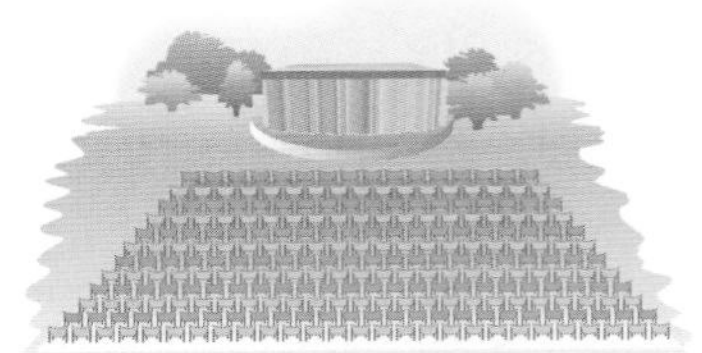

Putting Your Skills to Work

Gasoline Consumption on a 27-Foot Outboard

Frank and his father have a 27-foot outboard sport fishing boat that they charter for part of the year. The boat can be equipped with either two 225-horsepower outboard motors or one 250-horsepower outboard motor. They tested the consumption of gasoline per hour at various speeds for each choice of motor and made the following chart.

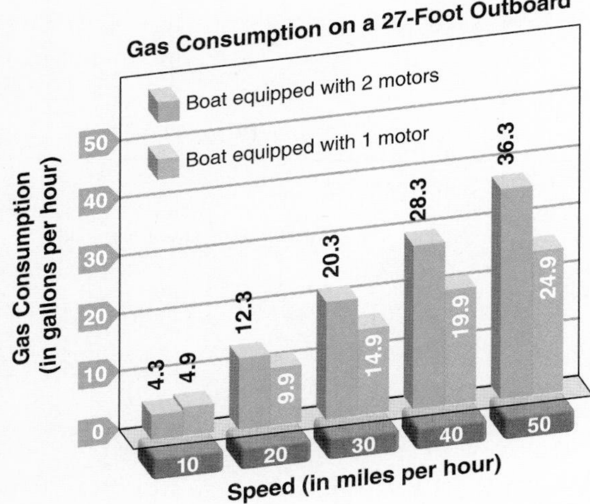

Problems for Individual Study and Analysis

1. How many more gallons per hour does the boat use at 40 miles per hour if it is equipped with two 225-horsepower outboard motors rather than one 250-horsepower motor?

2. If the boat is used for 30 hours of fishing per week and the usual cruising speed is 40 miles per hour, how many more gallons per week will be consumed if the boat is equipped with two 225-horsepower outboard motors rather than one 250-horsepower motor?

Problems for Group Investigation and Cooperative Learning

For the boat equipped with two 225-horsepower outboard motors the rate of gasoline consumption in gallons per hour (y) can be approximated from knowing the speed in miles per hour (x) using the equation $y = 0.8x - 3.7$. Use this equation for problems 3 and 4.

3. How many gallons per hour are consumed if the boat travels at 45 miles per hour?

4. If the boat is consuming 40.3 gallons per hour, how fast is the boat traveling?

For the boat equipped with one 250-horsepower outboard motor the rate of gasoline consumption in gallons per hour (y) can be approximated from knowing the speed in miles per hour (x) using the equation $y = 0.5x - 0.1$. Use this equation for problems 5 and 6.

5. Solve the above equation for x.

6. Use the result of problem 5 to find how many miles per hour the boat is traveling if it is consuming 17.4 gallons per hour.

Chapter 2 Organizer

Topic	Procedure	Examples
Solving equations without parentheses or fractions, p. 146.	**1.** On each side of the equation, combine like terms if possible. **2.** Add or subtract terms on both sides of the equation in order to get all terms with the variable on one side of the equation. **3.** Add or subtract a value on both sides of the equation to get all terms not containing the variable on the other side of the equation. **4.** Divide both sides of the equation by the coefficient of the variable. **5.** If possible, simplify the solution. **6.** Check your solution by substituting the obtained value into the original equation.	Solve for x. $5x + 2 + 2x = -10 + 4x + 3$ $7x + 2 = -7 + 4x$ $7x - 4x + 2 = -7 + 4x - 4x$ $3x + 2 = -7$ $3x + 2 - 2 = -7 - 2$ $3x = -9$ $\frac{3x}{3} = \frac{-9}{3}$ $x = -3$ *Check:* Is -3 the solution of $5x + 2 + 2x = -10 + 4x + 3$? $5(-3) + 2 + 2(-3) \stackrel{?}{=} -10 + 4(-3) + 3$ $-15 + 2 - 6 \stackrel{?}{=} -10 + (-12) + 3$ $-13 - 6 \stackrel{?}{=} -22 + 3$ $-19 = -19$ ✓
Solving equations with parentheses and/or fractions, p. 148 and p. 153.	**1.** Remove any parentheses. **2.** Simplify, if possible. **3.** If fractions exist, multiply all terms on both sides by the least common denominator of all the fractions. **4.** Now follow the remaining steps for solving an equation without parentheses or fractions.	Solve for y. $5(3y - 4) = \frac{1}{4}(6y + 4) - 48$ $15y - 20 = \frac{3}{2}y + 1 - 48$ $15y - 20 = \frac{3}{2}y - 47$ $2(15y) - 2(20) = 2\left(\frac{3}{2}y\right) - 2(47)$ $30y - 40 = 3y - 94$ $30y - 3y - 40 = 3y - 3y - 94$ $27y - 40 = -94$ $27y - 40 + 40 = -94 + 40$ $27y = -54$ $\frac{27y}{27} = \frac{-54}{27}$ $y = -2$
Solving formulas, p. 162	**1.** Remove any parentheses. **2.** If fractions exist, multiply all terms on both sides by the LCD, which may be a variable. **3.** Add or subtract terms on both sides of the equation in order to get all terms containing the *desired variable* on one side of the equation. **4.** Add or subtract terms on both sides of the equation in order to get all other terms on the opposite side of the equation. **5.** Divide both side of the equation by the coefficient of the desired variable. This division may involve other variables. **6.** Simplify, if possible. **7.** (Optional) Check your solution by substituting the obtained expression into the original equation.	Solve for z. $B = \frac{1}{3}(hx + hz)$ First we remove parentheses. $B = \frac{1}{3}hx + \frac{1}{3}hz$ Now we multiply each term by 3. $3(B) = 3\left(\frac{1}{3}hx\right) + 3\left(\frac{1}{3}hz\right)$ $3B = hx + hz$ $3B - hx = hx - hx + hz$ $3B - hx = hz$ The coefficient of z is h, so we divide each side by h. $\frac{3B - hx}{h} = z$

Topic	Procedure	Examples
Solving inequalities, *p. 176*	**1.** Follow the steps for solving an equation up until the division step. **2.** If you divide both sides of the inequality by a *positive number,* the direction of the inequality is not reversed. **3.** If you divide both sides of the inequality by a *negative number,* the direction of the inequality is reversed.	Solve for x and graph your solution. $\frac{1}{2}(3x - 2) \le -5 + 5x - 3$ First remove parentheses and simplify. $\frac{3}{2}x - 1 \le -8 + 5x$ Now multiply each term by 2. $2\left(\frac{3}{2}x\right) - 2(1) \le 2(-8) + 2(5x)$ $3x - 2 \le -16 + 10x$ $3x - 10x - 2 \le -16 + 10x - 10x$ $-7x - 2 \le -16$ $-7x - 2 + 2 \le -16 + 2$ $-7x \le -14$ When we divide both sides by a negative number, the inequality is reversed. $\frac{-7x}{-7} \ge \frac{-14}{-7}$ $x \ge 2$ Graphical solution: 0 1 2 3 4 5 x

Chapter 2 Review Problems

Sections 2.1–2.3

Solve for the variable. Noninteger answers may be left in fractional form or decimal form.

1. $5x = -35$

2. $x - 19 = -22$

3. $6 - 18x = 4 - 17x$

4. $18 - 10x = 63 + 5x$

5. $6x - 2(x + 3) = 5$

6. $1 - 2(6 - x) = 3x + 2$

7. $x - (0.5x + 2.6) = 17.6$

8. $-0.2(x + 1) = 0.3(x + 11)$

9. $3(x - 2) = -4(5 + x)$

10. $\frac{2}{3}x = -18$

11. $\frac{3}{4}x = 15$

12. $4(2x + 3) = 5(x - 3)$

13. $3(x - 3) = 13x + 21$

14. $0.9x + 1.0 = 0.3x + 0.4$

15. $2.4 - 0.3x = 0.4(x - 1)$

16. $12 - x + 2 = 3x - 10 + 4x$

17. $36 = 9x - (3x - 18)$

18. $12 - 5x = -7x - 2$

19. $2(3 - x) = 1 - (x - 2)$

20. $4(x + 5) - 7 = 2(x + 3)$

21. $0.9y + 3 = 0.4y + 1.5$

22. $7y - 3.4 = 11.3$

23. $3 = 2x + 5 - 3(x - 1)$

24. $2(5x - 1) - 7 = 3(x - 1) + 5 - 4x$

Section 2.4

Solve for the variable. Noninteger answers may be left in fractional form or decimal form.

25. $\frac{3}{4}x - 3 = \frac{1}{2}x + 2$

26. $1 = \frac{5x}{6} + \frac{2x}{3}$

27. $\frac{7x}{5} = 5 + \frac{2x}{5}$

28. $\frac{7x - 3}{2} - 4 = \frac{5x + 1}{3}$

29. $\frac{3x - 2}{2} + \frac{x}{4} = 2 + x$

30. $\frac{-3}{2}(x + 5) = 1 - x$

31. $\frac{-4}{3}(2x + 1) = -x - 2$

32. $\frac{1}{3}(x - 2) = \frac{x}{4} + 2$

33. $\frac{1}{5}(x - 3) = 2 - \frac{x}{2}$

34. $\frac{4}{5} + \frac{1}{2}x = \frac{1}{5}x + \frac{1}{2}$

35. $2x - \frac{3}{4} + \frac{7}{2}x = \frac{1}{2}x + \frac{1}{4}$

36. $\frac{3}{2}x - \frac{5}{6} + x = \frac{1}{2}x + \frac{2}{3}$

37. $-\frac{8}{3}x - 8 + 2x - 5 = -\frac{5}{3}$

38. $3.5(2x + 3) = 2.4x - 1$

39. $\frac{7}{12}(x - 3) = \frac{1}{3}x + 4$

40. $\frac{1}{6} + \frac{1}{3}(x - 3) = \frac{1}{2}(x + 9)$

41. $\frac{1}{7}(x + 5) - \frac{6}{14} = \frac{1}{2}(x + 3)$

42. $\frac{1}{6}(8x + 3) = \frac{1}{2}(2x + 7)$

43. $-\frac{2}{5}(3x + 1) = \frac{1}{3}(2 - x)$

44. $\frac{7}{9}x + \frac{2}{3} = 5 + \frac{1}{3}x$

Section 2.5

Solve for the variable indicated.

45. Solve for y. $3x - y = 10$

46. Solve for y. $5x + 2y + 7 = 0$

47. Solve for r. $A = P(1 + rt)$

48. Solve for h. $A = 4\pi r^2 + 2\pi rh$

49. Solve for p. $H = \frac{1}{3}(a + 2p + 3)$

50. Solve for y. $ax + by = c$

51. **(a)** Solve for T. $C = \frac{WRT}{1000}$.

(b) Use your result to find T if $C = 0.36$, $W = 30$, and $R = 0.002$.

52. **(a)** Solve for y. $5x - 3y = 12$

(b) Use your result to find y if $x = 9$.

53. **(a)** Solve for h: $V = lwh$.

(b) Use your result to find h when $V = 48$, $I = 2$, and $w = 4$.

Sections 2.6–2.7

Solve each inequality and graph the result.

54. $7 - 2x \geq 4x - 5$

−5 −4 −3 −2 −1 0 1 2 3 4 5 x

55. $2 - 3x \leq -5 + 4x$

−5 −4 −3 −2 −1 0 1 2 3 4 5 x

56. $2x - 3 + x > 5(x + 1)$

−7 −6 −5 −4 −3 −2 −1 0 1 2 3 x

57. $-x + 4 < 3x + 16$

−5 −4 −3 −2 −1 0 1 2 3 4 5 x

58. $8 - \frac{1}{3}x \leq x$

−1 0 1 2 3 4 5 6 7 8 9 x

59. $7 - \frac{3}{5}x > 4$

−3 −2 −1 0 1 2 3 4 5 6 7 x

60. $-4x - 14 < 4 - 2(3x - 1)$

7 8 9 10 11 12 13 14 15 16 17 x

61. $3(x - 2) + 8 < 7x + 14$

−5 −4 −3 −2 −1 0 1 2 3 4 5 x

62. $\frac{1}{2}(2x + 3) > 10$

5 $\frac{11}{2}$ 6 $\frac{13}{2}$ 7 $\frac{15}{2}$ 8 $\frac{17}{2}$ 9 $\frac{19}{2}$ 10 x

63. $5(1 - x) < 3(x - 1) - 2(3 - x)$

1 $\frac{6}{5}$ $\frac{7}{5}$ $\frac{8}{5}$ $\frac{9}{5}$ 2 $\frac{11}{5}$ $\frac{12}{5}$ $\frac{13}{5}$ $\frac{14}{5}$ 3 x

Use an inequality to solve.

64. ***Wages*** Julian earns \$15 per hour as a plasterer's assistant. His employer determines that the current job allows him to pay \$480 in wages to Julian. What are the maximum number of hours that Julian can work on this job? (*Hint:* Use $15h \leq 480$.)

65. ***Hiring a Temp*** The cost of hiring a temporary secretary for a day is \$85. Let $n =$ the number of temporary secretaries. Set up an inequality to determine how many times a temporary secretary may be hired if the company budget for temporary secretaries is \$1445 per month. What is the maximum number of days a temporary secretary may be hired during the month? (*Hint:* Use $85n \leq 1445$.)

Mixed Practice

Solve for the variable. Noninteger answers may be left in fractional form or decimal form.

66. $8(3x + 5) - 10 = 9(x - 2) + 13$

67. $8 - 3x + 5 = 13 + 4x + 2$

68. $-2(x - 3) = -4x + 3(3x + 2)$

69. $\frac{1}{2} + \frac{5}{4}x = \frac{2}{5}x - \frac{1}{10} + 4$

70. $\frac{1}{6}x - \frac{2}{3} = \frac{1}{3}(x - 4)$

71. $\frac{1}{2}(x - 3) = \frac{1}{4}(3x - 1)$

Solve for the variable indicated.

72. Solve for d. $H + 2d = 6c - 3d$

73. Solve for b. $H = \frac{3c + 2b}{4}$

Solve each inequality and graph the result.

74. $5 - \frac{1}{2}x > 4$

$-5 \quad -4 \quad -3 \quad -2 \quad -1 \quad 0 \quad 1 \quad 2 \quad 3 \quad 4 \quad 5 \quad x$

75. $2(x - 1) \geq 3(2 + x)$

$-10 \quad -9 \quad -8 \quad -7 \quad -6 \quad -5 \quad -4 \quad -3 \quad -2 \quad -1 \quad 0 \quad x$

76. $\frac{1}{3}(x + 2) \leq \frac{1}{2}(3x - 5)$

$\frac{12}{7} \quad \frac{13}{7} \quad 2 \quad \frac{15}{7} \quad \frac{16}{7} \quad \frac{17}{7} \quad \frac{18}{7} \quad \frac{19}{7} \quad \frac{20}{7} \quad 3 \quad \frac{22}{7} \quad x$

77. $4(2 - x) - (-5x + 1) \geq -8$

$-18 \quad -17 \quad -16 \quad -15 \quad -14 \quad -13 \quad -12 \quad -11 \quad -10 \quad -9 \quad -8 \quad x$

How Am I Doing? Chapter 2 Test

Remember to use your Chapter Test Prep Video CD to see the worked-out solutions to the test problems you want to review.

Solve for the variable. Noninteger answers may be left in fractional form or decimal form.

1. $3x + 5.6 = 11.6$

2. $9x - 8 = -6x - 3$

3. $2(2y - 3) = 4(2y + 2)$

4. $\frac{1}{7}y + 3 = \frac{1}{2}y$

5. $4(7 - 4x) = 3(6 - 2x)$

6. $0.8x + 0.18 - 0.4x = 0.3(x + 0.2)$

7. $\frac{2y}{3} + \frac{1}{5} - \frac{3y}{5} + \frac{1}{3} = 1$

8. $3 - 2y = 2(3y - 2) - 5y$

9. $5(20 - x) + 10x = 165$

10. $5(x + 40) - 6x = 9x$

11. $-2(2 - 3x) = 76 - 2x$

12. $20 - (2x + 6) = 5(2 - x) + 2x$

In questions 13–17, solve for x.

13. $2x - 3 = 12 - 6x + 3(2x + 3)$

14. $\frac{1}{3}x - \frac{3}{4}x = \frac{1}{12}$

15. $\frac{3}{5}x + \frac{7}{10} = \frac{1}{3}x + \frac{3}{2}$

16. $\frac{15x - 2}{28} = \frac{5x - 3}{7}$

17. $\frac{2}{3}(x + 8) + \frac{3}{5} = \frac{1}{5}(11 - 6x)$

18. Solve for w. $A = 3w + 2P$

19. Solve for w. $\frac{2w}{3} = 4 - \frac{1}{2}(x + 6)$

20. Solve for a. $A = \frac{1}{2}h(a + b)$

21. Solve for y. $5ax(2 - y) = 3axy + 5$

22. Solve for B; $V = \frac{1}{3}Bh$

▲ **23.** Use your result from question 22 to find the area of the base (B) of a pyramid if the volume (V) is 140 cubic inches and the height (h) is 14 inches.

Solve and graph the inequality.

24. $3(x - 2) \geq 5x$

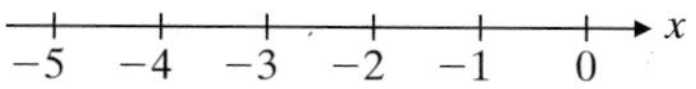

25. $2 - 7(x + 1) - 5(x + 2) < 0$

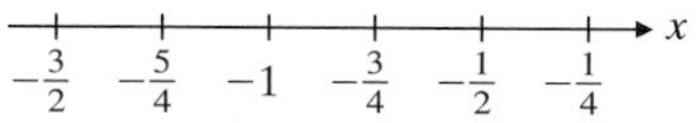

26. $5 + 8x - 4 < 2x + 13$

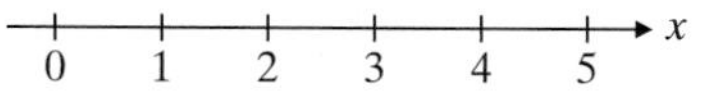

27. $\frac{1}{4}x + \frac{1}{16} \leq \frac{1}{8}(7x - 2)$

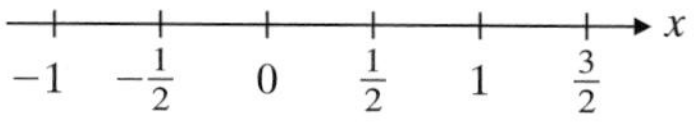

1. ____________
2. ____________
3. ____________
4. ____________
5. ____________
6. ____________
7. ____________
8. ____________
9. ____________
10. ____________
11. ____________
12. ____________
13. ____________
14. ____________
15. ____________
16. ____________
17. ____________
18. ____________
19. ____________
20. ____________
21. ____________
22. ____________
23. ____________
24. ____________
25. ____________
26. ____________
27. ____________

Cumulative Test for Chapters 0–2

1. ______
2. ______
3. ______
4. ______
5. ______
6. ______
7. ______
8. ______
9. ______
10. ______
11. ______
12. ______
13. ______
14. ______
15. ______
16. ______
17. ______
18. ______
19. ______
20. ______
21. ______
22. ______
23. ______

Approximately one-half of this test covers the content of Chapters 0 and 1. The remainder covers the content of Chapter 2. In questions 1–4, simplify.

1. $\frac{6}{7} - \frac{2}{3}$

2. $1\frac{3}{4} + 2\frac{1}{5}$

3. $3\frac{1}{5} \div 1\frac{1}{2}$

4. $(1.23)(0.56)$

5. Divide. $0.144 \div 1.2$

6. What is 4.3% of 830?

7. Multiply. $(-3)(-5)(-1)(2)(-1)$

8. Collect like terms. $5ab - 7ab^2 - 3ab - 12ab^2 + 10ab - 9ab^2$

9. Simplify. $(5x)^2$

10. Simplify: $2\{3x - 4[5 - 3y(2 - x)]\}$

11. Solve for x. $4(7 - 2x) = 3x - 12$

12. Solve for x. $\frac{1}{3}(x + 5) = 2x - 5$

13. Solve for y. $\frac{2y}{3} - \frac{1}{4} = \frac{1}{6} + \frac{y}{4}$

14. Solve for a: $5a - 8b = 6 + 2a$

15. Solve for b. $H = \frac{2}{3}(b + 4a)$

16. Solve for t. $I = Prt$

17. Solve for a. $A = \frac{ha}{2} + \frac{hb}{2}$

In questions 18–22, solve and graph the inequality.

18. $-6x - 3 < 2x - 10x + 7$

0 1 2 3 4 5 x

19. $\frac{1}{2}(x - 5) \geq x - 4$

0 1 2 3 4 5 x

20. $4(2 - x) > 1 - 5x - 8$

−17 −16 −15 −14 −13 −12 x

21. $x + \frac{5}{9} \leq \frac{1}{3} + \frac{7}{9}x$

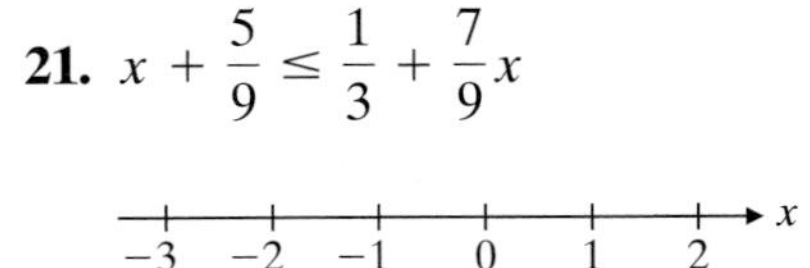

22. $7x - 13 \leq 3(4 - 5x) - 3$

−1 0 1 2 3 4 x

23. The football team will not let Chuck play unless he passes biology with a C (70 or better) average. There are five tests in the semester, and he has failed (0) the first one. However, he found a tutor and received an 82, an 89, and an 87 on the next three tests. Solve the inequality $\frac{0 + 82 + 89 + 87 + x}{5} \geq 70$ to find what his minimum score must be on the last test in order to pass the course and play football.

CHAPTER

3

Wild herds of caribou in Alaska are animals that are free to roam in one of the great wilderness areas of the world. Yet there is danger for these herds. Wildlife managers carefully measure the size of the herd and watch for population growth or losses. Predicting the size of the herd of caribou using a mathematical equation is highly desirable. Can you use your mathematical ability to create such an equation? Turn to the Putting Your Skills to Work problems on page 241 to find out.

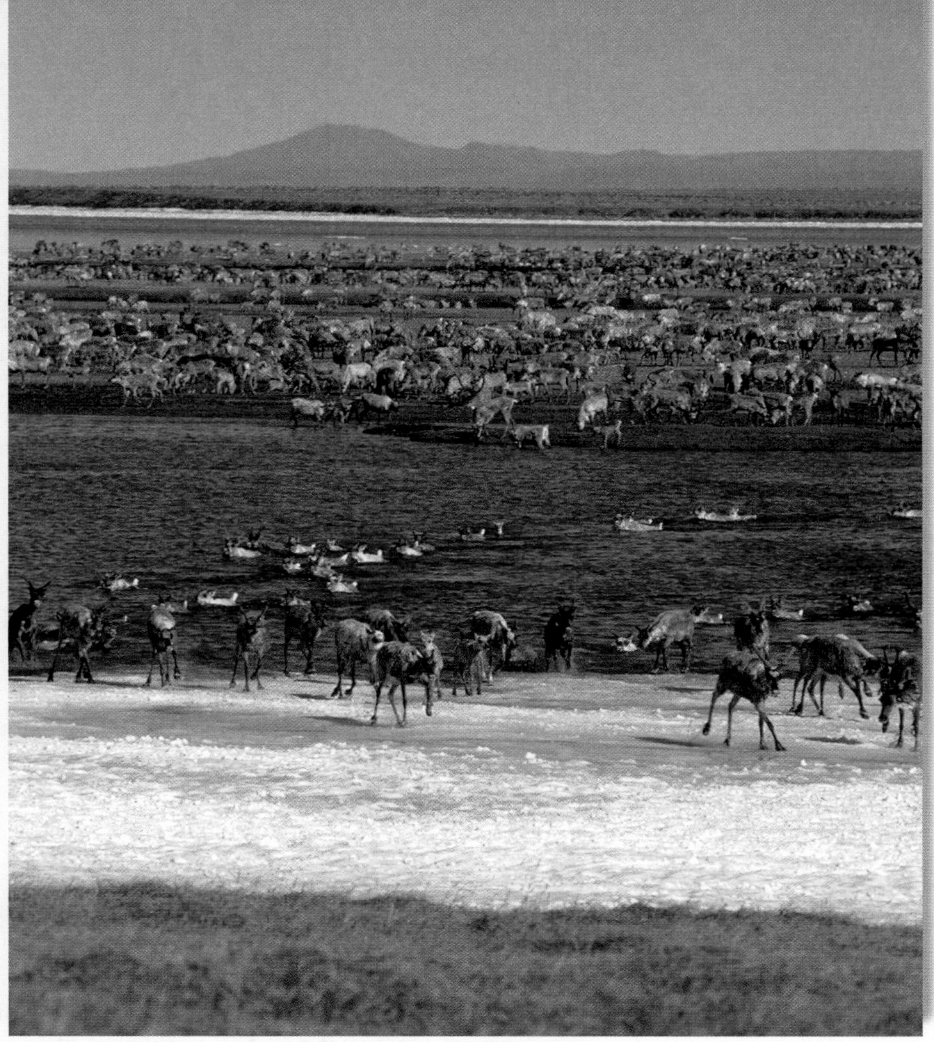

Solving Applied Problems

3.1 Translating English Phrases into Algebraic Expressions

Student Learning Objectives

After studying this section, you will be able to:

 **Translate English phrases into algebraic expressions.**

 **Write an algebraic expression to compare two or more quantities.**

 Translating English Phrases into Algebraic Expressions

One of the most useful applications of algebra is solving word problems. One of the first steps in solving word problems is translating the conditions of the problem into algebra. In this section we show you how to translate common English phrases into algebraic symbols. This process is similar to translating between languages like Spanish and French.

Several English phrases describe the operation of addition. If we represent an unknown number by the variable x, all of the following phrases can be translated into algebra as $x + 3$.

English Phrases Describing Addition	Algebraic Expression	Diagram
Three *more than* a number		x, 3
The *sum of* a number and three		
A number *increased by* three	$\mathbf{x + 3}$	
Three is *added to* a number.		
Three *greater than* a number		$x + 3$
A number *plus* three		

In a similar way we can use algebra to express English phrases that describe the operations of subtraction, multiplication, and division.

CAUTION Since subtraction is not commutative, the order is essential. A number decreased by five is $x - 5$. It is not correct to say $5 - x$. Use extra care as you study each example. Make sure you understand the proper order.

English Phrases Describing Subtraction	Algebraic Expression	Diagram
A number *decreased by* four		x
Four *less than* a number		4
Four is *subtracted from* a number.		
Four *smaller than* a number	$\mathbf{x - 4}$	
Four *fewer than* a number		
A number *diminished by* four		$x - 4$
A number *minus* 4		
The *difference between* a number and four		

English Phrases Describing Multiplication	Algebraic Expression	Diagram
Double a number		x, x
Twice a number		
The *product* of two and a number	$\mathbf{2x}$	
Two *of* a number		
Two *times* a number		$2x$

Since division is not commutative, the order is essential. A number divided by 3 is $\frac{x}{3}$. It is not correct to say $\frac{3}{x}$. Use extra care as you study each example.

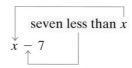

English Phrases Describing Division	Algebraic Expression	Diagram
A number *divided by* five One-*fifth* of a number The quotient of a number and five	$\frac{x}{5}$	x ; $\frac{x}{5}$

Often other words are used in English instead of the word *number*. We can use a variable, such as x, here also.

EXAMPLE 1

	English Phrase	Algebraic Expression
(a)	A *quantity* is increased by five.	$x + 5$
(b)	Double the *value*	$2x$
(c)	One-third of the *weight*	$\frac{x}{3}$ or $\frac{1}{3}x$
(d)	Twelve *more than* a number	$x + 12$
(e)	Seven *less than* a number	$x - 7$

Note that the algebraic expression for "seven less than a number" does not follow the order of the words in the English phrase. The variable or expression that follows the words *less than* always comes first.

seven less than x

$x - 7$

The variable or expression that follows the words *more than* technically comes before the plus sign. However, since addition is commutative, it also can be written after the plus sign.

NOTE TO STUDENT: Fully worked-out solutions to all of the Practice Problems can be found at the back of the text starting at page SP-1

Practice Problem 1 Write each English phrase as an algebraic expression.

(a) Four more than a number **(b)** Triple a value

(c) Eight less than a number **(d)** One-fourth of a height

More than one operation can be described in an English phrase. Sometimes parentheses must be used to make clear which operation is done first.

EXAMPLE 2

	English Phrase	Algebraic Expression
(a)	Seven more than double a number	$2x + 7$ *Note that these are **not** the same.*
(b)	The value of the number is increased by seven and then doubled.	$2(x + 7)$ *Note that the word **then** tells us to add x and 7 before doubling.*
(c)	One-half of the sum of a number and 3	$\frac{1}{2}(x + 3)$

Practice Problem 2 Write each English phrase as an algebraic expression.

(a) Eight more than triple a number

(b) A number is increased by eight and then it is tripled.

(c) One-third of the sum of a number and 4

Writing an Algebraic Expression to Compare Two or More Quantities

Often in a word problem two or more quantities are described in terms of another. We will want to use a variable to represent one quantity and then write an algebraic expression using *the same variable* to represent the other quantity. Which quantity should we let the variable represent? We usually let the variable represent the quantity that is the basis of comparison: the quantity that the others are being *compared to*.

EXAMPLE 3 Use a variable and an algebraic expression to describe the two quantities in the English sentence "Mike's salary is \$2000 more than Fred's salary."

Solution The two quantities that are being compared are Mike's salary and Fred's salary. Since Mike's salary is being *compared to* Fred's salary, we let the variable represent Fred's salary. The choice of the letter f helps us to remember that the variable represents Fred's salary.

Let f = Fred's salary.

Then $f + \$2000$ = Mike's salary. *Since Mike's salary is* \$2000 *more than Fred's.*

***NOTE TO STUDENT:** Fully worked-out solutions to all of the Practice Problems can be found at the back of the text starting at page SP-1*

Practice Problem 3 Use a variable and an algebraic expression to describe the two quantities in the English sentence "Marie works 17 hours per week less than Ann."

EXAMPLE 4 The length of a rectangle is 3 meters shorter than twice the width. Use a variable and an algebraic expression to describe the length and the width. Draw a picture of the rectangle and label the length and width.

Solution The length of the rectangle is being *compared to* the width. Use the letter w for width.

Let w = the width.

$\underbrace{\text{3 meters shorter than twice the width}}$

Then $2w - 3$ = the length.

A picture of the rectangle is shown.

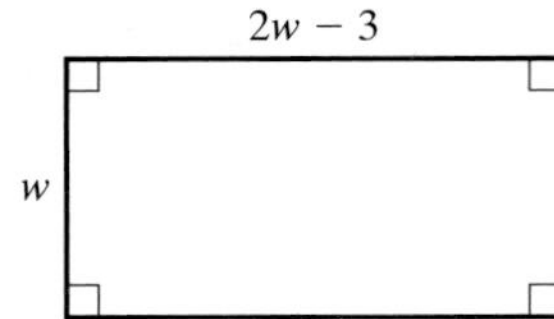

Practice Problem 4 The length of a rectangle is 5 meters longer than double the width. Use a variable and an algebraic expression to describe the length and the width. Draw a picture of the rectangle and label the length and width.

EXAMPLE 5 The first angle of a triangle is triple the second angle. The third angle of a triangle is 12° more than the second angle. Describe each angle algebraically. Draw a diagram of the triangle and label its parts.

Solution Since the first and third angles are described in terms of the second angle, we let the variable represent the number of degrees in the second angle.

Let s = the number of degrees in the second angle.

Then $3s$ = the number of degrees in the first angle.

And $s + 12$ = the number of degrees in the third angle.

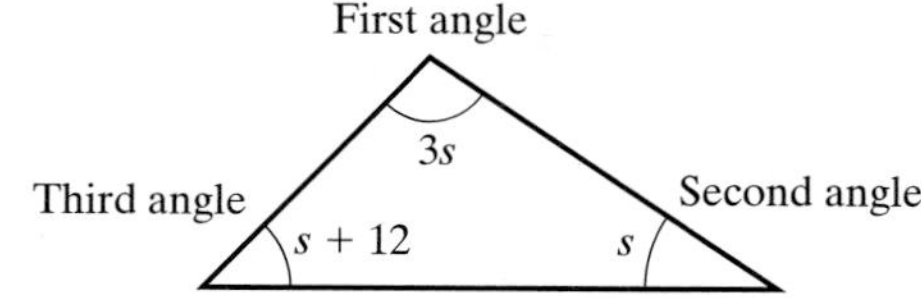

Practice Problem 5 The first angle of a triangle is 16° less than the second angle. The third angle is double the second angle. Describe each angle algebraically. Draw a diagram of the triangle and label its parts.

Some comparisons will involve fractions.

EXAMPLE 6 A theater manager was examining the records of attendance for last year. The number of people attending the theater in January was one-half of the number of people attending the theater in February. The number of people attending the theater in March was three-fifths of the number of people attending the theater in February. Use algebra to describe the attendance each month.

Solution What are we looking for? The *number of people* who attended the theater *each month*. The basis of comparison is February. That is where we begin.

Let f = the number of people who attended in February.

Then $\frac{1}{2}f$ = the number of people who attended in January.

And $\frac{3}{5}f$ = the number of people who attended in March.

Practice Problem 6 The college dean noticed that in the spring the number of students on campus was two-thirds of the number of students on campus in the fall. She also noticed that in the summer the number of students on campus was one-fifth the number of students on campus in the fall. Use algebra to describe the number of students on campus in each of these three time periods.

3.1 EXERCISES

Student Solutions Manual | CD/ Video | PH Math Tutor Center | MathXL®Tutorials on CD | MathXL® | MyMathLab® | Interactmath.com

Verbal and Writing Skills

Write an algebraic expression for each quantity. Let x represent the unknown value.

1. a quantity increased by 5

2. nine greater than a number

3. six fewer than a quantity

4. a value decreased by seven

5. one-eighth of a quantity

6. one-half of a quantity

7. twice a quantity

8. triple a number

9. three more than half of a number

10. five more than one-third of a number

11. double a quantity increased by nine

12. six times a number increased by eight

13. one-third of the sum of a number and seven

14. one-fourth of the sum of a number and 5

15. one-third of a number reduced by twice the same number

16. one-fifth of a number reduced by double the same number

17. seven less than triple a number

18. four less than seven times a number

Write an algebraic expression for each of the quantities being compared.

19. ***Stock Value*** The value of a share of IBM stock on that day was $74.50 more than the value of a share of AT&T stock.

20. ***Investments*** The annual income from Dr. Smith's mutual fund was $833 less than the annual income from her retirement fund.

▲ **21.** ***Geometry*** The length of the rectangle is 7 inches more than double the width.

▲ **22.** ***Geometry*** The length of the rectangle is 3 meters more than triple the width.

23. ***Cookie Sales*** The number of boxes of cookies sold by Sarah was 43 fewer than the number of boxes of cookies sold by Keiko. The number of boxes of cookies sold by Imelda was 53 more than the number sold by Keiko.

24. ***Fish Catch*** The number of pounds of fish caught by Captain Jack was 813 pounds more than the amount of fish caught by Captain Sally. The amount of fish caught by Captain Ben was 623 pounds less than the amount of fish caught by Captain Sally.

▲ **25.** ***Geometry*** The first angle of a triangle is 16 degrees less than the second angle. The third angle of a triangle is double the second angle.

▲ **26.** ***Geometry*** The first angle of a triangle is 19 degrees more than the third angle. The second angle is triple the third angle.

27. ***Exports*** The value of the exports of Japan was twice the value of the exports of Canada.

28. ***Olympic Medals*** Mark Spitz won two more Olympic medals than Carl Lewis did.

▲ **29.** ***Geometry*** The first angle of a triangle is triple the second angle. The third angle of a triangle is 14 degrees less than the second angle.

30. ***Book Cost*** The cost of Hiro's biology book was \$13 more than the cost of his history book. The cost of his English book was \$27 less than the cost of his history book.

Applications

Use algebra to describe the situation.

31. ***Land Area*** Kentucky has about half the land area of Minnesota. The land area of Maine is approximately two-fifths the land area of Minnesota. Describe the land area of each of these three states.

32. ***Middle School Population*** A census of El Cerrito Middle School found that the number of seventh graders was fifty more than the number of eighth graders. The number of sixth graders was three-fourths the number of eighth graders. Describe the population of each grade.

33. ***Archery*** In an archery tournament, the number of points awarded for an arrow in the gold circle (bull's eye) is six less than triple the points awarded for an arrow in the blue ring. Write an expression for each of these scores in an archery tournament.

34. ***Orbital Times*** The orbital time of Pluto is 82 years less than double the orbital time of Neptune.

To Think About

Kayak Rentals *The following bar graph depicts the number of people renting sea kayaks at Essex Boat Rental during July 2004. Use the bar graph to answer exercises 35 and 36.*

35. Write an expression for the number of men who rent Sea Kayaks at Essex Boat Rental in each age category. Start by using x for the number of men aged 16 to 24 who rented kayaks.

36. Write an expression for the number of women who rent Sea Kayaks at Essex Boat Rental. Start by using y for the number of women aged 35 to 44 who rented kyacks.

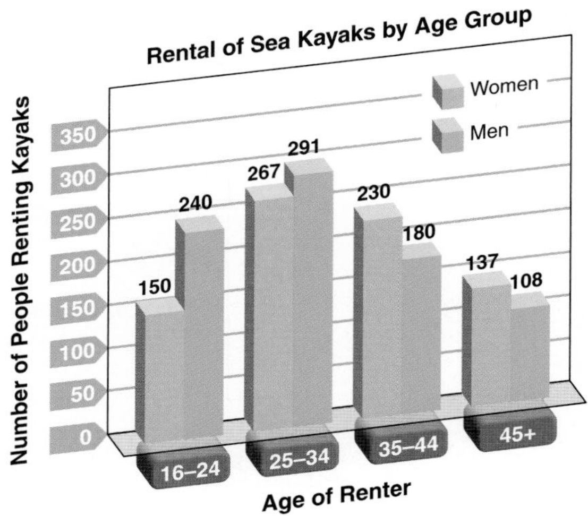

Cumulative Review

Solve for the variable.

37. $x + \frac{1}{2}(x - 3) = 9$

38. $\frac{3}{5}x - 3(x - 1) = 9$

39. $5(x - 8) = 13 + x - 5$

40. $6(w - 1) - 3(2 + w) = 9$

3.2 Using Equations to Solve Word Problems

Student Learning Objectives

After studying this section, you will be able to:

1. **Solve number problems.**
2. **Use the Mathematics Blueprint to solve applied word problems.**
3. **Use formulas to solve word problems.**

In Section 0.7 we introduced a simple three-step procedure to solve applied problems. You have had an opportunity to use that approach to solve word problems in Exercises 0.7 and in the Cumulative Review sections in Chapters 1 and 2. Now we are going to focus our attention on solving applied problems that require the use of variables, translating English phrases into algebraic expressions, and setting up equations. The process is a little more involved. Some students find the following outline a helpful way to keep organized while solving such problems.

1. *Understand the problem.*
   - **(a)** Read the word problem carefully to get an overview.
   - **(b)** Determine what information you will need to solve the problem.
   - **(c)** Draw a sketch. Label it with the known information. Determine what needs to be found.
   - **(d)** Choose a variable to represent one unknown quantity.
   - **(e)** If necessary, represent other unknown quantities in terms of that very same variable.
2. *Write an equation.*
   - **(a)** Look for key words to help you to translate the words into algebraic symbols and expressions.
   - **(b)** Use a given relationship in the problem or an appropriate formula to write an equation.
3. *Solve and state the answer.*
4. *Check.*
   - **(a)** Check the solution in the original equation. Is the answer reasonable?
   - **(b)** Be sure the solution to the equation answers the question in the word problem. You may need to do some additional calculations if it does not.

1 Solving Number Problems

EXAMPLE 1 Two-thirds of a number is eighty-four. What is the number?

Solution

1. ***Understand the problem.*** Draw a sketch.
   Let x = the unknown number.

2. ***Write an equation.***

$$\underbrace{\text{Two-thirds of a number}}_{\frac{2}{3}x} \quad \underset{=}{\text{is}} \quad \underbrace{\text{eighty-four.}}_{84}$$

3. ***Solve and state the answer.***

$$\frac{2}{3}x = 84$$

$$3\left(\frac{2}{3}x\right) = 3(84) \quad \text{Multiply both sides of the equation by 3.}$$

$$2x = 252$$

$$\frac{2x}{2} = \frac{252}{2} \quad \text{Divide both sides by 2.}$$

$$x = 126$$

The number is 126.

4. ***Check.*** Is two-thirds of 126 eighty-four?

$$\frac{2}{3}(126) \stackrel{?}{=} 84$$

$$84 = 84 \checkmark$$

Practice Problem 1 Three-fourths of a number is negative eighty-one. What is the number?

NOTE TO STUDENT: Fully worked-out solutions to all of the Practice Problems can be found at the back of the text starting at page SP-1

Learning to solve problems like Examples 1 and 2 is a very useful skill. You will find learning the material in Chapter 3 will be much easier if you can master the procedure used in these two examples.

EXAMPLE 2 Five more than six times a quantity is three hundred five. Find the number.

Solution

1. ***Understand the problem.*** Read the problem carefully. You may not need to draw a sketch.
Let $x =$ the unknown quantity.

2. ***Write an equation.***

$$\underbrace{\text{Five more than}}_{5\ +}\quad \underbrace{\text{six times a number}}_{6x}\quad \underbrace{\text{is}}_{=}\quad \underbrace{\text{three hundred five.}}_{305}$$

3. ***Solve and state the answer.*** You may want to rewrite the equation to make it easier to solve.

$$6x + 5 = 305$$

$$6x + 5 - 5 = 305 - 5 \quad \text{Subtract 5 from both sides.}$$

$$6x = 300$$

$$\frac{6x}{6} = \frac{300}{6} \quad \text{Divide both sides by 6.}$$

$$x = 50$$

The number is 50.

4. ***Check.*** Is five more than six times 50 three hundred five?

$$6(50) + 5 \stackrel{?}{=} 305$$

$$300 + 5 \stackrel{?}{=} 305$$

$$305 = 305 \checkmark$$

Practice Problem 2 Two less than triple a number is forty-nine. Find the number.

EXAMPLE 3 The larger of two numbers is three more than twice the smaller. The sum of the numbers is thirty-nine. Find each number.

Solution

1. ***Understand the problem.*** Read the problem carefully. The problem refers to *two* numbers. We must write an algebraic expression for *each number* before writing the equation. The larger number is being compared to the smaller number. We want to use *one variable* to describe each number.

$$\text{Let } s = \text{the smaller number.}$$

$$\text{Then } \underbrace{2s + 3 = \text{the larger number.}}_{\text{three more than twice the smaller number}}$$

2. ***Write an equation.*** The sum of the numbers is thirty-nine.

$$s + (2s + 3) = 39$$

3. ***Solve.***

$$s + (2s + 3) = 39$$
$$3s + 3 = 39 \quad \text{Collect like terms.}$$
$$3s = 36 \quad \text{Subtract 3 from each side.}$$
$$s = 12 \quad \text{Divide both sides by 3.}$$

4. ***Check.***

$$12 + [2(12) + 3] \stackrel{?}{=} 39$$
$$39 = 39 \checkmark$$

The solution checks, but have we solved the word problem? We need to find *each* number. 12 is the smaller number. Substitute 12 into the expression $2s + 3$ to find the larger number.

$$2s + 3 = 2(12) + 3 = 27$$

The smaller number is 12. The larger number is 27.

Practice Problem 3 Consider two numbers. The second number is twelve less than triple the first number. The sum of the two numbers is twenty-four. Find each number.

NOTE TO STUDENT: Fully worked-out solutions to all of the Practice Problems can be found at the back of the text starting at page SP-1

2 Using the Mathematics Blueprint to Solve Applied Word Problems

To facilitate understanding more involved word problems we will use a Mathematics Blueprint similar to the one we used in Section 0.7. This format is a simple way to organize facts, determine what to set variables equal to, and select a method or approach that will assist you in finding the desired quantity. You will find using this form helpful, particularly in those cases when you read through a word problem and mentally say to yourself, "Now where do I begin?" You begin by responding to the headings of the blueprint. Soon a procedure for solving the problem will emerge.

Mathematics Blueprint for Problem Solving

Gather the Facts	Assign the Variable	Basic Formula or Equation	Key Points to Remember

EXAMPLE 4 The mean annual snowfall in Juneau, Alaska, is 105.8 inches. This is 20.2 inches less than three times the annual snowfall in Boston. What is the annual snowfall in Boston?

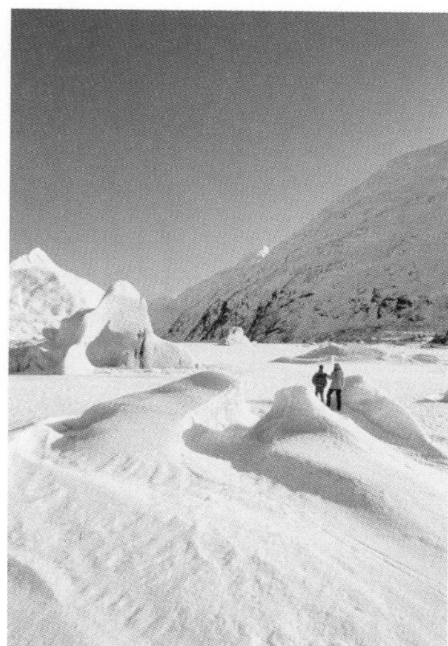

Solution

Understand the problem and write an equation.

Mathematics Blueprint for Problem Solving

Gather the Facts	Assign the Variable	Basic Formula or Equation	Key Points to Remember
Snowfall in Juneau is 105.8 inches. This is 20.2 inches less than three times the snowfall in Boston.	We do not know the snowfall in Boston. Let b = annual snowfall in Boston. Then $3b - 20.2$ = annual snowfall in Juneau.	Set $3b - 20.2$ equal to 105.8, which is the snowfall in Juneau.	All measurements of snowfall are recorded in inches.

Juneau's snowfall is 20.2 less than three times Boston's snowfall.

$$105.8 = 3b - 20.2$$

Solve and state the answer. You may want to rewrite the equation to make it easier to solve.

$$3b - 20.2 = 105.8$$

$$3b = 126 \quad \text{Add 20.2 to both sides.}$$

$$b = 42 \quad \text{Divide both sides by 3.}$$

The annual snowfall in Boston is 42 inches.

Check. Reread the word problem. Work backward.

Three times 42 is 126.

126 less 20.2 is 105.8.

Is this the annual snowfall in Juneau? Yes. ✓

Practice Problem 4 The maximum recorded rainfall for a 24-hour period in the United States occurred in Alvin, Texas, on July 25–26, 1979. The maximum recorded rainfall for a 24-hour period in Canada occurred in Ucluelet Brynnor Mines, British Columbia, on October 6, 1977. Alvin, Texas received 43 inches of rain in that period. The amount recorded in Texas was 14 inches less than three times the amount recorded in Canada. How much rainfall was recorded for Ucluelet Brynnor Mines in Canada? (*Source:* National Oceanic and Atmospheric Administration.)

Some word problems require a simple translation of the facts. Others require a little more detective work. You will not always need to use the Mathematics Blueprint to solve every word problem. As you gain confidence in problem solving, you will no doubt leave out some of the steps. We suggest that you use the procedure when you find yourself on unfamiliar ground. It is a powerful organizational tool.

3 Using Formulas to Solve Word Problems

Sometimes the relationship between two quantities is so well understood that we have developed a formula to describe that relationship. We have already done some work with formulas in Section 2.5. The following examples show how you can use a formula to solve a word problem.

EXAMPLE 5 Two people travel in separate cars. They each travel a distance of 330 miles on an interstate highway. To maximize fuel economy, Fred travels at exactly 50 mph. Sam travels at exactly 55 mph. How much time did the trip take each person? (Use the formula distance = rate · time or $d = rt$.)

Solution

Mathematics Blueprint for Problem Solving

Gather the Facts	Assign the Variable	Basic Formula or Equation	Key Points to Remember
Each person drives 330 miles. Fred drives at 50 mph. Sam drives at 55 mph.	Time is the unknown quantity for each driver. Use subscripts to denote different values of t. t_f = Fred's time t_s = Sam's time	distance = (rate)(time) or $d = rt$	The time is expressed in hours.

Substitute the known values into the formula and solve for t.

$$d = rt \qquad\qquad d = rt$$
$$330 = 50t_f \qquad\qquad 330 = 55t_s$$
$$6.6 = t_f \qquad\qquad 6 = t_s$$

It took Fred 6.6 hours to drive 330 miles. It took Sam 6 hours to drive 330 miles.

Check. Is this reasonable? Yes, you would expect Fred to take longer to drive the same distance because Fred is driving at a lower rate of speed.

Note: You may wish to express 6.6 hours in hours and minutes. To change 0.6 hours to minutes, proceed as follows:

$$0.6\ \cancel{\text{hour}} \cdot \frac{60 \text{ minutes}}{1\ \cancel{\text{hour}}} = (0.6)(60) \text{ minutes} = 36 \text{ minutes}$$

Thus, Fred drove for 6 hours and 36 minutes.

NOTE TO STUDENT: Fully worked-out solutions to all of the Practice Problems can be found at the back of the text starting at page SP-1

Practice Problem 5 Sarah left the city to visit her aunt and uncle, who live in a rural area north of the city. She traveled the 220-mile trip in 4 hours. On her way home she took a slightly longer route, which measured 225 miles on the car odometer. The return trip took 4.5 hours.

(a) What was her average speed on the trip leaving the city?

(b) What was her average speed on the return trip?

(c) On which trip did she travel faster and by how much?

EXAMPLE 6 A teacher told Melinda that she had a course average of 78 based on her six math tests. When she got home, Melinda found five of her tests. She had scores of 87, 63, 79, 71, and 96 on the five tests. She could not find her sixth test. What score did she obtain on that test? (Use the formula that an average = the sum of scores ÷ the number of scores.)

Solution

Mathematics Blueprint for Problem Solving

Gather the Facts	Assign the Variable	Basic Formula or Equation	Key Points to Remember
Her five known test scores are 87, 63, 79, 71, and 96. Her course average is 78.	We do not know the score Melinda received on her sixth test. Let x = the score on the sixth test.	average = $\dfrac{\text{sum of scores}}{\text{number of scores}}$	Since there are six test scores, we will need to divide the sum by 6.

When you average anything, you total up the sum of all the values and then divide it by the number of values.

We now write the equation for the average of six items. This involves adding all the tests and dividing by 6.

$$\frac{87 + 63 + 79 + 71 + 96 + x}{6} = 78$$

$$\frac{396 + x}{6} = 78 \qquad \text{Add the numbers in the numerator.}$$

$$6\left(\frac{396 + x}{6}\right) = 6(78) \qquad \text{Multiply both sides of the equation by 6 to remove the fraction.}$$

$$396 + x = 468 \qquad \text{Simplify.}$$

$$x = 72 \qquad \text{Subtract 396 from both sides to find } x.$$

Melinda's score on the sixth test was 72.

Check. To verify that this is correct, we check that the average of the 6 tests is 78.

$$\frac{87 + 63 + 79 + 71 + 96 + 72}{6} \stackrel{?}{=} 78$$

$$\frac{468}{6} \stackrel{?}{=} 78$$

$$78 = 78 \checkmark$$

The problem checks. We know that the score on the sixth test was 72.

Practice Problem 6 Barbara's math course has four tests and one final exam. The final exam counts as much as two tests. Barbara has test scores of 78, 80, 100, and 96 on her four tests. What grade does she need on the final exam if she wants to have a 90 average for the course?

     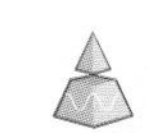

Student Solutions Manual | CD/Video | PH Math Tutor Center | MathXL®Tutorials on CD | MathXL® | MyMathLab® | Interactmath.com

Solve. Check your solution.

1. What number minus 543 gives 718?

2. What number added to 74 gives 265?

3. A number divided by eight is 296. What is the number?

4. Eighteen less than a number is 23. What is the number?

5. Seventeen greater than a number is 199. Find the number.

6. Three times a number is one. What is the number?

7. A number is doubled and then increased by seven. The result is ninety-three. What is the original number?

8. Four less than nine times a number is one hundred twenty-two. Find the original number.

9. When eighteen is reduced by two-thirds of a number, the result is 12. Find the number.

10. Twice a number is increased by one-third the same number. The result is 42. Find the number.

11. Five less than twice a number is the same as three times the number. Find the number.

12. Six less than five times a number is the same as seven times the number. Find the number.

13. A number, half of that number, and one-third of that number are added. The result is 22. What is the original number?

14. A number, twice that number, and one-third of that number are added. The result is 20. What is the original number?

Applications

Solve. Check to see if your answer is reasonable.

15. ***Motorcycle Inventory*** A Harley Davidson motorcycle shop maintains an inventory of four times as many new bikes as used bikes. If there are 60 new bikes, how many used bikes are now in stock?

16. ***Shirt Sizes*** The Enro Shirt Outlet store maintains an inventory of five times as many shirts in regular men's sizes (size XL and smaller) than it does in large men's sizes (size 2X and larger). There are 430 shirts in inventory in the store that are regular men's sizes. How many shirts in large men's sizes are in inventory?

17. ***Wildfires*** Between 1/1/02 and 7/27/02 there were 52,107 wildfires in the United States. This was 16,723 fewer than twice the number of wildfires between 1/1/03 and 7/27/03. Find the number of wildfires during the period 1/1/03 and 7/27/03. (*Source:* National Interagency Fire Center.)

18. ***DVD Rentals*** Harbor Video Rental charges \$8 per day to rent a DVD player, and \$2.25 per movie title. If Jeff rents the DVD player for 5 days, and he owes \$53.50 to Harbor Video Rental, how many movies did he rent?

19. ***CD Purchase*** The sale price of a new Panasonic compact disc player is \$218 at a local discount store. At the store where this sale is going on, each new CD is on sale for \$11 each. If Kyle purchases a player and some CDs for \$284, how many CDs did he purchase?

20. ***Online Charges*** Suellen subscribes to an online computer service that charges \$9.50 per month for 30 hours online and \$1.50 for each hour online in excess of 30 hours. Last month her bill was \$20. How many extra hours was she charged for?

21. ***One-Day Sale*** Raquelle went to Weller's Department Store one-day sale. She bought two blouses for \$38 each and a pair of shoes for \$49. She also wanted to but some jewelry. Each item of jewelry was bargain priced at \$11.50 each. If she brought \$171 with her, how many pieces of jewelry could she buy?

22. ***Waiting Tables*** Brad is a waiter at the "Steaks-Are-Us" restaurant. He gets paid \$5.75 per hour, and he can keep his tips. He knows that his tips average \$8.80 per table. If he worked an eight-hour shift and took home \$169.20, how many tables did he serve?

23. ***TGV*** On May 18, 1990 the fastest speed of any national railroad was achieved by the French high-speed train *Train à Grande Vitess* (TGV) as it traveled over a distance from Cortalain to Tours, France. A commentator said that this speed was so fast that if it continued at that rate, the train would travel 6404 miles in 20 hours. How fast did the train travel on that date? (*Source:* www.guinnessworld-records.com.)

24. ***Submarine Speed*** In 1958, the nuclear-powered submarine *Nautilus* took 6 days, 12 hours to travel submerged 5068 km across the Atlantic Ocean from Portsmouth, England, to New York City. What was its average speed, in kilometers per hour, for this trip? (Round to the nearest whole number.)

25. ***Gravity*** It has been shown that the force of gravity on a planet varies with the mass of the planet. The force of gravity on Jupiter, for example, is about two and a half times that of Earth. Using this information, approximately how much would a 220-lb astronaut weigh on Jupiter?

26. ***Sunday Comics*** Charles Schultz, the creator of *Peanuts,* once estimated that he had drawn close to 2600 Sunday comics over his career. At that time, about how many years had he been drawing *Peanuts?*

27. ***In-Line Skating*** Two in-line skaters, Nell and Kristin, start from the same point and skate in the same direction. Nell skates at 12 miles per hour and Kristin skates at 14 miles per hour. If they can keep up that pace for 2.5 hours, how far apart will they be at the end of that time?

28. ***Train Travel*** Two trains leave a train station at the same time. One train travels east at 50 miles per hour. The other train travels west at 55 miles per hour. In how many hours will the two trains be 315 miles apart?

29. ***Travel Routes*** Nella drove from Albuquerque, New Mexico, to the Garden of the Gods rock formation in Colorado Springs. It took her six hours to travel 312 miles over the mountain road. She came home on the highway. On the highway she took five hours to travel 320 miles. How fast did she travel using the mountain route? How much faster (in miles per hour) did she travel using the highway route?

30. ***Travel Speeds*** Allison drives 30 miles per hour through the city and 55 miles per hour on the New Jersey Turnpike. She drove 90 miles from Battery Park to the Jersey Shore. How much of the time was city driving if she spent 1.2 hours on the turnpike?

31. ***High Temperatures*** From July 13 to 21, 2003, Pueblo, Colorado had 9 consecutive days of temperatures above 100°F, with an average high temperature for that period of 104°F. Recently, Pueblo recorded eight days of high temperatures: 101°, 100°, 102.5°, 103°, 108°, 109°, 105.5°, and 102°. How high would the temperature need to be on the ninth day to tie that record from 2003? (*Source:* National Weather Service.)

32. ***Grading System*** Nyingwo's College Success Seminar teacher had a very complicated grading system. Each test counted once. Each project was worth two tests. The final exam was worth three tests. If Nyingwo received a 97, a 94, and an 89 on tests and a 91 and 93 on projects, what would she need to get on the final exam to receive an A for the course (A is 93 points)?

33. ***Gas Mileage*** The Ramirez family has three cars. The smallest car gets fuel mileage of 38 miles per gallon (mpg) in city driving. The second car gets 21 mpg in city driving. The third car is an ancient, heavy station wagon. Rita calculated that if all three cars were driven the same number of miles in city driving each year, the *average* miles-per-gallon rating of the three Ramirez cars would be $22\frac{2}{3}$ mpg in city driving. What is the miles-per-gallon rating of the old station wagon?

34. ***Executive Salaries*** A local hospital revealed that five officers of the hospital had an average salary of $125,000 per year. Three of the annual salaries were $50,000, $60,000, and $65,000. The annual salaries for the executive vice president and the president were not revealed. It was disclosed that the president makes double the salary of the executive vice president. Find the salaries of the president and the executive vice president.

To Think About

35. ***Cricket Chirps*** In warmer climates, approximate temperature predictions can be made by counting the number of chirps of a cricket during a minute. The Fahrenheit temperature decreased by forty is equivalent to one-fourth of the number of cricket chirps.

(a) Write an equation for this relationship.

(b) Approximately how many chirps per minute should be recorded if the temperature is 90°F?

(c) If a person recorded 148 cricket chirps in a minute, what would be the Fahrenheit temperature according to this formula?

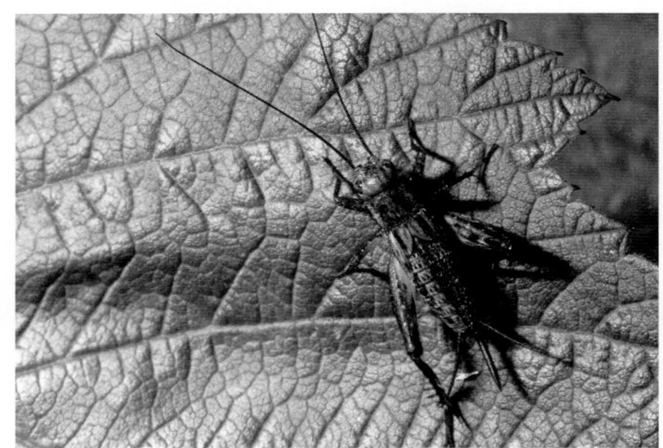

Cumulative Review

Simplify.

36. $5x(2x^2 - 6x - 3)$

37. $-2a(ab - 3b + 5a)$

38. $7x - 3y - 12x - 8y + 5y$

39. $5x^2y - 7xy^2 - 8xy - 9x^2y$

40. ***Apple Sales*** The local Apple Factory produce market sells premium MacIntosh apples at the price of four apples for $3.60. They purchase the apples from the apple orchards for $5.40 per dozen. How many apples will they have to sell to make a profit of $1350?

41. ***Anniversary Party*** Jennifer is hosting a party for her grandparents' 50th wedding anniversary, to be held in the church fellowship hall. She has a budget of $1425.00 to pay a caterer. If the caterer gives her a price of $23.75 per person, how many people can she invite?

3.3 Solving Word Problems: Comparisons

Student Learning Objective

After studying this section, you will be able to:

 **Solve word problems involving comparisons.**

 Solving Word Problems Involving Comparisons

Many real-life problems involve comparisons. We often compare quantities such as length, height, or income. Sometimes not all the information is known about the quantities that are being compared. You need to identify each quantity and write an algebraic expression that describes the situation in the word problem.

EXAMPLE 1 The Center City Animal Hospital treated a total of 18,360 dogs and cats last year. The hospital treated 1376 more dogs than cats. How many dogs were treated last year? How many cats were treated last year?

Solution

1. ***Understand the problem.***

What information is given? The combined number of dogs and cats is 18,360.

What is being compared? There were 1376 more dogs than cats.

If you compare one quantity to another, usually the second quantity is represented by the variable. Since we are comparing the number of dogs to the number of cats, we start with the number of cats.

Let $c =$ the number of cats treated at the hospital.

Then $c + 1376 =$ the number of dogs treated at the hospital.

2. ***Write an equation.***

The number of cats	plus	the number of dogs	is	18,360.
c	$+$	$(c + 1376)$	$=$	$18,360$

3. ***Solve and state the answer.***

$$c + c + 1376 = 18,360$$

$$2c + 1376 = 18,360 \quad \text{Combine like terms.}$$

$$2c + 1376 - 1376 = 18,360 - 1376 \quad \text{Subtract 1376 from both sides.}$$

$$2c = 16,984$$

$$\frac{2c}{2} = \frac{16,984}{2} \quad \text{Divide both sides by 2.}$$

$$c = 8492 \quad \text{The number of cats treated is 8492.}$$

$$c + 1376 = 8492 + 1376 = 9868 \quad \text{The number of dogs treated is 9868.}$$

4. ***Check.*** The number of dogs treated plus the number of cats treated should total 18,360.

$$8492 + 9868 \stackrel{?}{=} 18,360$$

$$18,360 = 18,360 \checkmark$$

Practice Problem 1 A deck hand on a fishing boat is working with a rope that measures 89 feet. He needs to cut it into two pieces. The long piece must be 17 feet longer than the short piece. Find the length of each piece of rope.

NOTE TO STUDENT: Fully worked-out solutions to all of the Practice Problems can be found at the back of the text starting at page SP-1

If the word problem contains three unknown quantities, determine the basis of comparison for two of the quantities.

EXAMPLE 2 An airport filed a report showing the number of plane departures that took off from the airport during each month last year. The number of departures in March was 50 more than the number of departures in January. In July, the number of departures was 150 less than triple the number of departures in January. In those three months, the airport had 2250 departures. How many departures were recorded for each month?

Solution

1. ***Understand the problem.*** What is the basis of comparison?

   The number of departures in March is compared to the number in January.
   The number of departures in July is compared to the number in January.

   Express this algebraically. It may help to underline the key phrases.

   Let j = the departures in January.

   $\underbrace{\text{March was 50 more than January}}$

   Then $j + 50$ = the departures in March.

   $\underbrace{\text{July was 150 less than triple January}}$

   And $3j - 150$ = the departures in July.

2. ***Write an equation.***

   $$\begin{array}{ccccccc} \text{number of} & & \text{number of} & & \text{number of} & & \text{three months'} \\ \text{departures} & + & \text{departures} & + & \text{departures} & = & \text{total} \\ \text{in January} & & \text{in March} & & \text{in July} & & \text{departures} \\ & & & & & & \\ j & + & (j + 50) & + & (3j - 150) & = & 2250 \end{array}$$

3. ***Solve and state the answer.***

   $$\begin{aligned} j + (j + 50) + (3j - 150) &= 2250 \\ 5j - 100 &= 2250 && \text{Collect like terms.} \\ 5j &= 2350 && \text{Add 100 to each side.} \\ j &= 470 && \text{Divide both sides by 5.} \end{aligned}$$

   Now, if $j = 470$, then

   $$j + 50 = 470 + 50 = 520$$

   and

   $$3j - 150 = 3(470) - 150 = 1410 - 150 = 1260.$$

   The number of departures in January was 470; the number of departures in March was 520; the number of departures in July was 1260.

4. ***Check.*** Do these answers seem reasonable? Yes. Do these answers agree with all the statements in the word problem?

   Is the number of departures in March 50 more than those in January?

   $$\begin{aligned} 520 &\stackrel{?}{=} 50 + 470 \\ 520 &= 520 \checkmark \end{aligned}$$

   Is the number of departures in July 150 less than triple those in January?

   $$\begin{aligned} 1260 &\stackrel{?}{=} 3(470) - 150 \\ 1260 &\stackrel{?}{=} 1410 - 150 \\ 1260 &= 1260 \checkmark \end{aligned}$$

   Is the total number of departures in the three months equal to 2250?

   $$\begin{aligned} 470 + 520 + 1260 &\stackrel{?}{=} 2250 \\ 2250 &= 2250 \checkmark \end{aligned}$$

   Yes, all conditions are satisfied. The three answers are correct.

Practice Problem 2 A social services worker was comparing the cost incurred by three families in heating their homes for the year. The first family had an annual heating bill that was \$360 more than that of the second family. The third family had a heating bill that was \$200 less than double the heating bill of the second family. The total annual heating bill for the three families was \$3960. What was the annual heating bill for each family?

***NOTE TO STUDENT:** Fully worked-out solutions to all of the Practice Problems can be found at the back of the text starting at page SP-1*

▲ **EXAMPLE 3** A small plot of land is in the shape of a rectangle. The length is 7 meters longer than the width. The perimeter of the rectangle is 86 meters. Find the dimensions of the rectangle.

Solution

1. ***Understand the problem.*** Read the problem: What information is given?

   The perimeter of a rectangle is 86 meters.

   What is being compared?

   The length is being compared to the width.

   Express this algebraically and draw a picture.

   Let w = the width.

   Then $w + 7$ = the length.

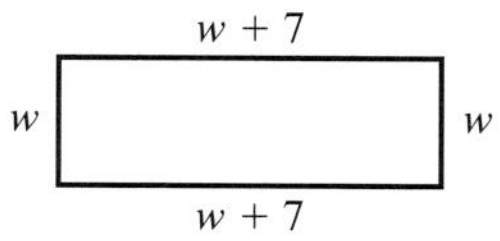

   Reread the problem: What are you being asked to do?

   Find the dimensions of the rectangle. The dimensions of the rectangle are the length and the width of the rectangle.

2. ***Write an equation.*** The perimeter is the total distance around the rectangle.

$$w + (w + 7) + w + (w + 7) = 86$$

3. ***Solve and state the answer.***

$$w + (w + 7) + w + (w + 7) = 86$$
$$4w + 14 = 86 \quad \text{Combine like terms.}$$
$$4w = 72 \quad \text{Subtract 14 from both sides.}$$
$$w = 18 \quad \text{Divide both sides by 4.}$$

   The width of the rectangle is 18 meters. What is the length?

$$w + 7 = \text{the length}$$
$$18 + 7 = 25$$

   The length of the rectangle is 25 meters.

4. ***Check.*** Put the actual dimensions in your drawing and add the lengths of the sides. Is the sum 86 meters? ✓

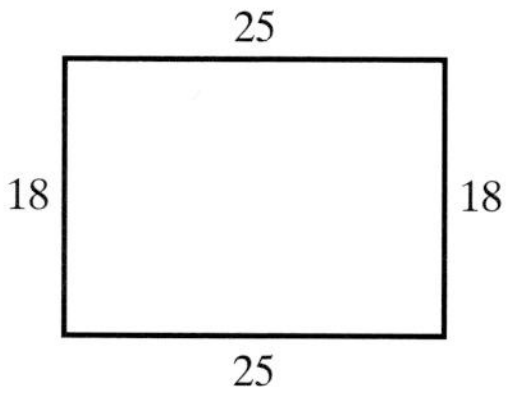

▲ **Practice Problem 3** A farmer purchased 720 meters of wire fencing to enclose a pasture. The pasture is in the shape of a triangle. The first side of the triangle is 30 meters less than the second side. The third side is one-half as long as the second side. Find the dimensions of the triangle.

3.3 Exercises

Student Solutions Manual | CD/ Video | PH Math Tutor Center | MathXL®Tutorials on CD | MathXL® | MyMathLab® | Interactmath.com

Applications

Solve. Check to see if your answer is reasonable. Have you answered the question that was asked?

1. ***Parade Banner*** For their homecoming parade, the students of Wheaton College have created a colorful banner, 47 meters in length, that is made of two pieces of parachute material. The short piece is 17 meters shorter than the long piece. Find the length of each piece.

2. ***Copper Wire*** A copper conducting wire measures 84 centimeters in length. It is cut into two pieces. The shorter piece is 5 centimeters shorter than the long piece. Find the length of each piece.

3. ***Salaries*** Dave and Elsie moved to Hamilton after they got married and they both began new jobs. Elsie earned $2600 per year more than Dave. The total salary for the year for Dave and Elsie was $71,200. How much did each of them earn for the year?

4. ***Auto Insurance*** Dick and Barbara moved to Ipswich and purchased a home. They paid $ 1856 per year to insure their two cars. Dick said it cost $358 more per year to insure his car than it did to insure Barbara's car. How much did it cost to insure Dick's car? How much did it cost to insure Barbara's car?

5. ***Volunteering*** Three siblings—David, Kate, and Sarah—committed themselves to volunteer 100 hours for Habitat for Humanity to build new housing. Sarah worked 15 hours more than Dave. Kate worked 5 hours fewer than Dave. How many hours did each of these siblings volunteer?

6. ***Fruit Basket*** Jerome counted 24 pieces of fruit in a fruit basket. There were twice as many apples as pears. There were four fewer peaches than pears. How many of each fruit were there?

7. ***Home States*** Professor Fullerton was demonstrating the ease of making a bar graph using information of student's home states. He was amazed that his class of 32 represented only 3 states. There were 8 more students born in Texas than were born in Oklahoma. The number of students born in Arizona was 9 fewer than the number born in Oklahoma. How many were born in each state?

8. ***Multiplex*** An 800-seat multiplex is divided into three theaters. Theater One is the smallest. Theater Two has 180 more seats than Theater One. Theater Three has 60 seats fewer than twice the number in Theater One. How large is each theater?

▲ **9.** ***Bridge Support*** The length of a rectangular piece of steel in a bridge is 3 meters less than double the width. The perimeter of the piece of steel is 42 meters. Find the length of the piece of steel. Find the width of the piece of steel.

▲ **10.** ***State Park*** A state park in Colorado has a perimeter of 92 miles. The park is in the shape of a rectangle. The length of the park is 30 miles less than triple the width of the park. Find the length of the park. Find the width of the park.

▲ **11.** ***Painting Frame*** Rashau made a rectangular frame for her latest oil painting. The length is 20 centimeters more than triple the width. The perimeter of the frame is 96 centimeters. Find the length and the width of the frame.

▲ **12.** ***Rug Dimensions*** Theresa purchased a small rectangular rug for her dorm room. The perimeter of the rug is 1438 inches. The length of the rug is 23 inches more than double the width. Find the length and the width of the rug.

▲ **13.** ***Jewelry Box*** A solid-gold jewelry box was found in the underwater palace of Cleopatra just off the shore of Alexandria. The length of the rectangular box is 35 centimeters less than triple the width. The perimeter of the box is 190 centimeters. Find the length and width of Cleopatra's solid-gold jewelry box.

▲ **14.** ***Giant Chocolate Bar*** A giant rectangular chocolate bar was made for a special promotion. The length was 6 meters more than half the width. The perimeter of the chocolate bar was 24 meters. Find the length and width of the giant chocolate bar.

15. ***Running Speed*** The top running speed of a cheetah is double the top running speed of a jackal. The top running speed of an elk is 10 miles per hour faster than that of a jackal. If each of these three animals could run at top speed for an hour (which, of course, is not possible), they could run a combined distance of 150 miles. What is the top running speed of each of these three animals? (*Source:* American Museum of Natural History.)

16. ***River Length*** The Missouri River is 149 miles longer than double the length of the Snake River. The Potomac River is 796 miles shorter than the Snake River. The combined lengths of these three rivers is 3685 miles. What is the length of each of the three rivers? (*Source:* U.S. Department of the Interior.)

▲ **17.** ***Kite Design*** Mr. Shen wished to enter the Orange County Kite Competition with an innovative kite of his own design. He did tests that showed an irregular quadrilateral design was best. (See diagram.) The longest side (A) was twice the length of the shortest side (C). Side B was one and one-half times the shortest side (C). Side D needed to be 3" (3 inches) longer than side C. If the competition required that the perimeter of your kite must be 58", what were the dimensions of Mr. Shen's kite?

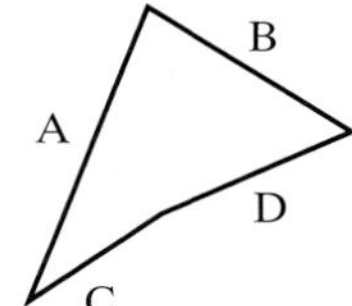

▲ **18.** ***Pennant Design*** The Tri-County schools are participating in a Renaissance Faire. The team from Appleton High School has designed a pennant to fly over its team tent. The pennant is in the shape of a triangle. The longest side is 5" (5 inches) less than twice the middle length side. The shortest side is 3" longer than half the middle length side. If the team captain bought 72" of satin edging for the banner, and there were 4" left over after the pennant was made, what are the dimensions of the pennant?

19. ***Balloon Trip*** A balloonist is trying to complete a nonstop trip around the world. During the course of his trip, he traveled 684 miles over land from Rockford, Illinois, to Washington, D.C. He traveled 1197 miles over water from Washington, D.C., to San Juan, Puerto Rico. The total trip was 39 hours. He traveled 3 more hours over water than he traveled over land.

(a) How long did he travel over land?
(b) How long did he travel over water?
(c) How much faster did he travel over water than over land?

20. ***Waterline Breaks*** In a typical year in New York City, 600 waterline breaks are reported along the 6181 miles of water pipes that twist and turn underground. Water breaks occur five times more often during the period from October to March than they do during the period from April to September.

(a) On average, how many waterline breaks would be expected during the period from October to March?

(b) On average, how many waterline breaks would be expected during the period from April to September?

(c) A water department official once complained to city hall that he expects a break in the waterline every five miles during the course of a year. Is his comment correct? Why?

To Think About

▲ **21.** ***Geometry*** A small square is constructed. Then a new square is made by increasing each side by 2 meters. The perimeter of the new square is 3 meters shorter than five times the length of one side of the original square. Find the dimensions of the original square.

▲ **22.** ***Geometry*** A rectangle is constructed. The length of this rectangle is double the width. Then a new rectangle is made by increasing each side by 3 meters. The perimeter of the new rectangle is 2 meters greater than four times the length of the old rectangle. Find the dimensions of the original rectangle.

Cumulative Review

Simplify.

23. $-4x(2x^2 - 3x + 8)$

24. $5a(ab + 6b - 2a)$

25. $-7x + 10y - 12x - 8y - 2$

26. $3x^2y - 6xy^2 + 7xy + 6x^2y$

27. ***Hardware Shopping*** Today there were 650 people shopping for hardware products in a home improvement store. Of the 650 shoppers, 117 were professional contractors and laborers. What percent of the shoppers were not professional contractors and laborers?

28. ***Dance Lessons*** A dance instructor is doing her best to teach engaged couples how to dance well before their wedding days. After giving lessons to 60 couples, she notes that only 48 couples are able to dance well without coaching. What percent of couples are not dancing very well?

How Am I Doing? Sections 3.1–3.3

How are you doing with your homework assignments in Sections 3.1 to 3.3? Do you feel you have mastered the material so far? Do you understand the concepts you have covered? Before you go further in the textbook, take some time to do each of the following problems.

3.1 *Write an algebraic expression. Use the variable x to represent the unknown number.*

1. Three times a quantity is then decreased by 40.

2. One-half of a number is increased by 12.

3. First a number is multiplied by five. Then the result is divided by 12.

4. One-fourth of the sum of a number and 10.

3.2 *Translate the information into an equation. Then solve the equation in order to answer the question.*

5. A number is doubled and then increased by five. The result is -47. What is the original number?

6. A number is divided by two. Then nine is subtracted from the result. A value of 43 is obtained. What is the original number?

7. At Lucas Ford, the monthly rental on a Ford Focus is \$310. The cost of a new car is \$12,400. In how many months will the rental cost equal the cost of purchasing a new car?

8. Bill Tupper makes \$24 per hour for a 40 hour week. He earns time and a half for every hour over 40 hours during that one week. If Bill earned \$1140 last week, how many overtime hours did he work?

9. The average salary of five workers at Verizon is \$50,200. The first person earns \$40,000 per year. A second person earns \$35,000 per year. A third person earns \$13,500 more per year than the first person. The fourth person earns an unknown annual salary. The fifth person earns \$2,500 per year more than the fourth person. How much is the annual salary of the fourth person? How much is the annual salary of the fifth person?

3.3

10. A rope measures 84 feet in length. It is cut into two pieces. The long piece is 18 feet longer than twice the length of the short piece. How long is each piece?

11. Andy is doing his reading for his History of World Civilizations class. He must read a total of 260 pages in the next three days. On Monday he reads 25 pages less than twice the number of pages he read on Sunday. On Tuesday he reads 15 pages less than three times the number of pages he read on Sunday. If he reached his reading goal, how many pages did he read on each day?

12. A farmer in southern New Jersey has three fields to plow. The first field takes three times as long to plow as the second field. The third field takes one fourth as long to plow as the second field. The farmer requires 510 hours to plow all three fields. How long does it take to plow each field?

Now turn to page SA-8 for the answer to each of these problems. Each answer also includes a reference to the objective in which the problem is first taught. If you missed any of these problems, you should stop and review the Examples and Practice Problems in the referenced objective. A little review now will help you master the material in the upcoming sections of the text.

1. ______
2. ______
3. ______
4. ______
5. ______
6. ______
7. ______
8. ______
9. ______
10. ______
11. ______
12. ______

3.4 Solving Word Problems: The Value of Money and Percents

Student Learning Objectives

After studying this section, you will be able to:

1. **Solve problems involving periodic rate charges.**
2. **Solve percent problems.**
3. **Solve investment problems involving simple interest.**
4. **Solve coin problems.**

The problems we now present are frequently encountered in business. They deal with money: buying, selling, and renting items; earning and borrowing money; and the value of collections of stamps or coins. Many applications require an understanding of the use of percents and decimals. Review Sections 0.4 and 0.5 if you are weak in these skills.

1 Solving Problems Involving Periodic Rate Charges

EXAMPLE 1 A business executive rented a car. The Supreme Car Rental Agency charged \$39 per day and \$0.28 per mile. The executive rented the car for two days and the total rental cost was computed to be \$176. How many miles did the executive drive the rented car?

Solution

1. ***Understand the problem.*** How do you calculate the cost of renting a car?

   total cost = per-day cost + mileage cost

   What is known?

   It cost \$176 *to rent the car for two days.*

   What do you need to find?

   The number of miles the car was driven.

   Choose a variable:

   Let m = the number of miles driven in the rented car.

2. ***Write an equation.*** Use the relationship for calculating the total cost.

$$\begin{array}{ccccc} \text{per-day cost} & + & \text{mileage cost} & = & \text{total cost} \\ (39)(2) & + & (0.28)m & = & 176 \end{array}$$

3. ***Solve and state the answer.***

$$(39)(2) + (0.28)(m) = 176$$

$$78 + 0.28m = 176 \quad \text{Simplify the equation.}$$

$$0.28m = 98 \quad \text{Subtract 78 from both sides.}$$

$$\frac{0.28m}{0.28} = \frac{98}{0.28} \quad \text{Divide both sides by 0.28.}$$

$$m = 350 \quad \text{Simplify.}$$

   The executive drove 350 miles.

4. ***Check.*** Does this seem reasonable? If he drove the car 350 miles in two days, would it cost \$176?

$$(\text{cost of \$39 per day for 2 days}) + (\text{cost of \$0.28 per mile for 350 miles}) \stackrel{?}{=} \text{total cost of \$176}$$

$$(\$39)(2) + (350)(\$0.28) \stackrel{?}{=} \$176$$

$$\$78 + \$98 \stackrel{?}{=} \$176$$

$$\$176 = \$176 \checkmark$$

Practice Problem 1 Alfredo wants to rent a truck to move to Florida. He has determined that the cheapest rental rates for a truck of the correct size are from a local company that will charge him \$25 per day and \$0.20 per mile. He has not yet completed an estimate of the mileage of the trip, but he knows that he will need the truck for three days. He has allowed \$350 in his moving budget for the truck. How far can he travel for a rental cost of exactly \$350?

NOTE TO STUDENT: Fully worked-out solutions to all of the Practice Problems can be found at the back of the text starting at page SP-1

Solving Percent Problems

Many applied situations require finding a percent of an unknown number. If we want to find 23% of \$400, we multiply 0.23 by 400: $0.23(400) = 92$. If we want to find 23% of an unknown number, we can express this using algebra by writing $0.23n$, where n represents the unknown number.

EXAMPLE 2 A sofa was marked with the following sign: "The price of this sofa has been reduced by 23%. You can save \$138 if you buy now." What was the original price of the sofa?

Solution

1. ***Understand the problem.***

   Let s = the original price of the sofa.

   Then $0.23s$ = the amount of the price reduction, which is \$138.

2. ***Write an equation and solve.***

   $0.23s = 138$ Write the equation.

   $\frac{0.23s}{0.23} = \frac{138}{0.23}$ Divide each side of the equation by 0.23.

   $s = 600$ Simplify.

   The original price of the sofa was \$600.

3. ***Check.*** Is \$600 a reasonable answer? ✓ Does 23% of \$600 = \$138? ✓

Practice Problem 2 John earns a commission of 38% of the cost of every set of encyclopedias that he sells. Last year he earned \$4560 in commissions. What was the cost of the encyclopedias that he sold last year?

EXAMPLE 3 Hector received a pay raise this year. The raise was 6% of last year's salary. This year he will earn \$15,900. What was his salary last year before the raise?

Solution

1. ***Understand the problem.*** What do we need to find?

   Hector's salary last year.

   What do we know?

   Hector received a 6% *pay raise and now earns* \$15,900.

   What does this mean?

   Reword the problem: *This year's salary of* \$15,900 *is* 6% *more than last year's salary.*

Choose a variable:

Let x = Hector's salary last year.
Then $0.06x$ = the amount of the raise.

2. ***Write an equation and solve.***

Last year's salary	+	the amount of his raise	=	this year's salary	
x	+	$0.06x$	=	15,900	Write the equation.
$1.00x$	+	$0.06x$	=	15,900	Rewrite x as $1.00x$.
		$1.06x$	=	15,900	Combine like terms.
x			=	$\frac{15{,}900}{1.06}$	Divide by 1.06.
x			=	15,000	Simplify.

Thus Hector's salary was $15,000 last year before the raise.

3. ***Check.*** Does it seem reasonable that Hector's salary last year was $15,000? The check is up to you.

Practice Problem 3 The price of Betsy's new car is 7% more than the price of a similar model last year. She paid $13,910 for her car this year. What would a similar model have cost last year?

Calculator

Interest

You can use a calculator to find simple interest. Find the interest on $450 invested at an annual rate of 6.5% for 15 months. Notice that the time is in months. Since the interest formula $I = prt$ is in years, you need to change 15 months to years by dividing 15 by 12.

Enter: 15 [÷] 12 [=]

Display: [1.25]

Leave this on the display and multiply as follows:

1.25 [×] 450 [×]

6.5 [%] [=]

The display should read

[36.5625]

which would round to $36.56.

Try finding the simple interest in the following investments.

(a) $9516 invested at 12% for 30 months

(b) $593 borrowed at 8% for 5 months

Answers:

(a) $2854.80

(b) $19.97

3 Solving Investment Problems Involving Simple Interest

Interest is a charge for borrowing money or an income from investing money. Interest rates affect our lives. They affect the national economy and they affect a consumer's ability to borrow money for big purchases. For these reasons, a student of mathematics should be able to solve problems involving interest.

There are two basic types of interest: simple and compound. **Simple interest** is computed by multiplying the amount of money borrowed or invested (which is called the *principal*) times the rate of interest times the period of time over which it is borrowed or invested (usually measured in years unless otherwise stated).

$$\text{Interest} = \text{principal} \times \text{rate} \times \text{time}$$
$$I = prt$$

You often hear of banks offering a certain interest rate *compounded* quarterly, monthly, weekly, or daily. In **compound interest** the amount of interest is added to the amount of the original principal at the end of each time period, so future interest is based on the sum of both principal and previous interest. Most financial institutions use compound interest in their transactions.

Problems involving compound interest may be solved by:

1. Repeated calculations using the simple interest formula.
2. Using a compound interest table.
3. Using exponential functions, a topic that is usually covered in a higher-level college algebra course.

All examples and exercises in this chapter will involve **simple interest.**

EXAMPLE 4 Find the interest on \$3000 borrowed at a simple interest rate of 18% for one year.

Solution

$I = prt$ The simple interest formula.

$I = (3000)(0.18)(1)$ Substitute the values of the variables: principal = 3000, the rate = 18% = 0.18, the time = one year.

$I = 540$

Thus the interest charge for borrowing \$3000 for one year at a simple interest rate of 18% is \$540.

Practice Problem 4 Find the interest on \$7000 borrowed at a simple interest rate of 12% for one year.

NOTE TO STUDENT: Fully worked-out solutions to all of the Practice Problems can be found at the back of the text starting at page SP-1

Now we apply this concept to a word problem about investments.

EXAMPLE 5 A woman invested an amount of money in two accounts for one year. She invested some at 8% simple interest and the rest at 6% simple interest. Her total amount invested was \$1250. At the end of the year she had earned \$86 in interest. How much money had she invested in each account?

Solution

Mathematics Blueprint for Problem Solving

Gather the Facts	Assign the Variable	Basic Formula or Equation	Key Points to Remember
\$1250 is invested: part at 8% interest, part at 6% interest. The total interest for the year is \$86.	x = amount invested at 8%. $1250 - x$ = amount invested at 6%. $0.08x$ = amount of interest for x dollars at 8%. $0.06(1250 - x)$ = amount of interest for $1250 - x$ dollars at 6%.	Interest earned at 8% + interest earned at 6% = total interest earned during the year, which is \$86.	Be careful to write $1250 - x$ for the amount of money invested at 6%. The order of the amounts is $1250 - x$. Do not use $x - 1250$.

interest earned at 8%	+	interest earned at 6%	=	total interest earned during the year
$0.08x$	+	$0.06(1250 - x)$	=	86

Note: Be sure you write $(1250 - x)$ for the amount of money invested at 6%. Students often write it backwards by mistake. It is *not* correct to use $(x - 1250)$ instead of $(1250 - x)$. The order of the terms is very important.

Solve and state the answer.

$0.08x + 75 - 0.06x = 86$	Remove parentheses.
$0.02x + 75 = 86$	Combine like terms.
$0.02x = 11$	Subtract 75 from both sides.
$\dfrac{0.02x}{0.02} = \dfrac{11}{0.02}$	Divide both sides by 0.02.
$x = 550$	The amount invested at 8% interest is \$550.
$1250 - x = 1250 - 550 = 700$	The amount invested at 6% interest is \$700.

Check. Are these values reasonable? Yes. Do the amounts equal \$1250?

$$\$550 + \$700 \stackrel{?}{=} \$1250$$
$$\$1250 = \$1250 \checkmark$$

Would these amounts earn \$86 interest in one year invested at the specified rates?

$$0.08(\$550) + 0.06(\$700) \stackrel{?}{=} \$86$$
$$\$44 + \$42 \stackrel{?}{=} \$86$$
$$\$86 = \$86 \checkmark$$

Practice Problem 5 A woman invested her savings of \$8000 in two accounts that each calculate interest only once per year. She placed one amount in a special notice account that yields 9% annual interest. The remainder she placed in a tax-free All-Savers account that yields 7% annual interest. At the end of the year, she had earned \$630 in interest from the two accounts together. How much had she invested in each account?

***NOTE TO STUDENT:** Fully worked-out solutions to all of the Practice Problems can be found at the back of the text starting at page SP-1*

Solving Coin Problems

Coin problems provide an unmatched opportunity to use the concept of *value*. We must make a distinction between *how many coins* there are and the *value* of the coins.

Consider the next example. Here we know *the value* of some coins, but do not know *how many* we have.

EXAMPLE 6 When Bob got out of math class, he had to make a long-distance call. He had exactly enough dimes and quarters to make a phone call that would cost \$2.55. He had one less quarter than he had dimes. How many coins of each type did he have?

Solution Let d = the number of dimes.

Then $d - 1$ = the number of quarters.

The total value of the coins was \$2.55. How can we represent the value of the dimes and the value of the quarters? Think.

Each dime is worth \$0.10.	Each quarter is worth \$0.25.
5 dimes are worth $(5)(0.10) = 0.50$.	8 quarters are worth $(8)(0.25) = 2.00$.
d dimes are worth $(d)(0.10) = 0.10d$.	$(d - 1)$ quarters are worth $(d - 1)(0.25) = 0.25(d - 1)$.

Now we can write an equation for the total value.

$$\text{(value of dimes)} + \text{(value of quarters)} = \$2.55$$
$$0.10d + 0.25(d - 1) = 2.55$$

$$0.10d + 0.25d - 0.25 = 2.55 \quad \text{Remove parentheses.}$$
$$0.35d - 0.25 = 2.55 \quad \text{Combine like terms.}$$
$$0.35d = 2.80 \quad \text{Add 0.25 to both sides.}$$
$$\frac{0.35d}{0.35} = \frac{2.80}{0.35} \quad \text{Divide both sides by 0.35.}$$
$$d = 8 \quad \text{Simplify.}$$
$$d - 1 = 7$$

Thus Bob had eight dimes and seven quarters.

Check. Is this answer reasonable? Yes. Does Bob have one less quarter than he has dimes?

$$8 - 7 \stackrel{?}{=} 1$$
$$1 = 1 \checkmark$$

Are eight dimes and seven quarters worth \$2.55?

$$8(\$0.10) + 7(\$0.25) \stackrel{?}{=} \$2.55$$
$$\$0.80 + \$1.75 \stackrel{?}{=} \$2.55$$
$$\$2.55 = \$2.55 \checkmark$$

Practice Problem 6 Ginger has five more quarters than dimes. She has \$5.10 in change. If she has only quarters and dimes, how many coins of each type does she have?

EXAMPLE 7 Michele and her two children returned from the grocery store with only \$2.80 in change. She had twice as many quarters as nickels. She had two more dimes than nickels. How many nickels, dimes, and quarters did she have?

Solution

Mathematics Blueprint for Problem Solving

Gather the Facts	Assign the Variable	Basic Formula or Equation	Key Points to Remember
Michele had \$2.80 in change. She had twice as many quarters as nickels. She had two more dimes than nickels.	x = number of nickels. $2x$ = number of quarters. $x + 2$ = number of dimes. $0.05x$ = value of the nickels. $0.25(2x)$ = value of the quarters. $0.10(x + 2)$ = value of the dimes.	The value of the nickels + the value of the dimes + the value of the quarters = \$2.80.	Don't add the number of coins to get \$2.80. You must add the value of the coins!

$$\text{(value of nickels)} + \text{(value of dimes)} + \text{(value of quarters)} = \$2.80$$
$$0.05x + 0.10(x + 2) + 0.25(2x) = 2.80$$

Solve.

$$0.05x + 0.10x + 0.20 + 0.50x = 2.80 \quad \text{Remove parentheses.}$$
$$0.65x + 0.20 = 2.80 \quad \text{Combine like terms.}$$
$$0.65x = 2.60 \quad \text{Subtract 0.20 from both sides.}$$
$$\frac{0.65x}{0.65} = \frac{2.60}{0.65} \quad \text{Divide both sides by 0.65.}$$
$$x = 4 \quad \text{Simplify. Michele had four nickels.}$$
$$2x = 8 \quad \text{She had eight quarters.}$$
$$x + 2 = 6 \quad \text{She had six dimes.}$$

When Michele left the grocery store she had four nickels, eight quarters, and six dimes.

Check. Is the answer reasonable? Yes. Did Michele have twice as many quarters as nickels?

$$(4)(2) \stackrel{?}{=} 8 \qquad 8 = 8 \checkmark$$

Did she have two more dimes than nickels?

$$4 + 2 \stackrel{?}{=} 6 \qquad 6 = 6 \checkmark$$

Do four nickels, eight quarters, and six dimes have a value of \$2.80?

$$4(\$0.05) + 8(\$0.25) + 6(\$0.10) \stackrel{?}{=} \$2.80$$
$$\$0.20 + \$2.00 + \$0.60 \stackrel{?}{=} \$2.80$$
$$\$2.80 = \$2.80 \checkmark$$

NOTE TO STUDENT: Fully worked-out solutions to all of the Practice Problems can be found at the back of the text starting at page SP-1

Practice Problem 7 A young boy told his friend that he had twice as many nickels as dimes in his pocket. He also said that he had four more quarters than dimes. He said that he had \$2.35 in change in his pocket. Can you determine how many nickels, dimes, and quarters he had?

Developing Your Study Skills

Applications or Word Problems

Applications or word problems are the very life of mathematics! They are the reason for doing mathematics because they teach you how to put into use the mathematical skills you have developed. Learning mathematics without ever doing word problems is similar to learning all the skills of a sport without ever playing a game or learning all the notes on an instrument without ever playing a song.

The key to success is practice. Make yourself do as many problems as you can. If you need help organizing your facts, use the Mathematics Blueprint. You may not be able to do all problems correctly at first, but keep trying. Do not give up whenever you reach a difficult one. If you cannot solve it, just try another one. Then come back and try it again later.

A misconception among students when they begin studying word problems is that each problem is different. At first the problems may seem this way, but as you practice more and more, you will begin to see the similarities, the different "types." You will see patterns in solving problems, which will enable you to solve them more easily.

3.4 Exercises

Student Solutions Manual | CD/ Video | PH Math Tutor Center | MathXL®Tutorials on CD | MathXL® | MyMathLab® | Interactmath.com

Applications

Solve. All problems involving interest refer to simple interest.

1. ***Raking Leaves*** Paul has a job raking leaves for a neighbor. He makes \$6.50 an hour, plus \$0.75 for each bag he fills. Last Saturday he worked three hours and made a total of \$27.75. How many bags of leaves did he fill?

2. ***Waiting Tables*** Marybelle is contemplating a job as a waitress. She would be paid \$4 per hour plus tips. The other waitresses have told her that an average tip at that restaurant is \$3 per table served. If she works 20 hours per week, how many tables would she have to serve in order to make \$191 during the week?

3. ***Overtime*** Ramon has a summer job as a lifeguard to earn his college tuition. He gets paid \$6.00 per hour for the first 40 hours and \$9.00 per hour for each hour in the week worked more than 40 hours. This summer his goal is to earn at least \$303.00 per week. How many hours of overtime per week will he need to achieve his goal?

4. ***Overtime*** Maria has a summer job as a tennis instructor to earn her college tuition. She gets paid \$6.50 per hour for the first 40 hours and \$9.75 for each hour in the week worked more than 40 hours. This summer her goal is to earn at least \$338.00 per week. How many hours of overtime per week will she need to achieve her goal?

5. ***Layaway*** Mrs. Peterson's triplets all want to attend the local private academy, where they are required to wear uniforms. Mrs. Peterson knows that the only way she can afford these uniforms is to shop early, put the uniforms on layaway, and pay a little every week. The total uniform cost for the three girls is \$1817.75. If she put down a deposit of \$600 and she could afford \$105 per week, how long would it take her to pay off the uniforms? (Round to nearest whole number.)

6. ***Party Costs*** The Swedish Chef Catering Company charges \$50.00 for setup, \$85.00 for cleanup, and the special menu that Judy Carter ordered cost \$23.50 per person. If Judy Carter's bill came to \$558.00, how many people came to the party?

7. ***Camera Sale*** The camera Melissa wanted for her birthday is on sale at 28% off the usual price. The amount of the discount is \$100.80. What was the original price of the camera?

8. ***Work Force*** The number of women working full-time in Springfield has risen 12% this year. This means 216 more women have full-time jobs. What was the number of women working full-time last year?

9. ***Salary*** The cost of living last year went up 3%. Fortunately, Alice Swanson got a 3% raise in her salary from last year. This year she is earning \$22,660. How much did she make last year?

10. ***Stock Profit*** A speculator bought stocks and later sold them for \$5136, making a profit of 7%. How much did the stocks cost him?

11. ***Investments*** Don Williams invested some money at 9% simple interest. At the end of the year, the total amount of his original principal and the interest was \$6540. How much did he originally invest?

12. ***Investments*** Robert Campbell invested some money at 8% simple interest. At the end of the year, the total amount of his original principal and the interest was \$7560. How much did he originally invest?

13. ***Trust Fund*** Mr. and Mrs. Wright set up a trust fund for their children last year. Part of it is earning 7% simple interest per year while the rest of it is earning 5% simple interest per year. They placed \$5000 in the trust fund. In one year the trust fund has earned \$310. How much did they invest at each interest rate?

14. ***Investments*** Anne and Michael invested \$8000 last year in tax-free bonds. Some of the bonds earned 8% simple interest while the rest earned 6% simple interest. At the end of the year, they had earned \$580 in interest. How much did they invest at each interest rate?

15. ***Investments*** Plymouth Rock Bank invested \$400,000 last year in mutual funds. The conservative fund earned 8% simple interest. The growth fund earned 12% simple interest. At the end of the year, the bank had earned \$38,000 from these mutual funds. How much did it invest in each fund?

16. ***Investments*** Millennium Securities last year invested \$600,000 in mutual funds. The international fund earned 11% simple interest. The high-tech fund earned 7% simple interest. At the end of the year, the company had earned \$50,000 in interest. How much did it invest in each fund?

17. ***Investments*** Dave Horn invested half of his money at 5%, one-third of his money at 4%, and the rest of his money at 3.5%. If his total annual investment income was \$530, how much had he invested?

18. ***Investments*** Last year Pete Pfeffer decided to invest half of his money in a credit union paying 4.5% interest, one-third of his money in a mutual fund paying 5% interest, and the rest of his money in a bank CD paying 4% interest. If his annual investment income was \$357.50 last year, how much money had he invested?

19. ***Coin Bank*** Little Melinda has nickels and quarters in her bank. She has four fewer nickels than quarters. She has \$3.70 in the bank. How many coins of each type does she have?

20. ***Coin Change*** Reggie's younger brother had several coins when he returned from his paper route. He had a total of \$5.35 in dimes and quarters. He had six more quarters than he had dimes. How many of each coin did he have?

21. ***Coin Change*** A newspaper carrier has \$3.75 in change. He has three more quarters than dimes but twice as many nickels as quarters. How many coins of each type does he have?

22. ***Coin Change*** Tim Whitman has \$4.50 in change in his desk drawer to use on the vending machines downstairs. He has four more quarters than dimes. He has three times as many nickels as dimes. How many coins of each type does he have?

23. ***Stamps*** Ramon was office manager for a small law firm. He made the weekly postage purchase. He bought regular 37¢ stamps for most of the firm, but he also picked up some 40¢ breast cancer stamps at the request of some of the lawyers. He noticed that the number of breast cancer stamps was 8 fewer than the number of regular stamps and that he spent \$19.90. How many of each stamp did he buy?

24. ***Ticket Prices*** Mario's Marionettes donated free tickets for their show to the local Boys & Girls Club. They claimed that the ticket value was \$176.75. A child's ticket cost \$5.50 and an adult ticket cost \$8.75. If there were three times as many children's tickets as adult tickets, how many adults and children got to attend the show for free?

25. ***Paper Currency*** Charlie Saulnier cashed his paycheck and came home from the bank with \$100 bills, \$20 bills, and \$10 bills. He has twice as many \$20 bills as he has \$10 bills. He has three more \$100 bills than he has \$10 bills. He is carrying \$1500 in bills. How many of each denomination does he have?

26. ***Paper Currency*** Roberta Burgess came home with \$325 in tips from two nights on her job as a waitress. She had \$20 bills, \$10 bills, and \$5 bills. She discovered that she had three times as many \$5 bills as she had \$10 bills. She also found that she had 4 fewer \$20 bills than she had \$10 bills. How many of each denomination did she have?

27. ***Salary*** Madelyn Logan is an office furniture dealer who earns an \$18,000 base salary. She also earns a 4% commission on sales. How much must she sell to earn a total of \$55,000?

28. ***Animal Shelter*** The local animal shelter accepts abandoned cats and dogs. They usually receive twice as many cats as dogs. They estimate that 80% of the cats and 60% of the dogs that come in need some kind of medical treatment. If they treated 286 animals last year, how many cats and dogs did they take in?

To Think About

29. ***Car Rentals*** The West Suburban Car Rental Agency will rent a compact car for \$35 per day and an additional charge of \$0.24 per mile. The Golden Gate Car Rental Agency charges only \$0.16 per mile but charges \$41 per day. If a salesperson wanted to rent a car for three days, how many miles would that person have to drive to make the Golden Gate Car Rental Agency car a better bargain?

30. ***Pumping Station*** A Peabody pumping station pumps 2000 gallons of water per hour into an empty reservoir tank for a town's drinking supply. The station pumps for three hours. Then a leak in the reservoir tank is created by a large crack. Some water flows out of the reservoir tank at a constant rate. The pumping station continues pumping for six more hours while the leak is undetected. At the end of nine hours the reservoir contains 17,640 gallons of water. During the last six hours, how many gallons per hour are leaking from the reservoir?

Cumulative Review

Perform the operations in the proper order.

31. $5(3) + 6 \div (-2)$

32. $5(-3) - 2(12 - 15)^2 \div 9$

Evaluate for $x = -2$ *and* $y = 3$.

33. $2x^2 + 3xy - 2y^2$

34. $x^3 - 5x^2 + 3y - 6$

Satellite Parts *Brian sells high-tech parts to satellite communications companies. In his negotiations he originally offers to sell one company 200 parts for a total of \$22,400. However, after negotiations, he offers to sell that company the same parts at a 15% discount if the company agrees to sign a purchasing contract for 200 additional parts at some future date.*

35. What is the average cost per part if the parts are sold at the discounted price?

36. How much will the total bill be for the 200 parts at the discounted price?

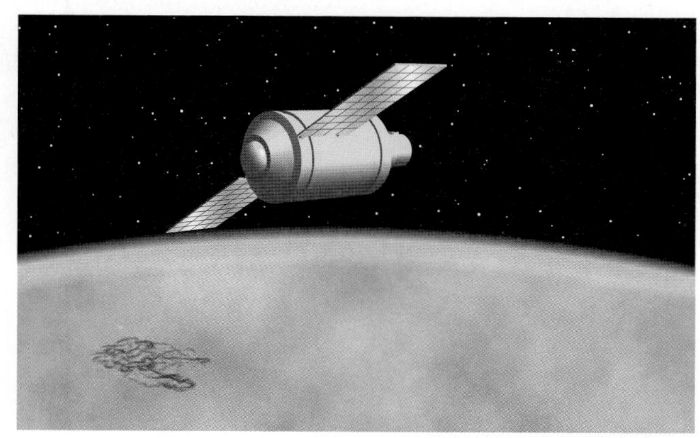

3.5 Solving Word Problems Using Geometric Formulas

Student Learning Objectives

After studying this section, you will be able to:

1. **Find the area and the perimeter of two-dimensional objects. Find the missing angle of a triangle.**
2. **Find the volume and the surface area of three-dimensional objects. Find a missing dimension.**
3. **Solve more-involved geometric problems.**

1 Finding Area, Perimeter, and Missing Angles

In Section 1.8 we reviewed a number of area and perimeter formulas. We repeat this list of formulas here for convenience.

AREA AND PERIMETER FORMULAS

A **parallelogram** is a four-sided figure with opposite sides parallel. In a parallelogram, opposite sides are equal and opposite angles are equal.

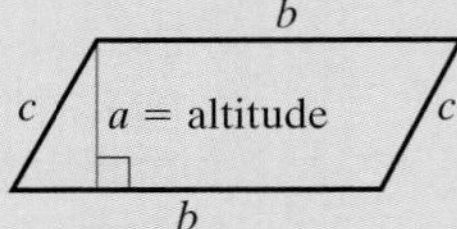

Perimeter = the sum of all four sides

Area $= ab$

A **rectangle** is a parallelogram with all interior angles measuring 90°.

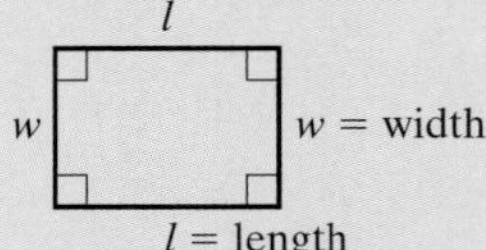

Perimeter $= 2l + 2w$

Area $= lw$

A **square** is a rectangle with all four sides equal.

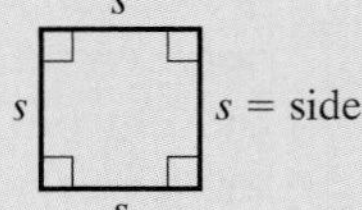

Perimeter $= 4s$

Area $= s^2$

A **trapezoid** is a four-sided figure with two sides parallel. The parallel sides are called the bases of the trapezoid.

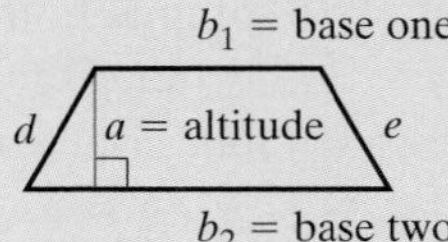

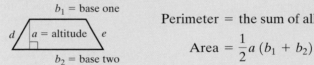

Perimeter = the sum of all four sides

Area $= \frac{1}{2}a\,(b_1 + b_2)$

A **triangle** is a closed plane figure with three sides.

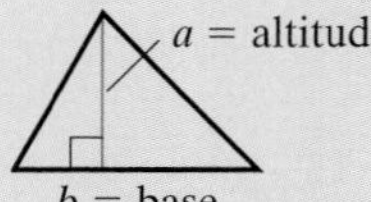

Perimeter = the sum of the three sides

Area $= \frac{1}{2}ab$

A **circle** is a plane curve consisting of all points at an equal distance from a given point called the center.

Circumference is the distance around a circle. The **radius** is a line segment from the center of the circle to a point on the circle. The **diameter** is a line segment across the circle that passes through the center with endpoints on the circle.

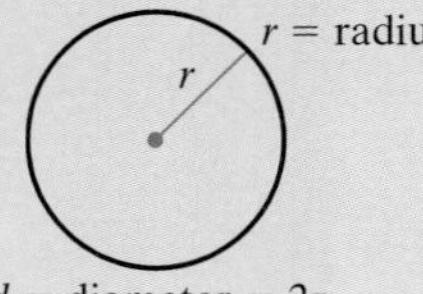

Circumference $= 2\pi r$

Area $= \pi r^2$

π is a constant associated with circles. It is an irrational number that is approximately 3.141592654. We usually use 3.14 as a sufficiently accurate approximation. Thus we write $\pi \approx 3.14$ for most of our calculations involving π.

We frequently encounter triangles in word problems. There are four important facts about triangles, which we list for convenient reference.

TRIANGLE FACTS

1. The sum of the interior angles of any triangle is 180°. That is,

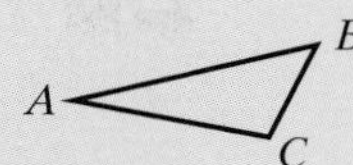

measure of $\angle A$ + measure of $\angle B$ + measure of $\angle C = 180°$.

2. An **equilateral** triangle is a triangle with three sides equal in length and three angles that measure 60° each.

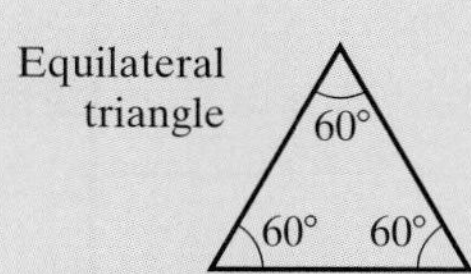

3. An **isosceles** triangle is a triangle with two equal sides. The two angles opposite the equal sides are also equal.

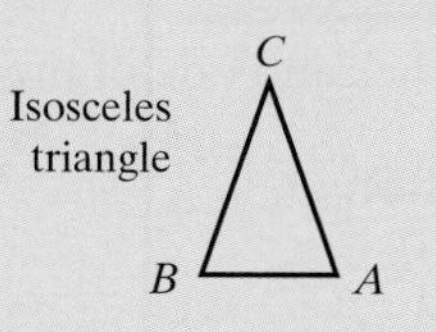

measure $\angle A$ = measure $\angle B$

4. A **right** triangle is a triangle with one angle that measures 90°.

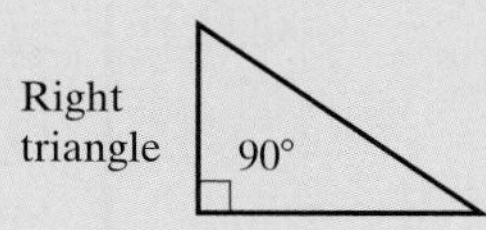

▲ **EXAMPLE 1** Find the area of a triangular window whose base is 16 inches and whose altitude is 19 inches.

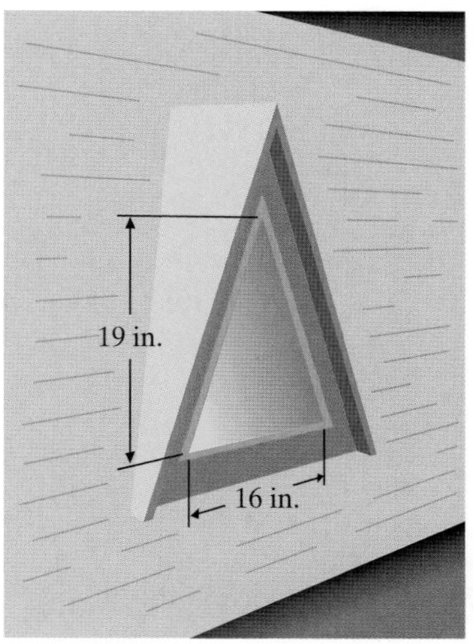

Solution We can use the formula for the area of a triangle. Substitute the known values in the formula and solve for the unknown.

$$A = \frac{1}{2}ab \quad \text{Write the formula for the area of a triangle.}$$

$$= \frac{1}{2}(16 \text{ in.})(19 \text{ in.}) \quad \text{Substitute the known values in the formula.}$$

$$= \frac{1}{2}(16)(19)(\text{in.})(\text{in.}) \quad \text{Simplify.}$$

$$A = 152 \text{ in.}^2 \quad \text{or} \quad 152 \text{ square inches}$$

The area of the triangle is 152 square inches.

▲ **Practice Problem 1** Find the area of a triangle whose base is 14 inches and whose altitude is 20 inches.

NOTE TO STUDENT: Fully worked-out solutions to all of the Practice Problems can be found at the back of the text starting at page SP-1

▲ **EXAMPLE 2** The area of an NBA basketball court is 4700 square feet. Find the width of the court if the length is 94 feet.

Solution Draw a diagram.

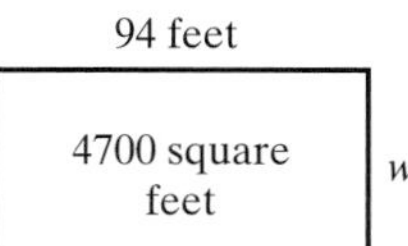

Write the formula for the area of a rectangle and solve for the unknown value.

$$A = lw$$

$$4700\ (\text{ft})^2 = (94\ \text{ft})(w) \quad \text{Substitute the known values into the formula.}$$

$$\frac{4700\ (\text{ft})(\text{ft})}{94\ \text{ft}} = \frac{94\ \text{ft}}{94\ \text{ft}}w \quad \text{Divide both sides by 94 feet.}$$

$$50\ \text{feet} = w$$

The width of the basketball court is 50 feet.

Practice Problem 2 The area of a rectangular field is 120 square yards. If the width of the field is 8 yards, what is the length?

EXAMPLE 3 The area of a trapezoid is 400 square inches. The altitude is 20 inches and one of the bases is 15 inches. Find the length of the other base.

15 in.

20 in.

Solution

$$A = \frac{1}{2}a\,(b_1 + b_2) \quad \text{Write the formula for the area of a trapezoid.}$$

$$400(\text{in.})^2 = \frac{1}{2}(20\ \text{in.})(15\ \text{in.} + b_2) \quad \text{Substitute the known values.}$$

$$400(\text{in.})(\text{in.}) = 10(\text{in.})(15\ \text{in.} + b_2) \quad \text{Simplify.}$$

$$400(\text{in.})(\text{in.}) = 150(\text{in.})(\text{in.}) + (10\ \text{in.})b_2 \quad \text{Remove parentheses.}$$

$$250(\text{in.})(\text{in.}) = (10\ \text{in.})b_2 \quad \text{Subtract 150 in.}^2 \text{ from both sides.}$$

$$25\ \text{in.} = b_2 \quad \text{Divide both sides by 10 in.}$$

The other base is 25 inches long.

Practice Problem 3 The area of a trapezoid is 256 square feet. The bases are 12 feet and 20 feet. Find the altitude.

EXAMPLE 4 Find the area of a circular sign whose diameter is 14 inches. (Use 3.14 for π.) Round to the nearest square inch.

Solution $A = \pi r^2$ Write the formula for the area of a circle.

Note that the length of the diameter is given in the word problem. We need to know the length of the radius to use the formula. Since $d = 2r$, then 14 in. $= 2r$ and $r = 7$ in.

$$A = \pi(7\ \text{in.})(7\ \text{in.}) \quad \text{Substitute known values into the formula.}$$

$$= (3.14)(7\ \text{in.})(7\ \text{in.})$$

$$= (3.14)(49\ \text{in.}^2)$$

$$= 153.86\ \text{in.}^2$$

Rounded to the nearest square inch, the area of the circle is approximately 154 square inches.

In this example, you were asked to find the area of the circle. Do not confuse the formula for area with the formula for circumference. $A = \pi r^2$, while $C = 2\pi r$. Remember that area involves square units, so it is only natural that in the area formula you would square the radius.

Practice Problem 4 Find the circumference of a circle whose radius is 15 meters. (Use 3.14 for π.) Round your answer to the nearest meter.

▲ **EXAMPLE 5** Find the perimeter of a parallelogram whose longer sides are 4 feet and whose shorter sides are 2.6 feet.

Solution Draw a picture.

4 ft

2.6 ft

The perimeter is the distance around a figure. To find the perimeter, add the lengths of the sides. Since the opposite sides of a parallelogram are equal, we can write the following.

$$\begin{aligned} P &= 2(4 \text{ feet}) + 2(2.6 \text{ feet}) \\ &= 8 \text{ feet} + 5.2 \text{ feet} \\ &= 13.2 \text{ feet} \end{aligned}$$

The perimeter of the parallelogram is 13.2 feet.

▲ **Practice Problem 5** Find the perimeter of an equilateral triangle with a side that measures 15 centimeters.

▲ **EXAMPLE 6** The smallest angle of an isosceles triangle measures 24°. The other two angles are larger. What are the measurements of the other two angles?

Solution We know that in an isosceles triangle the measures of two angles are equal. We know that the sum of the measures of all three angles is 180°. Both of the larger angles must be different from 24°, therefore these two larger angles must be equal.

Let $x =$ the measure in degrees of each of the larger angles.

Then we can write

$$\begin{aligned} 24° + x + x &= 180° & \\ 24° + 2x &= 180° & \text{Add like terms.} \\ 2x &= 156° & \text{Subtract 24 from each side.} \\ x &= 78° & \text{Divide each side by 2.} \end{aligned}$$

24°

Thus the measures of each of the other two angles of the triangle must be 78°.

▲ **Practice Problem 6** The largest angle on an isosceles triangle measures 132°. The other two angles are smaller. What are the measurements of the other two angles?

2 Finding Volume and Surface Area

Now let's examine three-dimensional figures. **Surface area** is the total area of the faces of a figure. You can find surface area by calculating the area of each face and then finding the sum. **Volume** is the measure of the amount of space inside a figure. Some formulas for the surface area and the volume of regular figures can be found in the following table.

GEOMETRIC FORMULAS: THREE-DIMENSIONAL FIGURES

Rectangular prism

Note that all of the faces are rectangles.

$$\text{Surface area} = 2lw + 2wh + 2lh$$

$$\text{Volume} = lwh$$

GEOMETRIC FORMULAS: THREE-DIMENSIONAL FIGURES (continued)

Sphere

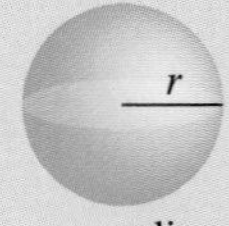

r = radius

Surface area $= 4\pi r^2$

Volume $= \frac{4}{3}\pi r^3$

Right circular cylinder

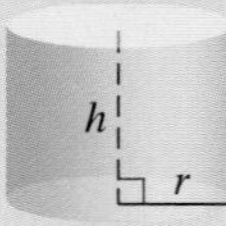

r = radius
h = height

Surface area $= 2\pi rh + 2\pi r^2$

Volume $= \pi r^2 h$

▲ **EXAMPLE 7** Find the volume of a sphere with radius 4 centimeters. (Use 3.14 for π.) Round your answer to the nearest cubic centimeter.

Solution

$$V = \frac{4}{3}\pi r^3 \quad \text{Write the formula for the volume of a sphere.}$$

$$= \frac{4}{3}(3.14)(4 \text{ cm})^3 \quad \text{Substitute the known values into the formula.}$$

$$= \frac{4}{3}(3.14)(64) \text{ cm}^3 \approx 267.946667 \text{ cm}^3$$

Rounded to the nearest whole number, the volume of the sphere is 268 cubic centimeters.

NOTE TO STUDENT: Fully worked-out solutions to all of the Practice Problems can be found at the back of the text starting at page SP-1

▲ **Practice Problem 7** Find the surface area of a sphere with radius 5 meters. Round your answer to the nearest square meter.

▲ **EXAMPLE 8** A can is made of aluminum. It has a flat top and a flat bottom. The height is 5 inches and the radius is 2 inches. How much aluminum is needed to make the can? How much aluminum is needed to make 10,000 cans?

Solution

Understand the problem. What do we need to find? Reword the problem.

We need to find the total surface area of a cylinder.

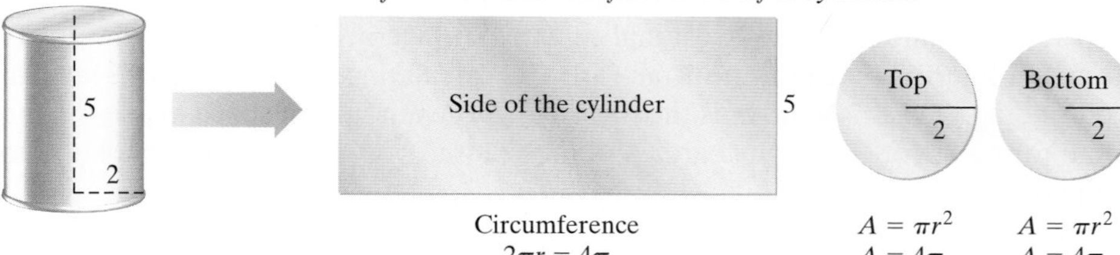

You may calculate the area of each piece and find the sum or you may use the formula.

We will use 3.14 to approximate π.

$$\text{Surface area} = 2\pi rh + 2\pi r^2$$

$$= 2(3.14)(2 \text{ in.})(5 \text{ in.}) + 2(3.14)(2 \text{ in.})^2$$

$$= 62.8 \text{ in.}^2 + 25.12 \text{ in.}^2 = 87.92 \text{ in.}^2$$

87.92 square inches of aluminum is needed to make each can.

Have we answered all the questions in the word problem? Reread the problem. How much aluminum is needed to make 10,000 cans?

$$(\text{aluminum for 1 can})(10{,}000) = (87.92 \text{ in.}^2)(10{,}000) = 879{,}200 \text{ square inches}$$

It would take 879,200 square inches of aluminum to make 10,000 cans.

▲ **Practice Problem 8** Sand is stored in a cylindrical drum that is 4 feet high and has a radius of 3 feet. How much sand can be stored in the drum?

3 Solving More-Involved Geometric Problems

▲ **EXAMPLE 9** A quarter-circle (of radius 1.5 yards) is connected to two rectangles with dimensions as labeled on the sketch in the margin. You need to lay a strip of carpet in your house according to this sketch. How many square yards of carpeting will be needed on the floor? (Use $\pi \approx 3.14$. Round your final answer to the nearest tenth.)

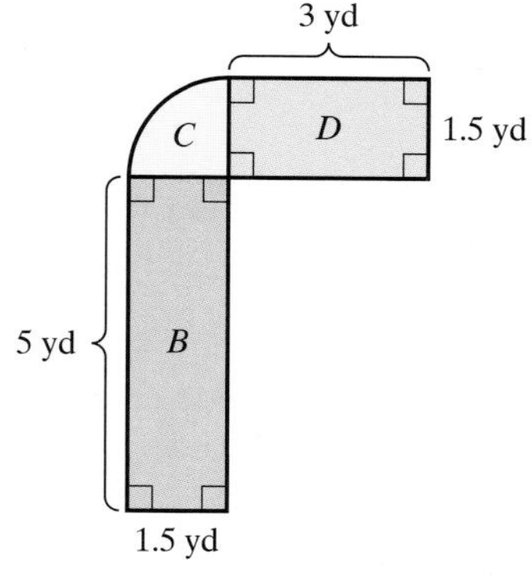

Solution The desired area is the sum of three areas, which we will call B, C, and D. Area B and area D are rectangular in shape. It is relatively easy to find the areas of these shapes.

$$A_B = (5 \text{ yd})(1.5 \text{ yd}) = 7.5 \text{ yd}^2 \qquad A_D = (3 \text{ yd})(1.5 \text{ yd}) = 4.5 \text{ yd}^2$$

Area C is one-fourth of a circle. The radius of the circle is 1.5 yd.

$$A_C = \frac{\pi r^2}{4} \approx \frac{(3.14)(1.5 \text{ yd})^2}{4} = \frac{(3.14)(2.25) \text{ yd}^2}{4} = 1.76625 \text{ yd}^2 \approx 1.8 \text{ yd}^2$$

The total area is $A_B + A_D + A_C \approx 7.5 \text{ yd}^2 + 4.5 \text{ yd}^2 + 1.8 \text{ yd}^2 \approx 13.8 \text{ yd}^2$.

13.8 square yards of carpeting will be needed to cover the floor.

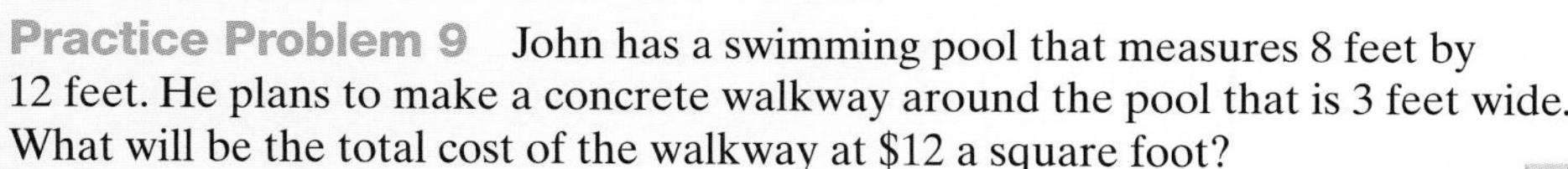

▲ **Practice Problem 9** John has a swimming pool that measures 8 feet by 12 feet. He plans to make a concrete walkway around the pool that is 3 feet wide. What will be the total cost of the walkway at \$12 a square foot?

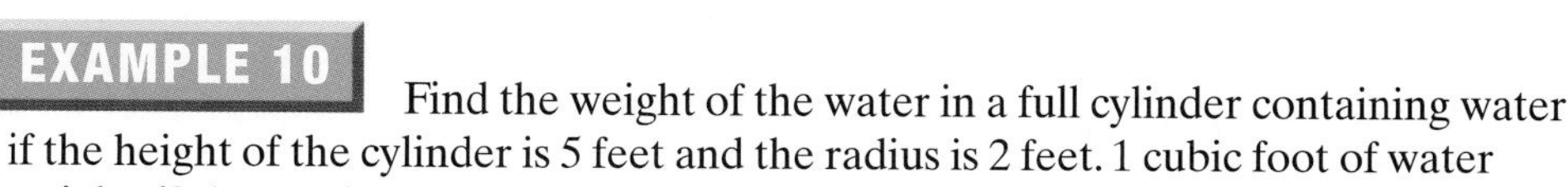

▲ **EXAMPLE 10** Find the weight of the water in a full cylinder containing water if the height of the cylinder is 5 feet and the radius is 2 feet. 1 cubic foot of water weighs 62.4 pounds. Round your answer to the nearest ten pounds. Use 3.14 for π.

Solution

Understand the problem.

Draw a diagram.

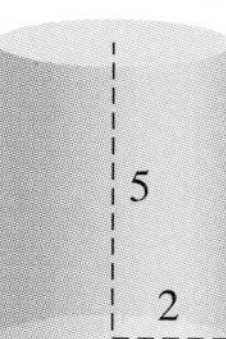

Write the formula for the volume of a cylinder.

$$\begin{aligned} V &= \pi r^2 h \\ &= (3.14)(2 \text{ ft})^2(5 \text{ ft}) \\ &= (3.14)(4 \text{ ft}^2)(5 \text{ ft}) \\ &= 62.8 \text{ ft}^3 \end{aligned}$$

The volume of the cylinder is 62.8 cubic feet.

Each cubic foot of water weighs 62.4 pounds. This can be written as 62.4 lb/ft^3. Since the volume of the cylinder is 62.8 ft^3, we multiply.

$$\begin{aligned} \text{Weight of the water} &= (62.8 \cancel{\text{ft}^3})\left(\frac{62.4 \text{ lb}}{1 \cancel{\text{ft}^3}}\right) \\ &= (62.8)(62.4) \text{ lb} = 3918.72 \text{ lb} \end{aligned}$$

The weight of the water in the cylinder is 3920 rounded to the nearest ten pounds.

▲ **Practice Problem 10** Find the weight of the water in a full rectangular container that is 5 feet wide, 6 feet long, and 8 feet high. Remember, 1 cubic foot of water weighs 62.4 pounds. Round your answer to the nearest 100 pounds.

3.5 Exercises

Student Solutions Manual

CD/ Video

PH Math Tutor Center

MathXL®Tutorials on CD
MathXL®

MyMathLab®

Interactmath.com

Verbal and Writing Skills

Geometry *Fill in the blank to complete each sentence.*

▲ **1.** Perimeter is the _______________ a plane figure.

▲ **2.** _______________ is the distance around a circle.

▲ **3.** Area is a measure of the amount of _______ in a region.

▲ **4.** A __________ is a four-sided figure with exactly two sides parallel.

▲ **5.** The sum of the interior angles of any triangle is ___________.

▲ **6.** ***Geometry*** An isosceles triangle is a triangle with _______________.

▲ **7.** ***Geometry*** Find the area of a triangle whose altitude is 24 inches and whose base is 13 inches.

▲ **8.** ***Geometry*** Find the area of a triangle whose altitude is 7 feet and whose base is 22 feet.

▲ **9.** ***Geometry*** Find the area of a parallelogram whose altitude is 14 inches and whose base is 7 inches.

▲ **10.** ***Geometry*** Find the area of a parallelogram whose altitude is 15 meters and whose base is 10 meters

▲ **11.** ***Geometry*** The area of a triangle is 80 square feet. Find the altitude if the base is 16 feet.

▲ **12.** ***Geometry*** The area of a triangle is 120 sq in. Find the altitude if the base is 24 in.

▲ **13.** ***Geometry*** The perimeter of a parallelogram is 46 inches. If the length of one side is 14 inches, what is the length of a side adjacent to it?

▲ **14.** ***Geometry*** If one side of a parallelogram measures 18.5 cm and an adjacent side measures 17.5 cm, what is the perimeter of the parallelogram?

▲ **15.** ***Geometry*** Find the area of a circular sign whose radius is 7.00 feet. (Use $\pi = 3.14$ as an approximate value.)

▲ **16.** ***Flower Bed*** Find the area of a circular flower bed whose diameter is 6 meters. (Use $\pi = 3.14$ as an approximate value.)

▲ **17.** ***Mercury*** The diameter of the planet Mercury is approximately 3032 miles. Find the distance around its equator. (Use 3.14 to approximate π.)

▲ **18.** ***Frisbees*** Find the area of an ultimate frisbee disc whose diameter is 27 cm. (Use 3.14 to approximate π.)

▲ **19.** ***Geometry*** The area of a trapezoid is 600 square inches and the bases are 20 inches and 30 inches. Find the altitude.

▲ **20.** ***Geometry*** The area of a trapezoid is 900 square inches. The bases are 40 inches and 50 inches. Find the altitude.

Applications

▲ **21.** ***Streets of Manhattan*** In midtown Manhattan, the street blocks have a uniform size of 80 meters north-south by 280 meters east-west. If a typical New York City neighborhood is two blocks east-west by three blocks north-south, how much area does it cover?

▲ **22.** ***Computer Cases*** A computer manufacturing plant makes its computer cases from plastic. Two sides of a triangular scrap of plastic measure 7 cm and 25 cm.

(a) If the perimeter of the plastic piece is 56 cm, how long is the third side?

(b) If each side of the triangular piece is decreased by 0.1 cm, what would the new perimeter be?

▲ **23.** ***Geometry*** The circumference of a circle is 31.4 centimeters. Find the radius. (Use $\pi = 3.14$ as an approximate value.)

▲ **24.** ***Geometry*** The perimeter of an equilateral triangle is 27 inches. Find the length of each side of the triangle.

▲ **25.** ***Tires*** An automobile tire has a diameter of 64 cm. What is the circumference of the tire? (Use $\pi = 3.14$ as an approximate value.)

▲ **26.** ***Golden Ratio*** The ancient Greeks discovered that rectangles where the length-to-width ratio was 8 to 5 (known as the golden ratio) were most pleasing to the eye. Kayla wants to create a painting that will be framed by some antique molding that she found. If she calculates that the molding can be used to make a frame of 104 inches in perimeter, what dimensions should her painting be so that it is visually appealing?

▲ **27.** ***Geometry*** Two angles of a triangle measure 47 degrees and 59 degrees. What is the measure of the third angle?

▲ **28.** ***Geometry*** A right triangle has one angle that measures 77 degrees. What does the other acute angle measure?

▲ **29.** ***Geometry*** Each of the equal angles of an isosceles triangle is 4 times as large as the third angle. What is the measure of each angle?

▲ **30.** ***Geometry*** In a triangle, the measure of the first angle is twice the measure of the second angle. The measure of the third angle is 20 degrees less than the second angle. What is the measure of each angle?

▲ **31.** ***Boat Frame*** The smallest angle of an isosceles triangle used in the wood frame of a boat measures 38°. The other two angles are larger. What are the measurements of the other two angles in this triangular part of the wood frame?

▲ **32.** ***TV Antenna*** The largest angle of an isosceles triangle used in holding a cable TV antenna measures 146°. The other two angles are smaller. What are the measurements of the other two angles in the triangular piece of the cable TV antenna?

▲ **33.** ***Parking Lot*** A triangular region of the community college parking lot was measured. The measure of the first angle of this triangle is double the measure of the second angle. The measure of the third angle is 19° greater than double the measure of the first angle. What are the measurements of all three angles?

▲ **34.** ***Lobster Pot*** A lobster pot used in Gloucester, Massachusetts, has a small triangular piece of wood at the entry point where the lobster enters. The measure of the first angle of this triangle is triple the measure of the second angle. The third angle of the triangle is 30° less than double the measure of the first angle. What are the measurements of all the three angles?

▲ **35.** ***Geometry*** A ladder makes a right triangle against a house. If the angle between the ladder and the house is 38°, what is the angle between the ladder and the ground?

▲ **36.** ***Geometry*** Two angles of a triangle measure 135° and 11°. What is the measure of the third angle?

▲ **37.** ***Painting a Shed*** The cost for paint to cover the exterior of the four sides of a shed was \$40. A 5-gallon can of paint costs \$20 and will cover 102 square feet. The shed consists of four sides, each shaped like a trapezoid. They each have one base of 8 feet and one base of 9 feet. What is the altitude of each trapezoid?

▲ **38.** ***Painting a Sign*** The cost for paint to cover both sides of a large road-side sign (front side and back side) was \$150. A 5-gallon can of paint costs \$25 and will cover 250 square feet. The sign is constructed in the shape of a trapezoid. It has one base measuring 35 feet and one base measuring 40 feet. What is the altitude of this trapezoid?

▲ **39.** ***Geometry*** What is the volume of a cylinder whose height is 8 inches and whose radius is 10 inches? (Use $\pi = 3.14$ as an approximate value.)

▲ **40.** ***Gas Cylinder*** A cylinder holds propane gas. The volume of the cylinder is 235.5 cubic feet. Find the height if the radius is 5 feet. (Use $\pi = 3.14$ as an approximate value.)

▲ **41.** ***Weather Balloon*** A spherical weather balloon needs to hold at least 175 cubic feet of helium to be buoyant enough to lift the meteorological instruments. Will a helium filled balloon with a diameter of 8 feet stay aloft?

▲ **42.** ***Storage Cabinet*** Mrs. Robinson has room for a storage cabinet that is 18 inches wide by 24 inches deep. If she calculates that she needs 15 cubic feet of storage space, how tall must the cabinet be?

▲ **43.** ***Milk Container*** A plastic cylinder made to hold milk is constructed with a solid top and bottom. The radius is 6 centimeters and the height is 4 centimeters. **(a)** Find the volume of the cylinder. **(b)** Find the total surface area of the cylinder. (Use $\pi = 3.14$ as an approximate value.)

▲ **44.** ***Pyrex Sphere*** A Pyrex glass sphere is made to hold liquids in a science lab. The radius of the sphere is 3 centimeters. **(a)** Find the volume of the sphere. **(b)** Find the total surface area of the sphere. (Use $\pi = 3.14$ as an approximate value.)

▲ **45.** ***Goat Tether*** Dan Perkin's goat is attached to the corner of the 8-foot-by-4-foot pump house by an 8-foot length of rope. The goat eats the grass around the pump house as shown in the diagram. This pattern consists of three-fourths of a circle of radius 8 feet and one-fourth of a circle of radius 4 feet. What area of grass can Dan Perkin's goat eat? (Use $\pi = 3.14$ as an approximate value.)

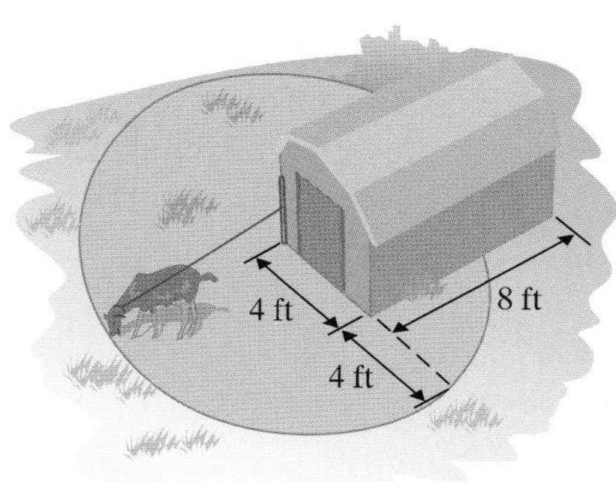

▲ **46.** ***Seven-Layer Torte*** For a party, Julian is making a seven-layer torte, which consists of seven 9-inch-diameter cake layers with a cream topping on each. He knows that one recipe of cream topping will cover 65 square inches of cake. How many batches of the topping must he make to complete his torte? (Use $\pi = 3.14$ as an approximate value.)

▲ **47.** ***Walkway*** A cement walkway is to be poured. It consists of the two rectangles with dimensions as shown in the diagram and a quarter of a circle with radius 1.5 yards. Use $\pi = 3.14$ as an approximate value. **(a)** How many square yards will the walkway be? **(b)** If a painter paints it for \$2.50 per square yard, how much will the painting cost?

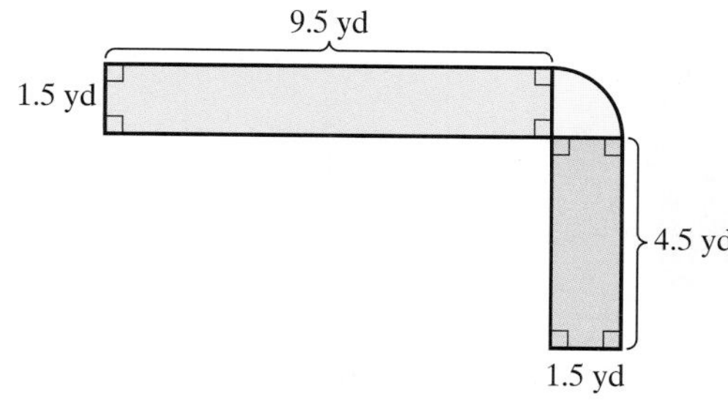

▲ **48.** ***Aluminum Plate*** An aluminum plate is made according to the following dimensions. The outer radius is 10 inches and the inner radius is 3 inches. (Use $\pi = 3.14$ as an approximate value.) **(a)** How many square inches in area is the aluminum plate (the shaded region in the sketch)? **(b)** If the cost to construct the plate is \$7.50 per square inch, what is the construction cost?

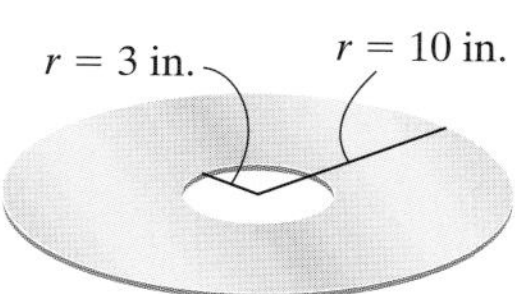

49. ***Toy Car Track*** New Toy Company is producing a racing car set, complete with plastic track. The track is a solid surface and has a straight edge with circular ends. See the following sketch for dimensions. **(a)** What is the distance around the track? **(b)** If it is 0.5 inches thick, how much plastic does it take to make the track?

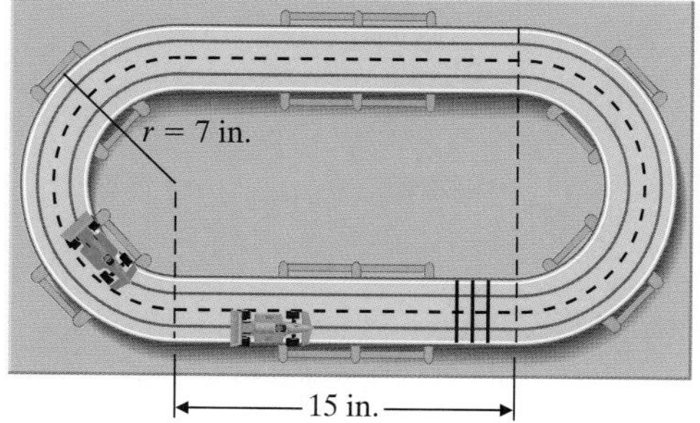

50. ***Uniform Design*** The Viceroy Soccer team has designed new uniforms. The front of their jerseys will have a blue rectangle, with a red V inside. (See the diagram.) The plain jersey shirt costs \$19.00. The red color costs \$0.05 per square inch and the blue color costs \$0.02 per square inch.

(a) What is the area of the red V?

(b) What is the area of the blue color?

(c) What is the cost per jersey?

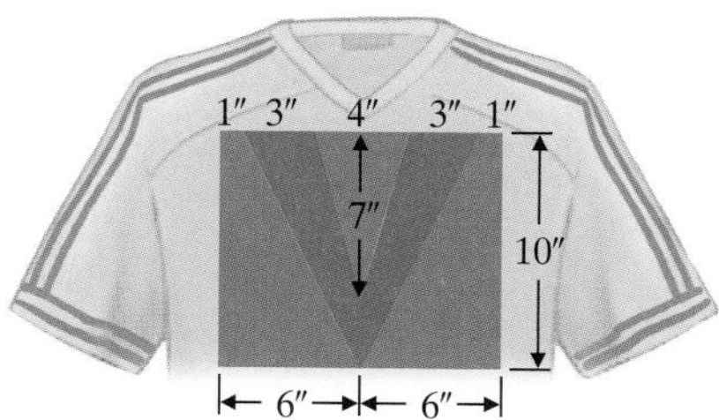

▲ **51.** ***Painting Frame*** It cost \$120.93 to frame a painting with a flat aluminum strip. This was calculated at \$1.39 per foot for materials and labor. Find the dimensions of the painting if its length is 3 feet less than four times its width.

▲ **52.** ***Driveway*** A concrete driveway measures 18 yards by 4 yards. The driveway will be 0.5 yards thick. **(a)** How many cubic yards of concrete will be needed? **(b)** How much will it cost if concrete is \$3.50 per cubic yard?

To Think About

▲ **53.** ***Geometry*** An isosceles triangle has one side that measures 4 feet and another that measures 7.5 feet. The third side was not measured. Can you find one unique perimeter for this triangle? What are the two possible perimeters?

▲ **54.** ***Geometry*** Find the total surface area of **(a)** a sphere of radius 3 inches and **(b)** a right circular cylinder with radius 2 inches and height 0.5 inch. Which object has a greater surface area? Use $\pi = 3.14$ as an approximate value.

▲ **55.** ***Moon*** Assume that a very long rope supported by poles that are 3 feet tall is stretched around the moon. (Neglect gravitational pull and assume that the rope takes the shape of a large circle.) The radius of the moon is approximately 1080 miles. How much longer would you need to make the rope if you wanted the rope to be supported by poles that are 4 feet tall? Use $\pi = 3.14$ as an approximate value.

Cumulative Review

Simplify.

56. $2(x - 6) - 3[4 - x(x + 2)]$

57. $-5(x + 3) - 2[4 + 3(x - 1)]$

58. $-\{3 - 2[x - 3(x + 1)]\}$

59. $-2\{x + 3[2 - 4(x - 3)]\}$

3.6 Using Inequalities to Solve Word Problems

 Translating English Sentences into Inequalities

Student Learning Objectives

After studying this section, you will be able to:

1. **Translate English sentences into inequalities.**
2. **Solve applied problems using inequalities.**

Real-life situations often involve inequalities. For example, if a student wishes to maintain a certain grade point average (GPA), you may hear him or her say, "I have to get a grade of at least an 87 on the final exam."

What does "at least an 87" mean? What grade does the student need to achieve? 87 would fit the condition. What about 88? The student would be happy with an 88. In fact the student would be happy with any grade that *is greater than or equal to* an 87. We can write this as

$$\text{grade} \geq 87.$$

Notice that the English phrase "at least an 87" translates mathematically as "greater than or equal to an 87."

Be careful when translating English phrases that involve inequalities into algebra. If you are not sure which symbol to use, try a few numbers to see if they fit the condition of the problem. Choose the mathematical symbol accordingly.

Here is a list that may help you.

English Phrases Describing Inequality	Algebraic Expression
Greater than Is more than Is greater than	$>$
Less than Is less than Is smaller than	$<$
Greater than or equal to Is greater than or equal to Is not less than Is at least Cannot be less than	$\geq$
Less than or equal to Is less than or equal to Is not greater than Is at most Is not more than	$\leq$

EXAMPLE 1 Translate each sentence into an inequality.

(a) The perimeter of the rectangle must be no more than 70 inches.
(b) The average number of errors must be less than two mistakes per page.
(c) His income must be at least \$950 per week.
(d) The new car will cost at most \$12,070.

Solution

(a) Perimeter must be *no more than* 70.

$$\text{Perimeter} \quad \leq \quad 70$$

Try 80. Does 80 satisfy this requirement? That is, is 80 more than 70? No. Do 60 and 50 satisfy this requirement? Yes. Use the "less than or equal to" symbol.

(b) Average number must be *less than* 2.

$$\text{Average} \quad < \quad 2$$

(c) Income must be *at least* \$950.

$$\text{Income} \quad \geq \quad 950$$

"At least" means, "not less than." The income must be \$950 or more. Use $\geq$.

(d) The new car will cost *at most* $12,070.

$$\text{Car} \leq 12{,}070$$

"At most $12,070" means it is the top price for the car. The cost of the car cannot be more than $12,070. Use ≤.

NOTE TO STUDENT: Fully worked-out solutions to all of the Practice Problems can be found at the back of the text starting at page SP-1

Practice Problem 1 Translate each sentence into an inequality.

(a) The height of the person must be no greater than 6 feet.
(b) The speed of the car must have been greater than 65 miles per hour.
(c) The area of the room must be greater than or equal to 560 square feet.
(d) The profit margin cannot be less than $50 per television set.

2 Solving Applied Problems Using Inequalities

We can use the same problem-solving techniques we used previously to solve word problems involving inequalities.

EXAMPLE 2 A manufacturing company makes 60-watt light bulbs. For every 1000 bulbs manufactured, a random sample of five bulbs is selected and tested. To meet quality control standards, the average number of hours these five bulbs last must be at least 900 hours. The test engineer tested five bulbs. Four of them lasted 850 hours, 1050 hours, 1000 hours, and 950 hours, respectively. How many hours must the fifth bulb last in order for the batch to meet quality control standards?

Solution

1. ***Understand the problem.***

Let n = the number of hours the fifth bulb must last

The average that the five bulbs last *must be at least* 900 hours. We could write

$$\text{Average} \geq 900 \text{ hours.}$$

2. ***Write an inequality.***

$$\text{Average of five bulbs} \geq 900 \text{ hours.}$$

$$\frac{850 + 1050 + 1000 + 950 + n}{5} \geq 900$$

3. ***Solve and state the answer.***

$$\frac{850 + 1050 + 1000 + 950 + n}{5} \geq 900$$

$$\frac{3850 + n}{5} \geq 900 \quad \text{Simplify the numerator.}$$

$$3850 + n \geq 4500 \quad \text{Multiply both sides by 5.}$$

$$n \geq 650 \quad \text{Subtract 3850 from each side.}$$

If the fifth bulb burns for 650 hours or more, the quality control standards will be met.

4. ***Check.*** Any value of 650 or larger should satisfy the original inequality. Suppose we pick $n = 650$ and substitute it into the inequality.

$$\frac{850 + 1050 + 1000 + 950 + 650}{5} \stackrel{?}{\geq} 900$$

$$\frac{4500}{5} \stackrel{?}{\geq} 900$$

$$900 \geq 900 \checkmark$$

If we try $n = 700$, the left side of the inequality will be 910. $910 \geq 900$. In fact, if we try any number greater than 650 for n, the left side of the inequality will be greater than 900. The inequality will be valid for $n = 650$ or any larger value.

Practice Problem 2 A manufacturing company makes coils of $\frac{1}{2}$-inch maritime rope. For every 300 coils of rope made, a random sample of four coils of rope is selected and tested. To meet quality control standards, the average number of pounds that each coil will hold must be at least 1100 pounds. The test engineer tested four coils of rope. The first three held 1050 pounds, 1250 pounds, and 950 pounds, respectively. How many pounds must the last coil hold if the sample is to meet quality control standards?

EXAMPLE 3 Juan is selling supplies for restaurants in the Southwest. He gets paid \$700 per month plus 8% of all the supplies he sells to restaurants. If he wants to earn more than \$3100 per month, what value of products will he need to sell?

Solution

1. ***Understand the problem.*** Juan earns a fixed salary and a salary that depends on how much he sells (commission salary) each month.

   Let x = the value of the supplies he sells each month.

   Then $0.08x$ = the amount of the commission salary he earns each month.

   He wants his total income to be more than \$3100 per month; thus

   $$\text{total income} > 3100.$$

2. ***Write the inequality.***

   The fixed income added to the commission income must be greater than 3100.

   $$\underset{700}{\downarrow} \quad \underset{+}{\downarrow} \quad \underset{0.08x}{\downarrow} \quad \underset{>}{\downarrow} \quad \underset{3100}{\downarrow}$$

3. ***Solve and state the answer.***

   $$700 + 0.08x > 3100$$
   $$0.08x > 2400 \quad \text{Subtract 700 from each side.}$$
   $$x > 30{,}000 \quad \text{Divide each side by 0.08.}$$

   Juan must sell more than \$30,000 worth of supplies each month.

4. ***Check.*** Any value greater than 30,000 should satisfy the original inequality.

   Suppose we pick $x = 30{,}001$ and substitute it into the inequality.

   $$700 + 0.08(30{,}001) \stackrel{?}{>} 3100$$
   $$700 + 2400.08 \stackrel{?}{>} 3100$$
   $$3100.08 > 3100 \checkmark$$

Practice Problem 3 Rita is selling commercial fire and theft alarm systems to local companies. She gets paid \$1400 per month plus 2% of the cost of all the systems she sells in one month. She wants to earn more than \$2200 per month. What value of products will she need to sell each month?

3.6 Exercises

Student Solutions Manual | CD/ Video | PH Math Tutor Center | MathXL®Tutorials on CD | MathXL® | MyMathLab® | Interactmath.com

Verbal and Writing Skills

Translate to an inequality.

1. The cost is greater than \$67,000.

2. The clearance of the bridge is less than 12 feet.

3. The number of people is not more than 120.

4. The tax increase is more than \$7890.

5. The height of stratocumulus clouds is not more than 1500 feet.

6. The volume of water in the aquarium must not drop below 35 gallons.

7. To earn an A in algebra, Ramon cannot get less than a 93 average.

8. The camp-ins at the Museum of Science in Boston cannot accommodate more than 600 people.

Applications

Solve using an inequality.

▲ **9.** ***Window Design*** A triangular window on Ross Camp's new Searay boat has two sides that measure 87 centimeters and 64 centimeters, respectively. The perimeter of the triangle must not exceed 291 centimeters. What are the possible values for the length of the third side of the window?

▲ **10.** ***Package Size*** The U.S. Postal Service provides guidelines for package size. One of the guidelines specifies the dimensions of the package: The length plus the girth (circumference around the widest part) cannot exceed 130 inches. If you are preparing a package that is 33 inches wide and 28 inches high, how long is the package permitted to be?

11. ***Flower Delivery*** Flora's Flowers shares the Speedy Delivery Service with Ruby's Rosebuds. Flora estimates that if she averages at least 24 deliveries per week, she will save money by hiring a student to deliver her flowers after school. Her contract with Speedy Delivery is up for renewal in 6 weeks. Flora tracks her deliveries for 5 weeks: 18, 40, 21, 7, and 36. At least how many deliveries must she average in week 6 to convince her to drop the delivery service?

12. ***Course Average*** Sophia has scored 85, 77, and 68 on three tests in her biology course. She has one final test to take and wants to obtain an average of 80 or more in the course. What possible values can she obtain on her final test and still achieve her goal?

▲ 13. ***Garden Design*** Joel plans to plant a flower garden in the front of his house, where he can fit a garden that is 8 feet wide. He wishes to use the can of wildflower mix that he got for his birthday. The can of seeds claims that it will luxuriously carpet an area of no more than 60 square feet. What are the possible dimensions for the depth of Joel's garden, so that it will be covered with wildflowers?

14. ***Class Size*** The Lee County Elementary School District noted that there was an increase of 1785 pupils during the fall semester. How many new teachers must they add to keep their average class size under 28? (Assume one teacher for each class.)

15. ***Truck Rental*** Suzie and Freddie decided that to save money, they would move themselves from their apartment to their new house. They had to rent a truck to do this. Because their budget was very strict, they could afford to spend no more than \$150. The truck costs \$37.50 per day and 19.5 cents per mile. If they decided they would need the truck for two days, what was the limit on the mileage they could put on the truck?

16. ***Salary*** Robin just graduated from college and has taken her first job. She is working for a computer sales company, Compusell. While she hopes to eventually get into management, she is presently working as a salesperson. Her earnings consist of a monthly salary of \$1300, plus 6% of all her sales. To meet her monthly obligations, Robin wants to earn at least \$2800 per month. What is the amount of sales she must make monthly to meet her goal?

17. ***Coolant*** The coolant in Tom's car is effective for radiator temperatures of less than 110 degrees Celsius. What would be the corresponding temperature range in degrees Fahrenheit? (Use $C = \frac{5}{9}(F - 32)$ in your inequality.)

18. ***IQ*** A person's IQ is found by multiplying mental age (m), as indicated by standard tests, by 100 and dividing this result by the chronological age (c). This gives the formula $\text{IQ} = 100\frac{m}{c}$. If a group of 14-year-old children has an IQ of not less than 80, what is the mental age range of this group?

19. ***Federal Aid*** The amount of federal aid in billions of dollars given to state and local governments can be approximated by the equation $A = 9.2x + 77.1$, where x is the number of years since 1980. Use this equation to determine those years for which the amount of federal aid to state and local governments will exceed \$307.1 billion. (*Source:* U.S. Office of Management and Budget)

20. ***Social Security*** The number of people in millions who are receiving Social Security benefits can be approximated by the equation $N = 0.57x + 34.8$, where x is the number of years since 1980. Use this equation to determine those years for which the number of people receiving Social Security benefits will exceed 50.19 million. (*Source:* U.S. Social Security Administration)

21. ***Car Repair*** Becky's car needed some major engine work in order to pass inspection. She decided that she would only have the work done if the total repair bill would be no more than than \$1200. The dealer told her that the parts she needed would cost \$840. He could not guarantee how many hours labor, at \$45 per hour, the job would take. At most how many hours of labor could the repairs take to stay within her price?

22. ***Apartment Furnishing*** Rachel and Alissa are renting their first apartment. They need to buy lamps and throw rugs to complete the apartment. Their budget for these items is a maximum of \$340. Rugs cost \$48 each and lamps cost \$35 each. They decide to buy 4 rugs. How many lamps can they buy?

To Think About

23. ***CD Manufacturing*** A compact disc recording company's weekly costs can be described by the equation cost $= 5000 + 7n$, where n is the number of compact discs manufactured in one week. The equation for the amount of income produced from selling these n discs is income $= 18n$. At least how many discs need to be manufactured and sold in one week for the income to be greater than the cost?

24. ***VCR Manufacturing*** A company that manufactures VCRs has weekly costs described by the equation cost $= 12{,}000 + 100n$, where n is the number of VCRs manufactured in one week. The equation for the amount of income produced from selling these n VCRs is income $= 210n$. At least how many VCRs need to be manufactured and sold in one week for the income to be greater than the cost?

Cumulative Review

Solve.

25. $10 - 3x > 14 - 2x$

26. $2x - 3 \geq 7x - 18$

27. $30 - 2(x + 1) \leq 4x$

28. $2(x + 3) - 22 < 4(x - 2)$

29. ***Leaky Faucet*** Frank has a leaky faucet in his bathtub. He closed the drain and measured that the faucet drips 8 gallons of water in one 24-hour period.

(a) If the faucet isn't fixed, how many gallons of water will be wasted in one year?

(b) If the faucet isn't fixed and water costs \$8.50 per 1000 gallons, how much extra money will Frank have to pay on his water bill for the year?

Putting Your Skills to Work

Predicting the Population of Caribou in Alaska

In the Fortymile River area of Alaska, there is a huge herd of caribou. The herd seems to be slowly growing in number and is carefully monitored by the Alaska State Department of Fish and Game. Wildlife managers find it helpful to have an equation that predicts the number of caribou that will be in this Fortymile herd from year to year. The herd has fluctuated greatly in size. In 1920 the herd was estimated to be 568,000. In 1975 the herd was reduced to only 3982. Thanks to wildlife management techniques, the herd seems to be experiencing slow but positive growth. During the period 1986 to 1990 the following growth was observed:

Year	Estimate of Herd Size
1986	15,303
1988	19,975
1990	22,766

The desired equation that models the slow growth of the caribou in this herd is in the form

$$y = ax + b$$

y is the size of the herd
a is the yearly growth factor
b is the size of the herd in 1986
x is the number of years since 1986

This type of equation will be discussed in more detail in Chapter 7. This type of linear equation can only be used to approximate change or growth that experiences approximately the same amount of growth or change each year.

Problems for Individual Investigation and Analysis

Use the preceding table to obtain the requested information.

1. Determine an estimate for the amount of increase in herd size per year by subtracting the 1986 figure from the 1990 figure and divide by 4. This will give you the value of a. Round your value of a to the nearest whole number. What is the value of b? Write the equation in the form $y = ax + b$.

2. Use your equation to predict what the herd size for 1995. Use the equation to predict the herd size for 1984.

Problems for Group Investigation and Cooperative Learning

3. Use the equation to predict the herd size for 2003. The actual measured population for 2003 was 43,375. How accurate was the equation? Does the equation predict a value that is too high or too low?

4. Using the population for 1986 in the table and the recorded population of 43,375 in the year 2003, calculate a new estimated value for the amount of increase in herd size per year. Round to the nearest whole number for a. Write a new equation that uses this value.

Chapter 3 Organizer

Procedure for Solving Applied Problems

1. **Understand the problem.**
   (a) Read the word problem carefully to get an overview.
   (b) Determine what information you will need to solve the problem.
   (c) Draw a sketch. Label it with the known information. Determine what needs to be found.
   (d) Choose a variable to represent one unknown quantity.
   (e) If necessary, represent other unknown quantities in terms of that same variable.
2. **Write an equation.**
   (a) Look for key words to help you to translate the words into algebraic symbols.
   (b) Use a given relationship in the problem or an appropriate formula in order to write an equation.
3. **Solve and state the answer.**
4. **Check.**
   (a) Check the solution in the original equation. Is the answer reasonable?
   (b) Be sure the solution to the equation answers the question in the word problem. You may need to do some additional calculations if it does not.

EXAMPLE A

The perimeter of a rectangle is 126 meters. The length of the rectangle is 6 meters less than double the width. Find the dimensions of the rectangle.

1. ***Understand the problem.***
   We want to find the length and the width of a rectangle whose perimeter is 126 meters.

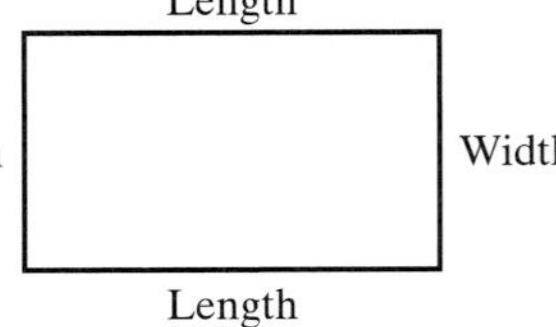

   The length is *compared to* the width, so we start with the width.
   Let w = width.

   The length is 6 meters less than double the width.
   Then $l = 2w - 6$.

2. ***Write an equation.***
   The perimeter of a rectangle is $P = 2w + 2l$.

$$126 = 2w + 2(2w - 6)$$

3. ***Solve.***

$$126 = 2w + 4w - 12$$
$$126 = 6w - 12$$
$$138 = 6w$$
$$23 = w$$

The width is 23 meters.

$$2w - 6 = 2(23) - 6 = 46 - 6 = 40$$

The length is 40 meters.

4. ***Check:***
   Is this reasonable? Yes. A rectangle 23 meters wide and 40 meters long seems to be about right for the perimeter to be 126 meters.

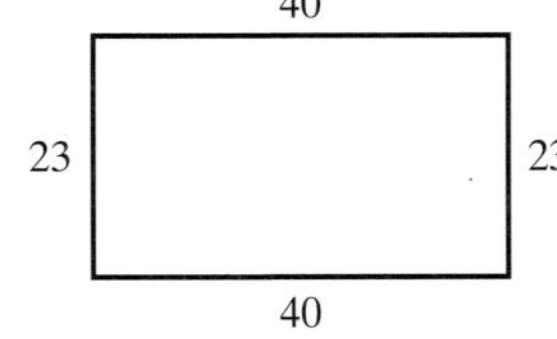

   Is the perimeter exactly 126 meters?

$$2(23) + 2(40) \stackrel{?}{=} 126$$
$$46 + 80 \stackrel{?}{=} 126$$
$$126 = 126 \checkmark$$

   Is the length exactly 6 meters less than double the width?

$$40 \stackrel{?}{=} 2(23) - 6$$
$$40 \stackrel{?}{=} 46 - 6$$
$$40 = 40 \checkmark$$

EXAMPLE B

Gina saved some money for college. She invested \$2400 for one year and earned \$225 in simple interest. She invested part of it at 12% and the rest of it at 9%. How much did she invest at each rate?

1. ***Understand the problem.***
   We want to find each amount that was invested.

   interest earned at 12% + interest earned at 9% = total interest of \$225

   We let x represent one quantity of money.
   Let x = amount of money invested at 12%.

   We started with \$2400. If we invest x at 12%, we still have $(2400 - x)$ left.
   Then $2400 - x$ = the amount of money invested at 9%.

   Interest = prt
   Interest at 12% $\quad I_1 = 0.12x$
   Interest at 9% $\quad I_2 = 0.09(2400 - x)$

2. ***Write an equation.***
   $I_1 + I_2 = 225$.

$$0.12x + 0.09(2400 - x) = 225$$

3. ***Solve.***

$$0.12x + 216 - 0.09x = 225$$
$$0.03x + 216 = 225$$
$$0.03x = 9$$
$$x = \frac{9}{0.03}$$
$$x = 300$$

\$300 was invested at 12%.

$$2400 - x = 2400 - 300 = 2100$$

\$2100 was invested at 9%.

4. ***Check:***
   Is this reasonable? Yes.
   Are the conditions of the problem satisfied? Does the total amount invested equal \$2400?

$$2100 + 300 \stackrel{?}{=} 2400$$
$$2400 = 2400 \checkmark$$

   Will \$2100 at 9% and \$300 at 12% yield \$225 in interest?

$$0.09(2100) + 0.12(300) \stackrel{?}{=} 225$$
$$189 + 36 \stackrel{?}{=} 225$$
$$225 = 225 \checkmark$$

25. ***Investments*** Peter and Shelly invested $9000 for one year. Part of it was invested at 12% and the remainder was invested at 8%. At the end of one year the couple had earned exactly $1000 in simple interest. How much did they invest at each rate?

26. ***Investments*** A man invests $5000 in a savings bank. He places part of it in a checking account that earns 4.5% and the rest in a regular savings account that earns 6%. His total annual income from this investment in simple interest is $270. How much was invested in each account?

27. ***Coin Change*** Mary has $3.75 in nickels, dimes, and quarters. She has three more quarters than dimes. She has twice as many nickels as quarters. How many of each coin does she have?

28. ***Coin Change*** Tim brought in $3.65 in coins. He had two more quarters than he had dimes. He had one fewer nickel than the number of dimes. How many coins of each type did he have?

Section 3.5

Solve.

▲ **29.** ***Geometry*** What is the surface area of a exercise ball with a diameter of 32 inches? (Use $\pi \approx 3.14$.)

▲ **30.** ***Trench Length*** Wilfredo and Tina bought a new screen house for camping. It was hexagonal (6 sides) in shape and 4 ft long on a side. If they wanted to dig a trench around their house so that rainwater would flow away, how long would the trench be? (You are looking for the perimeter of the screen house.)

▲ **31.** ***Geometry*** Find the third angle of a triangle if one angle measures 62 degrees and the second angle measures 47 degrees.

▲ **32.** ***Geometry*** Find the area of a triangle whose base is 8 miles and whose altitude is 10.5 miles.

▲ **33.** ***Geometry*** Find the volume of a rectangular solid whose width is 8 feet, whose length is 12 feet, and whose height is 20 feet.

▲ **34.** ***Geometry*** Find the volume of a sphere whose radius is 3 centimeters. (Use $\pi \approx 3.14$.)

▲ **35.** ***Geometry*** Find the area of a circle whose diameter is 18 centimeters. (Use $\pi \approx 3.14$.)

▲ **36.** ***Geometry*** The perimeter of an isosceles triangle is 46 inches. The two equal sides are each 17 inches long. How long is the third side?

▲ **37.** ***House Painting*** Jim wants to have the exterior siding on his house painted. Two sides of the house have a height of 18 feet and a length of 22 feet, and the other two sides of the house have a height of 18 feet and a length of 19 feet. The painter has quoted a price of $2.50 per square foot. The windows and doors of the house take up 100 square feet. How much will the painter charge to paint the siding?

▲ **38.** ***Aluminum Cylinder*** Find the cost to build a cylinder out of aluminum if the radius is 5 meters, the height is 14 meters, and the cylinder will have a flat top and flat bottom. The cost factor has been determined to be $40.00 per square meter. (*Hint:* First find the total surface area.) (Use $\pi \approx 3.14$.)

Section 3.6

Solve.

39. ***Car Rental*** Chelsea rents a car for $35 a day and 15 cents a mile. How far can she drive if she wants to rent the car for two days and does not want to spend more than $100?

40. ***Income*** Philip earns $12,000 per year in salary and 4% commission on his sales. How much were his sales if his annual income was more than $24,000?

41. ***Transcontinental Railroad*** In 1862, two companies were granted the rights to build the transcontinental railroad from Omaha, Nebraska to Sacramento, California. The Central Pacific railroad began in 1863 from Sacramento heading east. The Union Pacific began 24 months later, leaving from Omaha and heading west. The Central Pacific averaged 8.75 miles of track each month, while the Union Pacific averaged 20 miles of track per month. The two companies met at Promontory, Utah after completing 1590 miles of track. How much track did each build?

42. ***Clothes Shopping*** Michael plans to spend less than \$70 on shirts and ties. He bought three shirts for \$17.95 each. How much can he spend on ties?

Mixed Practice

Solve.

43. ***TV Show*** Wally timed a popular "30-minute" TV show. The show lasted 4 minutes longer than four times the amount of time that was devoted to commercials. How many minutes long was the actual show?

44. ***Balanced Weight*** Faye conducted an experiment. To verify the weight of four identical steel balls, she placed them on a balance. She placed three of the balls on one side of the balance. On the other side she placed an 8-ounce weight and one of the balls. She discovered that these two sides exactly balanced on the scale. How much does each steel ball weigh?

45. ***Electricity Use*** Fred and Nancy Sullivan are planning to purchase a new refrigerator. The most efficient model costs \$870, but the electricity to operate it would cost only \$41 per year. The less efficient model is the same size. It costs \$744, but the electricity to operate it would cost \$83 per year. How long will it be before the total cost is greater for the less efficient model?

46. ***Buying vs. Renting*** Custom Computer Works of Gloucester rents its office building and warehouse for \$1800 per month. The owner is thinking of buying the building. He could purchase it with a down payment of \$42,000. He would then make monthly mortgage payments of \$1100. How many months would it take for his total costs to be less to purchase the building rather than rent it?

▲ 47. ***Bookcase Construction*** Judy Carter is planning to build a bookcase for her home office. She has only 38 feet of lumber to make the unit. The bookcase is constructed of shelves as shown in the diagram. She wants the width of the bookcase to be 2.5 times the height. Find the width and the height of the bookcase she needs to construct.

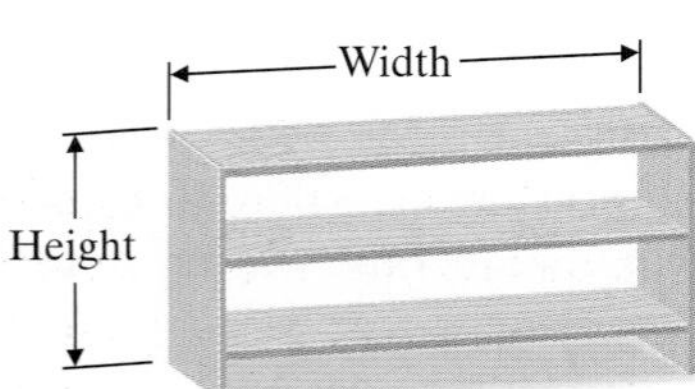

48. ***Retirement Plan*** Rick Ponticelli is investing some money in a retirement plan. He plans to invest \$100 a month the first year, \$200 a month the second year, \$300 a month the third year, and continue with that pattern. How many years will it be before he has invested \$66,000 in his retirement plan?

49. ***Basketball*** In a recent basketball game the Boston Celtics scored 99 points. They scored three times as many field goals as free throws. They also made 12 three-point baskets. How many field goals did they make? How many free throws did they make? (A field goal is worth two points and a free throw is worth one point.)

▲ **50.** ***Room Dimensions*** The perimeter of a rectangular room in Sally's house is 76 feet. The length of the room is 10 feet less than double the width of the room. Find the dimensions of the room.

51. ***Deck Building*** Ryan and Carl spent 28 hours building a deck. Ryan worked 8 less than twice as many hours as Carl. How many hours did each man put in?

52. ***Investments*** Sarah Tanguay has $2000 more invested at 8.5% than she does at 9.75%. Both investments are at simple interest rates. If the annual return from each investment is the same, how much is invested at each rate?

▲ **53.** ***Geometry*** The first angle of a triangle measures 20° larger than the second angle of a triangle. The third angle measures twice as large as the second angle. Find the measure of these three angles.

▲ **54.** ***Sign Construction*** A sign is made in the shape of a trapezoid. The altitude of the trapezoid is 12 feet. The two bases of the trapezoid are 15 feet and 19 feet. The sign is constructed of prime cedar that costs $6 per square foot. How much did the cedar that was used to make the sign cost?

55. ***Final Exam Score*** Thelma has a math final exam that counts twice as much as a test. She had four tests with grades of 88, 77, 95, and 92. What score does she need to obtain on the final exam to get an average of 90 for the course?

56. ***Mileage Deduction*** Barbara drove her car 27,000 miles last year. She drove twice as much for pleasure as she did for business. She can deduct $0.33 per mile for all business miles. Last year she claimed a business mileage deduction of $2000. Was her deduction correct? Please explain your answer. If her deduction was not correct, please indicate the correct deduction.

57. ***Jet Travel*** A jet plane travels 32 miles in three minutes. How far can the plane travel in one hour if it continues at that speed? How many minutes would it take the jet to travel from Boston to Denver (approximately 1800 miles) at that same speed?

58. ***Football*** A running back in a Wheaton College football game catches a pass and runs for the goal line 80 yards away. He can run a 50-yard dash in six seconds. If he runs at 80% of his speed in the 50-yard dash, how long will it take him teach to reach the goal line?

59. ***Field Trip*** A Ford Explorer can hold a driver and four passengers. A Dodge Caravan can hold a driver and six passengers. The biology department is taking a total of 95 people on a field trip. A total of 20 of the 95 people are available to drive. Not all potential drivers will be needed. The college wants to use twice as many Caravans as Explorers because the Caravans get better gas mileage. How many of each kind of vehicle are needed?

▲ **60.** ***Geometry*** The measure of the largest angle of a triangle is triple the measure of the smallest angle. The third angle is 12 degrees less than double the measure of the smallest angle. Find the measure of each angle.

61. ***Zorbing*** Zorbing is a sport, invented in New Zealand, where you are secured inside an inner capsule in a large transparent ball and rolled down a slope. The ball needs to be inflated with an inert gas before it can be used. An inflated zorb has a diameter of 3 meters. If the Zorb itself weighs 80 kg, the zorber weighs 75 kg, and the gas used to inflate the ball weighs 2 kg per cubic meter, what is the total weight of the zorb? (Use 3.14 to approximate π.)

How Am I Doing? Chapter 3 Test

Remember to use your Chapter Test Prep Video CD to see the worked-out solutions to the test problems you want to review.

Solve.

1. ________________

1. A number is doubled and then decreased by 11. The result is 59. What is the original number?

2. ________________

2. The sum of one-half of a number, one-ninth of the number, and one-twelfth of the number is twenty-five. Find the original number.

3. ________________

3. Double the sum of a number and 5 is the same as fourteen more than triple the same number. Find the number.

▲ **4.** A triangular region has a perimeter of 66 meters. The first side is two-thirds of the second side. The third side is 14 meters shorter than the second side. What are the lengths of the three sides of the triangular region?

4. ________________

▲ **5.** A rectangle has a length 7 meters longer than double the width. The perimeter is 134 meters. Find the dimensions of the rectangle.

5. ________________

6. Three harmful pollutants were measured by a consumer group in the city. The total sample contained 15 parts per million of three harmful pollutants. The amount of the first pollutant was double the second. The amount of the third pollutant was 75% of the second. How many parts per million of each pollutant were found?

6. ________________

7. Raymond has a budget of $1940 to rent a computer for his company office. The computer company he wants to rent from charges $200 for installation and service as a one-time fee. Then they charge $116 per month rental for the computer. How many months will Raymond be able to rent a computer with this budget?

7. ________________

8. ________________

8. Last year the yearly tuition at Westmont College went up 8%. This year's charge for tuition for the year is $22,680. What was it last year before the increase went into effect?

9. ________________

9. Franco invested $4000 in money market funds. Part was invested at 14% interest, the rest at 11% interest. At the end of each year the fund company pays interest. After one year he earned $482 in simple interest. How much was invested at each interest rate?

10. ________________

10. Mary has $3.50 in change. She has twice as many nickels as quarters. She has one less dime than she has quarters. How many of each coin does she have?

▲ **11.** Find the circumference of a circle with radius 34 inches. Use $\pi = 3.14$ as an approximation.

11. ______

▲ **12.** Find the area of a trapezoid if the two bases are 10 inches and 14 inches and the altitude is 16 inches.

12. ______

▲ **13.** Find the volume of a sphere with radius 10 inches. Use $\pi = 3.14$ as an approximation and round your answer to the nearest cubic inch.

13. ______

▲ **14.** Find the area of a parallelogram with a base of 12 centimeters and an altitude of 8 centimeters.

14. ______

▲ **15.** How much would it cost to carpet the area shown in the figure if carpeting costs \$12 per square yard?

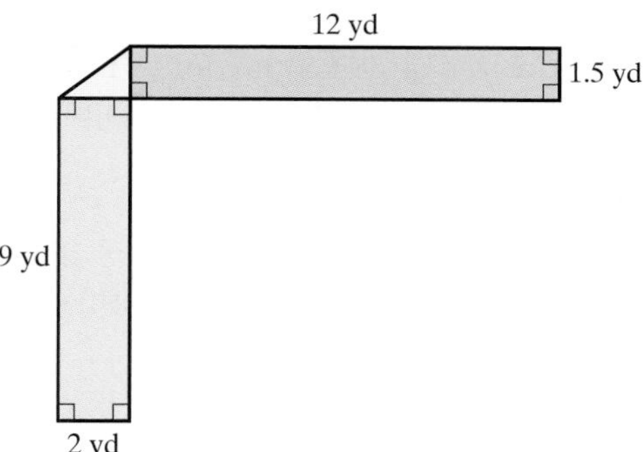

15. ______

16. ______

16. Cathy scored 76, 84, and 78 on three tests. How much must she score on the next test to have at least an 80 average?

17. Carol earns \$15,000 plus 5% commission on sales over \$10,000. How much must she make in sales to earn more than \$20,000?

17. ______

▲ **18.** Andrew is putting down tile for a new gymnasium. He can lay 25 square feet of tile in an hour. How long will it take him to do a gymnasium 150 feet long and 100 feet wide?

18. ______

Cumulative Test for Chapters 0–3

Approximately one-half of this test covers the content of Chapters 0–2. The remainder covers the content of Chapter 3.

1. ____________________
2. ____________________
3. ____________________
4. ____________________
5. ____________________
6. ____________________
7. ____________________
8. ____________________
9. ____________________
10. ____________________
11. ____________________
12. ____________________
13. ____________________
14. ____________________
15. ____________________

1. Divide. $2.4\overline{)8.856}$

2. Add. $\frac{3}{8} + \frac{5}{12} + \frac{1}{2}$

3. Simplify. $3(2x - 3y + 6) + 2(-3x - 7y)$

4. Evaluate. $12 - 3(2 - 4) + 12 \div 4$

5. Solve for b. $H = \frac{1}{2}(3a + 5b)$

6. Solve for x and graph your solution. $5x - 3 \leq 2(4x + 1) + 4$

7. When a number is doubled and then increased by 15, the result is 1. Find the number.

8. The number of students in the psychology class is 34 fewer than the number of students in world history. The total enrollment for the two classes is 134 students. How many students are in each class?

▲ **9.** A rectangle has a perimeter of 78 centimeters. The length of the rectangle is 11 centimeters longer than triple the width. Find the dimensions of the rectangle.

10. This year the sales for Homegrown Video are 35% higher than last year. This year the sales are \$182,250. What were the sales last year?

11. Hassan invested \$7000 for one year. He invested part of it in a high-risk fund that pays 15% interest. He placed the rest in a safe, low-risk fund that pays 7% interest. At the end of one year he earned \$730 in simple interest. How much did he invest in each of the two funds?

12. Linda has some dimes, nickels, and quarters in her purse. The total value of these coins is \$2.55. She has three times as many dimes as quarters. She has three more nickels than quarters. How many coins of each type does she have?

▲ **13.** Find the area of a triangle with an altitude of 13 meters and a base of 25 meters. What is the cost to construct such a triangle out of sheet metal that costs \$4.50 per square meter?

▲ **14.** Find the volume of a sphere that has a radius of 3.00 inches. How much will the contents of the sphere weigh if it is filled with a liquid that weighs 1.50 pounds per cubic inch? Use $\pi = 3.14$ as an approximation.

15. Melinda Tobey saw a glacier in Alaska that moves 65 feet per day. How long will it take the glacier to reach a cabin that is 1625 feet away?

CHAPTER

4

Polynomials are an important tool of mathematics. They are used to create formulas that model many real-world phenomena. Let us take a simple example. Suppose you wanted to know how much more you might make over your lifetime if you obtain a bachelor's degree as opposed to just an associate's degree. Suppose you wanted to know what the expected annual income will be in the future if you obtain a bachelor's degree. Do you think you could use your mathematical skills to determine these values? Turn to the Putting Your Skills to Work problems on page 295 to find out.

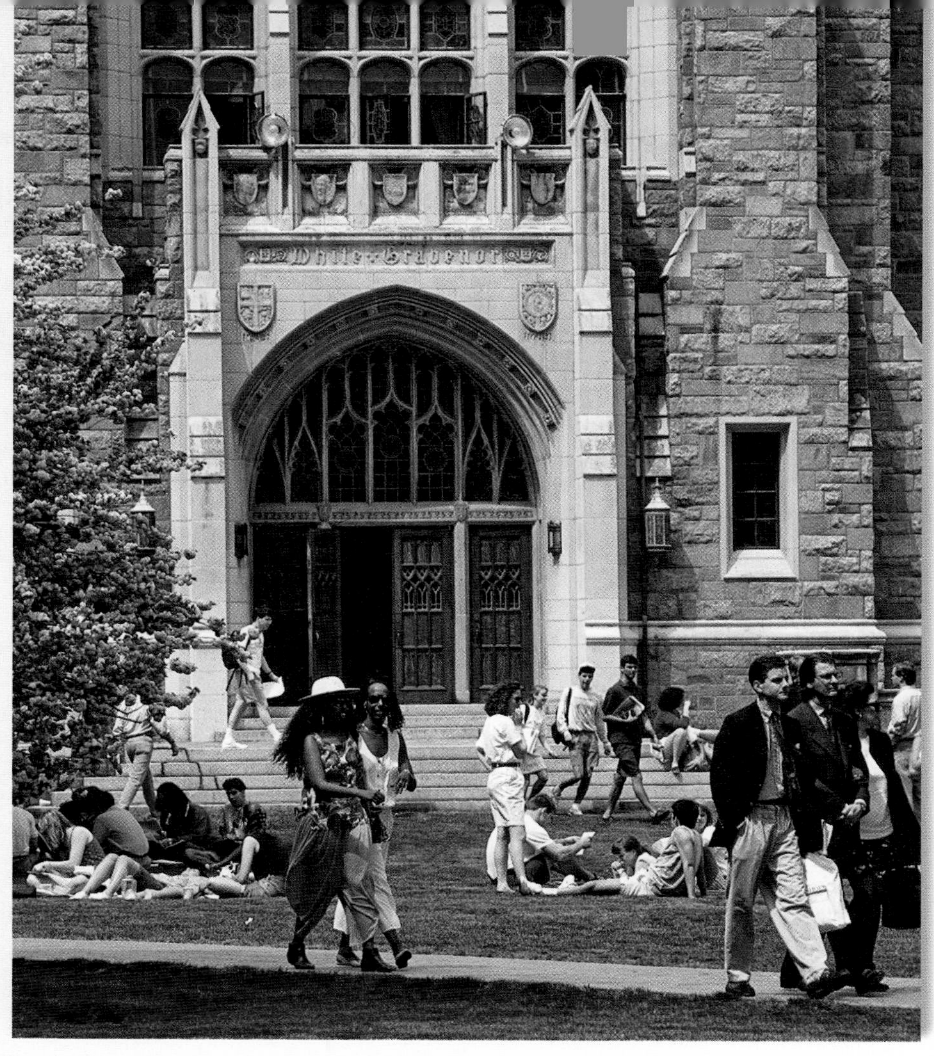

Exponents and Polynomials

4.1 The Rules of Exponents

Student Learning Objectives

After studying this section, you will be able to:

1. **Use the product rule to multiply exponential expressions with like bases.**
2. **Use the quotient rule to divide exponential expressions with like bases.**
3. **Raise exponential expressions to a power.**

1 Using the Product Rule to Multiply Exponential Expressions with Like Bases

Recall that x^2 means $x \cdot x$. That is, x appears as a factor two times. The 2 is called the **exponent.** The **base** is the variable x. The expression x^2 is called an **exponential expression.** What happens when we multiply $x^2 \cdot x^2$? Is there a pattern that will help us form a general rule?

$$(2^2)(2^3) = \overbrace{(2 \cdot 2)(2 \cdot 2 \cdot 2)}^{\text{5 twos}} = 2^5$$ The exponent means 2 occurs 5 times as a factor.

$$(3^3)(3^4) = \overbrace{(3 \cdot 3 \cdot 3)(3 \cdot 3 \cdot 3 \cdot 3)}^{\text{7 threes}} = 3^7$$ Notice that $3 + 4 = 7$.

$$(x^3)(x^5) = \overbrace{(x \cdot x \cdot x)(x \cdot x \cdot x \cdot x \cdot x)}^{8\ x\text{'s}} = x^8$$ The sum of the exponents is $3 + 5 = 8$.

$$(y^4)(y^2) = \overbrace{(y \cdot y \cdot y \cdot y)(y \cdot y)}^{6\ y\text{'s}} = y^6$$ The sum of the exponents is $4 + 2 = 6$.

We can state the pattern in words and then use variables.

THE PRODUCT RULE

To multiply two exponential expressions that have the same base, keep the base and *add the exponents.*

$$x^a \cdot x^b = x^{a+b}$$

Be sure to notice that this rule applies only to expressions that have the *same base*. Here x represents the base, while the letters a and b represent the exponents that are added.

It is important that you apply this rule even when an exponent is 1. Every variable that does not have a written exponent is understood to have an exponent of 1. Thus $x^1 = x$, $y^1 = y$, and so on.

EXAMPLE 1 Multiply. **(a)** $x^3 \cdot x^6$ **(b)** $x \cdot x^5$

Solution

(a) $x^3 \cdot x^6 = x^{3+6} = x^9$

(b) $x \cdot x^5 = x^{1+5} = x^6$ Note that the exponent of the first x is 1.

Practice Problem 1 Multiply. **(a)** $a^7 \cdot a^5$ **(b)** $w^{10} \cdot w$

NOTE TO STUDENT: Fully worked-out solutions to all of the Practice Problems can be found at the back of the text starting at page SP-1

EXAMPLE 2 Simplify. **(a)** $y^5 \cdot y^{11}$ **(b)** $2^3 \cdot 2^5$ **(c)** $x^6 \cdot y^8$

Solution

(a) $y^5 \cdot y^{11} = y^{5+11} = y^{16}$

(b) $2^3 \cdot 2^5 = 2^{3+5} = 2^8$ Note that the base does not change! Only the exponent changes.

(c) $x^6 \cdot y^8$ The rule for multiplying exponential expressions does not apply since the bases are not the same. This cannot be simplified.

Practice Problem 2 Simplify, if possible.

(a) $x^3 \cdot x^9$ **(b)** $3^7 \cdot 3^4$ **(c)** $a^3 \cdot b^2$

We can now look at multiplying expressions such as $(2x^5)(3x^6)$.

The number 2 in $2x^5$ is called the **numerical coefficient.** Recall that a numerical coefficient is a number that is multiplied by a variable. When we multiply two expressions such as $2x^5$ and $3x^6$, we first multiply the numerical coefficients; we multiply the variables with exponents separately.

EXAMPLE 3 Multiply. **(a)** $(2x^5)(3x^6)$ **(b)** $(5x^3)(x^6)$ **(c)** $(-6x)(-4x^5)$

Solution

(a) $(2x^5)(3x^6) = (2 \cdot 3)(x^5 \cdot x^6)$ Multiply the numerical coefficients.

$= 6(x^5 \cdot x^6)$ Use the rule for multiplying expressions with exponents. Add the exponents.

$= 6x^{11}$

(b) Every variable that does not have a visible numerical coefficient is understood to have a numerical coefficient of 1. Thus x^6 has a numerical coefficient of 1.

$$(5x^3)(x^6) = (5 \cdot 1)(x^3 \cdot x^6) = 5x^9$$

(c) $(-6x)(-4x^5) = (-6)(-4)(x^1 \cdot x^5) = 24x^6$ Remember that x has an exponent of 1.

Practice Problem 3 Multiply.

(a) $(-a^8)(a^4)$ **(b)** $(3y^2)(-2y^3)$ **(c)** $(-4x^3)(-5x^2)$

Problems of this type may involve more than one variable or more than two factors.

EXAMPLE 4 Multiply. $(5ab)\left(-\frac{1}{3}a\right)(9b^2)$

Solution

$$(5ab)\left(-\tfrac{1}{3}a\right)(9b^2) = (5)\left(-\tfrac{1}{3}\right)(9)(a \cdot a)(b \cdot b^2)$$
$$= -15a^2b^3$$

As you do the following problems, keep in mind the rule for multiplying numbers with exponents and the rules for multiplying signed numbers.

Practice Problem 4 Multiply. $(2xy)\left(-\frac{1}{4}x^2y\right)(6xy^3)$

2 Using the Quotient Rule to Divide Exponential Expressions with Like Bases

Frequently, we must divide exponential expressions. Since division by zero is undefined, in all problems in this chapter we assume that the denominator of any variable expression is not zero. We'll look at division in three separate parts.

Suppose that we want to simplify $x^5 \div x^2$. We could do the division the long way.

$$\frac{x^5}{x^2} = \frac{(x)(x)(x)\cancel{(x)}\cancel{(x)}}{\cancel{(x)}\cancel{(x)}} = x^3$$

Here we are using the arithmetical property of reducing fractions (see Section 0.1). When the same factor appears in both numerator and denominator, that factor can be removed.

A simpler way is to *subtract the exponents*. Notice that the base remains the same.

THE QUOTIENT RULE (PART 1)

$\dfrac{x^a}{x^b} = x^{a-b}$ Use this form if the larger exponent is in the numerator and $x \neq 0$.

EXAMPLE 5 Divide. **(a)** $\dfrac{2^{16}}{2^{11}}$ **(b)** $\dfrac{x^5}{x^3}$ **(c)** $\dfrac{y^{16}}{y^7}$

Solution

(a) $\dfrac{2^{16}}{2^{11}} = 2^{16-11} = 2^5$ Note that the base does *not* change.

(b) $\dfrac{x^5}{x^3} = x^{5-3} = x^2$

(c) $\dfrac{y^{16}}{y^7} = y^{16-7} = y^9$

Practice Problem 5 Divide. **(a)** $\dfrac{10^{13}}{10^7}$ **(b)** $\dfrac{x^{11}}{x}$ **(c)** $\dfrac{y^{18}}{y^8}$

NOTE TO STUDENT: Fully worked-out solutions to all of the Practice Problems can be found at the back of the text starting at page SP-1

Now we consider the situation where the larger exponent is in the denominator. Suppose that we want to simplify $x^2 \div x^5$.

$$\frac{x^2}{x^5} = \frac{\cancel{(x)}\cancel{(x)}}{\cancel{(x)}\cancel{(x)}(x)(x)(x)} = \frac{1}{x^3}$$

THE QUOTIENT RULE (PART 2)

$\dfrac{x^a}{x^b} = \dfrac{1}{x^{b-a}}$ Use this form if the larger exponent is in the denominator and $x \neq 0$.

EXAMPLE 6 Divide. **(a)** $\dfrac{12^{17}}{12^{20}}$ **(b)** $\dfrac{b^7}{b^9}$ **(c)** $\dfrac{x^{20}}{x^{24}}$

Solution

(a) $\dfrac{12^{17}}{12^{20}} = \dfrac{1}{12^{20-17}} = \dfrac{1}{12^3}$ Note that the base does *not* change.

(b) $\dfrac{b^7}{b^9} = \dfrac{1}{b^{9-7}} = \dfrac{1}{b^2}$

(c) $\dfrac{x^{20}}{x^{24}} = \dfrac{1}{x^{24-20}} = \dfrac{1}{x^4}$

Practice Problem 6 Divide. **(a)** $\dfrac{c^3}{c^4}$ **(b)** $\dfrac{10^{31}}{10^{56}}$ **(c)** $\dfrac{z^{15}}{z^{21}}$

When there are numerical coefficients, use the rules for dividing signed numbers to reduce fractions to lowest terms.

EXAMPLE 7 Divide. **(a)** $\frac{5x^5}{25x^7}$ **(b)** $\frac{-12x^8}{4x^3}$ **(c)** $\frac{-16x^7}{-24x^8}$

Solution

(a) $\frac{5x^5}{25x^7} = \frac{1}{5x^{7-5}} = \frac{1}{5x^2}$ **(b)** $\frac{-12x^8}{4x^3} = -3x^{8-3} = -3x^5$

(c) $\frac{-16x^7}{-24x^8} = \frac{2}{3x^{8-7}} = \frac{2}{3x}$

Practice Problem 7 Divide. **(a)** $\frac{-7x^7}{-21x^9}$ **(b)** $\frac{15x^{11}}{-3x^4}$ **(c)** $\frac{23x^8}{46x^9}$

You have to work very carefully if two or more variables are involved. Treat the coefficients and each variable separately.

EXAMPLE 8 Divide. **(a)** $\frac{x^3y^2}{5xy^6}$ **(b)** $\frac{-3x^2y^5}{12x^6y^8}$

Solution

(a) $\frac{x^3y^2}{5xy^6} = \frac{x^2}{5y^4}$ **(b)** $\frac{-3x^2y^5}{12x^6y^8} = -\frac{1}{4x^4y^3}$

Practice Problem 8 Divide. **(a)** $\frac{x^7y^9}{y^{10}}$ **(b)** $\frac{12x^5y^6}{-24x^3y^8}$

Suppose that a given base appears with the same exponent in the numerator and denominator of a fraction. In this case we can use the fact that *any nonzero number divided by itself is* 1.

EXAMPLE 9 Divide. **(a)** $\frac{x^6}{x^6}$ **(b)** $\frac{3x^5}{x^5}$

Solution

(a) $\frac{x^6}{x^6} = 1$ **(b)** $\frac{3x^5}{x^5} = 3\left(\frac{x^5}{x^5}\right) = 3(1) = 3$

Practice Problem 9 Divide. **(a)** $\frac{10^7}{10^7}$ **(b)** $\frac{12a^4}{15a^4}$

Do you see that if we had subtracted exponents when simplifying $\frac{x^6}{x^6}$ we would have obtained x^0 in Example 9? So we can surmise that any number (except 0) to the 0 power equals 1. We can write this fact as a separate rule.

THE QUOTIENT RULE (PART 3)

$$\frac{x^a}{x^a} = x^0 = 1 \quad \text{if } x \neq 0 \quad (0^0 \text{ remains undefined}).$$

TO THINK ABOUT: What Is 0 to the 0 Power? What about 0^0? Why is it undefined? $0^0 = 0^{1-1}$. If we use the quotient rule, $0^{1-1} = \frac{0}{0}$. Since division by zero is undefined, we must agree that 0^0 is undefined.

EXAMPLE 10 Divide. **(a)** $\dfrac{4x^0y^2}{8^0y^5z^3}$ **(b)** $\dfrac{5x^2y}{10x^2y^3}$

Solution

(a) $\dfrac{4x^0y^2}{8^0y^5z^3} = \dfrac{4(1)y^2}{(1)y^5z^3} = \dfrac{4y^2}{y^5z^3} = \dfrac{4}{y^3z^3}$ **(b)** $\dfrac{5x^2y}{10x^2y^3} = \dfrac{1x^0}{2y^2} = \dfrac{(1)(1)}{2y^2} = \dfrac{1}{2y^2}$

Practice Problem 10 Divide. **(a)** $\dfrac{-20a^3b^8c^4}{28a^3b^7c^5}$ **(b)** $\dfrac{5x^0y^6}{10x^4y^8}$

We can combine all three parts of the quotient rule we have developed.

THE QUOTIENT RULE

$\dfrac{x^a}{x^b} = x^{a-b}$ Use this form if the larger exponent is in the numerator and $x \neq 0$.

$\dfrac{x^a}{x^b} = \dfrac{1}{x^{b-a}}$ Use this form if the larger exponent is in the denominator and $x \neq 0$.

$\dfrac{x^a}{x^a} = x^0 = 1$ if $x \neq 0$.

We can combine the product rule and the quotient rule to simplify algebraic expressions that involve both multiplication and division.

EXAMPLE 11 Simplify. $\dfrac{(8x^2y)(-3x^3y^2)}{-6x^4y^3}$

Solution $\dfrac{(8x^2y)(-3x^3y^2)}{-6x^4y^3} = \dfrac{-24x^5y^3}{-6x^4y^3} = 4x$

Practice Problem 11 Simplify. $\dfrac{(-6ab^5)(3a^2b^4)}{16a^5b^7}$

NOTE TO STUDENT: Fully worked-out solutions to all of the Practice Problems can be found at the back of the text starting at page SP-1

3 Raising Exponential Expressions to a Power

How do we simplify an expression such as $(x^4)^3$? $(x^4)^3$ is x^4 raised to the third power. For this type of problem we say that we are raising a power to a power. A problem such as $(x^4)^3$ could be done by writing the following.

$$(x^4)^3 = x^4 \cdot x^4 \cdot x^4 \quad \text{By definition}$$
$$= x^{12} \quad \text{By adding exponents}$$

Notice that when we add the exponents we get $4 + 4 + 4 = 12$. This is the same as multiplying 4 by 3. That is, $4 \cdot 3 = 12$. This process can be summarized by the following rule.

RAISING A POWER TO A POWER

To raise a power to a power, keep the same base and multiply the exponents.

$$(x^a)^b = x^{ab}$$

Recall what happens when you raise a negative number to a power. $(-1)^2 = 1$. $(-1)^3 = -1$. In general,

$$(-1)^n = \begin{cases} +1 & \text{if } n \text{ is even} \\ -1 & \text{if } n \text{ is odd.} \end{cases}$$

EXAMPLE 12 Simplify. **(a)** $(x^3)^5$ **(b)** $(2^7)^3$ **(c)** $(-1)^8$

Solution

(a) $(x^3)^5 = x^{3 \cdot 5} = x^{15}$ **(b)** $(2^7)^3 = 2^{7 \cdot 3} = 2^{21}$ **(c)** $(-1)^8 = +1$

Note that in both parts (a) and (b) the base does not change.

Practice Problem 12 Simplify. **(a)** $(a^4)^3$ **(b)** $(10^5)^2$ **(c)** $(-1)^{15}$

Here are two rules involving products and quotients that are very useful: the product raised to a power rule and the quotient raised to a power rule. We'll illustrate each with an example.

If a product in parentheses is raised to a power, the parentheses indicate that *each factor* must be raised to that power.

$$(xy)^2 = x^2y^2 \qquad (xy)^3 = x^3y^3$$

PRODUCT RAISED TO A POWER

$$(xy)^a = x^ay^a$$

EXAMPLE 13 Simplify. **(a)** $(ab)^8$ **(b)** $(3x)^4$ **(c)** $(-2x^2)^3$

Solution

(a) $(ab)^8 = a^8b^8$ **(b)** $(3x)^4 = (3)^4x^4 = 81x^4$

(c) $(-2x^2)^3 = (-2)^3 \cdot (x^2)^3 = -8x^6$

Practice Problem 13 Simplify. **(a)** $(3xy)^3$ **(b)** $(yz)^{37}$ **(c)** $(-3x^3)^2$

If a fractional expression within parentheses is raised to a power, the parentheses indicate that both numerator and denominator must be raised to that power.

$$\left(\frac{x}{y}\right)^5 = \frac{x^5}{y^5} \qquad \left(\frac{x}{y}\right)^2 = \frac{x^2}{y^2} \qquad \text{if } y \neq 0$$

QUOTIENT RAISED TO A POWER

$$\left(\frac{x}{y}\right)^a = \frac{x^a}{y^a} \qquad \text{if } y \neq 0$$

EXAMPLE 14 Simplify. **(a)** $\left(\frac{x}{y}\right)^5$ **(b)** $\left(\frac{7}{w}\right)^4$

Solution

(a) $\left(\frac{x}{y}\right)^5 = \frac{x^5}{y^5}$ **(b)** $\left(\frac{7}{w}\right)^4 = \frac{7^4}{w^4} = \frac{2401}{w^4}$

Practice Problem 14 Simplify. **(a)** $\left(\frac{x}{5}\right)^3$ **(b)** $\left(\frac{4a}{b}\right)^6$

Many expressions can be simplified by using the previous rules involving exponents. Be sure to take particular care to determine the correct sign, especially if there is a negative numerical coefficient.

EXAMPLE 15 Simplify. $\left(\frac{-3x^2z^0}{y^3}\right)^4$

Solution

$$\left(\frac{-3x^2z^0}{y^3}\right)^4 = \left(\frac{-3x^2}{y^3}\right)^4$$ Simplify inside the parentheses first. Note that $z^0 = 1$.

$$= \frac{(-3)^4x^8}{y^{12}}$$ Apply the rules for raising a power to a power. Notice that we wrote $(-3)^4$ and not -3^4. We are raising -3 to the fourth power.

$$= \frac{81x^8}{y^{12}}$$ Simplify the coefficient: $(-3)^4 = +81$.

NOTE TO STUDENT: Fully worked-out solutions to all of the Practice Problems can be found at the back of the text starting at page SP-1

Practice Problem 15 Simplify. $\left(\frac{-2x^3y^0z}{4xz^2}\right)^5$

We list here the rules of exponents we have discussed in Section 4.1.

$$x^a \cdot x^b = x^{a+b}$$

$$\frac{x^a}{x^b} = \begin{cases} x^{a-b} & \text{if } a > b \\ \dfrac{1}{x^{b-a}} & \text{if } b > a \\ x^0 = 1 & \text{if } a = b \end{cases}$$

$$(x^a)^b = x^{ab}$$

$$(xy)^a = x^a y^a$$

$$\left(\frac{x}{y}\right)^a = \frac{x^a}{y^a} \quad y \neq 0$$

Developing Your Study Skills

Why Is Review Necessary?

You master a course in mathematics by learning the concepts one step at a time. Thus the study of mathematics is built step-by-step, with each step a supporting foundation for the next. The process is a carefully designed procedure, so no steps can be skipped. A student of mathematics needs to realize the importance of this building process to succeed.

Because new concepts depend on those previously learned, students often need to take time to review. The reviewing process will strengthen understanding and skills, which may be weak due to a lack of mastery or the passage of time. Review at the right time on the right concepts can strengthen previously learned skills and make progress possible.

Timely, periodic review of previously learned mathematical concepts is absolutely necessary for mastery of new concepts. You may have forgotten a concept or grown a bit rusty in applying it. Reviewing is the answer. Make use of the cumulative review problems in your textbook, whether they are assigned or not. Look back to previous chapters whenever you have forgotten how to do something. Review the chapter organizers from previous chapters. Study the examples and practice some exercises to refresh your understanding.

Be sure that you understand and can perform the computations of each new concept. This will enable you to move successfully on to the next one.

Remember, mathematics is a step-by-step building process. Learn each concept and reinforce and strengthen with review whenever necessary.

4.1 Exercises

Student Solutions Manual

CD/ Video
PH Math Tutor Center

MathXL®Tutorials on CD

MathXL®

MyMathLab®

Interactmath.com

Verbal and Writing Skills

1. Write in your own words the product rule for exponents.

2. To be able to use the rules of exponents, what must be true of the bases?

3. If the larger exponent is in the denominator, the quotient rule states that $\frac{x^a}{x^b} = \frac{1}{x^{b-a}}$. Provide an example to show why this is true.

In exercises 4 and 5, identify the numerical coefficient, the base(s), and the exponent(s).

4. $-8x^5y^2$

5. $6x^{11}y$

6. Evaluate **(a)** $3x^0$ and **(b)** $(3x)^0$. **(c)** Why are the results different?

Write in simplest exponent form.

7. $2 \cdot 2 \cdot a \cdot a \cdot a \cdot b$

8. $5 \cdot x \cdot x \cdot x \cdot y \cdot y$

9. $(-3)(a)(a)(b)(c)(b)(c)(c)$

10. $(-7)(x)(y)(z)(y)(x)$

Multiply. Leave your answer in exponent form.

11. $(7^4)(7^6)$

12. $(4^3)(4^5)$

13. $(5^{10})(5^{16})$

14. $(6^5)(6^8)$

15. $x^4 \cdot x^8$

16. $x^9 \cdot x^6$

17. $w^{12} \cdot w^{20}$

18. $z^{16} \cdot z^{10}$

Multiply.

19. $-5x^4(4x^2)$

20. $6x^2(-9x^3)$

21. $(5x)(10x^2)$

22. $(-4x^2)(-3x)$

23. $(3x^2y)(8x^3y^3)$

24. $(6xy^3)(5x^4y)$

25. $\left(\frac{2}{5}xy^3\right)\left(\frac{1}{3}x^2y^2\right)$

26. $\left(\frac{4}{5}x^5y\right)\left(\frac{15}{16}x^2y^4\right)$

27. $(1.1x^2z)(-2.5xy)$

28. $(2.3x^4w)(-3.5xy^4)$

29. $(8a)(2a^3b)(0)$

30. $(5ab)(2a^2)(0)$

31. $(-16x^2y^4)(-5xy^3)$

32. $(-12x^4y)(-7x^5y^3)$

33. $(-8x^3y^2)(3xy^5)$

34. $(9x^2y^6)(-11x^3y^3)$

35. $(-2x^3y^2)(0)(-3x^4y)$

36. $(-4x^8y^2)(13y^3)(0)$

37. $(8a^4b^3)(-3x^2y^5)$

38. $(5x^3y)(-2w^4z)$

39. $(2x^2y)(-3y^3z^2)(5xz^4)$

40. $(3ab)(5a^2c)(-2b^2c^3)$

Divide. Leave your answer in exponent form. Assume that all variables in any denominator are nonzero.

41. $\frac{y^{12}}{y^5}$

42. $\frac{x^{13}}{x^3}$

43. $\frac{y^5}{y^8}$

44. $\frac{b^{20}}{b^{23}}$

45. $\frac{11^{18}}{11^{30}}$

46. $\frac{8^9}{8^{12}}$

47. $\frac{3^{18}}{3^{14}}$

48. $\frac{5^{16}}{5^{12}}$

49. $\frac{a^{13}}{4a^5}$

50. $\frac{b^{16}}{5b^{13}}$

51. $\frac{x^7}{y^9}$

52. $\frac{x^{20}}{y^3}$

53. $\frac{48x^5y^3}{24xy^3}$

54. $\frac{45a^4b^3}{15a^4b^2}$

55. $\frac{16x^5y}{-32x^2y^3}$

56. $\frac{-36x^3y^7}{72x^5y}$ **57.** $\frac{1.8f^4g^3}{54f^2g^8}$ **58.** $\frac{3.1s^5t^3}{62s^8t}$ **59.** $\frac{-51x^6y^8}{17x^3y^8}$ **60.** $\frac{-30x^5y^4}{5x^3y^4}$

61. $\frac{8^0x^2y^3}{16x^5y}$ **62.** $\frac{3^2x^3y^7}{3^0x^5y^2}$ **63.** $\frac{18a^6b^3c^0}{24a^5b^3}$ **64.** $\frac{12a^7b^8}{16a^3b^8c^0}$ **65.** $\frac{85a^2b}{45c^3}$

66. $\frac{28x}{63y^2z}$

To Think About

67. What expression can be multiplied by $(-3x^3yz)$ to obtain $81x^8y^2z^4$?

68. $63a^5b^6$ is divided by an expression and the result is $-9a^4b$. What is this expression?

Simplify.

69. $(x^2)^6$ **70.** $(w^5)^8$ **71.** $(xy^2)^7$ **72.** $(a^3b)^4$ **73.** $(rs^2)^6$

74. $(m^3n^2)^5$ **75.** $(3a^3b^2c)^3$ **76.** $(2x^4yz^3)^2$ **77.** $(-3a^4)^2$ **78.** $(-2a^5)^4$

79. $\left(\frac{x}{2m^4}\right)^7$ **80.** $\left(\frac{p^5}{6x}\right)^5$ **81.** $\left(\frac{5x}{7y^2}\right)^2$ **82.** $\left(\frac{2a^4}{3b^3}\right)^4$ **83.** $(-3a^2b^3c^0)^4$

84. $(-2a^5b^2c^0)^5$ **85.** $(-2x^3y^0z)^3$ **86.** $(-4xy^0z^4)^3$ **87.** $\frac{(3x)^5}{(3x^2)^3}$ **88.** $\frac{(6y^3)^4}{(6y)^2}$

Mixed Practice

89. $(3ab^2)^3(ab)$ **90.** $(-2a^2b^3)^3(ab^2)$ **91.** $\left(\frac{8}{y^5}\right)^2$ **92.** $\left(\frac{4}{x^6}\right)^3$ **93.** $\left(\frac{2x}{y^3}\right)^4$

94. $\left(\frac{3x^5}{y}\right)^3$ **95.** $\left(\frac{ab^2}{c^3d^4}\right)^4$ **96.** $\left(\frac{a^3b}{c^5d}\right)^5$

To Think About

97. What expression raised to the third power is $-27x^9y^{12}z^{21}$?

98. What expression raised to the fourth power is $16x^{20}y^{16}z^{28}$?

Cumulative Review

Simplify.

99. $-3 - 8$ **100.** $-17 + (-32) + (-24) + 27$ **101.** $\left(\frac{2}{3}\right)\left(-\frac{21}{8}\right)$ **102.** $\frac{-3}{4} \div \frac{-12}{80}$

Rain Forests *Brazil, the largest country in South America, boasts a land area of approximately 8,511,960 sq km. Originally, 2,860,000 sq km in Brazil was covered by rain forest. As of 2002 the rain forest of that country only consists of 1,500,000 sq km. Round your answers to nearest tenth of a percent.*

103. What percentage of Brazil's land area was covered by rain forest 2002?

104. What was the percent decrease in the rain forest up to 2002?

105. If Brazil is said to lose 2.3% of its rain forest per year, how much rain forest was lost in the year after 2002?

(Information source: The Rain Forest Action Network)

4.2 Negative Exponents and Scientific Notation

1 Using Negative Exponents

If n is an integer, and $x \neq 0$, then x^{-n} is defined as follows:

DEFINITION OF A NEGATIVE EXPONENT

$$x^{-n} = \frac{1}{x^n}, \quad x \neq 0$$

EXAMPLE 1 Write with positive exponents.

(a) y^{-3} **(b)** z^{-6} **(c)** w^{-1}

Solution

(a) $y^{-3} = \frac{1}{y^3}$ **(b)** $z^{-6} = \frac{1}{z^6}$ **(c)** $w^{-1} = \frac{1}{w^1} = \frac{1}{w}$

Practice Problem 1 Write with positive exponents.

(a) x^{-12} **(b)** w^{-5} **(c)** z^{-2}

To evaluate a numerical expression with a negative exponent, first write the expression with a positive exponent. Then simplify.

EXAMPLE 2 Evaluate. **(a)** 3^{-2} **(b)** 2^{-5}

Solution

(a) $3^{-2} = \frac{1}{3^2} = \frac{1}{9}$ **(b)** $2^{-5} = \frac{1}{2^5} = \frac{1}{32}$

Practice Problem 2 Evaluate. **(a)** 4^{-3} **(b)** 2^{-4}

All the previously studied laws of exponents are true for any integer exponent. These laws are summarized in the following box. Assume that $x, y \neq 0$.

LAWS OF EXPONENTS

The Product Rule

$$x^a \cdot x^b = x^{a+b}$$

The Quotient Rule

$$\frac{x^a}{x^b} = x^{a-b} \quad \text{Use if } a > b, \qquad \frac{x^a}{x^b} = \frac{1}{x^{b-a}} \quad \text{Use if } a < b.$$

Power Rules

$$(xy)^a = x^a y^a, \qquad (x^a)^b = x^{ab}, \qquad \left(\frac{x}{y}\right)^a = \frac{x^a}{y^a}$$

Student Learning Objectives

After studying this section, you will be able to:

1. **Use negative exponents.**
2. **Write numbers in scientific notation.**

***NOTE TO STUDENT:** Fully worked-out solutions to all of the Practice Problems can be found at the back of the text starting at page SP-1*

By using the definition of a negative exponent and the properties of fractions, we can derive two more helpful properties of exponents. Assume that $x, y \neq 0$.

PROPERTIES OF NEGATIVE EXPONENTS

$$\frac{1}{x^{-n}} = x^n \qquad \frac{x^{-m}}{y^{-n}} = \frac{y^n}{x^m}$$

EXAMPLE 3 Simplify. Write the expression with no negative exponents.

(a) $\frac{1}{x^{-6}}$ **(b)** $\frac{x^{-3}y^{-2}}{z^{-4}}$ **(c)** $x^{-2}y^3$

Solution

(a) $\frac{1}{x^{-6}} = x^6$ **(b)** $\frac{x^{-3}y^{-2}}{z^{-4}} = \frac{z^4}{x^3y^2}$ **(c)** $x^{-2}y^3 = \frac{y^3}{x^2}$

NOTE TO STUDENT: Fully worked-out solutions to all of the Practice Problems can be found at the back of the text starting at page SP-1

Practice Problem 3 Simplify. Write the expression with no negative exponents.

(a) $\frac{3}{w^{-4}}$ **(b)** $\frac{x^{-6}y^4}{z^{-2}}$ **(c)** $x^{-6}y^{-5}$

EXAMPLE 4 Simplify. Write the expression with no negative exponents.

(a) $(3x^{-4}y^2)^{-3}$ **(b)** $\frac{x^2y^{-4}}{x^{-5}y^3}$

Solution

(a) $(3x^{-4}y^2)^{-3} = 3^{-3}x^{12}y^{-6} = \frac{x^{12}}{3^3y^6} = \frac{x^{12}}{27y^6}$

(b) $\frac{x^2y^{-4}}{x^{-5}y^3} = \frac{x^2x^5}{y^4y^3} = \frac{x^7}{y^7}$ First rewrite the expression so that only positive exponents appear. Then simplify using the product rule.

Practice Problem 4 Simplify. Write the expression with no negative exponents.

(a) $(2x^4y^{-5})^{-2}$ **(b)** $\frac{y^{-3}z^{-4}}{y^2z^{-6}}$

2 Writing Numbers in Scientific Notation

One common use of negative exponents is in writing numbers in scientific notation. Scientific notation is most useful in expressing very large and very small numbers.

SCIENTIFIC NOTATION

A positive number is written in **scientific notation** if it is in the form $a \times 10^n$, where $1 \leq a < 10$ and n is an integer.

EXAMPLE 5 Write in scientific notation. **(a)** 4567 **(b)** 157,000,000

Solution

(a) $4567 = 4.567 \times 1000$ To change 4567 to a number that is greater than 1 but less than 10, we move the decimal point three places to the left. We must then multiply the number by a power of 10 so that we do not change the value of the number. Use 1000.

$= 4.567 \times 10^3$

(b) $157{,}000{,}000 = 1.57000000 \times 100000000$ (8 places; 8 zeros)

$= 1.57 \times 10^8$

Practice Problem 5 Write in scientific notation.

(a) 78,200 **(b)** 4,786,000

Numbers that are smaller than 1 will have a negative power of 10 if they are written in scientific notation.

EXAMPLE 6 Write in scientific notation. **(a)** 0.061 **(b)** 0.000052

Solution

(a) We need to write 0.061 as a number that is greater than 1 but less than 10. In which direction do we move the decimal point?

$0.061 = 6.1 \times 10^{-2}$ Move the decimal point 2 places to the right.

(b) $0.000052 = 5.2 \times 10^{-5}$ Why?

Practice Problem 6 Write in scientific notation.

(a) 0.98 **(b)** 0.000092

The reverse procedure transforms scientific notation into ordinary decimal notation.

EXAMPLE 7 Write in decimal notation.

(a) 1.568×10^2 **(b)** 7.432×10^{-3}

Solution

(a) $1.568 \times 10^2 = 1.568 \times 100$

$= 156.8$

Alternative Method

$1.568 \times 10^2 = 156.8$ The exponent 2 tells us to move the decimal point 2 places to the right.

(b) $7.432 \times 10^{-3} = 7.432 \times \frac{1}{1000}$

$= 0.007432$

Alternative Method

$7.432 \times 10^{-3} = 0.007432$ The exponent -3 tells us to move the decimal point 3 places to the left.

Practice Problem 7 Write in decimal notation.

(a) 1.93×10^6 **(b)** 8.562×10^{-5}

Calculator

Scientific Notation

Most calculators can display only eight digits at one time. Numbers with more than eight digits are usually shown in scientific notation.

1.12 E 08 or 1.12 8 means 1.12×10^8. You can use the calculator to compute with large numbers by entering the numbers using scientific notation. For example,

$(7.48 \times 10^{24}) \times (3.5 \times 10^8)$

is entered as follows.

7.48 [EXP]

24 [×] 3.5

[EXP] 8 [=]

Display: [2.618 E 33]

or [2.618 33]

Note: Some calculators have an [EE] key instead of [EXP].

Compute on a calculator.

1. 35,000,000,000 + 77,000,000,000
2. $(6.23 \times 10^{12}) \times (4.9 \times 10^5)$
3. $(2.5 \times 10^7)^5$
4. $3.3284 \times 10^{32} \div (6.28 \times 10^{24})$
5. How many seconds are there in 1000 years?

The distance light travels in one year is called a *light-year*. A light-year is a convenient unit of measure to use when investigating the distances between stars.

EXAMPLE 8 A light-year is a distance of 9,460,000,000,000,000 meters. Write this in scientific notation.

Solution $9{,}460{,}000{,}000{,}000{,}000 = 9.46 \times 10^{15}$ meters

Practice Problem 8 Astronomers measure distances to faraway galaxies in parsecs. A parsec is a distance of 30,900,000,000,000,000 meters. Write this in scientific notation.

To perform a calculation involving very large or very small numbers, it is usually helpful to write the numbers in scientific notation and then use the laws of exponents to do the calculation.

EXAMPLE 9 Use scientific notation and the laws of exponents to find the following. Leave your answer in scientific notation.

(a) $(32{,}000{,}000)(1{,}500{,}000{,}000{,}000)$ **(b)** $\dfrac{0.00063}{0.021}$

Solution

(a) $(32{,}000{,}000)(1{,}500{,}000{,}000{,}000)$

$= (3.2 \times 10^7)(1.5 \times 10^{12})$ Write each number in scientific notation.

$= 3.2 \times 1.5 \times 10^7 \times 10^{12}$ Rearrange the order. Remember that multiplication is commutative.

$= 4.8 \times 10^{19}$ Multiply 3.2×1.5. Multiply $10^7 \times 10^{12}$.

(b) $\dfrac{0.00063}{0.021} = \dfrac{6.3 \times 10^{-4}}{2.1 \times 10^{-2}}$ Write each number in scientific notation.

$= \dfrac{6.3}{2.1} \times \dfrac{10^{-4}}{10^{-2}}$ Rearrange the order. We are actually using the definition of multiplication of fractions.

$= \dfrac{6.3}{2.1} \times \dfrac{10^2}{10^4}$ Rewrite with positive exponents.

$= 3.0 \times 10^{-2}$

Practice Problem 9 Use scientific notation and the laws of exponents to find the following. Leave your answer in scientific notation.

(a) $(56{,}000)(1{,}400{,}000{,}000)$ **(b)** $\dfrac{0.000111}{0.00000037}$

***NOTE TO STUDENT:** Fully worked-out solutions to all of the Practice Problems can be found at the back of the text starting at page SP-1*

When we use scientific notation, we are writing approximate numbers. We must include some zeros so that the decimal point can be properly located. However, all other digits except for these zeros are considered **significant digits.** The number 34.56 has four significant digits. The number 0.0049 has two significant digits. The zeros are considered placeholders. The number 634,000 has three significant digits (unless we have specific knowledge to the contrary). The zeros are considered placeholders. We sometimes round numbers to a specific number of significant digits. For example, 0.08746 rounded to two significant digits is 0.087. When we round 1,348,593 to three significant digits, we obtain 1,350,000.

EXAMPLE 10 The approximate distance from Earth to the star Polaris is 208 parsecs. A parsec is a distance of approximately 3.09×10^{13} kilometers. How long would it take a space probe traveling at 40,000 kilometers per hour to reach the star? Round to three significant digits.

Solution

1. ***Understand the problem.*** Recall that the distance formula is

$$\text{distance} = \text{rate} \times \text{time}.$$

We are given the distance and the rate. We need to find the time.

Let's take a look at the distance. The distance is given in parsecs, but the rate is given in kilometers per hour. We need to change the distance to kilometers. We are told that a parsec is approximately 3.09×10^{13} kilometers. That is, there are 3.09×10^{13} kilometers per parsec. We use this information to change 208 parsecs to kilometers.

$$208 \text{ parsecs} = \frac{(208 \text{ parsecs})(3.09 \times 10^{13} \text{ kilometers})}{1 \text{ parsec}} = 642.72 \times 10^{13} \text{ kilometers}$$

2. ***Write an equation.*** Use the distance formula.

$$d = r \times t$$

3. ***Solve the equation and state the answer.*** Substitute the known values into the formula and solve for the unknown, time.

$$642.72 \times 10^{13} \text{ km} = \frac{40{,}000 \text{ km}}{1 \text{ hr}} \times t$$

$$6.4272 \times 10^{15} \text{ km} = \frac{4 \times 10^{4} \text{ km}}{1 \text{ hr}} \times t \qquad \text{Change the numbers to scientific notation.}$$

$$\frac{6.4272 \times 10^{15} \text{ km}}{\dfrac{4 \times 10^{4} \text{ km}}{1 \text{ hr}}} = t \qquad \text{Divide both sides by } \frac{4 \times 10^{4} \text{ km}}{1 \text{ hr}}.$$

$$\frac{(6.4272 \times 10^{15} \cancel{\text{km}})(1 \text{ hr})}{4 \times 10^{4} \cancel{\text{km}}} = t$$

$$1.6068 \times 10^{11} \text{ hr} = t$$

1.6068×10^{11} is 160.68×10^{9} or 160.68 billion hours. The space probe will take approximately 160.68 billion hours to reach the star.

Reread the problem. Are we finished? What is left to do? We need to round the answer to three significant digits. Rounding to three significant digits, we have

$$160.68 \times 10^{9} \approx 161 \times 10^{9}.$$

This is approximately 161 billion hours or a little more than 18 million years.

4. ***Check.*** Unless you have had a great deal of experience working in astronomy, it would be difficult to determine whether this is a reasonable answer. You may wish to reread your analysis and redo your calculations as a check.

Practice Problem 10 The average distance from Earth to the distant star Betelgeuse is 159 parsecs. How many hours would it take a space probe to travel from Earth to Betelgeuse at a speed of 50,000 kilometers per hour? Round to three significant digits.

4.2 Exercises

     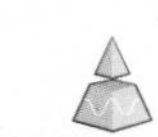

Student Solutions Manual | CD/ Video | PH Math Tutor Center | MathXL®Tutorials on CD | MathXL® | MyMathLab® | Interactmath.com

Simplify. Express your answer with positive exponents. Assume that all variables are nonzero.

1. x^{-4} **2.** y^{-5} **3.** 3^{-4} **4.** 5^{-3} **5.** $\dfrac{1}{y^{-8}}$ **6.** $\dfrac{1}{z^{-10}}$

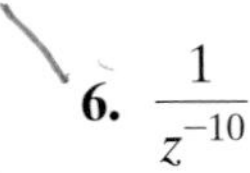

7. $\dfrac{x^{-4}y^{-5}}{z^{-6}}$ **8.** $\dfrac{x^{-6}y^{-2}}{z^{-5}}$ **9.** $x^{-5}y^{6}$ **10.** $x^{-4}y^{7}$ **11.** $(2x^{-3})^{-3}$ **12.** $(4x^{-4})^{-2}$

13. $3x^{-2}$ **14.** $4y^{-4}$ **15.** $(4x^2y)^{-2}$ **16.** $(2x^3y^5)^{-3}$

Mixed Practice

17. $\dfrac{3xy^{-2}}{z^{-3}}$ **18.** $\dfrac{4x^{-2}y^{-3}}{y^4}$ **19.** $\dfrac{(3x)^{-2}}{(3x)^{-3}}$ **20.** $\dfrac{(2ab^2)^{-3}}{(2ab^2)^{-4}}$

21. $wx^{-5}y^3z^{-2}$ **22.** $a^5b^{-3}c^{-4}$ **23.** $(8^{-2})(2^3)$ **24.** $(9^2)(3^{-3})$

25. $\left(\dfrac{3x^0y^2}{z^4}\right)^{-2}$ **26.** $\left(\dfrac{2a^3b^0}{c^2}\right)^{-3}$ **27.** $\dfrac{x^{-2}y^{-3}}{x^4y^{-2}}$ **28.** $\dfrac{a^{-6}b^3}{a^{-2}b^{-5}}$

Write in scientific notation.

29. 123,780 **30.** 5,786,100 **31.** 0.063 **32.** 0.000742

33. 889,610,000,000 **34.** 7,652,000,000 **35.** 0.00000001963 **36.** 0.000007618

In exercises 37–42, write in decimal notation.

37. 3.02×10^5 **38.** 8.137×10^7 **39.** 4.7×10^{-4} **40.** 6.53×10^{-3} **41.** 9.83×10^5 **42.** 3.5×10^{-8}

43. ***Bamboo Growth*** The growth rate of some species of bamboo is 0.0000237 miles per hour. Write this in scientific notation.

44. ***Neptune*** Neptune is 2.793×10^9 miles from the sun. Write this in decimal notation.

45. ***Red Blood Cell*** A single human red blood cell is about 7×10^{-6} meters in diameter. Write this in decimal notation.

46. ***Gold Atom*** The average volume of an atom of gold is 0.00000000000000000000001695 cubic centimeters. Write this in scientific notation.

Evaluate by using scientific notation and the laws of exponents. Leave your answer in scientific notation.

47. (56,000,000,000) (780,000,000)

48. (35,000,000) (84,000,000,000)

49. $\dfrac{(5{,}000{,}000)(16{,}000)}{8{,}000{,}000{,}000}$

50. (0.0075)(0.0000002)(0.001)

51. $(0.003)^4$

52. $(500{,}000)^4$

53. (150,000,000)(0.00005)(0.002)(30,000)

54. $\dfrac{(1{,}600{,}000)(0.00003)}{2400}$

Applications

National Debt *For fiscal year 2003, the national debt was determined to be approximately* 6.816×10^{12} *dollars. (Source: Treasury Department of Public Debt.)*

55. The census bureau estimates that in 2003, the entire population of the United States was 2.92×10^8 people. If the national debt were evenly divided among every person in the country, how much debt would be assigned to each individual? Round to three significant digits.

56. The census bureau estimates that in 2003, the number of people in the United States who were over age 18 was approximately 2.28×10^8 people. If the national debt were evenly divided among every person over age 18 in the country, how much debt would be assigned to each individual? Round to three significant digits.

Space Travel *A parsec is a distance of approximately* 3.09×10^{13} *kilometers.*

57. How long would it take a space probe to travel from Earth to the star Rigel, which is 276 parsecs from Earth? Assume that the space probe travels at 45,000 kilometers per hour. Round to three significant digits.

58. How long would it take a space probe to travel from Earth to the star Hadar, which is 150 parsecs from Earth? Assume that the space probe travels at 55,000 kilometers per hour. Round to three significant digits.

59. ***Watch Hand*** The tip of a $\frac{1}{3}$-inch-long hour hand on a watch travels at a speed of 0.00000275 miles per hour. How far has it traveled in a day?

60. ***Neutron Mass*** The mass of a neutron is approximately 1.675×10^{-27} kilogram. Find the mass of 180,000 neutrons.

61. ***007 Films*** The most profitable movie series made has been the James Bond series, which has grossed $\$3.2 \times 10^{9}$ over the 20 James Bond films. What is the average gross per film?

62. ***Moles per Molecule*** Avogadro's number says that there are approximately 6.02×10^{23} molecules/mole. How many molecules can one expect in 0.00483 mole?

63. ***Construction Cost*** In 1990 the cost for construction of new private buildings was estimated at $\$3.61 \times 10^{11}$. By 2010 the estimated cost for construction of new private buildings will be $\$9.36 \times 10^{11}$. What is the percent of increase from 1990 to 2010? Round to the nearest tenth of a percent. (*Source:* U.S. Census Bureau.)

64. ***Construction Cost*** In 1990 the cost for construction of new public buildings was estimated at $\$1.07 \times 10^{11}$. By 2010 the estimated cost for construction of new public buildings will be $\$3.06 \times 10^{11}$. What is the percent of increase from 1990 to 2010? Round to the nearest tenth of a percent. (*Source:* U.S. Census Bureau.)

Cumulative Review

Simplify.

65. $-2.7 - (-1.9)$

66. $(-1)^{33}$

67. $-\frac{3}{4} + \frac{5}{7}$

68. ***Hand Shakes*** A recent debate between two political candidates attracted 3540 people to a local gymnasium. At the conclusion of the debate, each person went to one side of the gymnasium to shake the hand of candidate #1 or to the other side of the room to shake the hand of candidate #2. Candidate #1 shook 524 less than triple the number of hands shaken by candidate #2. How many hands did each candidate shake?

69. ***Salaries*** Gina has a bachelor's degree. She earns \$12,460 more a year than Mario, who holds an associate's degree. Alfonso, who has not yet been able to attend college, earns \$8742 a year less than Mario. The combined annual salaries of the three people is \$112,000. What is the annual salary of each person?

4.3 Fundamental Polynomial Operations

Student Learning Objectives

After studying this section, you will be able to:

1. **Recognize polynomials and determine their degrees.**
2. **Add polynomials.**
3. **Subtract polynomials.**
4. **Evaluate polynomials to predict a value.**

1 Recognizing Polynomials and Determining Their Degrees

A **polynomial** in x is the sum of a finite number of terms of the form ax^n, where a is any real number and n is a whole number. Usually these polynomials are written in descending powers of the variable, as in

$$5x^3 + 3x^2 - 2x - 5 \quad \text{and} \quad 3.2x^2 - 1.4x + 5.6.$$

A **multivariable polynomial** is a polynomial with more than one variable. The following are multivariable polynomials:

$$5xy + 8, \qquad 2x^2 - 7xy + 9y^2, \qquad 17x^3y^9$$

The **degree of a term** is the sum of the exponents of all of the variables in the term. For example, the degree of $7x^3$ is three. The degree of $4xy$ is two. The degree of $10x^4y^2$ is six.

The **degree of a polynomial** is the highest degree of all of the terms in the polynomial. For example, the degree of $5x^3 + 8x^2 - 20x - 2$ is three. The degree of $6xy - 4x^2y + 2xy^3$ is four.

The polynomial 0 is said to have **no degree.** Likewise, a polynomial consisting of a constant is said to have no degree.

There are special names for polynomials with one, two, or three terms.

A **monomial** has *one* term:

$$5a, \qquad 3x^3yz^4, \qquad 12xy$$

A **binomial** has *two* terms:

$$7x + 9y, \qquad -6x - 4, \qquad 5x^4 + 2xy^2$$

A **trinomial** has *three* terms:

$$8x^2 - 7x + 4, \qquad 2ab^3 - 6ab^2 - 15ab, \qquad 2 + 5y + y^4$$

EXAMPLE 1 State the degree of the polynomial, and whether it is a monomial, a binomial, or a trinomial.

(a) $5xy + 3x^3$ **(b)** $-7a^5b^2$ **(c)** $8x^4 - 9x - 15$

Solution

(a) This polynomial is of degree 3. It has two terms, so it is a binomial.

(b) The sum of the exponents is $5 + 2 = 7$. Therefore this polynomial is of degree 7. It has one term, so it is a monomial.

(c) This polynomial is of degree 4. It has three terms, so it is a trinomial.

Practice Problem 1 State the degree of the polynomial, and whether it is a monomial, a binomial, or a trinomial.

(a) $-7x^5 - 3xy$ **(b)** $22a^3b^4$ **(c)** $-3x^3 + 3x^2 - 6x$

NOTE TO STUDENT: Fully worked-out solutions to all of the Practice Problems can be found at the back of the text starting at page SP-1

2 Adding Polynomials

We usually write a polynomial in x so that the exponents on x decrease from left to right. For example, the polynomial

$$5x^2 - 6x + 2$$

is said to be written in **decreasing order** since each exponent is decreasing as we move from left to right. You can add, subtract, multiply, and divide polynomials. Let us take a look at addition. To add two polynomials, we add their like terms.

EXAMPLE 2 Add. $(5x^2 - 6x - 12) + (-3x^2 - 9x + 5)$

Solution

$$\begin{aligned}(5x^2 - 6x - 12) + (-3x^2 - 9x + 5) &= [5x^2 + (-3x^2)] + [-6x + (-9x)] + [-12 + 5]\\ &= [(5 - 3)x^2] + [(-6 - 9)x] + [-12 + 5]\\ &= 2x^2 + (-15x) + (-7)\\ &= 2x^2 - 15x - 7\end{aligned}$$

Practice Problem 2 Add. $(-8x^3 + 3x^2 + 6) + (2x^3 - 7x^2 - 3)$

The numerical coefficients of the polynomials may be any real number. Thus the polynomials may have numerical coefficients that are decimals or fractions.

EXAMPLE 3 Add. $\left(\frac{1}{2}x^2 - 6x + \frac{1}{3}\right) + \left(\frac{1}{5}x^2 - 2x - \frac{1}{2}\right)$

Solution

$$\begin{aligned}\left(\tfrac{1}{2}x^2 - 6x + \tfrac{1}{3}\right) + \left(\tfrac{1}{5}x^2 - 2x - \tfrac{1}{2}\right) &= \left[\tfrac{1}{2}x^2 + \tfrac{1}{5}x^2\right] + [-6x + (-2x)] + \left[\tfrac{1}{3} + \left(-\tfrac{1}{2}\right)\right]\\ &= \left[\left(\tfrac{1}{2} + \tfrac{1}{5}\right)x^2\right] + [(-6 - 2)x] + \left[\tfrac{1}{3} + \left(-\tfrac{1}{2}\right)\right]\\ &= \left[\left(\tfrac{5}{10} + \tfrac{2}{10}\right)x^2\right] + [-8x] + \left[\tfrac{2}{6} - \tfrac{3}{6}\right]\\ &= \tfrac{7}{10}x^2 - 8x - \tfrac{1}{6}\end{aligned}$$

Practice Problem 3 Add. $\left(-\frac{1}{3}x^2 - 6x - \frac{1}{12}\right) + \left(\frac{1}{4}x^2 + 5x - \frac{1}{3}\right)$

EXAMPLE 4 Add. $(1.2x^3 - 5.6x^2 + 5) + (-3.4x^3 - 1.2x^2 + 4.5x - 7)$

Solution Group like terms.

$$\begin{aligned}(1.2x^3 - 5.6x^2 + 5) + (-3.4x^3 - 1.2x^2 + 4.5x - 7) &= (1.2 - 3.4)x^3 + (-5.6 - 1.2)x^2 + 4.5x + (5 - 7)\\ &= -2.2x^3 - 6.8x^2 + 4.5x - 2\end{aligned}$$

Practice Problem 4 Add.

$$(3.5x^3 - 0.02x^2 + 1.56x - 3.5) + (-0.08x^2 - 1.98x + 4)$$

As mentioned previously, polynomials may involve more than one variable.

3 Subtracting Polynomials

Recall that subtraction of real numbers can be defined as adding the opposite of the second number. Thus $a - b = a + (-b)$. That is, $3 - 5 = 3 + (-5)$. A similar method is used to subtract two polynomials.

To subtract two polynomials, change the sign of each term in the second polynomial and then add.

EXAMPLE 5 Subtract. $(7x^2 - 6x + 3) - (5x^2 - 8x - 12)$

Solution We change the sign of each term in the second polynomial and then add.

$$\begin{aligned}(7x^2 - 6x + 3) - (5x^2 - 8x - 12) &= (7x^2 - 6x + 3) + (-5x^2 + 8x + 12) \\ &= (7 - 5)x^2 + (-6 + 8)x + (3 + 12) \\ &= 2x^2 + 2x + 15\end{aligned}$$

NOTE TO STUDENT: Fully worked-out solutions to all of the Practice Problems can be found at the back of the text starting at page SP-1

Practice Problem 5 Subtract.

$$(5x^3 - 15x^2 + 6x - 3) - (-4x^3 - 10x^2 + 5x + 13)$$

When subtracting polynomials in two variables, you will need to use extra care in determining which terms are like terms. For example $6x^2y$ and $5x^2y$ are like terms. In a similar fashion, $3xy$ and $8xy$ are like terms. However $7xy^2$ and $15x^2y^2$ are not like terms. Every exponent of every variable in the two terms must be the same if the terms are to be like terms. You will use this concept in Example 6.

EXAMPLE 6 Subtract.

$$(-6x^2y - 3xy + 7xy^2) - (5x^2y - 8xy - 15x^2y^2)$$

Solution Change the sign of each term in the second polynomial and add. Look for like terms.

$$\begin{aligned}&(-6x^2y - 3xy + 7xy^2) + (-5x^2y + 8xy + 15x^2y^2) \\ &= (-6 - 5)x^2y + (-3 + 8)xy + 7xy^2 + 15x^2y^2 \\ &= -11x^2y + 5xy + 7xy^2 + 15x^2y^2\end{aligned}$$

Nothing further can be done to combine these four terms.

Practice Problem 6 Subtract.

$$(x^3 - 7x^2y + 3xy^2 - 2y^3) - (2x^3 + 4xy - 6y^3)$$

 Evaluating Polynomials to Predict a Value

Sometimes polynomials are used to predict a value. In such cases we need to **evaluate** the polynomial. We do this by substituting a known value for the variable and determining the value of the polynomial.

EXAMPLE 7 Automobiles sold in the United States have become more fuel efficient over the years due to regulations from Congress. The number of miles per gallon obtained by the average automobile in the United States can be described by the polynomial

$$0.3x + 12.9,$$

where x is the number of years since 1970. (*Source:* U.S. Federal Highway Administration.) Use this polynomial to estimate the number of miles per gallon obtained by the average automobile in

(a) 1972 **(b)** 2008

Solution

(a) The year 1972 is two years later than 1970, so $x = 2$.

Thus the number of miles per gallon obtained by the average automobile in 1972 can be estimated by evaluating $0.3x + 12.9$ when $x = 2$.

$$\begin{aligned} 0.3(2) + 12.9 &= 0.6 + 12.9 \\ &= 13.5 \end{aligned}$$

We estimate that the average car in 1972 obtained 13.5 miles per gallon.

(b) The year 2008 will be 38 years after 1970, so $x = 38$.

Thus the estimated number of miles per gallon obtained by the average automobile in 2008 can be predicted by evaluating $0.3x + 12.9$ when $x = 38$.

$$\begin{aligned} 0.3(38) + 12.9 &= 11.4 + 12.9 \\ &= 24.3 \end{aligned}$$

We therefore predict that the average car in 2008 will obtain 24.3 miles per gallon.

Practice Problem 7 The number of miles per gallon obtained by the average truck in the United States can be described by the polynomial $0.03x + 5.4$, where x is the number of years since 1970. (*Source:* U.S. Federal Highway Administration.) Use this polynomial to estimate the number of miles per gallon obtained by the average truck in

(a) 1974 **(b)** 2006

4.3 Exercises

Student Solutions Manual | CD/ Video | PH Math Tutor Center | MathXL®Tutorials on CD | MathXL® | MyMathLab® | Interactmath.com

Verbal and Writing Skills

1. State in your own words a definition for a polynomial in x and give an example.

2. State in your own words a definition for a multivariable polynomial and give an example.

3. State in your own words how to determine the degree of a polynomial in x.

4. State in your own words how to determine the degree of a multivariable polynomial.

State the degree of the polynomial and whether it is a monomial, a binomial, or a trinomial.

5. $6x^3y$

6. $5xy^6$

7. $20x^5 + 6x^3 - 7x$

8. $13x^4 - 12x + 20$

9. $5xy^2 - 3x^2y^3$

10. $7x^3y + 5x^4y^4$

Add.

11. $(-3x + 15) + (8x - 43)$

12. $(5x - 11) + (-7x + 34)$

13. $(6x^2 + 5x - 6) + (-8x^2 - 3x + 5)$

14. $(3x^2 - 2x - 5) + (-7x^2 + 8x - 2)$

15. $\left(\frac{1}{2}x^2 + \frac{1}{3}x - 4\right) + \left(\frac{1}{3}x^2 + \frac{1}{6}x - 5\right)$

16. $\left(\frac{1}{4}x^2 - \frac{2}{3}x - 10\right) + \left(-\frac{1}{3}x^2 + \frac{1}{9}x + 2\right)$

17. $(3.4x^3 - 7.1x + 3.4) + (2.2x^2 - 6.1x - 8.8)$

18. $(-4.6x^3 + 5.6x - 0.3) + (9.8x^2 + 4.5x - 1.7)$

Subtract.

19. $(2x - 19) - (-3x + 5)$

20. $(5x - 5) - (6x - 3)$

21. $\left(\frac{2}{5}x^2 - \frac{1}{2}x + 5\right) - \left(\frac{1}{3}x^2 - \frac{3}{7}x - 6\right)$

22. $\left(\frac{3}{8}x^2 - \frac{2}{3}x - 7\right) - \left(\frac{2}{3}x^2 - \frac{1}{2}x + 2\right)$

23. $(-3x^2 + 5x) - (2x^3 - 3x^2 + 10)$

24. $(7x^3 - 3x^2 - 5x + 4) - (x^3 - 7x + 3)$

25. $(0.5x^4 - 0.7x^2 + 8.3) - (5.2x^4 + 1.6x + 7.9)$

26. $(1.3x^4 - 3.1x^3 + 6.3x) - (x^4 - 5.2x^2 + 6.5x)$

Perform the indicated operations.

27. $(4x - 3) - (7x - 2) + (-5x + 8)$

28. $(3 - 8x) - (9x + 7) - (-3x - 2)$

29. $(5x^2y - 6xy^2 + 2) + (-8x^2y + 12xy^2 - 6)$

30. $(7x^2y^2 - 6xy + 5) + (-15x^2y^2 - 6xy + 18)$

31. $(3x^4 - 4x^2 - 18) - (2x^4 + 3x^3 + 6)$

32. $(2b^3 + 3b - 5) - (-3b^3 + 5b^2 + 7b)$

To Think About

Gas Mileage *Buses operated in this country have become more fuel efficient in recent years. The number of miles per gallon achieved by the average bus operated in the United States can be described by the polynomial* $0.04x + 5.2$, *where x is the number of years since 1970. (Source: U.S. Federal Highway Administration.)*

33. Estimate the number of miles per gallon obtained by the average bus in 1975.

34. Estimate the number of miles per gallon obtained by the average bus in 1995.

35. Estimate in what year the rating of the average bus will be 7.2 miles per gallon.

36. Estimate in what year the rating of the average bus will be 6.8 miles per gallon.

Prisons *The average number of prisoners held in federal and state prisons increases each year. The number of prisoners measured in thousands can be described by the polynomial* $1.8x^2 + 22.2x + 325$, *where x is the number of years since 1980. (Source: U.S. Bureau of Justice Statistics.)*

37. Estimate the number of prisoners in 1990.

38. Estimate the number of prisoners in 1995.

39. According to the polynomial, by how much will the prison population increase from 2002 to 2006?

40. According to the polynomial, by how much will the prison population increase from 2004 to 2010?

Applications

▲ **41.** ***Geometry*** The lengths and the widths of the following three rectangles are labeled. Create a polynomial that describes the sum of the *area* of these three rectangles.

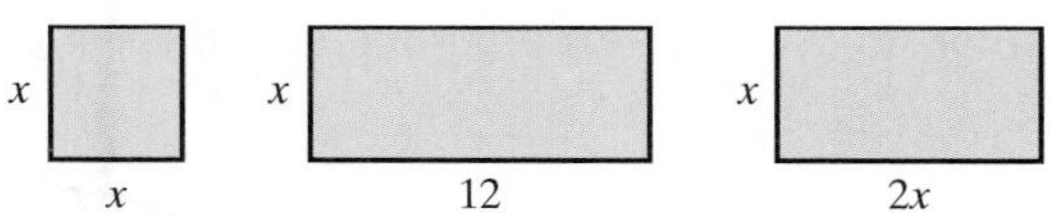

▲ **42.** ***Geometry*** The dimensions of the sides of the following figure are labeled. Create a polynomial that describes the *perimeter* of this figure.

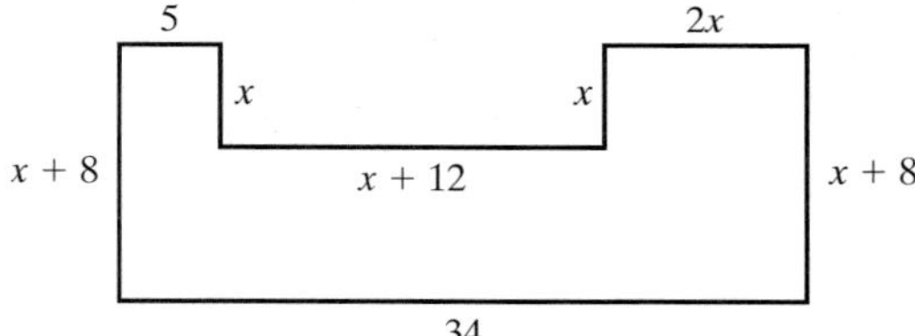

Cumulative Review

43. Solve for x. $3y - 8x = 2$

44. Solve for B. $3A = 2BCD$

45. Solve for b. $A = \frac{1}{2}h(b + c)$

46. Solve for d. $B = \frac{5xy}{d}$

47. ***Health Care Costs*** The total approximate expenditure for health care in the United States increased by 90% over the years 1990 to 2000. In 2000 a total of 1.324 trillion dollars was spent. How much was spent in 1990? (*Source:* U.S. Department of Health and Human Services.)

48. ***World Population*** In 1900, the population of the world was approximately 1.5×10^9. In 2000, the population had increased to 6×10^9. What was the percent of increase from 1900 to 2000?

How Am I Doing? Sections 4.1–4.3

1. __________

2. __________

3. __________

4. __________

5. __________

6. __________

7. __________

8. __________

9. __________

10. __________

11. __________

12. __________

How are you doing with your homework assignments in Sections 4.1 to 4.3? Do you feel you have mastered the material so far? Do you understand the concepts you have covered? Before you go further in the textbook, take some time to do each of the following problems.

Simplify all answers. Reduce all fractions.

4.1

Multiply

1. $(-5xy)(3x^2y^5)$

Divide. Assume that all variables are nonzero. Leave your answer with only positive exponents.

2. $-\dfrac{35xy^6}{25x^8y^3}$

3. $\dfrac{60x^7y^0}{15x^2y^9}$

Simplify.

4. $(-3x^5y)^4$

4.2

Simplify. Express your answer with positive exponents. Assume that all variables are nonzero.

5. $(4x^{-3}y^4)^{-2}$

6. $\dfrac{3x^{-2}y^6}{9xy^{-9}}$

7. Write in scientific notation. 58,740

8. Write in scientific notation. 0.00009362

4.3

Perform the indicated operations.

9. $(2x^2 + 0.5x - 2) + (0.3x^2 - 0.9x - 3.4)$

10. $(5x^2 + 8x - 14) - (-2x^2 - 9x + 12)$

11. $\left(\frac{1}{2}x^3 + \frac{1}{4}x^2 - 2x\right) - \left(\frac{1}{3}x^3 - \frac{1}{8}x^2 - 5x\right)$

12. $\left(\frac{1}{16}x^2 + \frac{1}{8}\right) + \left(\frac{1}{4}x^2 - \frac{3}{10}x - \frac{1}{2}\right)$

Now turn to page SA-10 for the answer to each of these problems. Each answer also includes a reference to the objective in which the problem is first taught. If you missed any of these problems, you should stop and review the Examples and Practice Problems in the referenced objective. A little review now will help you master the material in the upcoming sections of the text.

4.4 Multiplying Polynomials

Multiplying a Monomial by a Polynomial

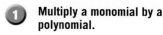

Student Learning Objectives

After studying this section, you will be able to:

1. **Multiply a monomial by a polynomial.**
2. **Multiply two binomials.**

NOTE TO STUDENT: Fully worked-out solutions to all of the Practice Problems can be found at the back of the text starting at page SP-1

We use the distributive property to multiply a monomial by a polynomial. Remember, the distributive property states that for real numbers a, b, and c,

$$a(b + c) = ab + ac.$$

EXAMPLE 1 Multiply. $3x^2(5x - 2)$

Solution

$$\begin{aligned} 3x^2(5x - 2) &= 3x^2(5x) + 3x^2(-2) && \text{Use the distributive property.} \\ &= (3\cdot5)(x^2\cdot x) + (3)(-2)x^2 \\ &= 15x^3 - 6x^2 \end{aligned}$$

Practice Problem 1 Multiply. $4x^3(-2x^2 + 3x)$

Try to do as much of the multiplication as you can mentally.

EXAMPLE 2 Multiply.

(a) $2x(x^2 + 3x - 1)$ **(b)** $-2xy^2(x^2 - 2xy - 3y^2)$

Solution

(a) $2x(x^2 + 3x - 1) = 2x^3 + 6x^2 - 2x$

(b) $-2xy^2(x^2 - 2xy - 3y^2) = -2x^3y^2 + 4x^2y^3 + 6xy^4$

Notice in part (b) that you are multiplying each term by the negative number $-2xy^2$. This will change the sign of each term in the product.

Practice Problem 2 Multiply.

(a) $-3x(x^2 + 2x - 4)$ **(b)** $6xy(x^3 + 2x^2y - y^2)$

When we multiply by a monomial, the monomial may be on the right side.

EXAMPLE 3 Multiply. $(x^2 - 2x + 6)(-2xy)$

Solution $(x^2 - 2x + 6)(-2xy) = -2x^3y + 4x^2y - 12xy$

Practice Problem 3 Multiply.

$$(-6x^3 + 4x^2 - 2x)(-3xy)$$

Multiplying Two Binomials

We can build on our knowledge of the distributive property and our experience with multiplying monomials to learn how to multiply two binomials. Let's suppose that we want to multiply $(x + 2)(3x + 1)$. We can use the distributive property. Since a can represent any number, let $a = x + 2$. Then let $b = 3x$ and $c = 1$. We now have the following.

$$\begin{aligned} a(b + c) &= \quad ab \quad + \quad ac \\ (x + 2)(3x + 1) &= (x + 2)(3x) + (x + 2)(1) \\ &= 3x^2 + 6x + x + 2 \\ &= 3x^2 + 7x + 2 \end{aligned}$$

Let's take another look at the original problem, $(x + 2)(3x + 1)$. This time we will assign a letter to each term in the binomials. That is, let $a = x$, $b = 2$, $c = 3x$, and $d = 1$. Using substitution, we have the following.

$$\begin{aligned}(x + 2)(3x + 1) &= (a + b)(c + d)\\ &= (a + b)c + (a + b)d\\ &= ac + bc + ad + bd\\ &= (x)(3x) + (2)(3x) + (x)(1) + (2)(1) \quad \text{By substitution}\\ &= 3x^2 + 6x + x + 2\\ &= 3x^2 + 7x + 2\end{aligned}$$

How does this compare with the preceding result?

The distributive property shows us *how* the problem can be done and *why* it can be done. In actual practice there is a memory device to help students remember the steps involved. It is often referred to as FOIL. The letters FOIL stand for the following.

F multiply the *F*irst terms
O multiply the *O*uter terms
I multiply the *I*nner terms
L multiply the *L*ast terms

The FOIL letters are simply a way to remember the four terms in the final product and how they are obtained. Let's return to our original problem.

$(x + 2)(3x + 1)$ F Multiply the *first* terms to obtain $3x^2$.

$(x + 2)(3x + 1)$ O Multiply the *outer* terms to obtain x.

$(x + 2)(3x + 1)$ I Multiply the *inner* terms to obtain $6x$.

$(x + 2)(3x + 1)$ L Multiply the *last* terms to obtain 2.

The result so far is $3x^2 + x + 6x + 2$. These four terms are the same four terms that we obtained when we multiplied using the distributive property. We can combine the like terms to obtain the final answer: $3x^2 + 7x + 2$. Now let's study the FOIL method in a few examples.

EXAMPLE 4 Multiply. $(2x - 1)(3x + 2)$

Solution

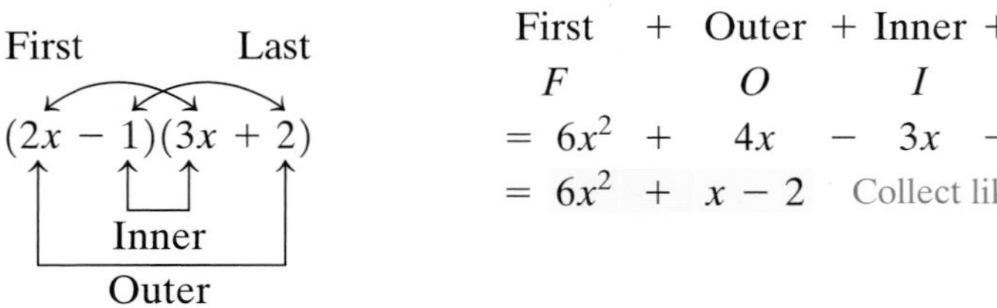

$$\begin{aligned}&\text{First} + \text{Outer} + \text{Inner} + \text{Last}\\ &\quad F \qquad\quad O \qquad\quad I \qquad\quad L\\ &= 6x^2 + 4x - 3x - 2\\ &= 6x^2 + x - 2 \quad \text{Collect like terms.}\end{aligned}$$

Practice Problem 4 Multiply. $(5x - 1)(x - 2)$

***NOTE TO STUDENT:** Fully worked-out solutions to all of the Practice Problems can be found at the back of the text starting at page SP-1*

EXAMPLE 5 Multiply. $(3a - 2b)(4a - b)$

Solution

First Last

$(3a - 2b)(4a - b)$ $= 12a^2 - 3ab - 8ab + 2b^2$

Inner

Outer

$= 12a^2 - 11ab + 2b^2$

Practice Problem 5 Multiply. $(8a - 5b)(3a - b)$

After you have done several problems, you may be able to combine the outer and inner products mentally.

In some problems the inner and outer products cannot be combined.

EXAMPLE 6 Multiply. $(3x + 2y)(5x - 3z)$

Solution

First Last

$(3x + 2y)(5x - 3z)$ $= 15x^2 - 9xz + 10xy - 6yz$

Inner

Outer

Since there are no like terms, we cannot combine any terms.

Practice Problem 6 Multiply. $(3a + 2b)(2a - 3c)$

EXAMPLE 7 Multiply. $(7x - 2y)^2$

Solution

$(7x - 2y)(7x - 2y)$ When we square a binomial, it is the same as multiplying the binomial by itself.

First Last

$(7x - 2y)(7x - 2y)$ $= 49x^2 - 14xy - 14xy + 4y^2$

Inner

Outer

$= 49x^2 - 28xy + 4y^2$

Practice Problem 7 Multiply. $(3x - 2y)^2$

We can multiply binomials containing exponents that are greater than 1. That is, we can multiply binomials containing x^2 or y^3, and so on.

EXAMPLE 8 Multiply. $(3x^2 + 4y^3)(2x^2 + 5y^3)$

Solution $(3x^2 + 4y^3)(2x^2 + 5y^3) = 6x^4 + 15x^2y^3 + 8x^2y^3 + 20y^6$

$= 6x^4 + 23x^2y^3 + 20y^6$

Practice Problem 8 Multiply. $(2x^2 + 3y^2)(5x^2 + 6y^2)$

▲ **EXAMPLE 9** The width of a living room is $(x + 4)$ feet. The length of the room is $(3x + 5)$ feet. What is the area of the room in square feet?

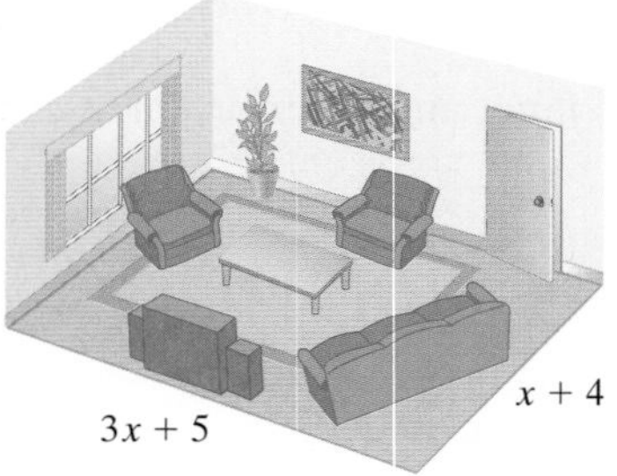

Solution

$$A = (\text{length})(\text{width}) = (3x + 5)(x + 4)$$
$$= 3x^2 + 12x + 5x + 20$$
$$= 3x^2 + 17x + 20$$

There are $(3x^2 + 17x + 20)$ square feet in the room.

NOTE TO STUDENT: Fully worked-out solutions to all of the Practice Problems can be found at the back of the text starting at page SP-1

▲ **Practice Problem 9** What is the area in square feet of a room that is $(2x - 1)$ feet wide and $(7x + 3)$ feet long?

Developing Your Study Skills

How to Review for an Exam

Reviewing adequately for an exam enables you to bring together the concepts you have learned over several sections. For your review, you will need to:

1. Reread your textbook. Make a list of any terms, rules, or formulas you need to know for the exam. Be sure you understand them all.
2. Reread your notes. Go over returned homework and quizzes. Redo the problems you missed.
3. Practice some of each type of problem covered in the chapter(s) you are to be tested on.
4. Use the end-of-chapter materials provided in your textbook. Read carefully through the chapter organizer. Do the review problems. Take the chapter test. When you are finished, check your answers. Redo any problems you missed.
5. Get help if any concepts give you difficulty.

4.4 EXERCISES

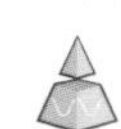

Student Solutions Manual | CD/ Video | PH Math Tutor Center | MathXL®Tutorials on CD | MathXL® | MyMathLab® | Interactmath.com

Multiply.

1. $-2x(6x^3 - x)$

2. $5x(-3x^4 + 4x)$

3. $3x^2(7x - 3)$

4. $2x^2(8x - 5)$

5. $2x^3(-2x^3 + 5x - 1)$

6. $5x^2(-3x^3 + 6x - 2)$

7. $\frac{1}{2}(2x + 3x^2 + 5x^3)$

8. $\frac{2}{3}(4x + 6x^2 - 2x^3)$

9. $(5x^3 - 2x^2 + 6x)(-3xy^2)$

10. $(2b^3 - 5b^2 + 3ab)(-3b^2)$

11. $(3x^3 + x^2 - 8x)(3xy)$

12. $(2x^3 + x^2 - 6x)(2xy)$

13. $(x^3 - 3x^2 + 5x - 2)(3x)$

14. $(-2x^3 + 4x^2 - 7x + 3)(2x)$

15. $(x^2y^2 - 6xy + 8)(-2xy)$

16. $(x^2y^2 + 5xy - 9)(-3xy)$

17. $(-7x^3 + 3x^2 + 2x - 1)(4x^2y)$

18. $(-5x^3 - 6x^2 + x - 1)(5xy^2)$

19. $(3d^4 - 4d^2 + 6)(-2c^2d)$

20. $(-4x^3 + 6x^2 - 5x)(-7xy^2)$

21. $6x^3(2x^4 - x^2 + 3x + 9)$

22. $8x^3(-2x^4 + 3x^2 - 5x - 14)$

23. $-7x^4(5x^3 - 8x^2 + 3x)$

24. $-5x^3(-2x^5 - 7x^2 + 4x)$

Multiply. Try to do most of the exercises mentally without writing down intermediate steps.

25. $(x + 10)(x + 3)$

26. $(x + 3)(x + 4)$

27. $(x + 6)(x + 2)$

28. $(x + 9)(x + 3)$

29. $(x - 8)(x + 2)$

30. $(x + 3)(x - 6)$

31. $(x - 5)(x - 4)$

32. $(x - 6)(x - 5)$

33. $(5x - 2)(-4x - 3)$

34. $(7x + 1)(-2x - 3)$

35. $(7x - 4)(x + 2y)$

36. $(x - 9)(3x + 4y)$

37. $(5x + 2)(3x - y)$

38. $(3x + 4)(5x - y)$

39. $(4y + 1)(5y - 3)$

40. $(5y + 1)(6y - 5)$

To Think About

41. What is wrong with this multiplication? $(x - 2)(-3) = 3x - 6$

42. What is wrong with this answer? $-(3x - 7) = -3x - 7$

43. What is the missing term? $(5x + 2)(5x + 2) = 25x^2 +$ ________ $+ 4$

44. Multiply the binomials and write a brief description of what is special about the result. $(5x - 1)(5x + 1)$

Mixed Practice

Multiply.

45. $(4x - 3y)(5x - 2y)$

46. $(3b - 5c)(2b - 7c)$

47. $(7x - 2)^2$

48. $(3x - 7)^2$

49. $(4a + 2b)^2$

50. $(5a + 3b)^2$

51. $(0.2x + 3)(4x - 0.3)$

52. $(0.5x - 2)(6x - 0.2)$

53. $\left(\frac{1}{2}x + \frac{1}{3}\right)\left(\frac{1}{2}x - \frac{1}{4}\right)$

54. $\left(\frac{1}{3}x + \frac{1}{5}\right)\left(\frac{1}{3}x - \frac{1}{2}\right)$

55. $(2a - 3b)(x - 5b)$

56. $(5b - 7c)(x - 2b)$

57. $(7x + 3y)(5x + 9y)$

58. $(4y - 3z)(5z - 3y)$

59. $(5y - 3z)(4y - 2z)$

Find the area of the rectangle.

▲ **60.**

5x + 2

2x − 3

▲ **61.**

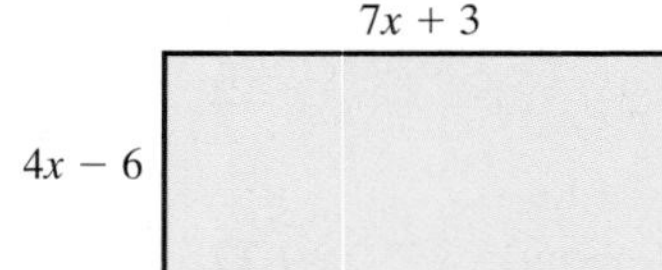

7x + 3

Cumulative Review

62. Solve for x. $3(x - 6) = -2(x + 4) + 6x$

63. Solve for w. $3(w - 7) - (4 - w) = 11w$

64. Twice the sum of a number and six is five more than three times the same number. Find the number.

65. Jamie was buying decorative marbles to re-create a table centerpiece she saw in a decorating magazine. She bought twice as many cat's eye marbles as tiger's eye marbles. If the cat'e eye marbles cost \$0.07 apiece and the tiger's eye marbles cost \$0.11 apiece, and Jamie spent \$6.00 for the marbles, how many of each kind did Jamie buy?

66. ***Paper Currency*** Heather returned from the bank with \$375. She had one more \$20 bill than she had \$10 bills. The number of \$5 bills she had was one less than triple the number of \$10 bills. How many of each denomination did she have?

Video Game Playing *The polynomial* $1.2x + 16$ *can be used to describe the number of hours per week that young people age 12–18 spend playing video games, where x is the number of years since 1992. (Source: U.S. Department of Health and Human Services.)*

67. What was the average number of hours per week young people spent playing video games in 1994?

68. What was the average number of hours per week young people spent playing video games in 1996?

69. Predict the number of hours per week young people will spend playing video games in 2008.

70. Predict the number of hours per week young people will spend playing video games in 2009.

 4.5 Multiplication: Special Cases

1 Multiplying Binomials of the Type $(a + b)(a - b)$

The case when you multiply $(x + y)(x - y)$ is interesting and deserves special consideration. Using the FOIL method, we find

$$(x + y)(x - y) = x^2 - xy + xy - y^2 = x^2 - y^2.$$

Notice that the sum of the inner product and the outer product is zero. We see that

$$(x + y)(x - y) = x^2 - y^2.$$

This works in all cases when the binomials are the sum and difference of the same two terms. That is, in one factor the terms are added, while in the other factor the same two terms are subtracted.

$$\begin{aligned}(5a + 2b)(5a - 2b) &= 25a^2 - 10ab + 10ab - 4b^2 \\ &= 25a^2 - 4b^2\end{aligned}$$

The product is the difference of the squares of the terms. That is, $(5a)^2 - (2b)^2$ or $25a^2 - 4b^2$.

Many students find it helpful to memorize this equation.

MULTIPLYING BINOMIALS: A SUM AND A DIFFERENCE

$$(a + b)(a - b) = a^2 - b^2$$

You may use this relationship to find the product quickly in cases where it applies. The terms must be the same and there must be a sum and a difference.

EXAMPLE 1 Multiply. $(7x + 2)(7x - 2)$

Solution

$$(7x + 2)(7x - 2) = (7x)^2 - (2)^2 = 49x^2 - 4$$

Practice Problem 1 Multiply. $(6x + 7)(6x - 7)$

EXAMPLE 2 Multiply. $(5x - 8y)(5x + 8y)$

Solution

$$(5x - 8y)(5x + 8y) = (5x)^2 - (8y)^2 = 25x^2 - 64y^2$$

Practice Problem 2 Multiply. $(3x - 5y)(3x + 5y)$

Student Learning Objectives

After studying this section, you will be able to:

1. Multiply binomials of the type $(a + b)(a - b)$.
2. Multiply binomials of the type $(a + b)^2$ and $(a - b)^2$.
3. Multiply polynomials with more than two terms.

NOTE TO STUDENT: Fully worked-out solutions to all of the Practice Problems can be found at the back of the text starting at page SP-1

2 Multiplying Binomials of the Type $(a + b)^2$ and $(a - b)^2$

A second case that is worth special consideration is a binomial that is squared. Consider the following problem.

$$\begin{aligned}(3x + 2)^2 &= (3x + 2)(3x + 2)\\ &= 9x^2 + 6x + 6x + 4\\ &= 9x^2 + 12x + 4\end{aligned}$$

If you complete enough problems of this type, you will notice a pattern. The answer always contains the square of the first term added to double the product of the first and last terms added to the square of the last term.

$3x$ is the first term		2 is the last term		Square the first term: $(3x)^2$		Double the product of the first and last terms: $2(3x)(2)$		Square the last term: $(2)^2$
↓		↓		↓		↓		↓
$(3x$	$+$	$2)^2$	$=$	$9x^2$	$+$	$12x$	$+$	4

We can show the same steps using variables instead of words.

$$(a + b)^2 = a^2 + 2ab + b^2$$

There is a similar formula for the square of a difference:

$$(a - b)^2 = a^2 - 2ab + b^2$$

We can use this formula to simplify $(2x - 3)^2$.

$$\begin{aligned}(2x - 3)^2 &= (2x)^2 - 2(2x)(3) + (3)^2\\ &= 4x^2 - 12x + 9\end{aligned}$$

You may wish to multiply this product using FOIL to verify.

These two types of products, the square of a sum and the square of a difference, can be summarized as follows.

A BINOMIAL SQUARED

$$(a + b)^2 = a^2 + 2ab + b^2$$
$$(a - b)^2 = a^2 - 2ab + b^2$$

EXAMPLE 3 Multiply.

(a) $(5y - 2)^2$ **(b)** $(8x + 9y)^2$

Solution

(a) $(5y - 2)^2 = (5y)^2 - (2)(5y)(2) + (2)^2$
$= 25y^2 - 20y + 4$

(b) $(8x + 9y)^2 = (8x)^2 + (2)(8x)(9y) + (9y)^2$
$= 64x^2 + 144xy + 81y^2$

Practice Problem 3 Multiply.

(a) $(4a - 9b)^2$ **(b)** $(5x + 4)^2$

NOTE TO STUDENT: Fully worked-out solutions to all of the Practice Problems can be found at the back of the text starting at page SP-1

CAUTION: $(a + b)^2 \neq a^2 + b^2$! The two sides are not equal! Squaring the sum $(a + b)$ does not give $a^2 + b^2$! Beginning algebra students often make this error. Make sure you remember that when you square a binomial there is always a *middle term*.

$$(a + b)^2 = a^2 + 2ab + b^2$$

Sometimes a numerical example helps you to see this.

$$\begin{aligned}(3 + 4)^2 &\neq 3^2 + 4^2\\ 7^2 &\neq 9 + 16\\ 49 &\neq 25\end{aligned}$$

Notice that what is missing on the right is $2ab = 2 \cdot 3 \cdot 4 = 24$.

3 Multiplying Polynomials with More Than Two Terms

We used the distributive property to multiply two binomials $(a + b)(c + d)$, and we obtained $ac + ad + bc + bd$. We could also use the distributive property to multiply the polynomials $(a + b)$ and $(c + d + e)$, and we would obtain $ac + ad + ae + bc + bd + be$. Let us see if we can find a direct way to multiply products such as $(3x - 2)(x^2 - 2x + 3)$. It can be done quickly using an approach similar to that used in arithmetic for multiplying whole numbers. Consider the following arithmetic problem.

$$\begin{array}{rll} & 128 & \\ \times & 43 & \\ \hline & 384 & \leftarrow \text{The product of 128 and 3} \\ 512 & & \leftarrow \text{The product of 128 and 4 moved one space to the left} \\ \hline 5504 & & \leftarrow \text{The sum of the two partial products} \end{array}$$

Let us follow a similar format to multiply the two polynomials. For example, multiply $(x^2 - 2x + 3)$ and $(3x - 2)$.

$$\begin{array}{rrrrl} & x^2 & -\ 2x & +\ 3 & \\ & & 3x & -\ 2 & \\ \hline & -\ 2x^2 & +\ 4x & -\ 6 & \leftarrow \text{The product } (x^2 - 2x + 3)(-2) \\ 3x^3 & -\ 6x^2 & +\ 9x & & \leftarrow \text{The product } (x^2 - 2x + 3)(3x) \text{ moved one space to the left so that like terms are underneath each other} \\ \hline 3x^3 & -\ 8x^2 & +\ 13x & -\ 6 & \leftarrow \text{The sum of the two partial products} \end{array}$$

This is often called **vertical multiplication.**

EXAMPLE 4 Multiply vertically. $(3x^3 + 2x^2 + x)(x^2 - 2x - 4)$

Solution

$$\begin{array}{rrrrrl} & & 3x^3 & +\ 2x^2 & +\ x & \text{We place one polynomial over the other.} \\ & & x^2 & -\ 2x & -\ 4 & \\ \hline & & -\ 12x^3 & -\ 8x^2 & -\ 4x & \leftarrow \text{The product } (3x^3 + 2x^2 + x)(-4) \\ & -\ 6x^4 & -\ 4x^3 & -\ 2x^2 & & \leftarrow \text{The product } (3x^3 + 2x^2 + x)(-2x) \\ 3x^5 & +\ 2x^4 & +\ x^3 & & & \leftarrow \text{The product } (3x^3 + 2x^2 + x)(x^2) \\ \hline 3x^5 & -\ 4x^4 & -\ 15x^3 & -\ 10x^2 & -\ 4x & \leftarrow \text{The sum of the three partial products} \end{array}$$

Note that the answers for each partial product are placed so that like terms are underneath each other.

Practice Problem 4 Multiply vertically. $(4x^3 - 2x^2 + x)(x^2 + 3x - 2)$

ALTERNATIVE METHOD: FOIL Horizontal Multiplication Some students prefer to do this type of multiplication using a horizontal format similar to the FOIL method. The following example illustrates this approach.

EXAMPLE 5 Multiply horizontally. $(x^2 + 3x + 5)(x^2 - 2x - 6)$

Solution We will use the distributive property repeatedly.

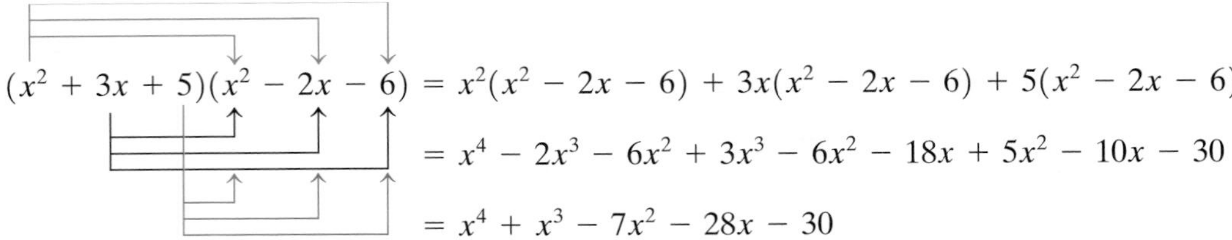

$$(x^2 + 3x + 5)(x^2 - 2x - 6) = x^2(x^2 - 2x - 6) + 3x(x^2 - 2x - 6) + 5(x^2 - 2x - 6)$$
$$= x^4 - 2x^3 - 6x^2 + 3x^3 - 6x^2 - 18x + 5x^2 - 10x - 30$$
$$= x^4 + x^3 - 7x^2 - 28x - 30$$

Practice Problem 5 Multiply horizontally. $(2x^2 + 5x + 3)(x^2 - 3x - 4)$

Some problems may need to be done in two or more separate steps.

EXAMPLE 6 Multiply. $(2x - 3)(x + 2)(x + 1)$

Solution We first need to multiply any two of the binomials. Let us select the first pair.

$$\underbrace{(2x - 3)(x + 2)}_{\text{Find this product first.}}(x + 1)$$

$$(2x - 3)(x + 2) = 2x^2 + 4x - 3x - 6$$
$$= 2x^2 + x - 6$$

Now we replace the first two factors with their resulting product.

$$\underbrace{(2x^2 + x - 6)}_{\text{Result of first product}}(x + 1)$$

We then multiply again.

$$(2x^2 + x - 6)(x + 1) = (2x^2 + x - 6)x + (2x^2 + x - 6)1$$
$$= 2x^3 + x^2 - 6x + 2x^2 + x - 6$$
$$= 2x^3 + 3x^2 - 5x - 6$$

The vertical format of Example 4 is an alternative method for this type of problem.

$$\begin{array}{r} 2x^2 + x - 6 \\ x + 1 \\ \hline 2x^2 + x - 6 \\ 2x^3 + x^2 - 6x \quad \\ \hline 2x^3 + 3x^2 - 5x - 6 \end{array}$$

Be sure to use special care in writing the exponents correctly in problems with more than one variable.

Thus we have

$$(2x - 3)(x + 2)(x + 1) = 2x^3 + 3x^2 - 5x - 6.$$

Note that it does not matter which two binomials are multiplied first. For example, you could first multiply $(2x - 3)(x + 1)$ to obtain $2x^2 - x - 3$ and then multiply that product by $(x + 2)$ to obtain the same result.

Practice Problem 6 Multiply. $(3x - 2)(2x + 3)(3x + 2)$
(*Hint:* Rearrange the factors.)

***NOTE TO STUDENT:** Fully worked-out solutions to all of the Practice Problems can be found at the back of the text starting at page SP-1*

Sometimes we encounter a binomial raised to a third power. In such cases we would write out the binomial three times as a product and then multiply. So to evaluate $(3x + 4)^3$ we would first write $(3x + 4)(3x + 4)(3x + 4)$ and then follow the method of Example 6.

4.5 Exercises

Student Solutions Manual

CD/ Video

PH Math Tutor Center

MathXL®Tutorials on CD
MathXL®

MyMathLab®

Interactmath.com

Verbal and Writing Skills

1. In the special case of $(a + b)(a - b)$, a binomial times a binomial is a ____________.

2. Identify which of the following could be the answer to a problem using the formula for $(a + b)(a - b)$. Why?
(a) $9x^2 - 16$
(b) $4x^2 + 25$
(c) $9x^2 + 12x + 4$
(d) $x^4 - 1$

3. A student evaluated $(4x - 7)^2$ as $16x^2 + 49$. What is missing? State the correct answer.

4. The square of a binomial, $(a - b)^2$, always produces which of the following?
(a) binomial
(b) trinomial
(c) four-term polynomial

Use the formula $(a + b)(a - b) = a^2 - b^2$ to multiply.

5. $(y - 7)(y + 7)$

6. $(x + 5)(x - 5)$

7. $(x - 9)(x + 9)$

8. $(x + 6)(x - 6)$

9. $(7x - 4)(7x + 4)$

10. $(4x - 9)(4x + 9)$

11. $(2x - 7)(2x + 7)$

12. $(3x - 10)(3x + 10)$

13. $(5x - 3y)(5x + 3y)$

14. $(8a - 3b)(8a + 3b)$

15. $(0.6x + 3)(0.6x - 3)$

16. $(5x - 0.2)(5x + 0.2)$

Use the formula for a binomial squared to multiply.

17. $(3y + 1)^2$

18. $(4x - 1)^2$

19. $(5x - 4)^2$

20. $(6x + 5)^2$

21. $(7x + 3)^2$

22. $(8x - 3)^2$

23. $(3x - 7)^2$

24. $(2x + 3y)^2$

25. $\left(\frac{2}{3}x + \frac{1}{4}\right)^2$

26. $\left(\frac{3}{4}x + \frac{1}{2}\right)^2$

27. $(9xy + 4z)^2$

28. $(7y - 3xz)^2$

Mixed Practice

Multiply. Use the special formula that applies.

29. $(7x + 3y)(7x - 3y)$

30. $(12x - 5y)(12x + 5y)$

31. $(7c - 6d)^2$

32. $(4c - 5d)^2$

Multiply.

33. $(9a - 10b)(9a + 10b)$

34. $(11a + 6b)(11a - 6b)$

35. $(5x + 9y)^2$

36. $(4x + 8y)^2$

37. $(x^2 + 5x - 3)(x - 2)$

38. $(x^2 - 4x + 5)(x - 3)$

39. $(4x + 1)(x^3 - 2x^2 + x - 1)$

40. $(3x - 1)(x^3 + x^2 - 4x - 2)$

41. $(a^2 - 3a + 2)(a^2 + 4a - 3)$

42. $(x^2 + 4x - 5)(x^2 - 3x + 4)$

43. $(x + 3)(x - 1)(3x - 8)$

44. $(x - 7)(x + 4)(2x - 5)$

45. $(3x + 5)(x - 2)(x - 4)$

46. $(2x - 7)(x + 1)(x - 2)$

47. $(a - 5)(2a + 3)(a + 5)$

48. $(b + 7)(3b - 2)(b - 7)$

To Think About

▲ **49.** Find the volume of this object.

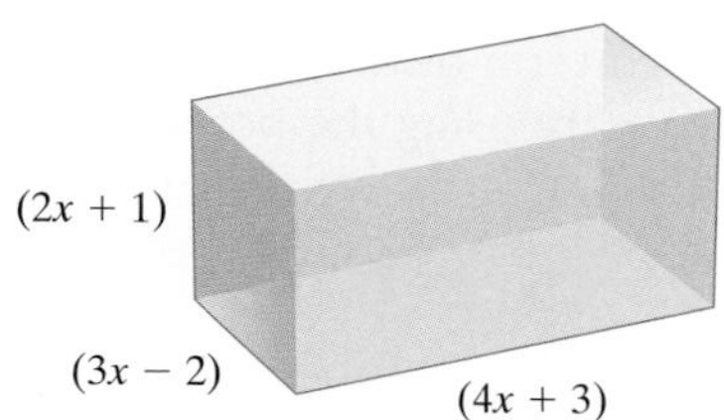

▲ **50.** ***Geometry*** The volume of a pyramid is $V = \frac{1}{3}Bh$, where B is the area of the base and H is the height. Find the volume of the following pyramid.

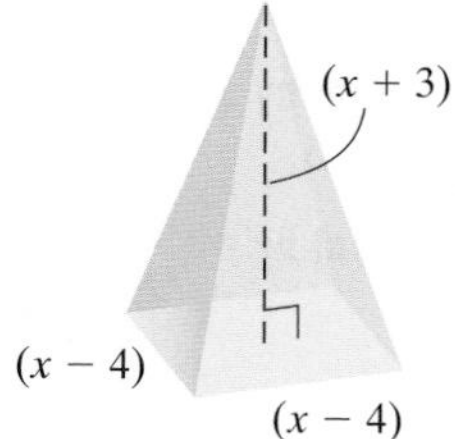

Cumulative Review

51. ***Investments*** An executive invested $18,000 in two accounts, one a cash-on-reserve account that yielded 7% simple interest, and the other a long-term certificate paying 11% simple interest. At the end of one year, the two accounts had earned her a total of $1540. How much had she invested in each account?

▲ **52.** ***Room Dimensions*** The perimeter of a rectangular room measures 34 meters. The width is 2 meters more than half the length. Find the dimensions of the room.

53. ***Boiling Point of Ammonia*** Ammonia has a boiling point of −33.4°C. What is the boiling point of ammonia measured in degrees Fahrenheit? (Use $F = 1.8C + 32$.)

54. ***Red Blood Cells*** A man with 5.5 liters of blood has approximately 2.75×10^{10} red blood cells. Each red blood cell is a small disk that measures 7.5×10^{-6} meters in diameter. If all of the red blood cells were arranged in a long straight line, how long would that line be?

4.6 Dividing Polynomials

Student Learning Objectives

After studying this section, you will be able to:

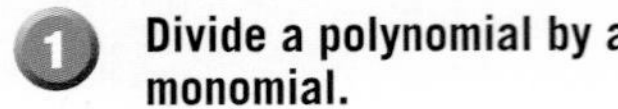

1 Divide a polynomial by a monomial.

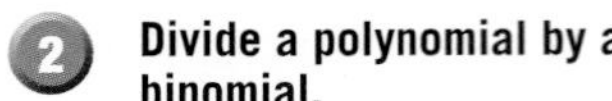

2 Divide a polynomial by a binomial.

1 Dividing a Polynomial by a Monomial

To divide a polynomial by a monomial, divide each term of the numerator by the denominator; then write the sum of the results. We are using the property of fractions that states that

$$\frac{a+b}{c} = \frac{a}{c} + \frac{b}{c}.$$

DIVIDING A POLYNOMIAL BY A MONOMIAL

1. Divide each term of the polynomial by the monomial.
2. When dividing variables, use the property $\dfrac{x^a}{x^b} = x^{a-b}$.

EXAMPLE 1 Divide. $\dfrac{8y^6 - 8y^4 + 24y^2}{8y^2}$

Solution $$\frac{8y^6 - 8y^4 + 24y^2}{8y^2} = \frac{8y^6}{8y^2} - \frac{8y^4}{8y^2} + \frac{24y^2}{8y^2} = y^4 - y^2 + 3$$

Practice Problem 1 Divide. $\dfrac{15y^4 - 27y^3 - 21y^2}{3y^2}$

NOTE TO STUDENT: Fully worked-out solutions to all of the Practice Problems can be found at the back of the text starting at page SP-1

2 Dividing a Polynomial by a Binomial

Division of a polynomial by a binomial is similar to long division in arithmetic. Notice the similarity in the following division problems.

Division of a three-digit number by a two-digit number

$$\begin{array}{r} 32 \\ 21\overline{)672} \\ \underline{63} \\ 42 \\ \underline{42} \\ 0 \end{array}$$

Division of a polynomial by a binomial

$$\begin{array}{r} 3x + 2 \\ 2x + 1\overline{)6x^2 + 7x + 2} \\ \underline{6x^2 + 3x}\phantom{{}+2} \\ 4x + 2 \\ \underline{4x + 2} \\ 0 \end{array}$$

DIVIDING A POLYNOMIAL BY A BINOMIAL

1. Place the terms of the polynomial and binomial in descending order. Insert a 0 for any missing term.
2. Divide the first term of the polynomial by the first term of the binomial. The result is the first term of the answer.
3. Multiply the first term of the answer by the binomial and subtract the result from the first two terms of the polynomial. Bring down the next term to obtain a new polynomial.
4. Divide the new polynomial by the binomial using the process described in step 2.
5. Continue dividing, multiplying, and subtracting until the degree of the remainder is less than the degree of the binomial divisor.
6. Write the remainder as the numerator of a fraction that has the binomial divisor as its denominator.

EXAMPLE 2 Divide. $(x^3 + 5x^2 + 11x + 14) \div (x + 2)$

Solution

Step 1 The terms are arranged in descending order. No terms are missing.

Step 2 Divide the first term of the polynomial by the first term of the binomial. In this case, divide x^3 by x to get x^2.

$$\begin{array}{r} x^2 \\ x + 2 \overline{)\, x^3 + 5x^2 + 11x + 14} \end{array}$$

Step 3 Multiply x^2 by $x + 2$ and subtract the result from the first two terms of the polynomial, $x^3 + 5x^2$ in this case.

$$\begin{array}{r l} x^2 & \\ x + 2 \overline{)\, x^3 + 5x^2 + 11x + 14} & \\ \underline{x^3 + 2x^2} \downarrow & \\ 3x^2 + 11x & \text{Bring down the next term.} \end{array}$$

Step 4 Continue to use the step 2 process. Divide $3x^2$ by x. Write the resulting $3x$ as the next term of the answer.

$$\begin{array}{r} x^2 + 3x \\ x + 2 \overline{)\, x^3 + 5x^2 + 11x + 14} \\ \underline{x^3 + 2x^2} \\ 3x^2 + 11x \end{array}$$

Step 5 Continue multiplying, dividing, and subtracting until the degree of the remainder is less than the degree of the divisor. In this case, we stop when the remainder does not have an x.

$$\begin{array}{r l} x^2 + 3x + 5 & \\ x + 2 \overline{)\, x^3 + 5x^2 + 11x + 14} & \\ \underline{x^3 + 2x^2} & \\ 3x^2 + 11x & \\ \underline{3x^2 + 6x} & \\ 5x + 14 & \\ \underline{5x + 10} & \\ 4 & \longleftarrow \text{The remainder is 4.} \end{array}$$

Step 6 The answer is $x^2 + 3x + 5 + \dfrac{4}{x + 2}$.

To check the answer, we multiply $(x + 2)(x^2 + 3x + 5)$ and add the remainder 4.

$$(x + 2)(x^2 + 3x + 5) + 4 = x^3 + 5x^2 + 11x + 10 + 4 = x^3 + 5x^2 + 11x + 14$$

This is the original polynomial. It checks.

Practice Problem 2 Divide. $(x^3 + 10x^2 + 31x + 35) \div (x + 4)$

Take great care with the subtraction step when negative numbers are involved.

EXAMPLE 3 Divide. $(5x^3 - 24x^2 + 9) \div (5x + 1)$

Solution We must first insert $0x$ to represent the missing x-term. Then we divide $5x^3$ by $5x$.

$$\begin{array}{r} x^2 \\ 5x + 1 \overline{\big) 5x^3 - 24x^2 + 0x + 9} \\ \underline{5x^3 + x^2} \\ -25x^2 \end{array}$$

Note that we are subtracting:
$-24x^2 - (+1x^2) = -24x^2 - 1x^2$
$= -25x^2$

Next we divide $-25x^2$ by $5x$.

$$\begin{array}{r} x^2 - 5x \\ 5x + 1 \overline{\big) 5x^3 - 24x^2 + 0x + 9} \\ \underline{5x^3 + x^2} \\ -25x^2 + 0x \\ \underline{-25x^2 - 5x} \\ 5x \end{array}$$

Note that we are subtracting:
$0x - (-5x) = 0x + 5x = 5x$

Finally, we divide $5x$ by $5x$.

$$\begin{array}{r} x^2 - 5x + 1 \\ 5x + 1 \overline{\big) 5x^3 - 24x^2 + 0x + 9} \\ \underline{5x^3 + x^2} \\ -25x^2 + 0x \\ \underline{-25x^2 - 5x} \\ 5x + 9 \\ \underline{5x + 1} \\ 8 \end{array}$$

$\longleftarrow$ The remainder is 8.

The answer is $x^2 - 5x + 1 + \dfrac{8}{5x + 1}$.

To check, multiply $(5x + 1)(x^2 - 5x + 1)$ and add the remainder 8.

$$(5x + 1)(x^2 - 5x + 1) + 8 = 5x^3 - 24x^2 + 1 + 8 = 5x^3 - 24x^2 + 9$$

This is the original polynomial. Our answer is correct.

NOTE TO STUDENT: Fully worked-out solutions to all of the Practice Problems can be found at the back of the text starting at page SP-1

Practice Problem 3 Divide. $(2x^3 - x^2 + 1) \div (x - 1)$

Now we will perform the division by writing a minimum of steps. See if you can follow each step.

EXAMPLE 4 Divide and check. $(12x^3 - 11x^2 + 8x - 4) \div (3x - 2)$

Solution

$$\begin{array}{r} 4x^2 - x + 2 \\ 3x - 2\overline{)12x^3 - 11x^2 + 8x - 4} \\ \underline{12x^3 - 8x^2} \\ -3x^2 + 8x \\ \underline{-3x^2 + 2x} \\ 6x - 4 \\ \underline{6x - 4} \\ 0 \end{array}$$

Check. $(3x - 2)(4x^2 - x + 2) = 12x^3 - 3x^2 + 6x - 8x^2 + 2x - 4$

$= 12x^3 - 11x^2 + 8x - 4$ Our answer is correct.

Practice Problem 4 Divide and check.

$$(20x^3 - 11x^2 - 11x + 6) \div (4x - 3)$$

Developing Your Study Skills

Taking the Exam

Allow yourself plenty of time to get to your exam. You may even find it helpful to arrive a little early in order to collect your thoughts and ready yourself. This will help you feel more relaxed.

After you get your exam, you will find it helpful to do the following.

1. Take two or three moderately deep breaths. Inhale, then exhale slowly. You will feel your entire body begin to relax.
2. Write down on the back of the exam any formulas or ideas that you need to remember.
3. Look over the entire test quickly in order to pace yourself and use your time wisely. Notice how many points each question is worth. Spend more time on items of greater worth.
4. Read directions carefully and be sure to answer all questions clearly. Keep your work neat and easy to read.
5. Ask your instructor about anything that is not clear to you.
6. Answer the questions that are easiest for you first. Then come back to the more difficult ones.
7. Do not get bogged down on one question for too long because it may jeopardize your chances of finishing other problems. Leave the tough question and come back to it when you have time later.
8. Check your work. This will help you to catch minor errors.
9. Stay calm if others leave before you do. You are entitled to use the full amount of allotted time. You will do better on the exam if you take your time and work carefully.

4.6 Exercises

Student Solutions Manual | CD/Video | PH Math Tutor Center | MathXL®Tutorials on CD | MathXL® | MyMathLab® | Interactmath.com

Divide.

1. $\dfrac{25x^4 - 15x^2 + 20x}{5x}$

2. $\dfrac{18b^5 - 12b^3 + 6b^2}{3b}$

3. $\dfrac{8y^4 - 12y^3 - 4y^2}{4y^2}$

4. $\dfrac{10y^4 - 35y^3 + 5y^2}{5y^2}$

5. $\dfrac{81x^7 - 36x^5 - 63x^3}{9x^3}$

6. $\dfrac{49x^8 - 35x^6 - 56x^3}{7x^3}$

7. $(48x^7 - 54x^4 + 36x^3) \div 6x^3$

8. $(72x^8 - 56x^5 - 40x^3) \div 8x^3$

Divide. Check your answers for exercises 9–16 by multiplication.

9. $\dfrac{6x^2 + 13x + 5}{2x + 1}$

10. $\dfrac{12x^2 + 19x + 5}{3x + 1}$

11. $\dfrac{x^2 - 8x - 17}{x - 5}$

12. $\dfrac{x^2 - 9x - 5}{x - 3}$

13. $\dfrac{3x^3 - x^2 + 4x - 2}{x + 1}$

14. $\dfrac{2x^3 - 3x^2 - 3x + 6}{x - 1}$

15. $\dfrac{4x^3 + 4x^2 - 19x - 15}{2x + 5}$

16. $\dfrac{6x^3 + 11x^2 - 8x + 5}{2x + 5}$

17. $\dfrac{10x^3 + 11x^2 - 11x + 2}{5x - 2}$

18. $\dfrac{5x^3 - 28x^2 - 20x + 21}{5x - 3}$

19. $\dfrac{12y^3 - 12y^2 - 25y + 31}{2y - 3}$

20. $\dfrac{9y^3 - 30y^2 + 31y - 4}{3y - 5}$

21. $(y^3 - y^2 - 13y - 12) \div (y + 3)$

22. $(y^3 - 2y^2 - 26y - 4) \div (y + 4)$

23. $(y^4 - 9y^2 - 5) \div (y - 2)$

24. $(2y^4 + 3y^2 - 5) \div (y - 2)$

To Think About

25. $(8y^3 + 3y - 7) \div (4y - 1)$

(*Hint:* The answer contains fractions.)

26. $(6y^3 - 3y^2 + 4) \div (2y + 1)$

(*Hint:* The answer contains fractions.)

Cumulative Review

27. ***Water Conservation*** The average home in the United States uses 110,000 gallons of water per year. Most environmental groups feel that with improved efficiency of water-using devices (washers, toilets, faucets, shower heads), this could be reduced by 30%. (*Source:* U.S. Energy Information Administration.) How many gallons of water per year would be used in the average home if this reduction were accomplished?

28. ***Flour Price*** In 1965, the price for 5 kg of flour was \$0.75. In 1970, the price increased by 15%. In 1971, the 1970 price decreased by 5%. What was the cost of 5 kg of flour in 1971? (Be sure to round each amount to the nearest cent.)

29. ***Cat Health*** In a veterinary study of a group of cats over age 5 who experienced regular exercise and playtime, 184 of the cats, or 92%, had no health problems. How many cats were in the study?

30. ***Internet Research*** Marlena's job requires doing research on the Internet for a marketing company. Today, she has downloaded a huge file. She has been reading all morning and has just completed two consecutive pages whose page numbers add to 1039. What are the page numbers?

31. ***Hurricane Pattern*** The National Hurricane Center has noticed an interesting pattern in the number of Atlantic Hurricanes that begin during the period August 1 to October 31 each year. Examine the bar graph. Then answer the following questions. Round all answers to the nearest tenth.

(a) What was the mean number of hurricanes per year during the years 1993 to 1997?

(b) What was the mean number of hurricanes per year during the years 1998 to 2002?

(c) What was the percent of increase from the five year period 1993 to 1997 to the five year period 1998 to 2002?

(d) If the same percent of increase for a five-year period continued to the years 2003 to 2007, what would be the mean number hurricanes during the period 2003 to 2007?

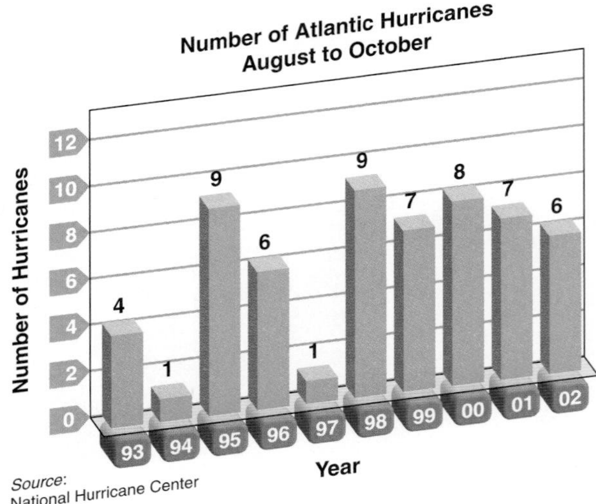

Putting Your Skills to Work

The Value of an Education

Is it worth your time, effort, and money to stay in school and earn a higher degree? Based on data from the Census Bureau's current population survey, the answer is yes! Below is a bar graph demonstrating the relationship between education and earnings, for people aged 18 and over, during the 1999 calendar year. You can see that more education means greater earnings over a year's time as well as greater earnings over a lifetime.

Problems for Individual Investigation and Analysis

1. You are trying to decide whether to continue on to a four-year college, or end your education with an associate's degree. How much more would you make per year if you continued on to earn a bachelor's degree?

2. You expect to have a working career of 42 years. How much more money will you expect to earn over your working career if you go on to complete your bachelor's degree?

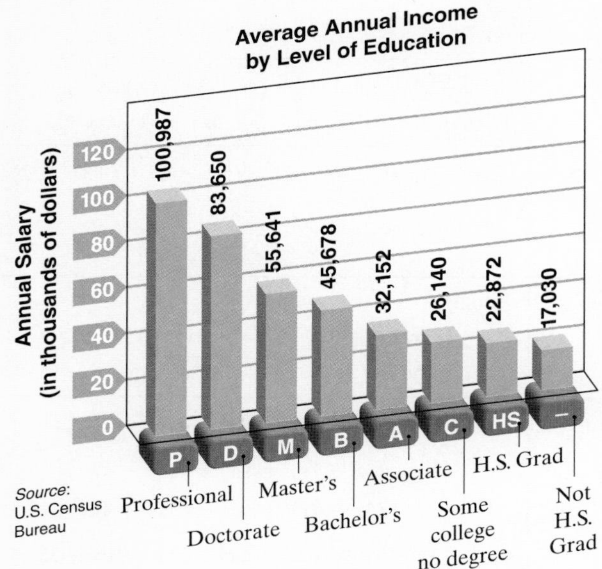

Problems for Group Investigation and Cooperative Learning

"Professional" denotes a person such as a doctor or lawyer who must obtain a doctorate and a professional license, as well.

3. You can calculate your lifetime earnings based on this chart of 1999 dollars, but it will not be completely accurate. The reality is that the value of the dollar continually changes.

   In 1992, professionals were estimated to earn \$74,560 per year. What percentage of growth in average annual income did professionals show from 1992 to 1999?

4. If this rate of growth remains constant for professionals over the next 7 years, what would a profession expect to earn in 2006?

5. Some economists use the income polynomial to predict the average annual income of people in the United States who have a bachelor's degree. It is given by the equation $I = 35x^3 - 620x^2 + 2820x + 43{,}112$, where x is the number of years since 1998 and I is the annual income in dollars. Using the income polynomial as just defined, predict the average annual income of a person with a bachelor's degree in the year 2004.

6. Using the income polynomial in exercise 5, predict the average annual income of a person with a bachelor's degree in the year 2006.

Chapter 4 Organizer

Topic	Procedure	Examples
Multiplying monomials, p. 252.	$x^a \cdot x^b = x^{a+b}$ **1.** Multiply the numerical coefficients. **2.** Add the exponents of a given base.	$3^{12} \cdot 3^{15} = 3^{27}$ $(-3x^2)(6x^3) = -18x^5$ $(2ab)(4a^2b^3) = 8a^3b^4$
Dividing monomials, p. 254.	$\frac{x^a}{x^b} = \begin{cases} x^{a-b} & \text{Use if } a \text{ is greater than } b. \\ \frac{1}{x^{b-a}} & \text{Use if } b \text{ is greater than } a. \end{cases}$ **1.** Divide or reduce the fraction created by the quotient of the numerical coefficients. **2.** Subtract the exponents of a given base.	$\frac{16x^7}{8x^3} = 2x^4$ $\frac{5x^3}{25x^5} = \frac{1}{5x^2}$ $\frac{-12x^5y^7}{18x^3y^{10}} = -\frac{2x^2}{3y^3}$
Exponent of zero, p. 255.	$x^0 = 1 \quad \text{if } x \neq 0$	$5^0 = 1 \qquad \frac{x^6}{x^6} = 1$ $w^0 = 1 \qquad 3x^0y = 3y$
Raising a power to a power, p. 256.	$(x^a)^b = x^{ab}$ $(xy)^a = x^ay^a$ $\left(\frac{x}{y}\right)^a = \frac{x^a}{y^a} \quad (y \neq 0)$ **1.** Raise the numerical coefficient to the power outside the parentheses. **2.** Multiply the exponent outside the parentheses times the exponent inside the parentheses.	$(x^9)^3 = x^{27}$ $(3x^2)^3 = 27x^6$ $\left(\frac{2x^2}{y^3}\right)^3 = \frac{8x^6}{y^9}$ $(-3x^4y^5)^4 = 81x^{16}y^{20}$ $(-5ab)^3 = -125a^3b^3$
Negative exponents, p. 261.	If $x \neq 0$ and $y \neq 0$, then $x^{-n} = \frac{1}{x^n}, \quad \frac{1}{x^{-n}} = x^n, \quad \frac{x^{-m}}{y^{-n}} = \frac{y^n}{x^m}$	Write with positive exponents. $x^{-6} = \frac{1}{x^6}, \quad \frac{1}{w^{-3}} = w^3, \quad \frac{w^{-12}}{z^{-5}} = \frac{z^5}{w^{12}}$
Scientific notation, p. 262.	A positive number is written in scientific notation if it is in the form $a \times 10^n$, where $1 \leq a < 10$ and n is an integer.	$2{,}568{,}000 = 2.568 \times 10^6$ $0.0000034 = 3.4 \times 10^{-6}$
Add polynomials, p. 268.	To add two polynomials, we add their like terms.	$(-7x^3 + 2x^2 + 5) + (x^3 + 3x^2 + x)$ $= -6x^3 + 5x^2 + x + 5$
Subtracting polynomials, p. 270.	To subtract the polynomials, change all signs of the second polynomial and add the result to the first polynomial. $(a) - (b) = (a) + (-b)$	$(5x^2 - 6) - (-3x^2 + 2) = (5x^2 - 6) + (+3x^2 - 2)$ $= 8x^2 - 8$
Multiplying a monomial by a polynomial, p. 275.	Use the distributive property. $a(b + c) = ab + ac$ $(b + c)a = ba + ca$	Multiply. $-5x(2x^2 + 3x - 4) = -10x^3 - 15x^2 + 20x$ $(6x^3 - 5xy - 2y^2)(3xy) = 18x^4y - 15x^2y^2 - 6xy^3$
Multiplying two binomials, p. 275.	**1.** The product of the sum and difference of the same two terms: $(a + b)(a - b) = a^2 - b^2$ **2.** The square of a binomial: $(a + b)^2 = a^2 + 2ab + b^2$ $(a - b)^2 = a^2 - 2ab + b^2$ **3.** Use FOIL for other binomial multiplication. The middle terms can often be combined, giving a trinomial.	$(3x + 7y)(3x - 7y) = 9x^2 - 49y^2$ $(3x + 7y)^2 = 9x^2 + 42xy + 49y^2$ $(3x - 7y)^2 = 9x^2 - 42xy + 49y^2$ $(3x - 5)(2x + 7) = 6x^2 + 21x - 10x - 35$ $= 6x^2 + 11x - 35$

Topic	Procedure	Examples
Multiplying two polynomials, p. 283.	To multiply two polynomials, multiply each term of one by each term of the other. This method is similar to the multiplication of many-digit numbers.	Vertical method: $$\begin{array}{r} 3x^2 - 7x + 4 \\ \times \qquad 3x - 1 \\ \hline -3x^2 + 7x - 4 \\ 9x^3 - 21x^2 + 12x \qquad \\ \hline 9x^3 - 24x^2 + 19x - 4 \end{array}$$ Horizontal method: $(5x + 2)(2x^2 - x + 3)$ $= 10x^3 - 5x^2 + 15x + 4x^2 - 2x + 6$ $= 10x^3 - x^2 + 13x + 6$
Multiplying three or more polynomials, p. 284.	**1.** Multiply any two polynomials. **2.** Multiply the result by any remaining polynomials.	$(2x + 1)(x - 3)(x + 4) = (2x^2 - 5x - 3)(x + 4)$ $= 2x^3 + 3x^2 - 23x - 12$
Dividing a polynomial by a monomial, p. 288.	**1.** Divide each term of the polynomial by the monomial. **2.** When dividing variables, use the property $\frac{x^a}{x^b} = x^{a-b}$.	Divide. $(15x^3 + 20x^2 - 30x) \div (5x)$ $= \frac{15x^3}{5x} + \frac{20x^2}{5x} + \frac{-30x}{5x}$ $= 3x^2 + 4x - 6$
Dividing a polynomial by a binomial, p. 288.	**1.** Place the terms of the polynomial and binomial in descending order. Insert a 0 for any missing term. **2.** Divide the first term of the polynomial by the first term of the binomial. **3.** Multiply the partial answer by the binomial, and subtract the result from the first two terms of the polynomial. Bring down the next term to obtain a new polynomial. **4.** Divide the new polynomial by the binomial using the process described in step 2. **5.** Continue dividing, multiplying, and subtracting until the degree of the remainder is less than the degree of the binomial divisor. **6.** Write the remainder as the numerator of a fraction that has the binomial divisor as its denominator.	Divide. $(8x^3 - 13x + 2x^2 + 7) \div (4x - 1)$ We rearrange the terms. $$\begin{array}{r} 2x^2 + x - 3 \\ 4x - 1 \overline{)\,8x^3 + 2x^2 - 13x + 7} \\ \underline{8x^3 - 2x^2} \qquad\qquad \\ 4x^2 - 13x \qquad \\ \underline{4x^2 - x} \qquad \\ -12x + 7 \\ \underline{-12x + 3} \\ 4 \end{array}$$ The answer is $2x^2 + x - 3 + \frac{4}{4x - 1}$.

Chapter 4 Review Problems

Section 4.1

Simplify. Leave your answer in exponent form.

1. $(-6a^2)(3a^5)$ **2.** $(5^{10})(5^{13})$ **3.** $(3xy^2)(2x^3y^4)$ **4.** $(2x^3y^4)(-7xy^5)$

5. $\frac{7^{15}}{7^{27}}$ **6.** $\frac{x^{12}}{x^{17}}$ **7.** $\frac{y^{30}}{y^{16}}$ **8.** $\frac{9^{13}}{9^{24}}$

9. $\frac{-15xy^2}{25x^6y^6}$ **10.** $\frac{-12a^3b^6}{18a^2b^{12}}$ **11.** $(x^3)^8$ **12.** $(b^5)^6$

13. $(-3a^3b^2)^2$ **14.** $(3x^3y)^4$ **15.** $\left(\frac{5ab^2}{c^3}\right)^2$ **16.** $\left(\frac{x^0y^3}{4w^5z^2}\right)^3$

Section 4.2

Simplify. Write with positive exponents.

17. $a^{-3}b^5$

18. m^8p^{-5}

19. $\dfrac{2x^{-6}}{y^{-3}}$

20. $(3x^{-4}y^3)^{-2}$

21. $(5x^2y^{-4})^{-2}$

22. $\dfrac{3x^{-3}}{y^{-2}}$

23. $\dfrac{4x^{-5}y^{-6}}{w^{-2}z^8}$

24. $\dfrac{3^{-3}a^{-2}b^5}{c^{-3}d^{-4}}$

Write in scientific notation.

25. 156,340,200,000

26. 179,632

27. 0.0078

28. 0.00006173

Write in decimal notation.

29. 1.2×10^5

30. 6.034×10^6

31. 3×10^6

32. 2.5×10^{-1}

33. 4.32×10^{-5}

34. 6×10^{-9}

Perform the indicated calculation. Leave your answer in scientific notation.

35. $\dfrac{(28{,}000{,}000)(5{,}000{,}000{,}000)}{7000}$

36. $(3.12 \times 10^5)(2.0 \times 10^6)(1.5 \times 10^8)$

37. $(1.6 \times 10^{-3})(3.0 \times 10^{-5})(2.0 \times 10^{-2})$

38. $\dfrac{(0.00078)(0.000005)(0.00004)}{0.002}$

39. ***Space Travel*** If a space probe travels at 40,000 kilometers per hour for 1 year, how far will it travel? (Assume that 1 year = 365 days.)

40. ***Atomic Clock*** An atomic clock is based on the fact that cesium emits 9,192,631,770 cycles of radiation in one second. How many of these cycles occur in one day? Round to three significant digits.

41. ***Computer Speed*** Today's fastest modern computers can perform one operation in 1×10^{-8} second. How many operations can such a computer perform in 1 minute?

Section 4.3

Combine.

42. $(4.3x^2 - 2.6x - 3.1) + (7.1x^2 - 4.7x + 8.4)$

43. $(1.2x^2 - 3.4x + 6) + (5.5x^2 - 7.6x - 3)$

44. $(x^3 + x^2 - 6x + 2) - (2x^3 - x^2 - 5x - 6)$

45. $(4x^3 - x^2 - x + 3) - (-3x^3 + 2x^2 + 5x - 1)$

46. $\left(\dfrac{3}{5}x^2y - \dfrac{1}{3}x + \dfrac{3}{4}\right) - \left(\dfrac{1}{2}x^2y + \dfrac{2}{7}x + \dfrac{1}{3}\right)$

47. $\dfrac{1}{2}x^2 - \dfrac{3}{4}x + \dfrac{1}{5} - \left(\dfrac{1}{4}x^2 - \dfrac{1}{2}x + \dfrac{1}{10}\right)$

48. $(5x^2 + 3x) + (-6x^2 + 2) - (5x - 8)$

49. $(2x^2 - 7) - (3x^2 - 4) + (-5x^2 - 6x)$

Section 4.4

Multiply.

50. $(3x + 1)(5x - 1)$

51. $(7x - 2)(4x - 3)$

52. $(2x + 3)(10x + 9)$

53. $5x(2x^2 - 6x + 3)$

54. $(6x^3 - 2x^2 + x - 4)(-3x)$

55. $(2xy^2 - 3xy - 4y)(-3x^2y)$

56. $(5a + 7b)(a - 3b)$

57. $(2x^2 - 3)(4x^2 - 5y)$

58. $-3x^2y(5x^4y + 3x^2 - 2)$

Section 4.5

Multiply.

59. $(3x - 2)^2$

60. $(5x + 3)(5x - 3)$

61. $(7x + 6y)(7x - 6y)$

62. $(5a - 2b)^2$

63. $(8x + 9y)^2$

64. $(x^2 + 7x + 3)(4x - 1)$

65. $(x - 6)(2x - 3)(x + 4)$

Section 4.6

Divide.

66. $(12y^3 + 18y^2 + 24y) \div (6y)$

67. $(30x^5 + 35x^4 - 90x^3) \div (5x^2)$

68. $(16x^3y^2 - 24x^2y + 32xy^2) \div (4xy)$

69. $(106x^6 - 24x^5 + 38x^4 + 26x^3) \div (2x^3)$

70. $(15x^2 + 11x - 14) \div (5x + 7)$

71. $(12x^2 - x - 63) \div (4x + 9)$

72. $(6x^3 + x^2 + 6x + 5) \div (2x - 1)$

73. $(2x^3 - x^2 + 3x - 1) \div (x + 2)$

74. $(12x^2 + 11x + 2) \div (3x + 2)$

75. $(8x^2 - 6x + 6) \div (2x + 1)$

76. $(x^3 - x - 24) \div (x - 3)$

77. $(2x^3 - 3x + 1) \div (x - 2)$

Mixed Practice

Simplify. Leave your answer in exponent form.

78. $(4^6)(4^{23})$

79. $\dfrac{6^{50}}{6^{35}}$

Simplify. Write your answer with only positive exponents.

80. $(-5x^3y^4)(-25x^5y^{10})$

81. $\dfrac{-36x^6y^5}{18xy^8}$

82. $(-4x^5y^6)^3$

83. Write in Scientific notation. 0.0000786

Remove parentheses and simplify.

84. $(-6x^3 - 7x + 8) - (-2x^3 + 5x - 9)$

85. $-6x^2(2x^3 + 5x^2 - 2)$

86. Multiply. $(7x - 3)(2x - 1)(x + 2)$

87. Divide. $(6x^3 + 11x^2 - x - 2) \div (3x - 2)$

Applications

Solve. Express your answer in scientific notation.

88. ***Foreign Aid*** In 2002, the United States donated $\$12.9 \times 10^9$ in foreign aid to poor countries. If the population of the United States in 2002 was estimated at 2.8×10^8 people, how much foreign aid per person did the United States donate? Leave your answer in dollars and cents.

89. ***Population*** In 2002, the estimated population of India was 1.132×10^9 people, while the estimated population of Bangladesh was 1.31×10^8 people. (*Source:* United Nations Statistical Bureau.) What was the total population in those two countries?

90. ***Electron Mass*** The mass of an electron is approximately 9.11×10^{-28} gram. Find the mass of 30,000 electrons.

91. ***Sun Energy*** The sun radiates energy into space at the rate of 3.9×10^{26} joules per second. How many joules are emitted in a day?

To Think About

Find a polynomial that describes the shaded area.

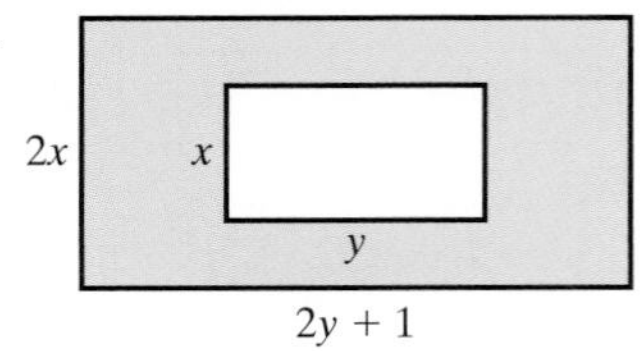

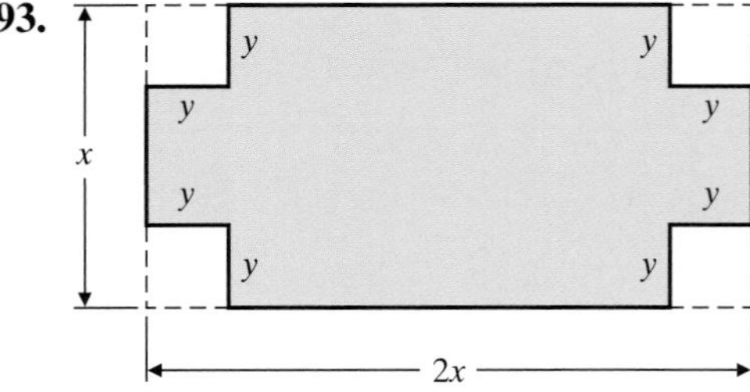

How Am I Doing? Chapter 4 Test

Remember to use your Chapter Test Prep Video CD to see the worked-out solutions to the test problems you want to review.

Simplify. Leave your answer in exponent form.

1. $(3^{10})(3^{24})$ **2.** $\frac{25^{18}}{25^{34}}$ **3.** $(8^4)^6$

In questions 4–8, simplify.

4. $(-3xy^4)(-4x^3y^6)$ **5.** $\frac{-35x^8y^{10}}{25x^5y^{10}}$ **6.** $(-5xy^6)^3$

7. $\left(\frac{7a^7b^2}{3c^0}\right)^2$ **8.** $\frac{(3x^2)^3}{(6x)^2}$ **9.** Evaluate. 4^{-3}

In questions 10 and 11, simplify and write with only positive exponents.

10. $6a^{-4}b^{-3}c^5$ **11.** $\frac{3x^{-3}y^2}{x^{-4}y^{-5}}$

12. Write in scientific notation. 0.0005482

13. Write in decimal notation. 5.82×10^8

14. Multiply. Leave your answer in scientific notation.
$(4.0 \times 10^{-3})(3.0 \times 10^{-8})(2.0 \times 10^4)$

Combine.

15. $(2x^2 - 3x - 6) + (-4x^2 + 8x + 6)$

16. $(3x^3 - 4x^2 + 3) - (14x^3 - 7x + 11)$

Multiply.

17. $-7x^2(3x^3 - 4x^2 + 6x - 2)$ **18.** $(5x^2y^2 - 6xy + 2)(3x^2y)$

19. $(5a - 4b)(2a + 3b)$ **20.** $(3x + 2)(2x + 1)(x - 3)$

21. $(7x^2 + 2y^2)^2$ **22.** $(5s - 11t)(5s + 11t)$

23. $(3x - 2)(4x^3 - 2x^2 + 7x - 5)$ **24.** $(3x^2 - 5xy)(x^2 + 3xy)$

Divide.

25. $15x^6 - 5x^4 + 25x^3 \div 5x^3$ **26.** $(8x^3 - 22x^2 - 5x + 12) \div (4x + 3)$

27. $(2x^3 - 6x - 36) \div (x - 3)$

Solve. Express your answer in scientific notation. Round to the nearest hundredth.

28. At the end of 2002, Saudi Arabia was estimated to have 2.618×10^{11} barrels of oil reserves. By one estimate, they have 86 years of reserves remaining. If they disbursed the oil by an equal amount each year, how many barrels of oil would they pump each year? (*Source:* United Nations Review of World Energy, 2003)

29. A space probe is traveling from Earth to the planet Pluto at a speed of 2.49×10^4 miles per hour. How far would this space probe travel in one week?

1. ____
2. ____
3. ____
4. ____
5. ____
6. ____
7. ____
8. ____
9. ____
10. ____
11. ____
12. ____
13. ____
14. ____
15. ____
16. ____
17. ____
18. ____
19. ____
20. ____
21. ____
22. ____
23. ____
24. ____
25. ____
26. ____
27. ____
28. ____
29. ____

Cumulative Test for Chapters 0–4

1. ______
2. ______
3. ______
4. ______
5. ______
6. ______
7. ______
8. ______
9. ______
10. ______
11. ______
12. ______
13. ______
14. ______
15. ______
16. ______
17. ______
18. ______
19. ______
20. ______
21. ______
22. ______
23. ______
24. ______
25. ______
26. ______

Approximately one-half of this test covers the content of Chapters 0 through 3. The remainder covers the content of Chapter 4.

In questions 1–5, simplify.

1. $\frac{5}{12} - \frac{7}{8}$ **2.** $(-3.7) \times (0.2)$ **3.** $\left(-4\frac{1}{2}\right) \div \left(5\frac{1}{4}\right)$

4. Find 6% of 1842.5 **5.** $7x(3x - 4) - 5x(2x - 3) - (3x)^2$

6. Evaluate $2x^2 - 3xy + y^2$ when $x = -2$ and $y = 3$.

In questions 7–9, solve.

7. $7x - 3(4 - 2x) = 14x - (3 - x)$

8. $\frac{2}{3}x + 6 = 4(x - 11)$ **9.** $4 - 7x < 11$

10. Solve for d: $8(x + d) = 3(y - d)$

11. A national walkout of 11,904 employees of the VBM Corp. occurred last month. This was 96% of the total number of employees. How many employees does VBM have?

12. How much interest would \$3320 earn in one year if invested at 6% simple interest?

13. Multiply. $(5x + 6)(4x - 3)$ **14.** Multiply. $(3x - 5)^2$

15. Multiply. $(3x + 2)(2x + 1)(x - 4)$

In questions 16–18, simplify.

16. $(-4x^4y^5)(5xy^3)$ **17.** $\frac{14x^8y^3}{-21x^5y^{12}}$ **18.** $(-2x^3y^2z^0)^4$

19. Write with only positive exponents. $\frac{9x^{-3}y^{-4}}{w^2z^{-8}}$

20. Write in scientific notation. 1,360,000,000,000,000

21. Write in scientific notation. 0.00056

22. Calculate. Leave your answer in scientific notation. $\frac{(2.0 \times 10^{-12})(8.0 \times 10^{-20})}{4.0 \times 10^3}$

23. Subtract. $(x^3 - 3x^2 - 5x + 20) - (-4x^3 - 10x^2 + x - 30)$

Multiply.

24. $-6xy^2(6x^2 - 3xy + 8y^2)$ **25.** $(2x^2 - 3x + 1)(3x - 5)$

26. Divide. $(x^2 + 2x - 12) \div (x - 3)$

CHAPTER

5

A touchdown. An exciting time for any NFL game. But was there a penalty on the play? Is the call of the official correct? Should there be an instant replay to determine whether the call is correct? If current trends continue, more replay reviews will take place each year. Can you determine the mathematical pattern? Turn to the Putting Your Skills to Work problems on page 347 to find out.

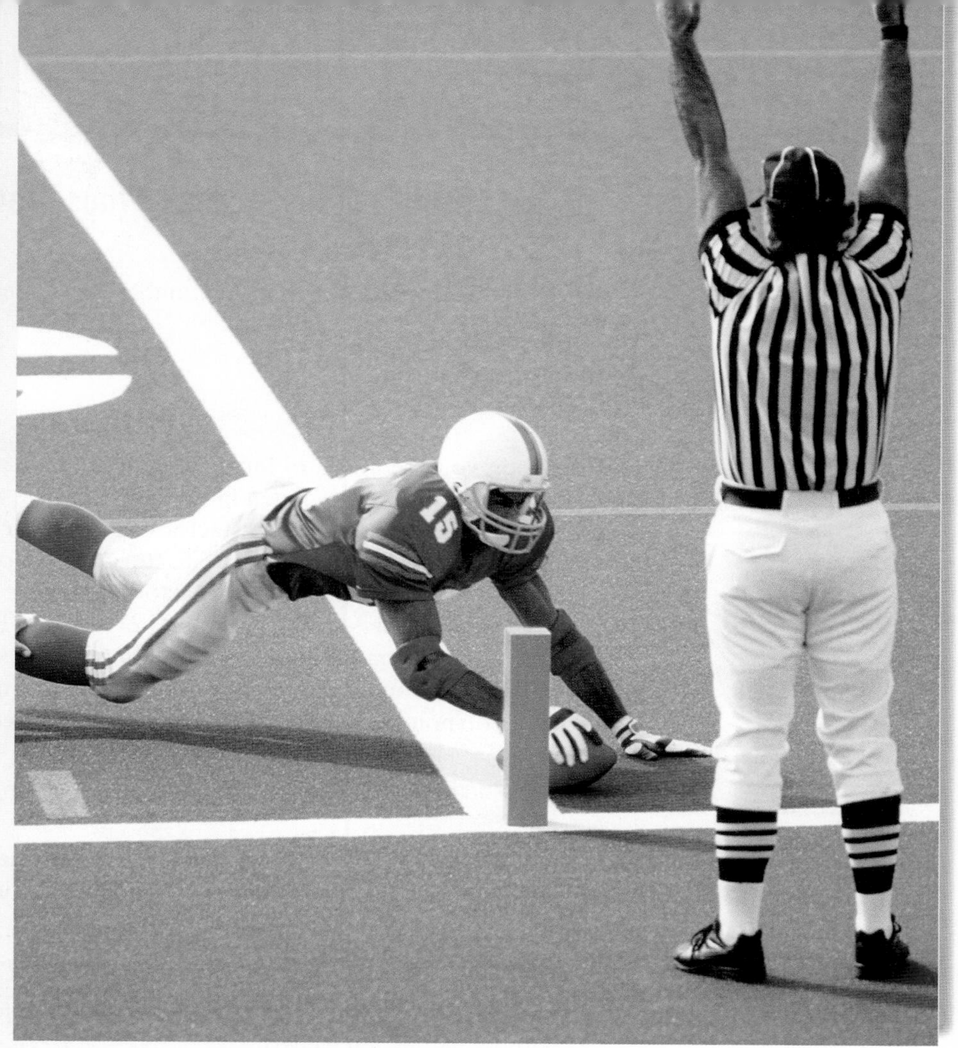

Factoring

5.1 Removing a Common Factor

Student Learning Objective

After studying this section, you will be able to:

Factor polynomials whose terms contain a common factor.

1 Factoring Polynomials Whose Terms Contain a Common Factor

Recall that when two or more numbers, variables, or algebraic expressions are multiplied, each is called a **factor.**

$$\underbrace{3}_{\text{factor}} \cdot \underbrace{2}_{\text{factor}} \qquad \underbrace{3x^2}_{\text{factor}} \cdot \underbrace{5x^3}_{\text{factor}} \qquad \underbrace{(2x-3)}_{\text{factor}}\underbrace{(x+4)}_{\text{factor}}$$

When you are asked **to factor** a number or an algebraic expression, you are being asked, "What factors, when multiplied, will give that number or expression?"

For example, you can factor 6 as $3 \cdot 2$ since $3 \cdot 2 = 6$. You can factor $15x^5$ as $3x^2 \cdot 5x^3$ since $3x^2 \cdot 5x^3 = 15x^5$. Factoring is simply the reverse of multiplying. 6 and $15x^5$ are simple expressions to factor and can be factored in different ways.

The factors of the polynomial $2x^2 + x - 12$ are not so easy to recognize. Factoring a polynomial changes an addition and/or subtraction problem into a multiplication problem. In this chapter we will be learning techniques for finding the factors of a polynomial. We will begin with **common factors.**

EXAMPLE 1 Factor. **(a)** $3x - 6y$ **(b)** $9x + 2xy$

Solution Begin by looking for a common factor, a factor that both terms have in common. Then rewrite the expression as a product.

(a) $3x - 6y = 3(x - 2y)$ This is true because $3(x - 2y) = 3x - 6y$.

(b) $9x + 2xy = x(9 + 2y)$ This is true because $x(9 + 2y) = 9x + 2xy$.

Some people find it helpful to think of factoring as the distributive property in reverse. When we write $3x - 6y = 3(x - 2y)$, we are doing the reverse of distributing the 3. This is the main point of this section. We are doing problems of the form $ca + cb = c(a + b)$. The common factor c becomes the first factor of our answer.

NOTE TO STUDENT: Fully worked-out solutions to all of the Practice Problems can be found at the back of the text starting at page SP-1

Practice Problem 1 Factor. **(a)** $21a - 7b$ **(b)** $5xy + 8x$

When we factor, we begin by looking for the greatest **common factor.** For example, in the polynomial $48x - 16y$, a common factor is 2. We could factor $48x - 16y$ as $2(24x - 8y)$. However, this is not complete. To factor $48x - 16y$ completely, we look for the greatest common factor of 48 and of 16.

$$48x - 16y = 16(3x - y)$$

EXAMPLE 2 Factor. $24xy + 12x^2 + 36x^3$. Remember to remove the greatest common factor.

Solution Find the greatest common factor of 24, 12, and 36. You may want to factor each number, or you may notice that 12 is a common factor. 12 is the greatest numerical common factor.

Notice also that x is a factor of each term. Thus, $12x$ is the greatest common factor.

$$24xy + 12x^2 + 36x^3 = 12x(2y + x + 3x^2)$$

Practice Problem 2 Factor. $12a^2 + 16ab^2 - 12a^2b$. Be careful to remove the greatest common factor.

FACTORING A POLYNOMIAL WITH COMMON FACTORS

1. Determine the greatest common numerical factor by asking, "What is the largest integer that will divide into the coefficient of all the terms?"
2. Determine the greatest common variable factor by asking, "What variables are common to all the terms, and what is the smallest exponent on each of those variables?"
3. The common factors are the first part of the answer.
4. After removing the common factors what remains is placed in a parentheses as the second factor.

EXAMPLE 3 Factor. **(a)** $12x^2 - 18y^2$ **(b)** $x^2y^2 + 3xy^2 + y^3$

Solution

(a) Note that the largest integer that is common to both terms is 6 (not 3 or 2).

$$12x^2 - 18y^2 = 6(2x^2 - 3y^2)$$

(b) Although y is common to all of the terms, we factor out y^2 since 2 is the largest exponent of y that is common to all terms. We do not factor out x, since x is not common to all of the terms.

$$x^2y^2 + 3xy^2 + y^3 = y^2(x^2 + 3x + y)$$

Practice Problem 3 Factor. **(a)** $16a^3 - 24b^3$ **(b)** $r^3s^2 - 4r^4s + 7r^5$

Checking Is Very Important! You can check any factoring problem by multiplying the factors you obtain. The result should be the same as the original polynomial.

EXAMPLE 4 Factor. $8x^3y + 16x^2y^2 - 24x^3y^3$

Solution We see that 8 is the largest integer that will divide evenly into the three numerical coefficients. We can factor an x^2 out of each term. We can also factor y out of each term.

$$8x^3y + 16x^2y^2 - 24x^3y^3 = 8x^2y(x + 2y - 3xy^2)$$

Check.

$$8x^2y(x + 2y - 3xy^2) = 8x^3y + 16x^2y^2 - 24x^3y^3 \quad ✓$$

Practice Problem 4 Factor. $18a^3b^2c - 27ab^3c^2 - 45a^2b^2c^2$

EXAMPLE 5 Factor. $9a^3b^2 + 9a^2b^2$

Solution We observe that both terms contain a common factor of 9. We can factor a^2 and b^2 out from each term. Thus the common factor is $9a^2b^2$.

$$9a^3b^2 + 9a^2b^2 = 9a^2b^2(a + 1)$$

CAUTION Don't forget to include the 1 inside the parentheses in Example 5. The solution is wrong without it. You will see why if you try to check a result written without the 1.

Practice Problem 5 Factor and check. $30x^3y^2 - 24x^2y^2 + 6xy^2$

EXAMPLE 6 Factor. $3x(x - 4y) + 2(x - 4y)$

Solution Be sure you understand what are terms and what are factors of the polynomial in this example. There are two terms. The expression $3x(x - 4y)$ is one term. The expression $2(x - 4y)$ is the second term. Each term is made up of two factors. Observe that the binomial $(x - 4y)$ is a common factor of the terms. A common factor may be any type of polynomial. Thus we can factor out the common factor $(x - 4y)$.

$$3x(x - 4y) + 2(x - 4y) = (x - 4y)(3x + 2)$$

Practice Problem 6 Factor. $3(a + 5b) + x(a + 5b)$

EXAMPLE 7 Factor. $7x^2(2x - 3y) - (2x - 3y)$

Solution The common factor of the terms is $(2x - 3y)$. What happens when we factor out $(2x - 3y)$? What are we left with in the second term?

Recall that $(2x - 3y) = 1(2x - 3y)$. Thus

$7x^2(2x - 3y) - (2x - 3y) = 7x^2(2x - 3y) - 1(2x - 3y)$ Rewrite the original expression.

$= (2x - 3y)(7x^2 - 1)$ Factor out $(2x - 3y)$.

NOTE TO STUDENT: Fully worked-out solutions to all of the Practice Problems can be found at the back of the text starting at page SP-1

Practice Problem 7 Factor. $8y(9y^2 - 2) - (9y^2 - 2)$

EXAMPLE 8 A computer programmer is writing a program to find the area of 4 circles. She uses the formula $A = \pi r^2$. The radii of the circles are a, b, c, and d, respectively. She wants the final answer to be in factored form with the value of π occurring only once, in order to minimize round-off error. Write the total area with a formula that has π occurring only once.

Solution

For each circle, $A = \pi r^2$, where $r = a, b, c,$ or d.

The total area is $\pi a^2 + \pi b^2 + \pi c^2 + \pi d^2$.

In factored form the total area $= \pi(a^2 + b^2 + c^2 + d^2)$.

Practice Problem 8 Use $A = \pi r^2$ to find the shaded area. The radius of the larger circle is b. The radius of the smaller circle is a. Write the total area formula in factored form so that π appears only once.

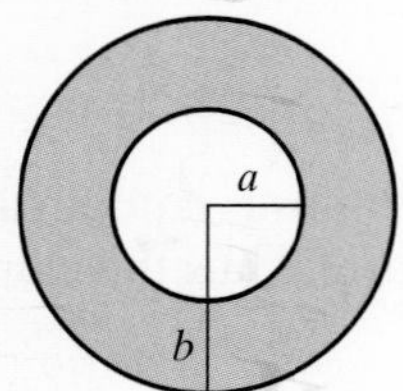

5.1 Exercises

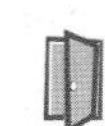
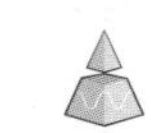

Student Solutions Manual | CD/Video | PH Math Tutor Center | MathXL®Tutorials on CD | MathXL® | MyMathLab® | Interactmath.com

Verbal and Writing Skills

In exercises 1 and 2, write a word or words to complete each sentence.

1. In the expression $3x^2 \cdot 5x^3$, $3x^2$ and $5x^3$ are called __________.

2. In the expression $3x^2 + 5x^3$, $3x^2$ and $5x^3$ are called __________.

3. We can factor $30a^4 + 15a^3 - 45a^2$ as $5a(6a^3 + 3a^2 - 9a)$. Is the factoring complete? Why or why not?

4. We can factor $4x^3 - 8x^2 + 20x$ as $4(x^3 - 2x^2 + 10x)$. Is the factoring complete?

Remove the largest possible common factor. Check your answers for exercises 5–28 by multiplication.

5. $3a^2 + 3a$

6. $2c^2 + 2c$

7. $21ab - 14ab^2$

8. $18wz - 27w^2z$

9. $2\pi rh + 2\pi r^2$

10. $9a^2b^2 - 36ab$

11. $5x^3 + 25x^2 - 15x$

12. $8x^3 - 10x^2 - 14x$

13. $12ab - 28bc + 20ac$

14. $12xy - 18yz - 36xz$

15. $16x^5 + 24x^3 - 32x^2$

16. $36x^6 + 45x^4 - 18x^2$

17. $14x^2y - 35xy - 63x$

18. $40a^2 - 16ab - 24a$

19. $54x^2 - 45xy + 18x$

20. $48xy - 24y^2 + 40y$

21. $3xy^2 - 2ay + 5xy - 2y$

22. $2ab^3 + 3xb^2 - 5b^4 + 2b^2$

23. $24x^2y - 40xy^2$

24. $35abc^2 - 49ab^2c$

25. $7x^3y^2 + 21x^2y^2$

26. $8x^3y^2 + 32xy^2$

27. $9x^2y - 18xy^2 - 27xy$

28. $10x^2y - 15xy^2 + 20xy$

Hint: In exercises 29–42, refer to Examples 6 and 7.

29. $7a(x + 2y) - b(x + 2y)$

30. $6(3a + b) - z(3a + b)$

31. $3x(x - 4) - 2(x - 4)$

32. $5x(x - 7) + 3(x - 7)$

33. $6b(2a - 3c) - 5d(2a - 3c)$

34. $7x(3y + 5z) - 6t(3y + 5z)$

35. $7c(b - a^2) - 5d(b - a^2) + 2f(b - a^2)$

36. $3b(y^2 - x) - 4a(y^2 - x) + 6c(y^2 - x)$

37. $2a(xy - 3) - 4(xy - 3) - z(xy - 3)$

38. $3c(bc - 3a) - 2(bc - 3a) - 6b(bc - 3a)$

39. $4a^3(a - 3b) + (a - 3b)$

40. $(c + 4d) + 7c^2(c + 4d)$

41. $(2a + 3) - 7x(2a + 3)$

42. $d(5x - 3) - (5x - 3)$

To Think About

▲ **43.** ***Geometry*** Find a formula for the area of four rectangles of width 2.786 inches. The lengths of the rectangles are a, b, c, and d inches. Write the formula in factored form.

44. ***Wholesale Purchases*** Find a formula for the total cost of all purchases by four people. Each person went to the local wholesale warehouse and spent \$29.95 per item. Harry bought a items, Richard bought b items, Lyle bought c items, and Selena bought d items. Write the formula in factored form.

Cumulative Review

45. ***Integers*** The sum of three consecutive odd integers is 40 more than the smallest of these integers. Find each of these three consecutive odd integers. (*Hint:* Consecutive odd integers are numbers included in the following pattern: $-3, -1, 1, 3, 5, 7, 9, \ldots, x, x + 2, \ldots$).

46. ***College Costs*** Tuition, room, and board at a college in Colorado cost Lisa \$27,040. This was a 4% increase over the cost of these items last year. What did Lisa pay last year for tuition, room, and board?

47. ***Videotape Speed*** A videotape plays 6.72 feet per minute for 2 hours at standard speed. It plays for 6 hours at extended long play speed. What is the rate of the tape at the slower speed?

Fruit Production *In 2001 the top six fruit producing countries of the world produced 258,000,000 tons of fruit. The percent of this 258 million tons produced by each of these countries is shown in the following graph. Use the graph to answer the following questions.*

Percent of Fruit Produced by the Top Six Fruit Producing Countries of the World

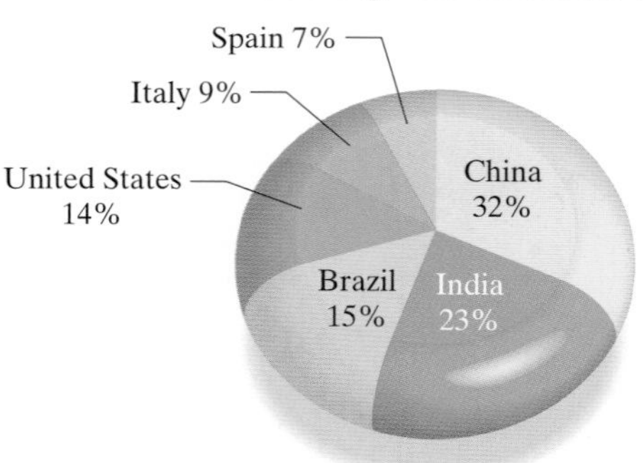

Source: Food and Agriculture Organization of the United Nations

48. How many tons of fruit were produced in Italy in 2001?

49. How many tons of fruit were produced in Brazil in 2001?

50. The population of Italy in 2001 was approximately 57,000,000 people. How many pounds of fruit was produced in the country for each person? (Round your answer to nearest whole number. Remember than 1 ton = 2000 pounds.)

51. The population of Brazil in 2001 was approximately 174,000,000 people. How many pounds of fruit was produced in the country for each person? (Round your answer to nearest whole number.)

5.2 Factoring by Grouping

Factoring Expressions with Four Terms by Grouping

A common factor of a polynomial can be a number, a variable, or an algebraic expression. Sometimes the polynomial is written so that it is easy to recognize the common factor. This is especially true when the common factor is enclosed by parentheses.

Student Learning Objective

After studying this section, you will be able to:

1. **Factor expressions with four terms by grouping.**

EXAMPLE 1 Factor. $x(x - 3) + 2(x - 3)$

Solution Observe each term:

$$\underbrace{x(x - 3)}_{\text{first term}} + \underbrace{2(x - 3)}_{\text{second term}}$$

The common factor of the first and second terms is the quantity $(x - 3)$, so we have

$$x(x - 3) + 2(x - 3) = (x - 3)(x + 2).$$

Practice Problem 1 Factor. $3y(2x - 7) - 8(2x - 7)$

NOTE TO STUDENT: Fully worked-out solutions to all of the Practice Problems can be found at the back of the text starting at page SP-1

Now let us face a new challenge. Think carefully. Try to follow this new idea. Suppose the polynomial in Example 1, $x(x - 3) + 2(x - 3)$, were written in the form $x^2 - 3x + 2x - 6$. (Note that this form is obtained by multiplying the factors of the first and second terms.) How would we factor a four-term polynomial like this?

In such cases we remove a common factor from the first two terms and a different common factor from the second two terms. That is, we would factor x from $x^2 - 3x$ and 2 from $2x - 6$.

$$x^2 - 3x + 2x - 6 = x(x - 3) + 2(x - 3)$$

Because the resulting terms have a common factor (the binomial enclosed by the parentheses), we would then proceed as we did in Example 1. This procedure for factoring is often called **factoring by grouping.**

EXAMPLE 2 Factor. $2x^2 + 3x + 6x + 9$

Solution

$2x^2 + 3x$	+	$6x + 9$
Factor out a common factor of x from the first two terms.		Factor out a common factor of 3 from the second two terms.
$x(2x + 3)$		$3(2x + 3)$

Note that the sets of parentheses in the two terms contain the same expression at this step.

The expression in parentheses is now a common factor of the terms.

Now we finish the factoring.

$$2x^2 + 3x + 6x + 9 = x(2x + 3) + 3(2x + 3)$$
$$= (2x + 3)(x + 3)$$

Practice Problem 2 Factor. $6x^2 - 15x + 4x - 10$

EXAMPLE 3 Factor. $4x + 8y + ax + 2ay$

Solution

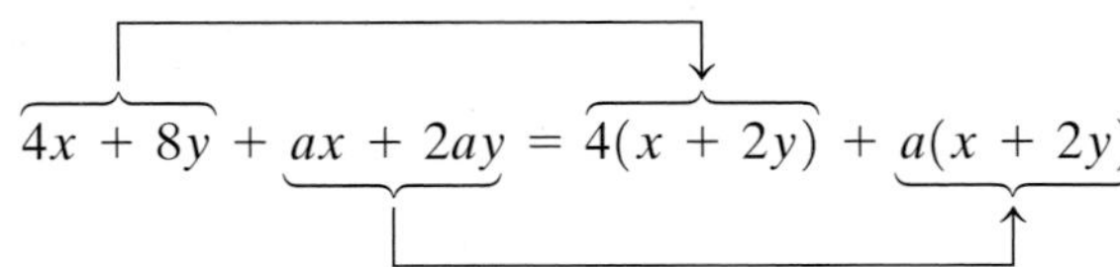
Factor out a common
factor of 4 from
the first two terms.

$$4x + 8y + ax + 2ay = 4(x + 2y) + a(x + 2y)$$

Factor out a common factor of a from the second two terms.

$4(x + 2y) + a(x + 2y) = (x + 2y)(4 + a)$ The common factor of the terms is the expression in parentheses, $x + 2y$.

***NOTE TO STUDENT:** Fully worked-out solutions to all of the Practice Problems can be found at the back of the text starting at page SP-1*

Practice Problem 3 Factor by grouping. $ax + 2a + 4bx + 8b$

In some problems the terms are out of order. We have to rearrange the order of the terms first so that the first two terms have a common factor.

EXAMPLE 4 Factor. $bx + 4y + 4b + xy$

Solution

$bx + 4y + 4b + xy = bx + 4b + xy + 4y$ Rearrange the terms so that the first terms have a common factor.

$= b(x + 4) + y(x + 4)$ Factor out the common factor of b from the first two terms.

$= (x + 4)(b + y)$ Factor out the common factor of y from the second two terms.

Practice Problem 4 Factor. $6a^2 + 5bc + 10ab + 3ac$

Sometimes you will need to factor out a negative common factor from the second two terms to obtain two terms that contain the same parenthetical expression.

EXAMPLE 5 Factor. $2x^2 + 5x - 4x - 10$

Solution

$2x^2 + 5x - 4x - 10 = x(2x + 5) - 2(2x + 5)$ Factor out the common factor of x from the first two terms and the common factor of -2 from the second two terms.

$= (2x + 5)(x - 2)$

Notice that if you factored out a common factor of $+2$ in the first step, the two resulting terms would not contain the same parenthetical expression. If the expressions inside the two sets of parentheses are not exactly the same, you cannot express the polynomial as a product of two factors!

Practice Problem 5 Factor. $6xy + 14x - 15y - 35$

EXAMPLE 6 Factor. $2ax - a - 2bx + b$

Solution

$2ax - a - 2bx + b = a(2x - 1) - b(2x - 1)$ Factor out the common factor of a from the first two terms. Factor out the common factor of $-b$ from the second two terms.

$= (2x - 1)(a - b)$ Since the two resulting terms contain the same parenthetical expression, we can complete the factoring.

Practice Problem 6 Factor. $3x - 10ay + 6y - 5ax$

CAUTION Many students find that they make a factoring error in the first step of problems like Example 6. Watch that step very carefully. If you take your answer and multiply it by FOIL, you should obtain the original problem.

EXAMPLE 7 Factor and check your answer. $8ad + 21bc - 6bd - 28ac$

Solution We observe that the first two terms do not have a common factor.

$8ad + 21bc - 6bd - 28ac = 8ad - 6bd - 28ac + 21bc$ Rearrange the order using the commutative property of addition.

$= 2d(4a - 3b) - 7c(4a - 3b)$ Factor out the common factor of $2d$ from the first two terms and the common factor of $-7c$ from the last two terms.

$= (4a - 3b)(2d - 7c)$ Factor out the common factor of $(4a - 3b)$.

To check, we multiply the two binomials using the FOIL procedure.

$(4a - 3b)(2d - 7c) = 8ad - 28ac - 6bd + 21bc$

$= 8ad + 21bc - 6bd - 28ac$ ✓ Rearrange the order of the terms. This is the original problem. Thus it checks.

Practice Problem 7 Factor and check your answer.

$10ad + 27bc - 6bd - 45ac$

5.2 Exercises

Student Solutions Manual | CD/ Video | PH Math Tutor Center | MathXL®Tutorials on CD | MathXL® | MyMathLab® | Interactmath.com

Verbal and Writing Skills

1. To factor $3x^2 - 6xy + 5x - 10y$, we must first remove a common factor of $3x$ from the first two terms. What do we do with the last two terms? What should we get for the answer?

2. To factor $5x^2 + 15xy - 2x - 6y$, we must first remove a common factor of $4x$ from the first two terms. What do we do with the last two terms? What should we get for the answer?

Factor by grouping. Check your answers for exercises 3–26.

3. $ab - 3a + 4b - 12$

4. $xy - x + 4y - 4$

5. $x^3 - 4x^2 + 3x - 12$

6. $x^3 - 6x^2 + 2x - 12$

7. $2ax + 6bx - ay - 3by$

8. $4x + 8y - 3wx - 6wy$

9. $3ax + bx - 6a - 2b$

10. $ad + 3a - d^2 - 3d$

11. $5a + 12bc + 10b + 6ac$

12. $4u^2 + v + 4uv + u$

13. $5a - 5b - 2ax + 2xb$

14. $xy - 4x - 3y + 12$

15. $y^2 - 2y - 3y + 6$

16. $x^2 - 4x + 3x - 12$

17. $14 - 7y + 2y - y^2$

18. $xa + 2bx - a - 2b$

19. $6ax - y + 2ay - 3x$

20. $6tx + r - 3t - 2rx$

21. $2x^2 + 8x - 3x - 12$

22. $3y^2 - y + 9y - 3$

23. $t^3 - t^2 + t - 1$

24. $x^2 - 2x - xy + 2y$

25. $28x^2 + 8xy^2 + 21xw + 6y^2w$

26. $8xw + 10x^2 + 35xy^2 + 28y^2w$

To Think About

27. Although $6a^2 - 12bd - 8ad + 9ab = 6(a^2 - 2bd) - a(8d - 9b)$ is true, it is not the correct solution to the problem "Factor $6a^2 - 12bd - 8ad + 9ab$." Explain. Can this expression be factored?

28. Tim was trying to factor $5x^2 - 3xy - 10x + 6y$. In his first step he wrote down $x(5x - 3y) + 2(-5x + 3y)$. Was he doing the problem correctly? What is the answer?

Cumulative Review

29. ***Braking*** A train was traveling at 73 miles per hour when the engineer spotted a stalled truck on the railroad crossing ahead. He jammed on the brakes but was unable to stop the train before it collided with the stalled truck. For every second the engineer applied the brakes, the train slowed down by 4 miles per hour. The accident reconstruction team found that the train was still traveling at 41 miles per hour at the time of impact. For how many seconds were the brakes applied?

30. ***Car Sales*** Tim Brown made an average profit of \$320 per car for each car he sold at Donahue Motors over the first 5 months of the year. In January and February, he averaged only \$200 per car. In March, he averaged \$300 per car, but in April he averaged \$480 per car. Assuming that he sells around the same number of cars each month, what was his average profit per car for the month of May?

31. ***Music Sales*** In 1998, the Recording Industry Association of America reported a 6.8% increase from the previous year in U.S. unit sales of all musical recordings. This translates to an 11.9% increase in dollar value, or a 15.1 million increase. (*Source:* Bureau of Economic Analysis.) If the dollar value increase is equal to \$15.1 million dollars, what was the total dollar value of musical recordings in the United States in 1997? Round to the nearest tenth of a million.

32. ***Ticket Sales*** A community theater sold 900 tickets to a play. Floor seats cost \$12 each and balcony seats cost \$10. The total receipts were \$9780. How many of each type of ticket were sold?

33. ***Coffee Production*** In 1995, 5.5 million metric tons of coffee were produced in the world. By the year 2000, total world production had increased by 33%. How many metric tons were produced in the world in 2000? It is estimated that from 2000 to 2005 the total world production of coffee will increase by 28%. If that is true, how many metric tons will be produced in 2005? (*Source:* Statistical Division of the United Nations)

5.3 Factoring Trinomials of the Form $x^2 + bx + c$

Student Learning Objectives

After studying this section, you will be able to:

1. **Factor polynomials of the form $x^2 + bx + c$.**
2. **Factor polynomials that have a common factor and a factor of the form $x^2 + bx + c$.**

1 Factoring Polynomials of the Form $x^2 + bx + c$

Suppose that you wanted to factor $x^2 + 5x + 6$. After some trial and error you *might* obtain $(x + 2)(x + 3)$, or you might get discouraged and not get an answer. If you did get these factors, you could check this answer by the FOIL method.

$$(x + 2)(x + 3) = x^2 + 3x + 2x + 6$$
$$= x^2 + 5x + 6$$

But trial and error can be a long process. There is another way. Let's look at the preceding equation again.

$$(x + 2)(x + 3) = \overset{F}{x^2} + \underbrace{\overset{O}{3x} + \overset{I}{2x}} + \overset{L}{6}$$
$$= x^2 \quad + 5x \quad + 6$$

The first thing to notice is that the product of the first terms in the factors gives the first term of the polynomial. That is, $x \cdot x = x^2$.

The first term is the product of these terms.

$$x^2 + 5x + 6 \quad = \quad (x + 2)(x + 3)$$

The next thing to notice is that the sum of the products of the outer and inner terms in the factors produces the middle term of the polynomial. That is, $(x \cdot 3) + (2 \cdot x) = 3x + 2x = 5x$. Thus we see that the sum of the second terms in the factors, $2 + 3$, gives the coefficient of the middle term, 5.

Finally, note that the product of the last terms of the factors gives the last term of the polynomial. That is, $2 \cdot 3 = 6$.

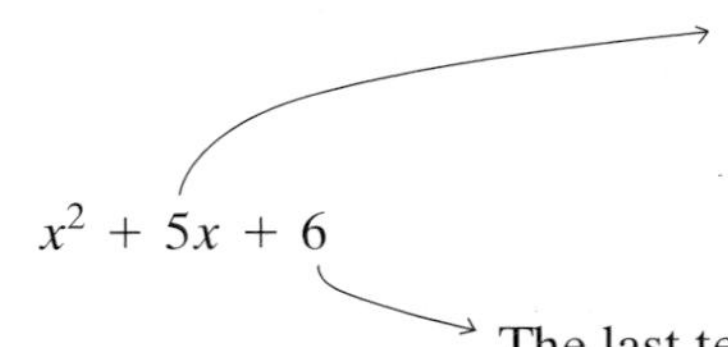

The coefficient of the middle term is the *sum* of these two numbers.

$$x^2 + 5x + 6 \qquad (x + 2)(x + 3)$$

The last term is the *product* of these two numbers.

Let's summarize our observations in general terms and then try a few examples.

FACTORING TRINOMIALS OF THE FORM $x^2 + bx + c$

1. The answer will be of the form $(x + m)(x + n)$.
2. m and n are numbers such that:
   (a) When you multiply them, you get the last term, which is c.
   (b) When you add them, you get the coefficient of the middle term, which is b.

EXAMPLE 1 Factor. $x^2 + 7x + 12$

Solution The answer is of the form $(x + m)(x + n)$. We want to find the two numbers, m and n, that you can multiply to get 12 and add to get 7. The numbers are 3 and 4.

$$x^2 + 7x + 12 = (x + 3)(x + 4)$$

Practice Problem 1 Factor. $x^2 + 8x + 12$

NOTE TO STUDENT: Fully worked-out solutions to all of the Practice Problems can be found at the back of the text starting at page SP-1

EXAMPLE 2 Factor. $x^2 + 12x + 20$

Solution We want two numbers that have a product of 20 and a sum of 12. The numbers are 10 and 2.

$$x^2 + 12x + 20 = (x + \underline{10})(x + \underline{2})$$

Note: If you cannot think of the numbers in your head, write down the possible factors whose product is 20.

Product	Sum
$1 \cdot 20 = 20$	$1 + 20 = 21$
$2 \cdot 10 = 20$	$2 + 10 = 12$ ←
$4 \cdot 5 = 20$	$4 + 5 = 9$

Then select the pair whose sum is 12. Select this pair.

Practice Problem 2 Factor. $x^2 + 17x + 30$
You may find that it is helpful to list all the factors whose product is 30 first.

So far we have factored only trinomials of the form $x^2 + bx + c$, where b and c are positive numbers. The same procedure applies if b is a negative number and c is positive. Because m and n have a positive product and a negative sum, they must both be negative.

EXAMPLE 3 Factor. $x^2 - 8x + 15$

Solution We want two numbers that have a product of $+15$ and a sum of -8. They must be negative numbers since the sign of the middle term is negative and the sign of the last term is positive.

the sum $-5 + (-3)$

$$x^2 - 8x + 15 = (x - 5)(x - 3)$$

the product $(-5)(-3)$

Think: $(-5)(-3) = +15$ *and* $-5 + (-3) = -8$.

Multiply using FOIL to check.

Practice Problem 3 Factor. $x^2 - 11x + 18$

EXAMPLE 4 Factor. $x^2 - 9x + 14$

Solution We want two numbers whose product is 14 and whose sum is -9. The numbers are -7 and -2. So

$$x^2 - 9x + 14 = (x - 7)(x - 2) \text{ or } (x - 2)(x - 7).$$

Practice Problem 4 Factor. $x^2 - 11x + 24$

All the examples so far have had a positive last term. What happens when the last term is negative? If the last term is negative, one of the numbers m or n must be a positive and the other must be a negative. Why? The product of a positive number and a negative number is negative.

NOTE TO STUDENT: Fully worked-out solutions to all of the Practice Problems can be found at the back of the text starting at page SP-1

EXAMPLE 5 Factor. $x^2 - 3x - 10$

Solution We want two numbers whose product is -10 and whose sum is -3. The two numbers are -5 and $+2$.

$$x^2 - 3x - 10 = (x - 5)(x + 2)$$

Practice Problem 5 Factor. $x^2 - 5x - 24$

What if we made a sign error and *incorrectly* factored the trinomial $x^2 - 3x - 10$ as $(x + 5)(x - 2)$? We could detect the error immediately since the sum of $+5$ and -2 is 3. We need a sum of -3!

EXAMPLE 6 Factor. $y^2 + 10y - 24$. Check your answer.

Solution The two numbers whose product is -24 and whose sum is $+10$ are the numbers $+12$ and -2.

$$y^2 + 10y - 24 = (y + 12)(y - 2)$$

CAUTION It is very easy to make a sign error in these problems. Make sure that you mentally multiply your answer back by FOIL to obtain the original expression. Check each sign carefully.

Check. $(y + 12)(y - 2) = y^2 - 2y + 12y - 24 = y^2 + 10y - 24$ ✓

Practice Problem 6 Factor. $y^2 + 17y - 60$
Multiply your answer to check.

EXAMPLE 7 Factor. $x^2 - 16x - 36$

Solution We want two numbers whose product is -36 and whose sum is -16.

List all the possible factors of 36 (without regard to sign). Find the pair that has a difference of 16. We are looking for a difference because the signs of the factors are different.

Factors of 36	The Difference Between the Factors
36 and 1	35
18 and 2	16 ← This is the value we want.
12 and 3	9
9 and 4	5
6 and 6	0

Once we have picked the pair of numbers (18 and 2), it is not difficult to find the signs. For the coefficient of the middle term to be -16, we will have to add the numbers -18 and $+2$.

$$x^2 - 16x - 36 = (x - 18)(x + 2)$$

Practice Problem 7 Factor. $x^2 - 7x - 60$
You may find it helpful to list the pairs of numbers whose product is 60.

At this point you should work several problems to develop your factoring skill. This is one section where you really need to drill by doing many problems.

Feel a little confused about the signs? If you do, you may find these facts helpful.

FACTS ABOUT FACTORING TRINOMIALS OF THE FORM $x^2 + bx + c$

The *two numbers m* and *n* will have the *same sign* if the last term of the polynomial is *positive*.

$$x^2 + bx + c = (x \quad m)(x \quad n)$$

1. They will both be *positive* if the *coefficient* of the *middle* term is *positive*. $x^2 + 5x + 6 = (x + 2)(x + 3)$
2. They will both be *negative* if the *coefficient* of the *middle* term is *negative*. $x^2 - 5x + 6 = (x - 2)(x - 3)$

The two numbers *m* and *n* will have *opposite signs* if the last term is *negative*.

1. The *larger* of the absolute values of the two numbers will be given a plus sign if the coefficient of the *middle term* is *positive*. $x^2 + 6x - 7 = (x + 7)(x - 1)$
2. The larger of the absolute values of the two numbers will be given a negative sign if the coefficient of the *middle term* is *negative*. $x^2 - 6x - 7 = (x - 7)(x + 1)$

Do not memorize these facts; rather, try to understand the pattern.

Sometimes the exponent of the first term of the polynomial will be greater than 2. If the exponent is an even power, it is a square. For example, $x^4 = (x^2)(x^2)$. Likewise, $x^6 = (x^3)(x^3)$.

EXAMPLE 8 Factor. $y^4 - 2y^2 - 35$

Solution Think: $y^4 = (y^2)(y^2)$ This will be the first term of each parentheses.

$(y^2 \quad)(y^2 \quad)$

$(y^2 + \quad)(y^2 - \quad)$ The last term of the polynomial is negative.

$(y^2 + 5)(y^2 - 7)$ Thus the signs of *m* and *n* will be different. Now think of factors of 35 whose difference is 2.

Practice Problem 8 Factor. $a^4 + a^2 - 42$

2 Factoring Polynomials That Have a Common Factor and a Factor of the Form $x^2 + bx + c$

Some factoring problems require two steps. Often we must first factor out a common factor from each term of the polynomial. Once this is done, we may find that the other factor is a trinomial that can be factored using the methods previously discussed in this section.

EXAMPLE 9 Factor. $2x^2 + 36x + 160$

Solution

$2x^2 + 36x + 160 = 2(x^2 + 18x + 80)$ First factor out the common factor of 2 from each term of the polynomial.

$= 2(x + 8)(x + 10)$ Then factor the remaining polynomial.

The final answer is $2(x + 8)(x + 10)$. *Be sure to list all parts of the answer.*

Check. $2(x + 8)(x + 10) = 2(x^2 + 18x + 80) = 2x^2 + 36x + 160$ ✓

Thus we are sure that the answer is $2(x + 8)(x + 10)$.

Practice Problem 9 Factor. $3x^2 + 45x + 150$

EXAMPLE 10 Factor. $3x^2 + 9x - 162$

Solution

$$3x^2 + 9x - 162 = 3(x^2 + 3x - 54)$$ First factor out the common factor of 3 from each term of the polynomial.

$$= 3(x - 6)(x + 9)$$ Then factor the remaining polynomial.

The final answer is $3(x - 6)(x + 9)$. *Be sure you included the 3.*

Check. $3(x - 6)(x + 9) = 3(x^2 + 3x - 54) = 3x^2 + 9x - 162$ ✓

Thus we are sure that the answer is $3(x - 6)(x + 9)$.

NOTE TO STUDENT: Fully worked-out solutions to all of the Practice Problems can be found at the back of the text starting at page SP-1

Practice Problem 10 Factor. $4x^2 - 8x - 140$

CAUTION. Don't forget the common factor!

It is quite easy to forget to look for a greatest common factor as the first step of factoring a trinomial. Therefore, it is a good idea to examine your final answer in any factoring problem and ask yourself, "Can I factor out a common factor from any binomial contained inside a set of parentheses?" Often you will be able to see a common factor at that point if you missed it in the first step of the problem.

▲ **EXAMPLE 11** Find a polynomial in factored form for the shaded area in the figure.

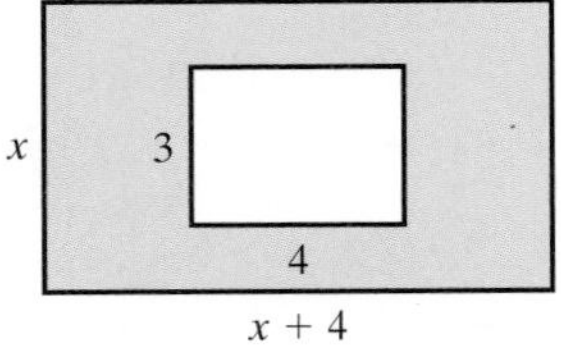

Solution To obtain the shaded area, we find the area of the larger rectangle and subtract from it the area of the smaller rectangle. Thus we have the following:

$$\text{shaded area} = x(x + 4) - (4)(3)$$
$$= x^2 + 4x - 12$$

Now we factor this polynomial to obtain the shaded area $= (x + 6)(x - 2)$.

▲ **Practice Problem 11** Find a polynomial in factored form for the shaded area in the figure.

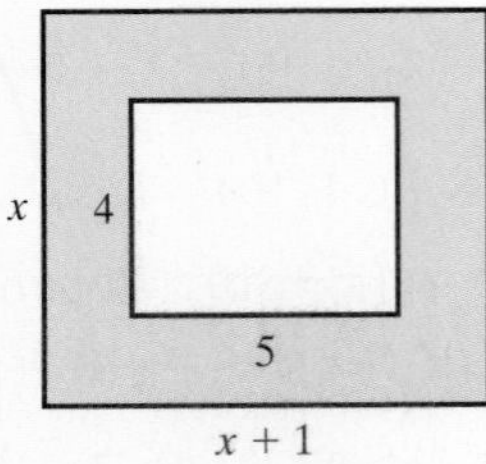

5.3 Exercises

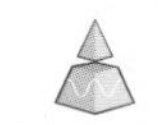

Student Solutions Manual | CD/ Video | PH Math Tutor Center | MathXL®Tutorials on CD | MathXL® | MyMathLab® | Interactmath.com

Verbal and Writing Skills

Fill in the blanks.

1. To factor $x^2 + 5x + 6$, find two numbers whose __________ is 6 and whose __________ is 5.

2. To factor $x^2 + 5x - 6$, find two numbers whose __________ is -6 and whose __________ is 5.

Factor.

3. $x^2 + 2x + 1$
4. $x^2 + 11x + 30$
5. $x^2 + 12x + 20$
6. $x^2 + 10x + 21$
7. $x^2 - 4x + 3$
8. $x^2 - 6x + 8$
9. $x^2 - 11x + 28$
10. $x^2 - 13x + 12$
11. $x^2 + x - 20$
12. $x^2 + x - 42$
13. $x^2 - 13x - 14$
14. $x^2 - 6x - 16$
15. $x^2 + 2x - 35$
16. $x^2 + 4x - 12$
17. $x^2 - 2x - 24$
18. $x^2 - 11x - 26$
19. $x^2 + 12x + 32$
20. $x^2 + 18x + 72$
21. $x^2 - 10x + 24$
22. $x^2 - 13x + 42$
23. $x^2 + 13x + 30$
24. $x^2 + 9x + 20$
25. $x^2 - 6x + 5$
26. $y^2 - 8y + 7$

Mixed Practice

Look over your answers to exercises 3–26 carefully. Be sure that you are clear on your sign rules. Exercises 27–42 contain a mixture of all the types of problems in this section. Make sure you can do them all. Check your answers by multiplication.

27. $a^2 + 6a - 16$
28. $a^2 - 13a + 30$
29. $x^2 - 12x + 32$
30. $x^2 - 6x - 27$
31. $x^2 + 4x - 21$
32. $x^2 - 9x + 18$
33. $x^2 + 15x + 56$
34. $x^2 + 20x + 99$
35. $x^2 - 21x - 46$
36. $x^2 + 12x - 45$
37. $x^2 + 9x - 36$
38. $x^2 - 13x + 36$
39. $x^2 - 2xy - 15y^2$
40. $x^2 - 2xy - 35y^2$
41. $x^2 - 16xy + 63y^2$
42. $x^2 + 19xy + 48y^2$

In exercises 43–54, first factor out the greatest common factor from each term. Then factor the remaining polynomial. Refer to Examples 9 and 10.

43. $4x^2 + 24x + 20$
44. $4x^2 + 28x + 40$
45. $6x^2 + 18x + 12$
46. $6x^2 + 24x + 18$
47. $2x^2 - 20x + 42$
48. $2x^2 - 22x + 56$
49. $3x^2 - 6x - 72$
50. $3x^2 - 12x - 63$
51. $7x^2 + 21x - 70$
52. $7x^2 + 7x - 84$
53. $3x^2 - 18x + 15$
54. $3x^2 - 33x + 54$

▲ 55. ***Geometry*** The circle just touches the middle of each side of the square in this sketch. Find a formula for the shaded area. Place the formula in factored form. Evaluate it when $x = 8$. Use $\pi \approx 3.14$.

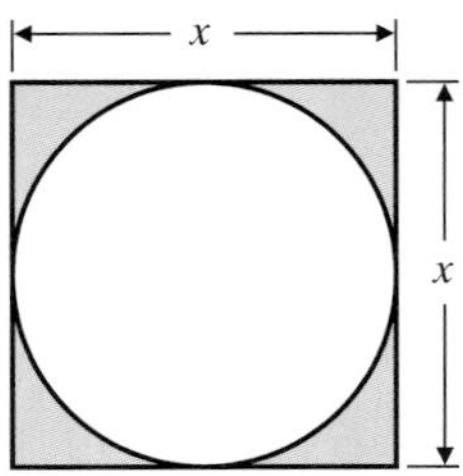

▲ 56. ***Geometry*** Find a polynomial that describes how much greater the perimeter of the square is than the circumference of the circle in the sketch for exercise 55. (*Hint:* Find the perimeter of the square. Find the circumference of the circle. Subtract the circumference from the perimeter. Use $\pi \approx 3.14$.)

▲ 57. ***Geometry*** Find a polynomial in factored form for the shaded area. Both figures are rectangles with dimensions as labeled.

▲ 58. ***Geometry*** How much larger is the perimeter of the large rectangle than the perimeter of the small rectangle?

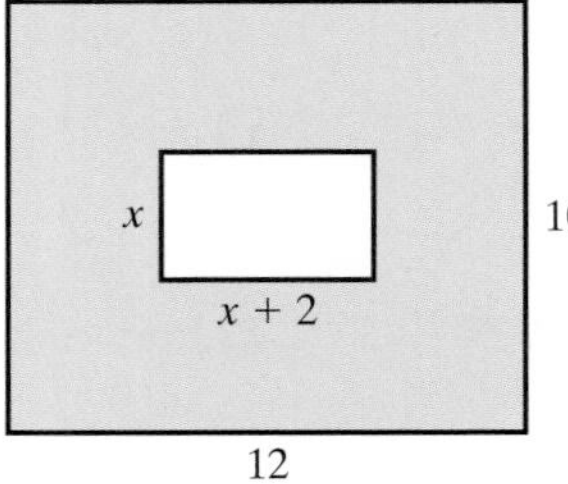

Cumulative Review

59. Solve for t. $A = P + Prt$

60. Solve $2 - 3x \leq 7$ for x. Graph the solution on the number line.

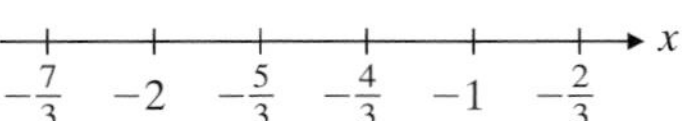

61. ***Travel Speed*** A new car that maintains a constant speed travels from Watch Hill, Rhode Island, to Greenwich, Connecticut, in 2 hours. A train, traveling 20 mph faster, makes the trip in $1\frac{1}{2}$ hours. How far is it from Watch Hill to Greenwich? (*Hint:* Let c = the car's speed. First find the speed of the car and the speed of the train. Then be sure to answer the question.)

62. ***Salary*** Kerri works as a radio advertising sales rep. She earns a guaranteed minimum salary of \$500 per month plus 3% commission on her sales. She wants to earn \$4400 or more this month. At least how much must she generate in sales?

DJ Charges *The Golden Sounds DJ Service charges \$65 per hour plus \$85 for each 30-minute period after midnight.*

63. If the bill for Marcia's wedding reception was \$515 and the reception started at 8 P.M., when did the reception end?

64. If the bill for Melissa's wedding reception was \$535 and the reception ended at 2 A.M., when did the reception start?

Average Temperature *The equation $T = 19 + 2M$ has been used by some meteorologists to predict the monthly average temperature for the small island of Menorca off the coast of Spain during the first 6 months of the year. The variable T represents the average monthly temperature measured in degrees Celsius. The variable M represents the number of months since January.*

65. What is the average temperature of Menorca during the month of April?

66. During what month will the average temperature be 29°C?

5.4 Factoring Trinomials of the Form $ax^2 + bx + c$

1 Using the Trial-and-Error Method

When the coefficient of the x^2-term in a trinomial of the form $ax^2 + bx + c$ is not 1, the trinomial is more difficult to factor. Several possibilities must be considered.

Student Learning Objectives

After studying this section, you will be able to:

1. **Factor a trinomial of the form $ax^2 + bx + c$ by the trial-and-error method.**
2. **Factor a trinomial of the form $ax^2 + bx + c$ by the grouping method.**
3. **Factor a trinomial of the form $ax^2 + bx + c$ after a common factor has been factored out of each term.**

EXAMPLE 1 Factor. $2x^2 + 5x + 3$

Solution In order for the coefficient of the x^2-term of the polynomial to be 2, the coefficients of the x-terms in the factors must be 2 and 1. Thus $2x^2 + 5x + 3 = (2x \quad)(x \quad)$.

In order for the last term of the polynomial to be 3, the constants in the factors must be 3 and 1.

Since all signs in the polynomial are positive, we know that each factor in parentheses will contain only positive signs. However, we still have two possibilities. They are as follows:

$$(2x + 3)(x + 1)$$
$$(2x + 1)(x + 3)$$

We check them by multiplying by the FOIL method.

$$(2x + 1)(x + 3) = 2x^2 + 7x + 3 \quad \text{Wrong middle term}$$
$$(2x + 3)(x + 1) = 2x^2 + 5x + 3 \quad \text{Correct middle term}$$

Thus the correct answer is

$$(2x + 3)(x + 1) \text{ or } (x + 1)(2x + 3).$$

Practice Problem 1 Factor. $2x^2 + 7x + 5$

Some problems have many more possibilities.

EXAMPLE 2 Factor. $4x^2 - 13x + 3$

Solution

The Different Factors of 4 Are:	The Factors of 3 Are:
2 and 2	1 and 3
1 and 4	

Let us list the possible factoring combinations and compute the middle term by the FOIL method. Note that the signs of the constants in both factors will be negative. Why?

Possible Factors	Middle Term	Correct?
$(2x - 3)(2x - 1)$	$-8x$	No
$(4x - 3)(x - 1)$	$-7x$	No
$(4x - 1)(x - 3)$	$-13x$	Yes

The correct answer is $(4x - 1)(x - 3)$ or $(x - 3)(4x - 1)$.
This method is called the **trial-and-error method.**

Practice Problem 2 Factor. $9x^2 - 64x + 7$

NOTE TO STUDENT: Fully worked-out solutions to all of the Practice Problems can be found at the back of the text starting at page SP-1

EXAMPLE 3 Factor. $3x^2 - 2x - 8$

Solution

Factors of 3	Factors of 8
3 and 1	8 and 1
	4 and 2

Let us list only one-half of the possibilities. We'll let the constant in the first factor of each product be positive.

Possible Factors	Middle Term	Correct Factors?
$(x + 8)(3x - 1)$	$+23x$	No
$(x + 1)(3x - 8)$	$-5x$	No
$(x + 4)(3x - 2)$	$+10x$	No
$(x + 2)(3x - 4)$	$+2x$	No (but only because the sign is wrong)

So we just *reverse* the signs of the constants in the factors.

	Middle Term	Correct Factor?
$(x - 2)(3x + 4)$	$-2x$	Yes

The correct answer is

$$(x - 2)(3x + 4) \text{ or } (3x + 4)(x - 2).$$

Practice Problem 3 Factor. $3x^2 - x - 14$

NOTE TO STUDENT: Fully worked-out solutions to all of the Practice Problems can be found at the back of the text starting at page SP-1

It takes a good deal of practice to readily factor problems of this type. The more problems you do, the more proficient you will become. The following method will help you factor more quickly.

2 Using the Grouping Method

One way to factor a trinomial of the form $ax^2 + bx + c$ is to write it with four terms and factor by grouping, as we did in Section 5.2. For example, the trinomial $2x^2 + 13x + 20$ can be written as $2x^2 + 5x + 8x + 20$. Using the methods of Section 5.2, we factor it as follows.

$$\begin{aligned} 2x^2 + 5x + 8x + 20 &= x(2x + 5) + 4(2x + 5) \\ &= (2x + 5)(x + 4) \end{aligned}$$

We can factor all factorable trinomials of the form $ax^2 + bx + c$ in this way. We will use the following procedure.

GROUPING NUMBER METHOD FOR FACTORING TRINOMIALS OF THE FORM $ax^2 + bx + c$

1. Obtain the grouping number ac.
2. Find the two numbers whose product is the grouping number and whose sum is b.
3. Use those numbers to write bx as the sum of two terms.
4. Factor by grouping.
5. Multiply to check.

Let's try the problem from Example 1.

EXAMPLE 4 Factor by grouping. $2x^2 + 5x + 3$

Solution

1. The grouping number is $(2)(3) = 6$.
2. The factors of 6 are $6 \cdot 1$ and $3 \cdot 2$. We choose the numbers 3 and 2 because their product is 6 and their sum is 5.
3. We write $5x$ as the sum $3x + 2x$.
4. Factor by grouping.

$$\begin{aligned} 2x^2 + 5x + 3 &= 2x^2 + 2x + 3x + 3 \\ &= 2x(x + 1) + 3(x + 1) \\ &= (x + 1)(2x + 3) \end{aligned}$$

5. Multiply to check.

$$\begin{aligned} (x + 1)(2x + 3) &= 2x^2 + 3x + 2x + 3 \\ &= 2x^2 + 5x + 3 \quad \checkmark \end{aligned}$$

Practice Problem 4 Factor by grouping. $2x^2 + 7x + 5$

EXAMPLE 5 Factor by grouping. $4x^2 - 13x + 3$

Solution

1. The grouping number is $(4)(3) = 12$.
2. The factors of 12 are (12)(1) or (4)(3) or (6)(2). Note that the middle term of the polynomial is negative. Thus we choose the numbers -12 and -1 because their product is still 12 and their sum is -13.
3. We write $-13x$ as the sum $-12x + (-1x)$.
4. Factor by grouping.

$$\begin{aligned} 4x^2 - 13x + 3 &= 4x^2 - 12x - 1x + 3 \\ &= 4x(x - 3) - 1(x - 3) \\ &= (x - 3)(4x - 1) \end{aligned}$$

Remember to factor out a -1 from the last two terms so that both sets of parentheses contain the same expression.

Practice Problem 5 Factor by grouping. $9x^2 - 64x + 7$

EXAMPLE 6 Factor by grouping. $3x^2 - 2x - 8$

Solution

1. The grouping number is $(3)(-8) = -24$.
2. We want two numbers whose product is -24 and whose sum is -2. They are -6 and 4.
3. We write $-2x$ as a sum $-6x + 4x$.
4. Factor by grouping.

$$\begin{aligned} 3x^2 - 6x + 4x - 8 &= 3x(x - 2) + 4(x - 2) \\ &= (x - 2)(3x + 4) \end{aligned}$$

Practice Problem 6 Factor by grouping. $3x^2 + 4x - 4$

To factor polynomials of the form $ax^2 + bx + c$, use the method, either trial-and-error or grouping, that works best for you.

3 Using the Common Factor Method

Some problems require first factoring out the greatest common factor and then factoring the trinomial by one of the two methods of this section.

EXAMPLE 7 Factor. $9x^2 + 3x - 30$

Solution

$9x^2 + 3x - 30 = 3(3x^2 + 1x - 10)$ We first factor out the common factor of 3 from each term of the trinomial.

$= 3(3x - 5)(x + 2)$ We then factor the trinomial by the grouping method or by the trial-and-error method.

NOTE TO STUDENT: Fully worked-out solutions to all of the Practice Problems can be found at the back of the text starting at page SP-1

Practice Problem 7 Factor. $8x^2 + 8x - 6$

Be sure to remove the greatest common factor in the very first step.

EXAMPLE 8 Factor. $32x^2 - 40x + 12$

Solution

$32x^2 - 40x + 12 = 4(8x^2 - 10x + 3)$ We first factor out the greatest common factor of 4 from each term of the trinomial.

$= 4(2x - 1)(4x - 3)$ We then factor the trinomial by the grouping method or by the trial-and-error method.

Practice Problem 8 Factor. $24x^2 - 38x + 10$

5.4 Exercises

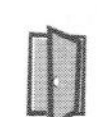

Student Solutions Manual | CD/ Video | PH Math Tutor Center | MathXL®Tutorials on CD | MathXL® | MyMathLab® | Interactmath.com

Factor by the trial-and-error method. Check your answers using FOIL.

1. $4x^2 + 13x + 3$ **2.** $3x^2 + 11x + 10$ **3.** $5x^2 + 7x + 2$ **4.** $3x^2 + 4x + 1$

5. $3x^2 - 4x - 7$ **6.** $5x^2 + 7x - 6$ **7.** $2x^2 - 5x - 3$ **8.** $2x^2 - x - 6$

Factor by the grouping number method. Check your answers by using FOIL.

9. $9x^2 + 9x + 2$ **10.** $4x^2 + 11x + 6$ **11.** $15x^2 - 34x + 15$ **12.** $10x^2 - 29x + 10$

13. $2x^2 + 3x - 20$ **14.** $6x^2 + 11x - 10$ **15.** $8x^2 + 10x - 3$ **16.** $5x^2 + 2x - 7$

Factor by any method.

17. $6x^2 - 5x - 6$ **18.** $3x^2 - 13x - 10$ **19.** $6x^2 + x - 15$ **20.** $12x^2 + 5x - 3$

21. $7x^2 - 5x - 18$ **22.** $9x^2 - 22x - 15$ **23.** $9y^2 - 13y + 4$ **24.** $5y^2 - 11y + 2$

25. $5a^2 - 13a - 6$ **26.** $3a^2 - 10a - 8$ **27.** $14x^2 - 3x - 5$ **28.** $40x^2 - x - 6$

29. $15x^2 + 4x - 4$ **30.** $8x^2 - 11x + 3$ **31.** $12x^2 + 28x + 15$ **32.** $24x^2 + 17x + 3$

33. $12x^2 - 16x - 3$ **34.** $12x^2 + x - 6$ **35.** $2x^4 + 15x^2 - 8$ **36.** $4x^4 - 11x^2 - 3$

37. $2x^2 + 11xy + 15y^2$ **38.** $15x^2 + 14xy + 3y^2$ **39.** $5x^2 + 16xy - 16y^2$ **40.** $12x^2 + 11xy - 5y^2$

Factor by first factoring out the greatest common factor. See Examples 7 and 8.

41. $4x^2 + 34x + 42$

42. $10x^2 + 22x + 12$

43. $8x^2 - 26x + 6$

44. $12x^2 - 24x + 9$

45. $10x^2 - 25x - 15$

46. $20x^2 - 25x - 30$

47. $6x^3 + 9x^2 - 60x$

48. $6x^3 - 16x^2 - 6x$

Mixed Practice

Factor.

49. $5x^2 + 3x - 2$

50. $6x^2 + x - 2$

51. $12x^2 - 38x + 20$

52. $20x^2 - 38x + 12$

53. $12x^2 - 20x + 3$

54. $6x^2 - 23x + 20$

55. $8x^2 + 16x - 10$

56. $16x^2 + 36x - 10$

Cumulative Review

57. Solve. $7x - 3(4 - 2x) = 2(x - 3) - (5 - x)$

58. Solve for x. $7x - 3y = 5$

Carbon Dioxide Emissions *Answer each of the following questions using the carbon dioxide emissions graph.*

59. From 1995 to the estimated value for 2010, what is the percent of increase for carbon dioxide emissions for the United States? (Round to the nearest tenth.)

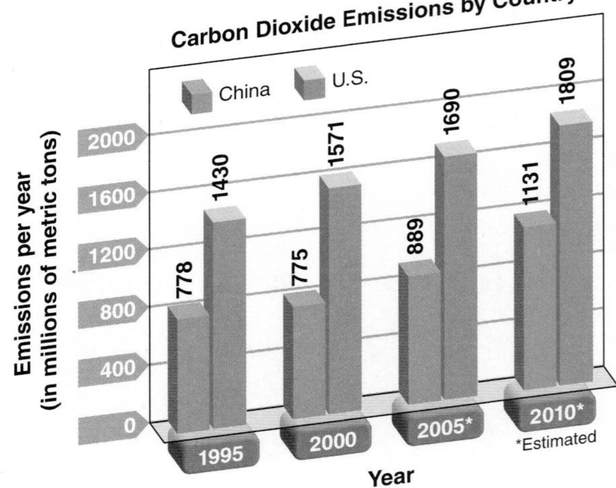

60. From 1995 to the estimated value for 2010, what is the percent of increase for carbon dioxide emissions for China? (Round to the nearest tenth.)

61. Which country has the greatest percent of increase for the period 1995 to the estimated value for 2010?

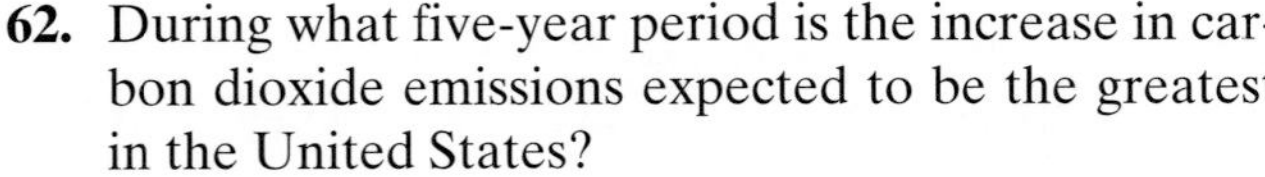

62. During what five-year period is the increase in carbon dioxide emissions expected to be the greatest in the United States?

How Am I Doing? Sections 5.1–5.4

How are you doing with your homework assignments in Sections 5.1 to 5.4? Do you feel you have mastered the material so far? Do you understand the concepts you have covered? Before you go further in the textbook, take some time to do each of the following problems.

Factor each of the following problems. Be sure to remove the greatest common factor in each case.

5.1

1. $6xy - 15z + 21$

2. $20x^2 - 32xy + 12x$

3. $7(4x - 5) - b(4x - 5)$

4. $2x(8y + 3z) - 5y(8y + 3z)$

5.2

5. $18 + 3x - 6y - xy$

6. $15x - 9xb + 20w - 12bw$

7. $x^3 - 5x^2 - 3x + 15$

8. $7a + 21b + 2ab + 6b^2$

5.3

9. $x^2 - 15x + 56$

10. $x^2 + 12x - 64$

11. $x^2 + 13xy + 40y^2$

12. $7x^2 - 14x - 245$
(*Hint:* First factor out the greatest common factor.)

5.4

13. $10x^2 + x - 2$

14. $3x^2 - 23x + 14$

15. $6x^2 + 17xy + 12y^2$

16. $14x^3 - 20x^2 - 16x$
(*Hint:* First factor out the greatest common factor.)

Now turn to page SA-12 for the answer to each of these problems. Each answer also includes a reference to the objective in which the problem is first taught. If you missed any of these problems, you should stop and review the Examples and Practice Problems in the referenced objective. A little review now will help you master the material in the upcoming sections of the text.

1. ______
2. ______
3. ______
4. ______
5. ______
6. ______
7. ______
8. ______
9. ______
10. ______
11. ______
12. ______
13. ______
14. ______
15. ______
16. ______

5.5 SPECIAL CASES OF FACTORING

Student Learning Objectives

After studying this section, you will be able to:

1. **Recognize and factor expressions of the type $a^2 - b^2$ (difference of two squares).**
2. **Recognize and factor expressions of the type $a^2 + 2ab + b^2$ (perfect-square trinomial).**
3. **Recognize and factor expressions that require factoring out a common factor and then using a special-case formula.**

As we proceed in this section you will be able to reduce the time it takes you to factor a polynomial by quickly recognizing and factoring two special types of polynomials: the difference of two squares and perfect-square trinomials.

1 Factoring the Difference of Two Squares

Recall the formula from Section 4.5:

$$(a + b)(a - b) = a^2 - b^2.$$

In reverse form we can use it for factoring.

DIFFERENCE OF TWO SQUARES

$$a^2 - b^2 = (a + b)(a - b)$$

We can state it in words in this way: "The difference of two squares can be factored into the sum and difference of those values that were squared."

EXAMPLE 1 Factor. $9x^2 - 1$

Solution We see that the problem is in the form of the difference of two squares. $9x^2$ is a square and 1 is a square. So using the formula we can write the following.

$$9x^2 - 1 = (3x + 1)(3x - 1) \quad \text{Because } 9x^2 = (3x)^2 \text{ and } 1 = (1)^2$$

NOTE TO STUDENT: Fully worked-out solutions to all of the Practice Problems can be found at the back of the text starting at page SP-1

Practice Problem 1 Factor. $64x^2 - 1$

EXAMPLE 2 Factor. $25x^2 - 16$

Solution Again we use the formula for the difference of squares.

$$25x^2 - 16 = (5x + 4)(5x - 4) \quad \text{Because } 25x^2 = (5x)^2 \text{ and } 16 = (4)^2$$

Practice Problem 2 Factor. $36x^2 - 49$

Sometimes the polynomial contains two variables.

EXAMPLE 3 Factor. $4x^2 - 49y^2$

Solution We see that

$$4x^2 - 49y^2 = (2x + 7y)(2x - 7y).$$

Practice Problem 3 Factor. $100x^2 - 81y^2$

CAUTION Please note that the Difference of Two Squares formula only works if the last term is negative. So if Example 3 had been to factor $4x^2 + 49y^2$ we would **not** have been able to factor the problem. We will examine this in more detail in Section 5.6.

Some problems may involve more than one step.

EXAMPLE 4 Factor. $81x^4 - 1$

Solution We see that

$$81x^4 - 1 = (9x^2 + 1)(9x^2 - 1) \qquad \text{Because } 81x^4 = (9x^2)^2 \text{ and } 1 = (1)^2$$

Is the factoring complete? We can factor $9x^2 - 1$.

$$81x^4 - 1 = (9x^2 + 1)(3x - 1)(3x + 1) \qquad \text{Because } (9x^2 - 1) = (3x - 1)(3x + 1)$$

Practice Problem 4 Factor. $x^8 - 1$

2 Factoring Perfect-Square Trinomials

There is a formula that will help us to factor very quickly certain trinomials, called **perfect-square trinomials.** Recall from Section 4.5 the formulas for a binomial squared.

$$(a + b)^2 = a^2 + 2ab + b^2$$
$$(a - b)^2 = a^2 - 2ab + b^2$$

We can use these two equations in reverse form for factoring.

PERFECT-SQUARE TRINOMIALS

$$a^2 + 2ab + b^2 = (a + b)^2$$
$$a^2 - 2ab + b^2 = (a - b)^2$$

A perfect-square trinomial is a trinomial that is the result of squaring a binomial. How can we recognize a perfect-square trinomial?

1. The first and last terms are *perfect squares.*
2. The middle term is twice the product of the values whose squares are the first and last terms.

EXAMPLE 5 Factor. $x^2 + 6x + 9$

Solution This is a perfect-square trinomial.

1. The first and last terms are perfect squares because $x^2 = (x)^2$ and $9 = (3)^2$.
2. The middle term, $6x$, is twice the product of x and 3.

Since $x^2 + 6x + 9$ is a perfect-square trinomial, we can use the formula

$$a^2 + 2ab + b^2 = (a + b)^2$$

with $a = x$ and $b = 3$. So we have

$$x^2 + 6x + 9 = (x + 3)^2.$$

Practice Problem 5 Factor. $x^2 + 10x + 25$

EXAMPLE 6 Factor. $4x^2 - 20x + 25$

Solution This is a perfect-square trinomial. Note that $20x = 2(2x \cdot 5)$. Also note the negative sign. Thus we have the following.

$$4x^2 - 20x + 25 = (2x - 5)^2 \quad \text{Since } a^2 - 2ab + b^2 = (a - b)^2$$

NOTE TO STUDENT: Fully worked-out solutions to all of the Practice Problems can be found at the back of the text starting at page SP-1

Practice Problem 6 Factor. $25x^2 - 30x + 9$

A polynomial may have more than one variable and its exponents may be higher than 2. The same principles apply.

EXAMPLE 7 Factor.

(a) $49x^2 + 42xy + 9y^2$ **(b)** $36x^4 - 12x^2 + 1$

Solution

(a) This is a perfect-square trinomial. Why?

$$49x^2 + 42xy + 9y^2 = (7x + 3y)^2 \quad \text{Because } 49x^2 = (7x)^2, 9y^2 = (3y)^2, \text{ and } 42xy = 2(7x \cdot 3y)$$

(b) This is a perfect-square trinomial. Why?

$$36x^4 - 12x^2 + 1 = (6x^2 - 1)^2 \quad \text{Because } 36x^4 = (6x^2)^2, 1 = (1)^2, \text{ and } 12x^2 = 2(6x^2 \cdot 1)$$

Practice Problem 7 Factor.

(a) $25x^2 + 60xy + 36y^2$ **(b)** $64x^6 - 48x^3 + 9$

Some polynomials appear to be perfect-square trinomials but are not. They were factored in other ways in Section 5.4.

EXAMPLE 8 Factor. $49x^2 + 35x + 4$

Solution This is *not* a perfect-square trinomial! Although the first and last terms are perfect squares since $(7x)^2 = 49x^2$ and $(2)^2 = 4$, the middle term, $35x$, is not double the product of 2 and $7x$! $35x \neq 28x$! So we must factor by trial and error or by grouping to obtain

$$49x^2 + 35x + 4 = (7x + 4)(7x + 1).$$

Practice Problem 8 Factor. $9x^2 + 15x + 4$

Factoring Out a Common Factor Before Using a Special-Case Formula

For some polynomials, we will first factor out the greatest common factor. Then we will find an opportunity to use the difference-of-two-squares formula or one of the perfect-square trinomial formulas.

Look carefully at example 9. Do you know what is the greatest common factor?

EXAMPLE 9 Factor. $12x^2 - 48$

Solution

$12x^2 - 48 = 12(x^2 - 4)$ First we factor out the greatest common factor, 12.

$= 12(x + 2)(x - 2)$ Then we use the difference-of-two-squares formula, $a^2 - b^2 = (a + b)(a - b)$.

Practice Problem 9 Factor. $20x^2 - 45$

Look carefully at example 10. Do you know what is the greatest common factor?

EXAMPLE 10 Factor. $24x^2 - 72x + 54$

Solution

$24x^2 - 72x + 54 = 6(4x^2 - 12x + 9)$ First we factor out the greatest common factor, 6.

$= 6(2x - 3)^2$ Then we use the perfect-square trinomial formula, $a^2 - 2ab + b^2 = (a - b)^2$.

Practice Problem 10 Factor. $75x^2 - 60x + 12$

5.5 EXERCISES

Student Solutions Manual | CD/ Video | PH Math Tutor Center | MathXL®Tutorials on CD | MathXL® | MyMathLab® | Interactmath.com

Factor by using the difference-of-two-squares formula.

1. $9x^2 - 1$ **2.** $25x^2 - 1$ **3.** $81x^2 - 16$ **4.** $100x^2 - 49$

5. $x^2 - 49$ **6.** $x^2 - 100$ **7.** $4x^2 - 25$ **8.** $16x^2 - 25$

9. $x^2 - 25$ **10.** $x^2 - 36$ **11.** $1 - 16x^2$ **12.** $1 - 64x^2$

13. $16x^2 - 49y^2$ **14.** $25x^2 - 81y^2$ **15.** $36x^2 - 169y^2$ **16.** $64x^2 - 81y^2$

17. $81x^2 - 100$ **18.** $25a^2 - 16$ **19.** $25a^2 - 81b^2$ **20.** $9x^2 - 49y^2$

Factor by using the perfect-square trinomial formula.

21. $9x^2 + 6x + 1$ **22.** $25x^2 + 10x + 1$ **23.** $y^2 - 10y + 25$ **24.** $y^2 - 12y + 36$

25. $36x^2 - 60x + 25$ **26.** $16x^2 - 72x + 81$ **27.** $49x^2 + 28x + 4$ **28.** $25x^2 + 30x + 9$

29. $x^2 + 14x + 49$ **30.** $x^2 + 8x + 16$ **31.** $25x^2 - 40x + 16$ **32.** $49x^2 - 42x + 9$

33. $81x^2 + 36xy + 4y^2$ **34.** $36x^2 + 60xy + 25y^2$ **35.** $25x^2 - 30xy + 9y^2$ **36.** $4x^2 - 28xy + 49y^2$

Mixed Practice

Factor by using either the difference-of-two-squares or the perfect-square trinomial formulas.

37. $16a^2 + 72ab + 81b^2$ **38.** $169a^2 + 26ab + b^2$ **39.** $49x^2 - 42xy + 9y^2$ **40.** $9x^2 - 30xy + 25y^2$

41. $49x^2 + 42x + 9$ **42.** $25x^2 + 40x + 16$ **43.** $49x^2 - 9$ **44.** $9x^2 - 25$

45. $x^4 - 36$ **46.** $x^4 - 49$ **47.** $9x^4 - 12x^2 + 4$ **48.** $36x^4 - 60x^2 + 25$

To Think About

49. In Example 4, first we factored $81x^4 - 1$ as $(9x^2 + 1)(9x^2 - 1)$, and then we factored $9x^2 - 1$ as $(3x + 1)(3x - 1)$. Show why you cannot factor $9x^2 + 1$.

50. What two numbers could replace the b in $25x^2 + bx + 16$ so that the resulting trinomial would be a perfect square? (*Hint*: One number is negative.)

51. What value could you give to c so that $16y^2 - 56y + c$ would become a perfect-square trinomial? Is there only one answer or more than one?

52. Jerome says that he can find two values of b so that $100x^2 + bx - 9$ will be a perfect square. Kesha says there is only one that fits, and Larry says there are none. Who is correct and why?

Factor by first looking for a greatest common factor. See Examples 9 and 10.

53. $16x^2 - 36$

54. $27x^2 - 75$

55. $147x^2 - 3y^2$

56. $16y^2 - 100x^2$

57. $12x^2 - 36x + 27$

58. $125x^2 - 100x + 20$

59. $98x^2 + 84x + 18$

60. $128x^2 + 96x + 18$

Mixed Practice

Factor. Be sure to look for common factors first.

61. $x^2 - 15x + 44$

62. $x^2 - 16x + 63$

63. $2x^2 + 5x - 3$

64. $15x^2 - 11x + 2$

65. $16x^2 - 121$

66. $9x^2 - 100y^2$

67. $9x^2 + 42x + 49$

68. $9x^2 + 30x + 25$

69. $3x^2 + 6x - 45$

70. $4x^2 + 24x + 32$

71. $5x^2 - 80$

72. $13x^2 - 13$

73. $7x^2 + 42x + 63$

74. $6x^2 + 60x + 150$

75. $2x^2 - 32x + 126$

76. $2x^2 - 32x + 110$

Cumulative Review

77. Divide. $(x^3 + x^2 - 2x - 11) \div (x - 2)$

78. Divide. $(6x^3 + 11x^2 - 11x - 20) \div (3x + 4)$

Iguana Diet *The green iguana can reach a length of 6 feet and weigh up to 18 pounds. Of the basic diet of the iguana, 40% should consist of greens such as lettuce, spinach, and parsley; 35% should consist of bulk vegetables such as broccoli, zucchini, and carrots; and 25% should consist of fruit.*

79. If a certain iguana weighing 150 ounces has a daily diet equal to 2% of its body weight, compose a diet for it in ounces that will meet the iguana's one-day requirement for nutrition.

80. If another iguana weighing 120 ounces has a daily diet equal to 3% of its body weight, compose a diet for it in ounces that will meet the iguana's one-day requirement for nutrition.

Altitude *The peak of Mount Washington is at an altitude of 6288 feet above sea level. The altitude A in feet of a car driving down the mountain road from the peak a distance M measured in miles is given by* $A = 6288 - 700M$.

81. What is the altitude of a car that has driven from the mountain peak down a distance of 3.5 miles?

82. A car drives from the peak down the mountain road to a point where the altitude is 2788 feet above sea level. How many miles down the road has the car driven?

5.6 A Brief Review of Factoring

Student Learning Objectives

After studying this section, you will be able to:

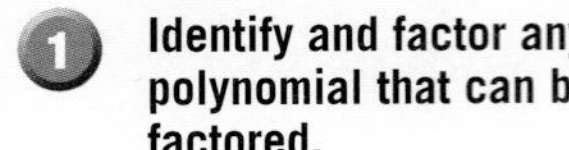

1. **Identify and factor any polynomial that can be factored.**
2. **Determine whether a polynomial is prime.**

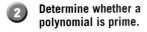

1 Identifying and Factoring Polynomials

Often the various types of factoring problems are all mixed together. We need to be able to identify each type of polynomial quickly. The following table summarizes the information we have learned about factoring.

Many polynomials require more than one factoring method. When you are asked to factor a polynomial, it is expected that you will factor it completely. Usually, the first step is factoring out a common factor; then the next step will become apparent.

Carefully go through each example in the following Factoring Organizer. Be sure you understand each step that is involved.

Factoring Organizer

Number of Terms in the Polynomial	Identifying Name and/or Formula	Example
A. Any number of terms	**Common factor** The terms have a common factor consisting of a number, a variable, or both.	$2x^2 - 16x = 2x(x - 8)$ $3x^2 + 9y - 12 = 3(x^2 + 3y - 4)$ $4x^2y + 2xy^2 - wxy + xyz = xy(4x + 2y - w + z)$
B. Two terms	**Difference of two squares** First and last terms are perfect squares. $a^2 - b^2 = (a + b)(a - b)$	$16x^2 - 1 = (4x + 1)(4x - 1)$ $25y^2 - 9x^2 = (5y + 3x)(5y - 3x)$
C. Three terms	**Perfect-square trinomial** First and last terms are perfect squares. $a^2 + 2ab + b^2 = (a + b)^2$ $a^2 - 2ab + b^2 = (a - b)^2$	$25x^2 - 10x + 1 = (5x - 1)^2$ $16x^2 + 24x + 9 = (4x + 3)^2$
D. Three terms	**Trinomial of the form $x^2 + bx + c$** It starts with x^2. The constants of the two factors are numbers whose product is c and whose sum is b.	$x^2 - 7x + 12 = (x - 3)(x - 4)$ $x^2 + 11x - 26 = (x + 13)(x - 2)$ $x^2 - 8x - 20 = (x - 10)(x + 2)$
E. Three terms	**Trinomial of the form $ax^2 + bx + c$** It starts with ax^2, where a is any number but 1.	Use trial-and-error or the grouping number method to factor $12x^2 - 5x - 2$. 1. The grouping number is -24. 2. The two numbers whose product is -24 and whose sum is -5 are -8 and 3. 3. $12x^2 - 5x - 2 = 12x^2 + 3x - 8x - 2$ $= 3x(4x + 1) - 2(4x + 1)$ $= (4x + 1)(3x - 2)$
F. Four terms	**Factor by grouping** Rearrange the order if the first two terms do not have a common factor.	$wx - 6yz + 2wy - 3xz = wx + 2wy - 3xz - 6yz$ $= w(x + 2y) - 3z(x + 2y)$ $= (x + 2y)(w - 3z)$

EXAMPLE 1 Factor.

(a) $25x^3 - 10x^2 + x$ **(b)** $20x^2y^2 - 45y^2$

(c) $2ax + 4ay + 4x + 8y$ **(d)** $15x^2 - 3x^3 + 18x$

Solution

(a) $25x^3 - 10x^2 + x = x(25x^2 - 10x + 1)$ Factor out the common factor of x. The other factor is a perfect-square trinomial.

$= x(5x - 1)^2$

(b) $20x^2y^2 - 45y^2 = 5y^2(4x^2 - 9)$ Factor out the common factor of $5y^2$. The other factor is a difference of squares.

$= 5y^2(2x - 3)(2x + 3)$

(c) $2ax + 4ay + 4x + 8y = 2[ax + 2ay + 2x + 4y]$ Factor out the common factor of 2.

$= 2[a(x + 2y) + 2(x + 2y)]$ Factor the terms inside the bracket by the grouping method.

$= 2[(x + 2y)(a + 2)]$ Factor out the common factor of $(x + 2y)$.

(d) $15x^2 - 3x^3 + 18x = -3x^3 + 15x^2 + 18x$ Rearrange the terms in descending order of powers of x.

$= -3x(x^2 - 5x - 6)$ Factor out the common factor of $-3x$.

$= -3x(x - 6)(x + 1)$ Factor the trinomial.

Practice Problem 1 Factor. Be careful. These practice problems are mixed.

(a) $3x^2 - 36x + 108$ **(b)** $9x^4y^2 - 9y^2$

(c) $5x^3 - 15x^2y + 10x^2 - 30xy$ **(d)** $12x - 9 - 4x^2$

***NOTE TO STUDENT:** Fully worked-out solutions to all of the Practice Problems can be found at the back of the text starting at page SP-1*

2 Determining Whether a Polynomial Is Prime

Not all polynomials can be factored using the methods in this chapter. If we cannot factor a polynomial by elementary methods, we will identify it as a **prime** polynomial. If, after you have mastered the factoring techniques in this chapter, you encounter a polynomial that you cannot factor with these methods, you should feel comfortable enough to say, "The polynomial cannot be factored with the methods in this chapter, so it is prime," rather than "I can't do it—I give up!"

EXAMPLE 2 Factor, if possible. $x^2 + 6x + 12$

Solution The factors of 12 are

$$(1)(12) \text{ or } (2)(6) \text{ or } (3)(4).$$

None of these pairs add up to 6, the coefficient of the middle term. Thus the problem cannot be factored by the methods of this chapter. It is prime.

Practice Problem 2 Factor. $x^2 - 9x - 8$

EXAMPLE 3 Factor, if possible. $25x^2 + 4$

Solution We have a formula to factor the difference of two squares. There is no way to factor the sum of two squares. That is, $a^2 + b^2$ cannot be factored. Thus

$$25x^2 + 4 \text{ is prime.}$$

Practice Problem 3 Factor, if possible. $25x^2 + 82x + 4$

Student Solutions Manual

CD/ Video

PH Math Tutor Center

MathXL®Tutorials on CD

MathXL®

MyMathLab®

Interactmath.com

Review the six basic types of factoring in the Factoring Organizer on page 334. Each of the six types is included in exercises 1–12. Be sure you can find two of each type.

Factor. Check your answer by multiplying.

1. $6a^2 + 2ab - 3a$

2. $6x^2 - 3xy + 5x$

3. $16x^2 - 25y^2$

4. $64x^2 - 9y^2$

5. $9x^2 - 12xy + 4y^2$

6. $16x^2 + 24xy + 9y^2$

7. $x^2 + 8x + 15$

8. $x^2 + 15x + 54$

9. $15x^2 + 7x - 2$

10. $6x^2 + 13x - 5$

11. $ax - 3cx + 3ay - 9cy$

12. $bx - 2dx + 5by - 10dy$

Mixed Practice

Factor, if possible. Be sure to factor completely. Always factor out the greatest common factor first, if one exists.

13. $y^2 + 14y + 49$

14. $y^2 + 16y + 64$

15. $4x^2 - 12x + 9$

16. $16x^2 - 40x + 25$

17. $2x^2 - 11x + 12$

18. $3x^2 - 10x + 8$

19. $x^2 - 3xy - 70y^2$

20. $x^2 - 6xy - 16y^2$

21. $ax - 5a + 3x - 15$

22. $by + 7b - 6y - 42$

23. $45x - 5x^3$

24. $18y^2 + 3y - 6$

25. $5x^3y^3 - 10x^2y^3 + 5xy^3$

26. $2x^4y - 12x^3y + 18x^2y$

27. $27xyz^2 - 12xy$

28. $12x^2 - 2x - 18x^3$

29. $3x^2 + 6x - 105$

30. $4x^2 - 28x - 72$

31. $3x^3 + 3x^2 - 36x$

32. $7x^2 + 3x - 2$

33. $7x^2 - 2x^4 + 4$

34. $14x^2 - x^3 + 32x$

35. $6x^2 - 3x + 2$

36. $4x^3 + 8x^2 - 60x$

Remove the greatest common factor first. Then continue to factor, if possible.

37. $5x^2 + 10xy - 30y$

38. $7a^2 + 21b - 42$

39. $30x^3 + 3x^2y - 6xy^2$

40. $30x^3 - 25x^2y - 30xy^2$

41. $24x^2 - 58x + 30$

42. $12x^2 - 30x + 12$

To Think About

43. A polynomial that cannot be factored by the methods of this chapter is called ___________.

44. A binomial of the form $x^2 - d$ can be quickly factored or identified as prime. If it can be factored, what is true of the number d?

Cumulative Review

45. ***DVD Player Sale*** A DVD player was reduced in price by \$19.56. This was 20% of the original price. Find the sale price.

46. ***Antiviral Drug*** A major pharmaceutical company is testing a new, powerful antiviral drug. It kills 13 strains of virus every hour. If there are presently 294 live strains of virus in the test container, how many live strains were there 6 hours ago?

Compensation Costs *If you were to compare the relative costs to produce items in different countries, you would need a basis of comparison. Let us assume that it costs \$100 in 1980 in the United States to pay production workers to manufacture some product. In the same year it would cost \$38 to pay production workers in Israel and \$117 to pay production workers in Norway to produce the same object. Use the chart below to compare these hourly compensation costs and answer the following questions:*

47. Suppose the same percent of increase in Israel that was observed from 1990 to 2000 continued from 2000 to 2010. If it cost \$100 for a production worker to produce an item in the United States in 2010, what would it cost for a production worker in Israel in 2010? Round to the nearest dollar.

48. Suppose the same percent of decrease in Norway that was observed from 1990 to 2000 continued from 2000 to 2010. If it cost \$100 for a production worker to produce an item in the United States in 2010, what would it cost for a production worker in Norway in 2010? Round to the nearest dollar.

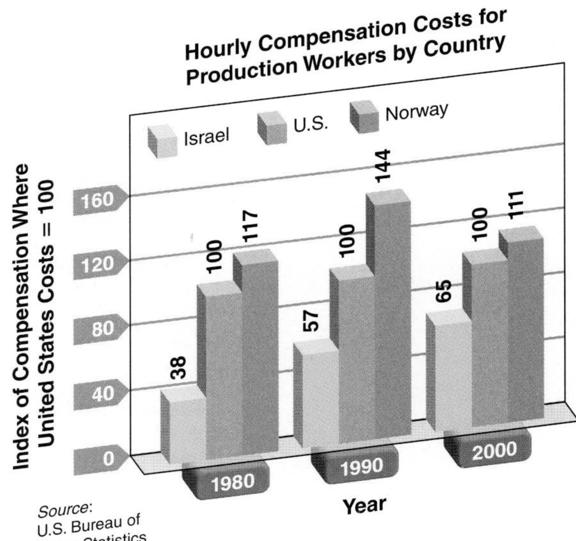

49. Write an equation of the form $y = ax + b$, where x is the number of years since 1990 that will predict the hourly compensation costs (y) for a production worker in Israel. Assume that the change over the period from 1990 to 2000 will continue at the same rate.

50. Write an equation of the form $y = ax + b$, where x is the number of years since 1990 that will predict the hourly compensation costs (y) for a production worker in Norway. Assume that the change over the period from 1990 to 2000 will continue at the same rate.

5.7 Solving Quadratic Equations by Factoring

Student Learning Objectives

After studying this section, you will be able to:

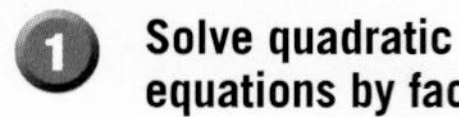

1. **Solve quadratic equations by factoring.**
2. **Use quadratic equations to solve applied problems.**

1 Solving Quadratic Equations by Factoring

In Chapter 2, we learned how to solve linear equations such as $3x + 5 = 0$ by finding the root (or value of x) that satisfied the equation. Now we turn to the question of how to solve equations like $3x^2 + 5x + 2 = 0$. Such equations are called **quadratic equations.** A quadratic equation is a polynomial equation in one variable that contains a variable term of degree 2 and no terms of higher degree.

> The *standard form* of a quadratic equation is $ax^2 + bx + c = 0$, where a, b, and c are real numbers and $a \neq 0$.

In this section, we will study quadratic equations in standard form, where a, b, and c are integers.

Many quadratic equations have two real number solutions (also called real **roots**). But how can we find them? The most direct approach is the factoring method. This method depends on a very powerful property.

> **ZERO FACTOR PROPERTY**
>
> If $a \cdot b = 0$, then $a = 0$ or $b = 0$.

Notice the word *or* in the zero factor property. When we make a statement in mathematics using this word, we intend it to mean *one or the other or both*. Therefore, the zero factor property states that if the product $a \cdot b$ is zero, then a can equal zero or b can equal zero or *both a and b* can equal zero. We can use this principle to solve a quadratic equation. Before you start, make sure that the equation is in standard form.

> 1. Make sure the equation is set equal to zero.
> 2. Factor, if possible, the quadratic expression that equals 0.
> 3. Set each factor containing a variable equal to 0.
> 4. Solve the resulting equations to find each root.
> 5. Check each root.

EXAMPLE 1 Solve the equation to find the two roots. $3x^2 + 5x + 2 = 0$

Solution

$$3x^2 + 5x + 2 = 0 \quad \text{The equation is in standard form.}$$

$$(3x + 2)(x + 1) = 0 \quad \text{Factor the quadratic expression.}$$

$$3x + 2 = 0 \qquad x + 1 = 0 \quad \text{Set each factor equal to 0.}$$

$$3x = -2 \qquad x = -1 \quad \text{Solve the equations to find the two roots.}$$

$$x = -\frac{2}{3}$$

The two roots (that is, solutions) are $-\frac{2}{3}$ and -1.

Check. We can determine if the two numbers $-\frac{2}{3}$ and -1 are solutions to the equation. Substitute $-\frac{2}{3}$ for x in the *original equation*. If an identity results, $-\frac{2}{3}$ is a solution. Do the same for -1.

$$\begin{aligned} 3x^2 + 5x + 2 &= 0 \\ 3\left(-\frac{2}{3}\right)^2 + 5\left(-\frac{2}{3}\right) + 2 &\stackrel{?}{=} 0 \\ 3\left(\frac{4}{9}\right) + 5\left(-\frac{2}{3}\right) + 2 &\stackrel{?}{=} 0 \\ \frac{4}{3} - \frac{10}{3} + 2 &\stackrel{?}{=} 0 \\ \frac{4}{3} - \frac{10}{3} + \frac{6}{3} &\stackrel{?}{=} 0 \\ 0 &= 0 \quad \checkmark \end{aligned}$$

$$\begin{aligned} 3x^2 + 5x + 2 &= 0 \\ 3(-1)^2 + 5(-1) + 2 &\stackrel{?}{=} 0 \\ 3(1) + 5(-1) + 2 &\stackrel{?}{=} 0 \\ 3 - 5 + 2 &\stackrel{?}{=} 0 \\ -2 + 2 &\stackrel{?}{=} 0 \\ 0 &= 0 \quad \checkmark \end{aligned}$$

Thus $-\frac{2}{3}$ and -1 are both roots of the equation $3x^2 + 5x + 2 = 0$.

Practice Problem 1 Solve the equation by factoring to find the two roots and check. $10x^2 - x - 2 = 0$

NOTE TO STUDENT: Fully worked-out solutions to all of the Practice Problems can be found at the back of the text starting at page SP-1

EXAMPLE 2 Solve the equation to find the two roots. $2x^2 + 13x - 7 = 0$

Solution

$$2x^2 + 13x - 7 = 0 \quad \text{The equation is in standard form.}$$
$$(2x - 1)(x + 7) = 0 \quad \text{Factor.}$$
$$2x - 1 = 0 \qquad x + 7 = 0 \quad \text{Set each factor equal to 0.}$$
$$2x = 1 \qquad x = -7 \quad \text{Solve the equations to find the two roots.}$$
$$x = \frac{1}{2}$$

The two roots are $\frac{1}{2}$ and -7.

Check. If $x = \frac{1}{2}$, then we have the following.

$$2\left(\frac{1}{2}\right)^2 + 13\left(\frac{1}{2}\right) - 7 = 2\left(\frac{1}{4}\right) + 13\left(\frac{1}{2}\right) - 7$$
$$= \frac{1}{2} + \frac{13}{2} - \frac{14}{2} = 0 \quad \checkmark$$

If $x = -7$, then we have the following.

$$2(-7)^2 + 13(-7) - 7 = 2(49) + 13(-7) - 7$$
$$= 98 - 91 - 7 = 0 \quad \checkmark$$

Thus $\frac{1}{2}$ and -7 are both roots of the equation $2x^2 + 13x - 7 = 0$.

Practice Problem 2 Solve the equation to find the two roots. $3x^2 + 11x - 4 = 0$

If the quadratic equation $ax^2 + bx + c = 0$ has no visible constant term, then $c = 0$. All such quadratic equations can be solved by factoring out a common factor and then using the zero factor property to obtain two solutions that are real numbers.

EXAMPLE 3 Solve the equation to find the two roots. $7x^2 - 3x = 0$

Solution

$7x^2 - 3x = 0$ The equation is in standard form. Here $c = 0$.

$x(7x - 3) = 0$ Factor out the common factor.

$x = 0 \quad 7x - 3 = 0$ Set each factor equal to 0 by the zero factor property.

$7x = 3$ Solve the equations to find the two roots.

$x = \frac{3}{7}$

The two roots are 0 and $\frac{3}{7}$.

Check. Verify that 0 and $\frac{3}{7}$ are the roots of $7x^2 - 3x = 0$.

***NOTE TO STUDENT:** Fully worked-out solutions to all of the Practice Problems can be found at the back of the text starting at page SP-1*

Practice Problem 3 Solve the equation to find the two roots. $7x^2 + 11x = 0$

If the quadratic equation is not in standard form, we use the same basic algebraic methods we studied in Sections 2.1–2.3 to place the terms on one side and zero on the other so that we can use the zero factor property.

EXAMPLE 4 Solve. $x^2 = 12 - x$

Solution

$x^2 = 12 - x$ The equation is not in standard form.

$x^2 + x - 12 = 0$ Add x and -12 to both sides of the equation so that the left side is equal to zero; we can now factor.

$(x - 3)(x + 4) = 0$ Factor.

$x - 3 = 0 \quad x + 4 = 0$ Set each factor equal to 0 by the zero factor property.

$x = 3 \quad x = -4$ Solve the equations for x.

Check. If $x = 3$: $(3)^2 \stackrel{?}{=} 12 - 3$; $9 \stackrel{?}{=} 12 - 3$; $9 = 9$ ✓

If $x = -4$: $(-4)^2 \stackrel{?}{=} 12 - (-4)$; $16 \stackrel{?}{=} 12 + 4$; $16 = 16$ ✓

Both roots check.

Practice Problem 4 Solve. $x^2 - 6x + 4 = -8 + x$

EXAMPLE 5 Solve. $\frac{x^2 - x}{2} = 6$

Solution We must first clear the fractions from the equation.

$2\left(\frac{x^2 - x}{2}\right) = 2(6)$ Multiply each side by 2.

$x^2 - x = 12$ Simplify.

$x^2 - x - 12 = 0$ Place in standard form.

$(x - 4)(x + 3) = 0$ Factor.

$x - 4 = 0 \quad x + 3 = 0$ Set each factor equal to zero.

$x = 4 \quad x = -3$ Solve the equations for x.

The check is left to the student.

Practice Problem 5 Solve. $\frac{2x^2 - 7x}{3} = 5$

2 Using Quadratic Equations to Solve Applied Problems

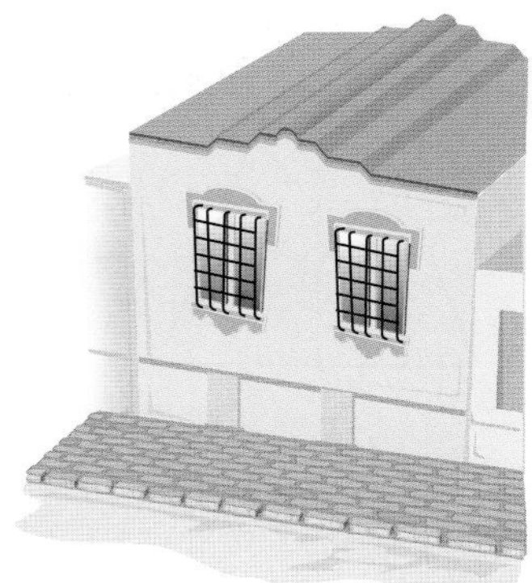

Certain types of word problems—for example, some geometry applications—lead to quadratic equations. We'll show how to solve such word problems in this section.

It is particularly important to check the apparent solutions to the quadratic equation with conditions stated in the word problem. Often a particular solution to the quadratic equation will be eliminated by the conditions of the word problem.

EXAMPLE 6 Carlos lives in Mexico City. He has a rectangular brick walkway in front of his house. The length of the walkway is 3 meters longer than twice the width. The area of the walkway is 44 square meters. Find the length and width of the rectangular walkway.

Solution

1. ***Understand the problem.***
   Draw a picture.

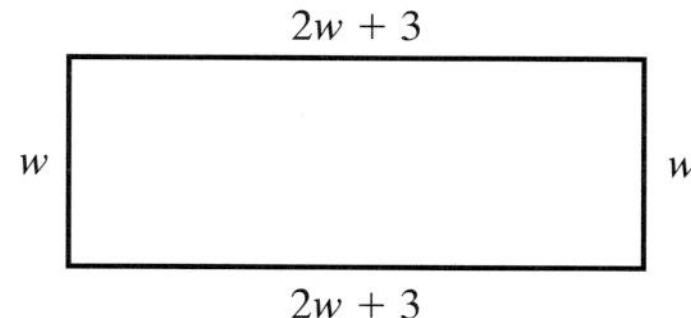

$$\text{Let } w = \text{the width in meters}$$
$$\text{Then } 2w + 3 = \text{the length in meters}$$

2. ***Write an equation.***

$$\text{area} = (\text{width})(\text{length})$$
$$44 = w(2w + 3)$$

3. ***Solve and state the answer.***

$44 = w(2w + 3)$

$44 = 2w^2 + 3w$ Remove parentheses.

$0 = 2w^2 + 3w - 44$ Subtract 44 from both sides.

$0 = (2w + 11)(w - 4)$ Factor.

$2w + 11 = 0 \quad w - 4 = 0$ Set each factor equal to 0.

$2w = -11 \quad w = 4$ Simplify and solve.

$w = -5\frac{1}{2}$ Although $-5\frac{1}{2}$ is a solution to the quadratic equation, it is not a valid solution to the word problem. It would not make sense to have a rectangle with a negative number as a width.

Since $w = 4$, the width of the walkway is 4 meters. The length is $2w + 3$, so we have $2(4) + 3 = 8 + 3 = 11$. Thus the length of the walkway is 11 meters.

4. ***Check.*** Is the length 3 meters more than twice the width?

$$11 \stackrel{?}{=} 3 + 2(4) \qquad 11 = 3 + 8 \checkmark$$

Is the area of the rectangle 44 square meters?

$$4 \times 11 \stackrel{?}{=} 44 \qquad 44 = 44 \checkmark$$

Practice Problem 6 The length of a rectangle is 2 meters longer than triple the width. The area of the rectangle is 85 square meters. Find the length and width of the rectangle.

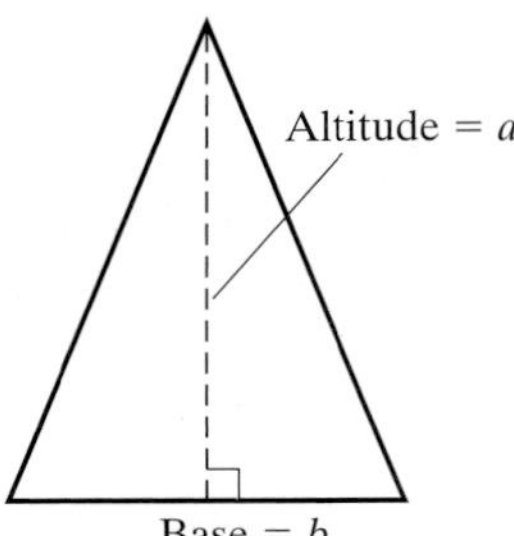

EXAMPLE 7

The top of a local cable television tower has several small triangular reflectors. The area of each triangle is 49 square centimeters. The altitude of each triangle is 7 centimeters longer than the base. Find the altitude and the base of one of the triangles.

Solution

Let b = the length of the base in centimeters
$b + 7$ = the length of the altitude in centimeters

To find the area of a triangle, we use

$$\text{area} = \frac{1}{2}(\text{altitude})(\text{base}) = \frac{1}{2}ab = \frac{ab}{2}.$$

$\frac{ab}{2} = 49$	Write an equation.
$\frac{(b+7)(b)}{2} = 49$	Substitute the expressions for altitude and base.
$\frac{b^2 + 7b}{2} = 49$	Simplify.
$b^2 + 7b = 98$	Multiply each side of the equation by 2.
$b^2 + 7b - 98 = 0$	Place the quadratic equation in standard form.
$(b - 7)(b + 14) = 0$	Factor.
$b - 7 = 0 \quad b + 14 = 0$	Set each factor equal to zero.
$b = 7 \quad b = -14$	Solve the equations for b.

We cannot have a base of -14 centimeters, so we reject the negative answer. The only possible solution is 7. So the base is 7 centimeters. The altitude is $b + 7 = 7 + 7 = 14$. The altitude is 14 centimeters. The triangular reflector has a base of 7 centimeters and an altitude of 14 centimeters.

Check. When you do the check, answer the following two questions.

1. Is the altitude 7 centimeters longer than the base?
2. Is the area of a triangle with a base of 7 centimeters and an altitude of 14 centimeters actually 49 square centimeters?

***NOTE TO STUDENT:** Fully worked-out solutions to all of the Practice Problems can be found at the back of the text starting at page SP-1*

Practice Problem 7 A triangle has an area of 35 square centimeters. The altitude of the triangle is 3 centimeters shorter than the base. Find the altitude and the base of the triangle.

Many problems in the sciences require the use of quadratic equations. You will study these in more detail if you take a course in physics or calculus in college. Often a quadratic equation is given as part of the problem.

When an object is thrown upward, its height (S) in meters is given, approximately, by the quadratic equation

$$S = -5t^2 + vt + h.$$

The letter h represents the initial height in meters. The letter v represents the initial velocity of the object thrown. The letter t represents the time in seconds starting from the time the object is thrown.

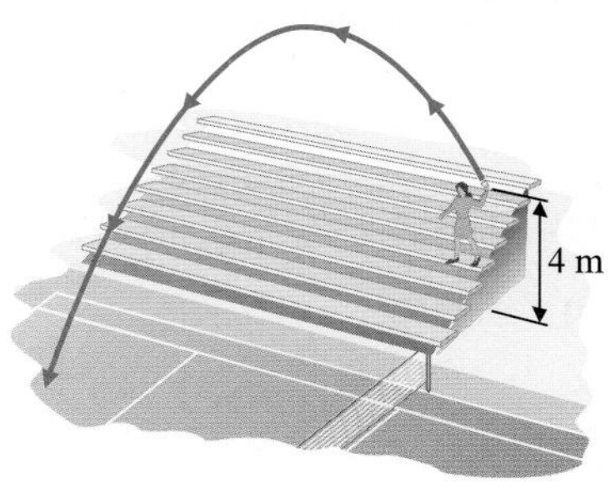

EXAMPLE 8 A tennis ball is thrown upward with an initial velocity of 8 meters/second. Suppose that the initial height above the ground is 4 meters. At what time t will the ball hit the ground?

Solution In this case $S = 0$ since the ball will hit the ground. The initial upward velocity is $v = 8$ meters/second. The initial height is 4 meters, so $h = 4$.

$S = -5t^2 + vt + h$	Write an equation.
$0 = -5t^2 + 8t + 4$	Substitute all values into the equation.
$5t^2 - 8t - 4 = 0$	Isolate the terms on the left side. (Most students can factor more readily if the squared variable is positive.)
$(5t + 2)(t - 2) = 0$	Factor.
$5t + 2 = 0 \qquad t - 2 = 0$	Set each factor = 0.
$5t = -2 \qquad t = 2$	Solve the equations for t.
$t = -\dfrac{2}{5}$	

We want a positive time t in seconds; thus we do not use $t = -\frac{2}{5}$. Therefore, the ball will strike the ground 2 seconds after it is thrown.

Check. Verify the solution.

Practice Problem 8 A Mexican cliff diver does a dive from a cliff 45 meters above the ocean. This constitutes free fall, so the initial velocity is $v = 0$, and if there is no upward spring, then $h = 45$ meters. How long will it be until he breaks the water's surface?

5.7 Exercises

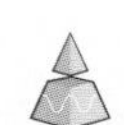

Student Solutions Manual | CD/ Video | PH Math Tutor Center | MathXL®Tutorials on CD | MathXL® | MyMathLab® | Interactmath.com

Using the factoring method, solve for the roots of each quadratic equation. Be sure to place the equation in standard form before factoring. Check your answers.

1. $x^2 - 4x - 21 = 0$

2. $x^2 - x - 20 = 0$

3. $x^2 + 16x + 39 = 0$

4. $x^2 + 11x + 18 = 0$

5. $2x^2 - 7x + 6 = 0$

6. $2x^2 - 11x + 12 = 0$

7. $6x^2 - 13x = -6$

8. $10x^2 + 19x = 15$

9. $x^2 + 13x = 0$

10. $8x^2 - x = 0$

11. $8x^2 = 72$

12. $9x^2 = 81$

13. $5x^2 + 3x = 8x$

14. $6x^2 - 4x = 3x$

15. $6x^2 = 16x - 8$

16. $24x^2 = -10x + 4$

17. $(x - 5)(x + 2) = -4(x + 1)$

18. $(x - 5)(x + 4) = 2(x - 5)$

19. $4x^2 - 3x + 1 = -7x$

20. $9x^2 - 2x + 4 = 10x$

21. $\frac{x^2}{2} - 8 + x = -8$

22. $4 + \frac{x^2}{3} = 2x + 4$

23. $\frac{x^2 + 7x}{4} = -3$

24. $\frac{x^2 + 5x}{6} = 4$

25. $\frac{10x^2 - 25x}{12} = 5$

26. $\frac{12x^2 - 4x}{5} = 8$

To Think About

27. Why can an equation in standard form with $c = 0$ (that is, an equation of the form $ax^2 + bx = 0$) always be solved?

28. Martha solved $(x + 3)(x - 2) = 14$ as follows:

$$x + 3 = 14 \quad \text{or} \quad x - 2 = 14$$
$$x = 11 \quad \text{or} \quad x = 16$$

Josette said this had to be wrong because these values do not check. Explain what is wrong with Martha's method.

Applications

▲ **29.** ***Geometry*** The area of a rectangular garden is 140 square meters. The width is 3 meters longer than one-half of the length. Find the length and the width of the garden.

▲ **30.** ***Geometry*** The area of a triangular sign is 33 square meters. The base of the triangle is 1 meter less than double the altitude. Find the altitude and the base of the sign.

Forming Groups *Suppose the number of students in a mathematics class is x. The teacher insists that each student participate in group work each class. The number of possible groups is:*

$$G = \frac{x^2 - 3x + 2}{2}$$

31. The class has 13 students. How many possible groups are there?

32. Three students withdraw from the class. How many fewer groups can be formed?

33. A teacher claims each student could be in 36 different groups. How many students are there?

34. The teacher wants each student to participate in a different group each day. There are 45 class days in the semester. How many students must be in the class?

Falling Object *Use the following information for exercises 35 and 36. When an object is thrown upward, its height (S), in meters, is given (approximately) by the quadratic equation*

$$S = -5t^2 + vt + h,$$

where v = the upward initial velocity in meters/second,

t = the time of flight in seconds, and

h = the height above level ground from which the object is thrown.

35. Johnny is standing on a platform 6 meters high and throws a ball straight up as high as he can at a velocity of 13 meters/second. At what time t will the ball hit the ground? How far from the ground is the ball after 2 seconds have elapsed from the time of the throw? (Assume that the ball is 6 meters from the ground when it leaves Johnny's hand.)

36. You are standing on the edge of a cliff near Acapulco, overlooking the ocean. The place where you stand is 180 meters from the ocean. You drop a pebble into the water. ("Dropping" the pebble implies that there is no initial velocity, so $v = 0$.) How many seconds will it take to hit the water? How far has the pebble dropped after 3 seconds?

37. ***Overtime Costs*** Paying overtime to employees can be very expensive, but if profits are realized, it is worth putting a shift on overtime. In a high-tech helicopter company, the extra hourly cost in dollars for producing x additional helicopters is given by the cost equation $C = 2x^2 - 7x$. If the extra hourly cost is \$15, how many additional helicopters are produced?

38. ***Producing Power*** A boat generator on a Gloucester fishing boat is required to produce 64 watts of power. The amount of current I measured in amperes needed to produce the power for this generator is given by the equation $P = 40I - 4I^2$. What is the *minimum* number of amperes required to produce the necessary power?

Internal Phone Calls *The technology and communication office of a local company has set up a new telephone system so that each employee has a separate telephone and extension number. They are studying the possible number of telephone calls that can be made from people in the office to other people in the office. They have discovered that the total number of possible telephone calls T is described by the equation $T = 0.5(x^2 - x)$, where x is the number of people in the office. Use this information to answer exercises 39–42.*

39. If 70 people are presently employed at the office, how many possible telephone calls can be made between these 70 people?

40. If the company hires 10 new employees next year, how many possible telephone calls can be made between the 80 people that will be employed next year?

41. One Saturday, only a small number of employees were working at the office. It has been determined that on that day, a total of 153 different phone calls could have been made from people working in the office to other people working in the office. How many people worked on that Saturday?

42. On the day after Thanksgiving, only a small number of employees were working at the office. It has been determined that on that day, a total of 105 different phone calls could have been made from people working in the office to other people working in the office. How many people worked on the day after Thanksgiving?

Cumulative Review

Simplify.

43. $(2x^2y^3)(-5x^3y)$

44. $(3a^4b^5)(4a^6b^8)$

45. $\dfrac{21a^5b^{10}}{-14ab^{12}}$

46. $\dfrac{18x^3y^6}{54x^8y^{10}}$

Putting Your Skills to Work

The Mathematics of Instant Replay

In the National Football League the outcome of the call of game officials can be challenged and reviewed by looking at a video replay of the play that is being considered. Over the years since 1999 the number of replay reviews during the regular season has been increasing steadily. The number of reversals (where the original decision of game officials has been overturned after careful review) has been increasing also.

Consider the following chart which displays the data for a five-year period.

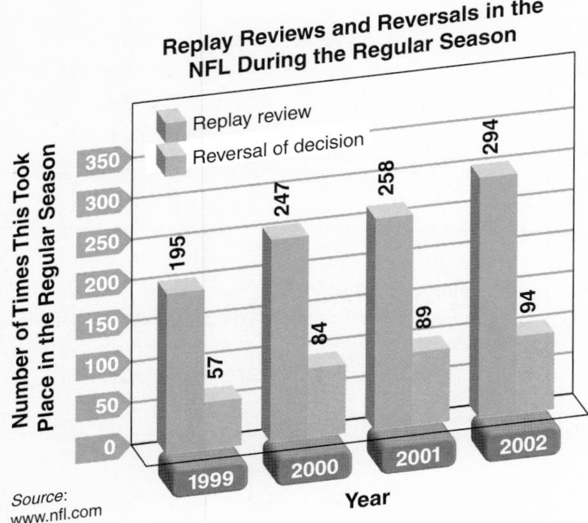

4. Find the percentage of reversals in 2001. Find the percentage of reversals in 2002. By how much did the percentage change? (Round your answer to nearest whole percent.)

Problems for Individual Investigation and Analysis

1. If the same pattern of yearly increase in the number of replay reviews continues from 2002 to 2005 that occurred from 2001 to 2002, how many replay reviews would you expect during the 2005 playing season?

2. If the same pattern of yearly increase in the number of reversals continues from 2002 to 2006 that occurred from 2001 to 2002, how many reversals of an official game decision would you expect during the 2006 playing season?

3. Find the percentage of reversals in 1999. Find the percentage of reversals in 2000. By how much did the percentage change? (Round your answer to nearest whole percent.)

Problems for Group Investigation and Cooperative Learning

5. A possible predictor of the number of replays (y) for a given NFL season is given by the equation $y = 30x + 294$, where x is the number of years after 2002. Use that equation to predict the number of replays in the 2004 season.

6. A possible predictor of the number of reversals (y) for a given NFL season is given by the equation $y = 11x + 99$, where x is the number of years after 2002. Use that equation to predict the number of reversals in the 2005 season.

7. Write the equation in Exercise 5 in factored form.

8. Write the equation in Exercise 6 in factored form.

Chapter 5 Organizer

Topic	Procedure	Examples
A. Common factor, p. 304.	Factor out the largest common factor from each term.	$2x^2 - 2x = 2x(x - 1)$ $3a^2 + 3ab - 12a = 3a(a + b - 4)$ $8x^4y - 24x^3 = 8x^3(xy - 3)$
Special cases ***B. Difference of squares, p. 328.*** ***C. Perfect-square trinomials, p. 329.***	If you recognize the special cases, you will be able to factor quickly. $a^2 - b^2 = (a + b)(a - b)$ $a^2 + 2ab + b^2 = (a + b)^2$ $a^2 - 2ab + b^2 = (a - b)^2$	$25x^2 - 36y^2 = (5x + 6y)(5x - 6y)$ $16x^4 - 1 = (4x^2 + 1)(2x + 1)(2x - 1)$ $25x^2 + 10x + 1 = (5x + 1)^2$ $49x^2 - 42xy + 9y^2 = (7x - 3y)^2$
D. Trinomials of the form $x^2 + bx + c$, p. 314.	Factor trinomials of the form $x^2 + bx + c$ by asking what two numbers have a product of c and a sum of b. If each term of the trinomial has a common factor, factor it out as the first step.	$x^2 - 18x + 77 = (x - 7)(x - 11)$ $x^2 + 7x - 18 = (x + 9)(x - 2)$ $5x^2 - 10x - 40 = 5(x^2 - 2x - 8)$ $= 5(x - 4)(x + 2)$
E. Trinomials of the form $ax^2 + bx + c$, where $a \neq 1$, p. 321.	Factor trinomials of the form $ax^2 + bx + c$ by the grouping number method or by the trial-and-error method.	$6x^2 + 11x - 10$ Grouping number $= -60$ Two numbers whose product is -60 and whose sum is $+11$ are $+15$ and -4. $6x^2 + 15x - 4x - 10 = 3x(2x + 5) - 2(2x + 5)$ $= (2x + 5)(3x - 2)$
F. Four terms. Factor by grouping, p. 302.	Rearrange the terms if necessary so that the first two terms have a common factor. Then factor out the common factors. $ax + ay - bx - by = a(x + y) - b(x + y)$ $= (a - b)(x + y)$	$2ax^2 + 21 + 3a + 14x^2$ $= 2ax^2 + 14x^2 + 3a + 21$ $= 2x^2(a + 7) + 3(a + 7)$ $= (a + 7)(2x^2 + 3)$
Prime polynomials, p. 335.	A polynomial that is not factorable is called prime.	$x^2 + y^2$ is prime. $x^2 + 5x + 7$ is prime.
Multistep factoring, p. 334.	Many problems require two or three steps of factoring. Always try to factor out the greatest common factor as the first step.	$3x^2 - 21x + 36 = 3(x^2 - 7x + 12)$ $= 3(x - 4)(x - 3)$ $2x^3 - x^2 - 6x = x(2x^2 - x - 6)$ $= x(2x + 3)(x - 2)$ $25x^3 - 49x = x(25x^2 - 49)$ $= x(5x + 7)(5x - 7)$ $8x^2 - 24x + 18 = 2(4x^2 - 12x + 9)$ $= 2(2x - 3)^2$
Solving quadratic equations by factoring, p. 338.	**1.** Write as $ax^2 + bx + c = 0$. **2.** Factor. **3.** Set each factor equal to 0. **4.** Solve the resulting equations.	Solve: $3x^2 + 5x = 2$ $3x^2 + 5x - 2 = 0$ $(3x - 1)(x + 2) = 0$ $3x - 1 = 0$ or $x + 2 = 0$ $x = \frac{1}{3}$ or $x = -2$

Topic	Procedure	Examples
Using quadratic equations to solve applied problems, p. 341.	Some word problems, like those involving the product of two numbers, area, and formulas with a squared variable, can be solved using the factoring methods we have shown.	The length of a rectangle is 4 less than three times the width. Find the length and width if the area is 55 square inches. Let w = width. Then $3w - 4$ = length. $55 = w(3w - 4)$ $55 = 3w^2 - 4w$ $0 = 3w^2 - 4w - 55$ $0 = (3w + 11)(w - 5)$ $w = -\frac{11}{3}$ or $w = 5$ $-\frac{11}{3}$ is not a valid solution. Thus width = 5 inches and length = 11 inches.

Chapter 5 Review Problems

Section 5.1

Factor out the greatest common factor.

1. $12x^3 - 20x^2y$

2. $10x^3 - 35x^3y$

3. $7x^2y - 14xy^2 - 21x^3y^3$

4. $50a^4b^5 - 25a^4b^4 + 75a^5b^5$

5. $3a^3 + 6a^2 - 9ab + 12a$

6. $2x - 4y + 6z + 12$

7. $2a(a + 3b) - 5(a + 3b)$

8. $15x^3y + 6xy^2 + 3xy$

Section 5.2

Factor by grouping.

9. $3ax - 7a - 6x + 14$

10. $a^2 + 5ab - 4a - 20b$

11. $x^2y + 3y - 2x^2 - 6$

12. $30ax - 15ay + 42x - 21y$

13. $15x^2 - 3x + 10x - 2$

14. $30w^2 - 18w + 5wz - 3z$

Section 5.3

Factor completely. Be sure to factor out any common factors as your first step.

15. $x^2 - 2x - 35$

16. $x^2 - 10x + 24$

17. $x^2 + 14x + 48$

18. $x^2 + 8xy + 15y^2$

19. $x^4 + 13x^2 + 42$

20. $x^4 - 2x^2 - 35$

21. $6x^2 + 30x + 36$

22. $3x^2 + 39x + 36$

23. $2x^2 - 28x + 96$

24. $4x^2 - 44x + 120$

Section 5.4

Factor completely. Be sure to factor out any common factors as your first step.

25. $4x^2 + 7x - 15$

26. $12x^2 + 11x - 5$

27. $15x^2 + 7x - 4$

28. $6x^2 - 13x + 6$

29. $2x^2 - x - 3$

30. $3x^2 + 2x - 8$

31. $20x^2 + 48x - 5$

32. $20x^2 + 21x - 5$

33. $6a^2 + 11a - 10$

34. $6a^2 - 19a + 10$

35. $6x^2 + 4x - 10$

36. $6x^2 - 4x - 10$

37. $4x^2 - 26x + 30$

38. $4x^2 - 20x - 144$

39. $12x^2 - 22x - 20$

40. $18x^2 + 51x - 42$

41. $6x^2 - 19xy + 10y^2$

42. $6x^2 - 32xy + 10y^2$

Section 5.5

Factor these special cases. Be sure to factor out any common factors.

43. $49x^2 - y^2$

44. $16x^2 - 36y^2$

45. $25x^2 + 30x + 9$

46. $49x^2 - 28x + 4$

47. $25x^2 - 36$

48. $100x^2 - 9$

49. $y^2 - 36x^2$

50. $9y^2 - 25x^2$

51. $36x^2 + 12x + 1$

52. $25x^2 - 20x + 4$

53. $16x^2 - 24xy + 9y^2$

54. $49x^2 - 28xy + 4y^2$

55. $2x^2 - 18$

56. $3x^2 - 75$

57. $28x^2 + 140x + 175$

58. $72x^2 - 192x + 128$

Section 5.6

If possible, factor each polynomial completely. If a polynomial cannot be factored, state that it is prime.

59. $4x^2 - 9y^2$

60. $x^2 + 6x + 9$

61. $x^2 - 9x + 18$

62. $x^2 + 13x - 30$

63. $6x^2 + x - 7$

64. $10x^2 + x - 2$

65. $24x - 60$

66. $8x^2y^2 - 4xy$

67. $50x^3y^2 + 30x^2y^2 - 10x^2y^2$

68. $26a^3b - 13ab^3 + 52a^2b^4$

69. $x^3 - 16x^2 + 64x$

70. $2x^2 + 40x + 200$

71. $3x^2 - 18x + 27$

72. $25x^3 - 60x^2 + 36x$

73. $7x^2 - 9x - 10$

74. $4x^2 - 13x - 12$

75. $9x^3y - 4xy^3$

76. $3x^3a^3 - 11x^4a^2 - 20x^5a$

77. $12a^2 + 14ab - 10b^2$

78. $121a^2 + 66ab + 9b^2$

79. $7a - 7 - ab + b$

Mixed Practice

If possible, factor each polynomial completely. If a polynomial cannot be factored, state that it is prime.

80. $8b - 10 + 28bc - 35c$

81. $18b - 21 + 14x - 12bx$

82. $5xb - 35x + 4by - 28y$

83. $2a^2x - 15ax + 7x$

84. $x^5 - 17x^3 + 16x$

85. $x^4 - 81y^{12}$

86. $6x^4 - x^2 - 15$

87. $28yz - 16xyz + x^2yz$

88. $12x^3 + 17x^2 + 6x$

89. $16w^2 - 2w - 5$

90. $12w^2 - 12w + 3$

91. $4y^3 + 10y^2 - 6y$

92. $10y^2 + 33y - 7$

93. $8y^{10} - 16y^8$

94. $9x^4 - 144$

95. $x^2 - 6x + 12$

96. $8x^2 - 19x - 6$

97. $8y^5 + 4y^3 - 60y$

98. $9xy^2 + 3xy - 42x$

99. $16x^4y^2 - 56x^2y + 49$

100. $128x^3y - 2xy$

101. $2ax + 5a - 10b - 4bx$

102. $2x^3 - 9 + x^2 - 18x$

Section 5.7

Solve the following equations by factoring.

103. $x^2 - 3x - 18 = 0$

104. $2x^2 + 5x - 12 = 0$

105. $5x^2 = 2x - 7x^2$

106. $5x^2 - x = 4x^2 + 12$

107. $2x^2 + 9x - 5 = 0$

108. $x^2 + 11x + 24 = 0$

109. $x^2 + 14x + 45 = 0$

110. $5x^2 = 7x + 6$

111. $3x^2 + 6x = 2x^2 - 9$

112. $4x^2 + 9x - 9 = 0$

113. $5x^2 - 11x + 2 = 0$

Solve.

▲ **114.** ***Geometry*** The area of a triangle is 35 square centimeters. The base is 3 centimeters longer than the altitude of the triangle. Find the length of the base and the altitude.

▲ **115.** ***Geometry*** The area of a rectangle is 105 square feet. The length of the rectangle is 1 foot longer than double the width. Find the length and width of the rectangle.

116. ***Rocket Height*** The height in feet that a model rocket attains is given by $h = -16t^2 + 80t + 96$, where t is the time measured in seconds. How many seconds will it take until the rocket finally reaches the ground? (*Hint:* At ground level $h = 0$.)

117. ***Output Power*** An electronic technician is working with a 100-volt electric generator. The output power of the generator is given by the equation $p = -5x^2 + 100x$, where x is the amount of current measured in amperes and p is measured in watts. The technician wants to find the value for x when the power is 480 watts. Can you find the two answers?

How Am I Doing? Chapter 5 Test

Remember to use your Chapter Test Prep Video CD to see the worked-out solutions to the test problems you want to review.

If possible, factor each polynomial completely. If a polynomial cannot be factored, state that it is prime.

1. $x^2 + 12x - 28$

2. $16x^2 - 81$

3. $10x^2 + 27x + 5$

4. $9a^2 - 30a + 25$

5. $7x - 9x^2 + 14xy$

6. $10xy + 15by - 8x - 12b$

7. $6x^3 - 20x^2 + 16x$

8. $5a^2c - 11ac + 2c$

9. $81x^2 - 100$

10. $9x^2 - 15x + 4$

11. $20x^2 - 45$

12. $36x^2 + 1$

13. $3x^3 + 11x^2 + 10x$

14. $60xy^2 - 20x^2y - 45y^3$

15. $81x^2 - 1$

16. $81y^4 - 1$

17. $2ax + 6a - 5x - 15$

18. $aw^2 - 8b + 2bw^2 - 4a$

19. $3x^2 - 3x - 90$

20. $2x^3 - x^2 - 15x$

Solve.

21. $x^2 + 14x + 45 = 0$

22. $14 + 3x(x + 2) = -7x$

23. $2x^2 + x - 10 = 0$

24. $x^2 - 3x - 28 = 0$

Solve using a quadratic equation.

▲ **25.** The park service is studying a rectangular piece of land that has an area of 91 square miles. The length of this piece of land is 1 mile shorter than double the width. Find the length and width of this rectangular piece of land.

1. ______
2. ______
3. ______
4. ______
5. ______
6. ______
7. ______
8. ______
9. ______
10. ______
11. ______
12. ______
13. ______
14. ______
15. ______
16. ______
17. ______
18. ______
19. ______
20. ______
21. ______
22. ______
23. ______
24. ______
25. ______

Cumulative Test for Chapters 0–5

1. ______
2. ______
3. ______
4. ______
5. ______
6. ______
7. ______
8. ______
9. ______
10. ______
11. ______
12. ______
13. ______
14. ______
15. ______
16. ______
17. ______
18. ______
19. ______
20. ______
21. ______
22. ______
23. ______
24. ______

Approximately one-half of this test covers the content of Chapters 0–4. The remainder covers the content of Chapter 5.

1. What % of 480 is 72?

2. What is 13% of 3.8?

Simplify.

3. $4.3 - 2(3.4 - 7.2) - 6.1$

4. $(-2x^3y^4)(-4xy^6)$

5. $(-3)^4$

6. $(9x - 4)(3x + 2)$

7. $(2x^2 - 6x + 1)(x - 3)$

Solve.

8. $3x - 4 \geq 6x + 5$

9. $3x - (7 - 5x) = 3(4x - 5)$

10. $\frac{1}{2}x - 3 = \frac{1}{4}(3x + 3)$

11. Solve for q: $3(q + 1) = 8q - p$

Factor each polynomial completely. If a polynomial cannot be factored, state that it is prime.

12. $6x^2 - 5x + 1$

13. $6x^2 + 5x - 4$

14. $9x^2 + 3x - 2$

15. $121x^2 - 64y^2$

16. $4x + 120 - 80x^2$

17. $x^2 + 5x + 9$

18. $16x^3 + 40x^2 + 25x$

19. $81x^4 - 16b^4$

20. $2ax - 4bx + 3a - 6b$

21. $15x^2 + 6x - 9$

Solve.

22. $x^2 + 5x - 24 = 0$

23. $3x^2 - 11x + 10 = 0$

Solve using a quadratic equation.

▲ **24.** Mr. Jerome's garden covered 300 square feet. If the width was 5 feet less than the length, find the measurements of the garden.

CHAPTER

6

Imagine you and a friend have begun a business venture. You have decided to open a calculator store in a shopping mall. The profits are good, but they seem to vary greatly depending on how much advertising you do for the business. Do you think you could use your mathematics to help predict your monthly profits? Turn to the Putting Your Skills to Work problems on page 395 to find out.

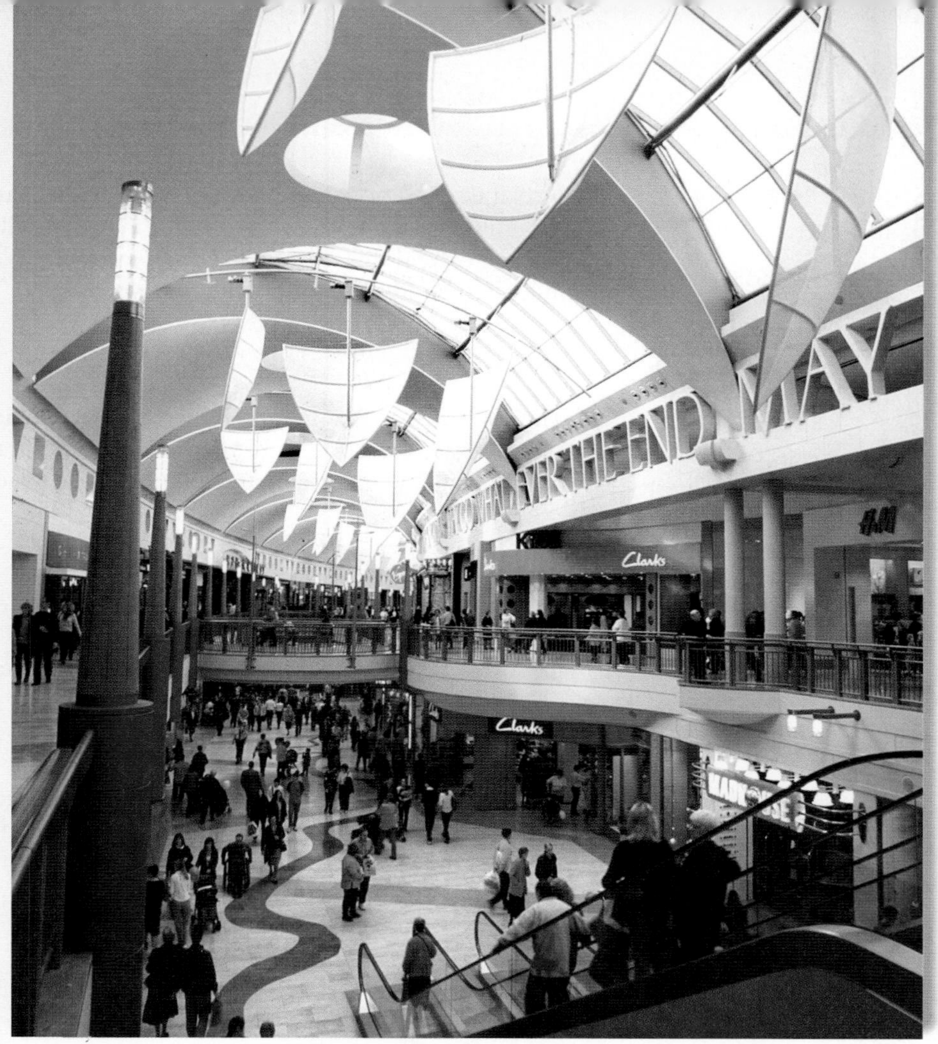

Rational Expressions and Equations

6.1 Simplifying Rational Expressions

Student Learning Objective

After studying this section, you will be able to:

 **Simplify rational expressions by factoring.**

Recall that a rational number is a number that can be written as one integer divided by another integer, such as $3 \div 4$ or $\frac{3}{4}$. We usually use the word *fraction* to mean $\frac{3}{4}$. We can extend this idea to algebraic expressions. A **rational expression** is a polynomial divided by another polynomial, such as

$$(3x + 2) \div (x + 4) \quad \text{or} \quad \frac{3x + 2}{x + 4}.$$

The last fraction is sometimes also called a **fractional algebraic expression.** There is a special restriction for all fractions, including fractional algebraic expressions. The denominator of the fraction cannot be 0. For example, in the expression

$$\frac{3x + 2}{x + 4},$$

the denominator cannot be 0. Therefore, the value of x cannot be -4. The following important restriction will apply throughout this chapter. We state it here to avoid having to mention it repeatedly throughout this chapter.

RESTRICTION

The denominator of a rational expression cannot be zero. Any value of the variable that would make the denominator zero is not allowed.

We have discovered that fractions can be simplified (or reduced) in the following way.

$$\frac{15}{25} = \frac{3 \cdot \cancel{5}}{5 \cdot \cancel{5}} = \frac{3}{5}$$

This is sometimes referred to as the **basic rule of fractions** and can be stated as follows.

BASIC RULE OF FRACTIONS

For any rational expression $\frac{a}{b}$ and any polynomial a, b, and c (where $b \neq 0$ and $c \neq 0$),

$$\frac{ac}{bc} = \frac{a}{b}.$$

We will examine several examples where a, b, and c are real numbers, as well as more involved examples where a, b, and c are polynomials. In either case we shall make extensive use of our factoring skills in this section.

One essential property is revealed by the basic rule of fractions: If the numerator and denominator of a given fraction are multiplied by the same nonzero quantity, an equivalent fraction is obtained. The rule can be used two ways. You can start with $\frac{ac}{bc}$ and end with the equivalent fraction $\frac{a}{b}$. Or, you can start with $\frac{a}{b}$ and end with the equivalent fraction $\frac{ac}{bc}$. In this section we focus on the first method.

EXAMPLE 1 Reduce $\frac{21}{39}$.

Solution $\frac{21}{39} = \frac{7 \cdot \cancel{3}}{13 \cdot \cancel{3}} = \frac{7}{13}$ Use the rule $\frac{ac}{bc} = \frac{a}{b}$. Let $c = 3$ because 3 is the greatest common factor of 21 and 39.

Practice Problem 1 Reduce $\frac{28}{63}$.

NOTE TO STUDENT: Fully worked-out solutions to all of the Practice Problems can be found at the back of the text starting at page SP-1

 Simplifying Rational Expressions by Factoring

The process of reducing the fraction shown previously is sometimes called *dividing out* common factors. Remember, only **factors** of both the numerator and the denominator can be divided out. To apply the basic rule of fractions, it is usually necessary that the numerator and denominator of the fraction be completely factored. You will need to use your factoring skills from Chapter 5 to accomplish this step. When you apply this rule, you are **simplifying the fraction.**

EXAMPLE 2 Simplify. $\dfrac{4x + 12}{5x + 15}$

Solution

$$\frac{4x + 12}{5x + 15} = \frac{4(x + 3)}{5(x + 3)}$$ Factor 4 from the numerator. Factor 5 from the denominator.

$$= \frac{4\cancel{(x + 3)}}{5\cancel{(x + 3)}}$$ Apply the basic rule of fractions.

$$= \frac{4}{5}$$

Practice Problem 2 Simplify. $\dfrac{12x - 6}{14x - 7}$

EXAMPLE 3 Simplify. $\dfrac{x^2 + 9x + 14}{x^2 - 4}$

Solution

$$= \frac{(x + 7)(x + 2)}{(x - 2)(x + 2)}$$ Factor the numerator. Factor the denominator.

$$= \frac{(x + 7)\cancel{(x + 2)}}{(x - 2)\cancel{(x + 2)}}$$ Apply the basic rule of fractions.

$$= \frac{x + 7}{x - 2}$$

CAUTION Do not try to remove terms that are added. In Example 3, do not try to remove the x^2 in the top and the x^2 in the bottom of the fraction. The basic rule of fractions only applies to quantities that are factors of both numerator and denominator.

Practice Problem 3 Simplify. $\dfrac{4x^2 - 9}{2x^2 - x - 3}$

Some problems may involve more than one step of factoring. Always remember to factor out any common factors as the first step, if it is possible to do so.

EXAMPLE 4 Simplify. $\dfrac{x^3 - 9x}{x^3 + x^2 - 6x}$

Solution

$$= \frac{x(x^2 - 9)}{x(x^2 + x - 6)}$$ Factor out a common factor from the polynomials in the numerator and the denominator.

$$= \frac{\cancel{x}\cancel{(x + 3)}(x - 3)}{\cancel{x}\cancel{(3 + x)}(x - 2)}$$ Factor each polynomial and apply the basic rule of fractions.

$$= \frac{x - 3}{x - 2}$$

Practice Problem 4 Simplify. $\dfrac{x^3 - 16x}{x^3 - 2x^2 - 8x}$

When you are simplifying, be on the lookout for the special situation where *a factor in the denominator is the opposite of a factor in the numerator*. In such a case you should factor a negative number from one of the factors so that it becomes equivalent to the other factor and it can be divided out. Look carefully at the following two examples.

EXAMPLE 5 Simplify. $\dfrac{5x - 15}{6 - 2x}$

Solution Notice that the variable term in the numerator, $5x$, and the variable term in the denominator, $-2x$, *are opposite in sign*. Likewise, the numerical terms -15 and 6 *are opposite in sign*. Factor out a negative number from the denominator.

$$\frac{5x - 15}{6 - 2x} = \frac{5(x - 3)}{-2(-3 + x)}$$

Factor 5 from the numerator.
Factor −2 from the denominator.
Note that $(x - 3)$ and $(-3 + x)$ are equivalent since $(+x - 3) = (-3 + x)$.

$$= \frac{5\cancel{(x - 3)}}{-2\cancel{(-3 + x)}}$$

Apply the basic rule of fractions.

$$= -\frac{5}{2}$$

Note that $\frac{5}{-2}$ is not considered to be in simple form. We usually avoid leaving a negative number in the denominator. Therefore, to simplify, give the result as $-\frac{5}{2}$ or $\frac{-5}{2}$.

***NOTE TO STUDENT:** Fully worked-out solutions to all of the Practice Problems can be found at the back of the text starting at page SP-1*

Practice Problem 5 Simplify. $\dfrac{2x - 5}{5 - 2x}$

EXAMPLE 6 Simplify. $\dfrac{2x^2 - 11x + 12}{16 - x^2}$

Solution

$$= \frac{(x - 4)(2x - 3)}{(4 - x)(4 + x)}$$

Factor the numerator and the denominator. Observe that $(x - 4)$ and $(4 - x)$ are opposites.

$$= \frac{(x - 4)(2x - 3)}{-1(-4 + x)(4 + x)}$$

Factor −1 out of $(+4 - x)$ to obtain $-1(-4 + x)$.

$$= \frac{\cancel{(x - 4)}(2x - 3)}{-1\cancel{(-4 + x)}(4 + x)}$$

Apply the basic rule of fractions since $(x - 4)$ and $(-4 + x)$ are equivalent.

$$= \frac{2x - 3}{-1(4 + x)}$$

$$= -\frac{2x - 3}{4 + x}$$

Practice Problem 6 Simplify. $\dfrac{4x^2 + 3x - 10}{25 - 16x^2}$

After doing Examples 5 and 6, you will notice a pattern. Whenever the factor in the numerator and the factor in the denominator are opposites, the value −1 results. We could actually make this a definition of that property.

For all monomials A and B where $A \neq B$, it is true that

$$\frac{A - B}{B - A} = -1.$$

You may use this definition in reducing fractions if it is helpful to you. Otherwise, you may use the factoring method discussed in Examples 5 and 6.

Some problems will involve two or more variables. In such cases, you will need to factor carefully and make sure that each set of parentheses contains the correct letters.

EXAMPLE 7 Simplify. $\dfrac{x^2 - 7xy + 12y^2}{2x^2 - 7xy - 4y^2}$

Solution

$$= \frac{(x - 4y)(x - 3y)}{(2x + y)(x - 4y)}$$ Factor the numerator. Factor the denominator.

$$= \frac{\cancel{(x - 4y)}(x - 3y)}{(2x + y)\cancel{(x - 4y)}}$$ Apply the basic rule of fractions.

$$= \frac{x - 3y}{2x + y}$$

Practice Problem 7 Simplify. $\dfrac{4x^2 - 9y^2}{4x^2 + 12xy + 9y^2}$

EXAMPLE 8 Simplify. $\dfrac{6a^2 + ab - 7b^2}{36a^2 - 49b^2}$

Solution

$$= \frac{(6a + 7b)(a - b)}{(6a + 7b)(6a - 7b)}$$ Factor the numerator. Factor the denominator.

$$= \frac{\cancel{(6a + 7b)}(a - b)}{\cancel{(6a + 7b)}(6a - 7b)}$$ Apply the basic rule of fractions.

$$= \frac{a - b}{6a - 7b}$$

Practice Problem 8 Simplify. $\dfrac{25a^2 - 16b^2}{10a^2 + 3ab - 4b^2}$

6.1 Exercises

Student Solutions Manual

CD/ Video

PH Math Tutor Center

MathXL®Tutorials on CD

MathXL®

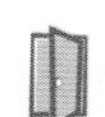
MyMathLab®

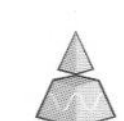
Interactmath.com

Simplify.

1. $\dfrac{3a - 9b}{a - 3b}$

2. $\dfrac{5x + 2y}{35x + 14y}$

3. $\dfrac{6x + 18}{x^2 + 3x}$

4. $\dfrac{8x - 12}{2x^3 - 3x^2}$

5. $\dfrac{9x^2 + 6x + 1}{1 - 9x^2}$

6. $\dfrac{4x^2 + 4x + 1}{1 - 4x^2}$

7. $\dfrac{3a^2b(a - 2b)}{6ab^2}$

8. $\dfrac{9ab^2}{6a^2b^2(b + 3a)}$

9. $\dfrac{x^2 + x - 2}{x^2 - x}$

10. $\dfrac{x^2 + x - 12}{x^2 - 3x}$

11. $\dfrac{x^2 - 3x - 10}{3x^2 + 5x - 2}$

12. $\dfrac{4x^2 - 10x + 6}{2x^2 + x - 3}$

13. $\dfrac{x^2 + 4x - 21}{x^3 - 49x}$

14. $\dfrac{x^3 - 3x^2 - 40x}{x^2 + 10x + 25}$

15. $\dfrac{3x^2 + 7x - 6}{x^2 + 7x + 12}$

16. $\dfrac{x^2 - 5x - 14}{2x^2 - x - 10}$

17. $\dfrac{3x^2 - 8x + 5}{4x^2 - 5x + 1}$

18. $\dfrac{3y^2 + 10y + 3}{3y^2 - 14y - 5}$

19. $\dfrac{5x^2 - 27x + 10}{5x^2 + 3x - 2}$

20. $\dfrac{2x^2 + 2x - 12}{x^2 + 3x - 4}$

Mixed Practice

Take some time to review exercises 1–20 before you proceed with exercises 21–34.

21. $\dfrac{10 - 2x}{4x^2 - 20x}$

22. $\dfrac{6 - 2ab}{ab^2 - 3b}$

23. $\dfrac{2x^2 - 7x - 15}{25 - x^2}$

24. $\dfrac{49 - x^2}{2x^2 - 9x - 35}$

25. $\dfrac{(4x + 5)^2}{8x^2 + 6x - 5}$

26. $\dfrac{6x^2 - 13x - 8}{(3x - 8)^2}$

27. $\dfrac{2x^2 + 9x - 18}{30 - x - x^2}$

28. $\dfrac{4y^2 - y - 3}{8 - 7y - y^2}$

29. $\dfrac{a^2 + 2ab - 3b^2}{2a^2 + 5ab - 3b^2}$

30. $\dfrac{a^2 + 3ab - 10b^2}{3a^2 - 7ab + 2b^2}$

31. $\dfrac{9x^2 - 4y^2}{9x^2 + 12xy + 4y^2}$

32. $\dfrac{16x^2 - 24xy + 9y^2}{16x^2 - 9y^2}$

To Think About

Be sure to remove a common factor first when solving exercises 33 and 34.

33. $\dfrac{x^3 - bx^2 - abx + ax^2}{bx^2 - b^2x - b^2c + bcx}$

34. $\dfrac{bxy + bx^2 - axy - ax^2}{ay^2 + axy + 2by^2 + 2bxy}$

Cumulative Review

Multiply.

35. Multiply. $(3x - 7)^2$

36. Multiply: $(7x + 6y)(7x - 6y)$

37. $(2x + 3)(x - 4)(x - 2)$

38. $(x^2 - 3x - 5)(2x^2 + x + 3)$

39. ***Dividing Acreage*** Walter and Ann Perkins wish to divide $4\frac{7}{8}$ acres of farmland into three equal-sized house lots. What will be the acreage of each lot?

40. ***Roasting a Turkey*** Ron and Mary Larson are planning to cook a $17\frac{1}{2}$-pound turkey. The directions suggest a cooking time of 22 minutes per pound for turkeys that weigh between 16 and 20 pounds. How many hours and minutes should they allow for an approximate cooking time?

Languages *The number of people on our planet who speak the Chinese Mandarin language is 158,000,000 more than twice the number of people who speak Spanish. The number of people on Earth who speak English is 17,000,000 less than the number of those who speak Spanish. There are 341,000,000 people who speak English on our planet. (*Source: *United Nations Statistical Division)*

41. How many people speak Chinese Mandarin?

42. How many people speak Spanish?

6.2 MULTIPLYING AND DIVIDING RATIONAL EXPRESSIONS

Student Learning Objectives

After studying this section, you will be able to:

1. **Multiply rational expressions.**
2. **Divide rational expressions.**

 Multiplying Rational Expressions

To multiply two rational expressions, we multiply the numerators and multiply the denominators. As before, the denominators cannot equal zero.

> For any two rational expressions $\frac{a}{b}$ and $\frac{c}{d}$ where $b \neq 0$ and $d \neq 0$,
> $$\frac{a}{b} \cdot \frac{c}{d} = \frac{ac}{bd}.$$

Simplifying or reducing fractions *prior to multiplying them* usually makes the computations easier to do. Leaving the reducing step until the end makes the simplifying process longer and increases the chance for error. This long approach should be avoided.

As an example, let's do the same problem two ways to see which one is easier. Let's simplify the following problem by multiplying first and then reducing the result.

$$\frac{5}{7} \times \frac{49}{125}$$

$$\frac{5}{7} \times \frac{49}{125} = \frac{245}{875}$$ Multiply the numerators and multiply the denominators.

$$= \frac{7}{25}$$ Reduce the fraction. (*Note:* It takes a bit of trial and error to discover how to reduce it.)

Compare this with the following method, where we reduce the fractions prior to multiplying them.

$$\frac{5}{7} \times \frac{49}{125}$$

$$\frac{5}{7} \times \frac{7 \cdot 7}{5 \cdot 5 \cdot 5}$$ **Step 1.** It is easier to factor first. We factor the numerator and denominator of the second fraction.

$$\frac{5 \cdot 7 \cdot 7}{7 \cdot 5 \cdot 5 \cdot 5}$$ **Step 2.** We express the product as one fraction (by the definition of multiplication of fractions).

$$\frac{\cancel{5} \cdot \cancel{7} \cdot 7}{\cancel{7} \cdot \cancel{5} \cdot 5 \cdot 5} = \frac{7}{25}$$ **Step 3.** Then we apply the basic rule of fractions to divide the common factors of 5 and 7 that appear in the numerator and in the denominator.

A similar approach can be used with the multiplication of rational expressions. We first factor the numerator and denominator of each fraction. Then we divide out any factor that is common to a numerator and a denominator. Finally, we multiply the remaining numerators and the remaining denominators.

EXAMPLE 1 Multiply. $\frac{x^2 - x - 12}{x^2 - 16} \cdot \frac{2x^2 + 7x - 4}{x^2 - 4x - 21}$

Solution

$$\frac{(x-4)(x+3)}{(x-4)(x+4)} \cdot \frac{(x+4)(2x-1)}{(x+3)(x-7)}$$ Factoring is always the first step.

$$= \frac{\cancel{(x-4)}\cancel{(x+3)}}{\cancel{(x-4)}\cancel{(x+4)}} \cdot \frac{\cancel{(x+4)}(2x-1)}{\cancel{(x+3)}(x-7)}$$ Apply the basic rule of fractions. (Three pairs of factors divide out.)

$$= \frac{2x-1}{x-7}$$ The final answer.

Practice Problem 1 Multiply. $\frac{6x^2 + 7x + 2}{x^2 - 7x + 10} \cdot \frac{x^2 + 3x - 10}{2x^2 + 11x + 5}$

NOTE TO STUDENT: Fully worked-out solutions to all of the Practice Problems can be found at the back of the text starting at page SP-1

In some cases, a given numerator can be factored more than once. You should always check for a *common factor* as your first step.

EXAMPLE 2 Multiply. $\dfrac{x^4 - 16}{x^3 + 4x} \cdot \dfrac{2x^2 - 8x}{4x^2 + 2x - 12}$

Solution

$$= \frac{(x^2 + 4)(x^2 - 4)}{x(x^2 + 4)} \cdot \frac{2x(x - 4)}{2(2x^2 + x - 6)}$$

Factor each numerator and denominator. Factoring out the common factor first is very important.

$$= \frac{(x^2 + 4)(x + 2)(x - 2)}{x(x^2 + 4)} \cdot \frac{2x(x - 4)}{2(x + 2)(2x - 3)}$$

Factor again where possible.

$$= \frac{\cancel{(x^2 + 4)}\cancel{(x + 2)}(x - 2)}{\cancel{x}\cancel{(x^2 + 4)}} \cdot \frac{\cancel{2x}(x - 4)}{\cancel{2}\cancel{(x + 2)}(2x - 3)}$$

Divide out factors that appear in both the numerator and the denominator. (There are four such pairs of factors.)

$$= \frac{(x - 2)(x - 4)}{(2x - 3)} \quad \text{or} \quad \frac{x^2 - 6x + 8}{2x - 3}$$

Write the answer as one fraction. (Usually, if there is more than one factor in a numerator, the answer is left in factored form.)

Practice Problem 2 Multiply. $\dfrac{2y^2 - 6y - 8}{y^2 - y - 2} \cdot \dfrac{y^2 - 5y + 6}{2y^2 - 32}$.

Dividing Rational Expressions

For any two fractions $\frac{a}{b}$ and $\frac{c}{d}$, the operation of division can be performed by inverting the second fraction and multiplying it by the first fraction. When we invert a fraction, we are finding its *reciprocal*. Two numbers are **reciprocals** of each other if their product is 1. The reciprocal of $\frac{3}{5}$ is $\frac{5}{3}$. The reciprocal of 7 is $\frac{1}{7}$. The reciprocal of $\frac{a}{b}$ is $\frac{b}{a}$. Sometimes people state the rule for dividing fractions this way: "To divide two fractions, keep the first fraction unchanged and multiply by the reciprocal of the second fraction."

The definition for division of fractions is

$$\frac{a}{b} \div \frac{c}{d} = \frac{a}{b} \cdot \frac{d}{c}.$$

This property holds whether a, b, c, and d are polynomials or numerical values. (It is assumed, of course, that no denominator is zero.)

In the first step for dividing two rational expressions, invert the second fraction and rewrite the quotient as a product. Then follow the procedure for multiplying rational expressions.

EXAMPLE 3 Divide. $\dfrac{6x + 12y}{2x - 6y} \div \dfrac{9x^2 - 36y^2}{4x^2 - 36y^2}$

Solution

$$= \frac{6x + 12y}{2x - 6y} \cdot \frac{4x^2 - 36y^2}{9x^2 - 36y^2}$$

Invert the second fraction and write the problem as the product of two fractions.

$$= \frac{6(x + 2y)}{2(x - 3y)} \cdot \frac{4(x^2 - 9y^2)}{9(x^2 - 4y^2)}$$

Factor each numerator and denominator.

$$= \frac{(3)(2)(x + 2y)}{2(x - 3y)} \cdot \frac{(2)(2)(x + 3y)(x - 3y)}{(3)(3)(x + 2y)(x - 2y)}$$ Factor again where possible.

$$= \frac{\cancel{(3)}\cancel{(2)}\cancel{(x + 2y)}}{\cancel{2}\cancel{(x - 3y)}} \cdot \frac{(2)(2)(x + 3y)\cancel{(x - 3y)}}{\cancel{(3)}(3)\cancel{(x + 2y)}(x - 2y)}$$ Divide out factors that appear in both numerator and denominator.

$$= \frac{(2)(2)(x + 3y)}{3(x - 2y)}$$ Write the result as one fraction.

$$= \frac{4(x + 3y)}{3(x - 2y)}$$ Simplify. (Usually, answers are left in this form.)

Although it is correct to write this answer as $\frac{4x + 12y}{3x - 6y}$, it is customary to leave the answer in factored form to ensure that the final answer is simplified.

***NOTE TO STUDENT:** Fully worked-out solutions to all of the Practice Problems can be found at the back of the text starting at page SP-1*

Practice Problem 3 Divide. $\frac{x^2 + 5x + 6}{x^2 + 8x} \div \frac{2x^2 + 5x + 2}{2x^2 + x}$

A polynomial that is not in fraction form can be written as a fraction if you give it a denominator of 1.

EXAMPLE 4 Divide. $\frac{15 - 3x}{x + 6} \div (x^2 - 9x + 20)$

Solution Note that $x^2 - 9x + 20$ can be written as $\frac{x^2 - 9x + 20}{1}$.

$$= \frac{15 - 3x}{x + 6} \cdot \frac{1}{x^2 - 9x + 20}$$ Invert and multiply.

$$= \frac{-3(-5 + x)}{x + 6} \cdot \frac{1}{(x - 5)(x - 4)}$$ Factor where possible. Note that we had to factor -3 from the first numerator so that it would contain a factor in common with the second denominator.

$$= \frac{-3\cancel{(-5 + x)}}{x + 6} \cdot \frac{1}{\cancel{(x - 5)}(x - 4)}$$ Divide out the common factor. $(-5 + x)$ is equivalent to $(x - 5)$.

$$= \frac{-3}{(x + 6)(x - 4)}$$ The final answer. Note that the answer can be written in several equivalent forms.

or $-\frac{3}{(x + 6)(x - 4)}$ or $\frac{3}{(x + 6)(4 - x)}$

Practice Problem 4 Divide. $\frac{x + 3}{x - 3} \div (9 - x^2)$

CAUTION: It is logical to assume that the problems included in Section 6.2 have at least one common factor that can be divided out. Therefore if, after factoring, you do not observe any common factors, you should be somewhat suspicious. In such cases, it would be wise to double check your factoring steps to see if an error has been made.

6.2 EXERCISES

Student Solutions Manual | CD/Video | PH Math Tutor Center | MathXL®Tutorials on CD | MathXL® | MyMathLab® | Interactmath.com

Verbal and Writing Skills

1. Before multiplying rational expressions, we should always first try to

____

____________________.

2. Division of two rational expressions is done by keeping the first fraction unchanged and then

____________________.

Multiply.

3. $\dfrac{2x - 10}{x - 4} \cdot \dfrac{x^2 + 5x + 4}{x^2 - 4x - 5}$

4. $\dfrac{7x + 7}{x + 4} \cdot \dfrac{x^2 - x - 20}{7x^2 - 42x - 49}$

5. $\dfrac{24x^3}{4x^2 - 36} \cdot \dfrac{2x^2 + 6x}{16x^2}$

6. $\dfrac{14x^2}{10x + 50} \cdot \dfrac{5x^3 - 125x}{35x^4}$

7. $\dfrac{x^2 + 3x - 10}{x^2 + x - 20} \cdot \dfrac{x^2 - 3x - 4}{x^2 + 4x + 3}$

8. $\dfrac{x^2 - x - 20}{x^2 - 3x - 10} \cdot \dfrac{x^2 + 7x + 10}{x^2 + 4x - 5}$

Divide.

9. $\dfrac{x + 6}{x - 8} \div \dfrac{x + 5}{x^2 - 6x - 16}$

10. $\dfrac{x - 4}{x + 9} \div \dfrac{x - 7}{x^2 + 13x + 36}$

11. $(6x - 5) \div \dfrac{36x^2 - 25}{6x^2 + 17x + 10}$

12. $\dfrac{4x^2 - 9}{4x^2 + 12x + 9} \div (6x - 9)$

13. $\dfrac{3x^2 + 12xy + 12y^2}{x^2 + 4xy + 3y^2} \div \dfrac{4x + 8y}{x + y}$

14. $\dfrac{5x^2 + 10xy + 5y^2}{x^2 + 5xy + 6y^2} \div \dfrac{3x + 3y}{x + 2y}$

Mixed Practice

Perform the operation indicated.

15. $\dfrac{(x + 5)^2}{3x^2 - 7x + 2} \cdot \dfrac{x^2 - 4x + 4}{x + 5}$

16. $\dfrac{3x^2 - 10x - 8}{(4x + 5)^2} \cdot \dfrac{4x + 5}{(x - 4)^2}$

17. $\dfrac{x^2 + x - 30}{10 - 2x} \div \dfrac{x^2 + 4x - 12}{5x + 15}$

18. $\dfrac{x^2 + 3x - 28}{x^2 + 14x + 49} \div \dfrac{12 - 3x^2}{x^2 + 5x - 14}$

19. $\dfrac{y^2 + 4y - 12}{y^2 + 2y - 24} \cdot \dfrac{y^2 - 16}{y^2 + 2y - 8}$

20. $\dfrac{5y^2 + 17y + 6}{10y^2 + 9y + 2} \cdot \dfrac{4y^2 - 1}{2y^2 + 5y - 3}$

21. $\dfrac{x^2 + 7x + 12}{2x^2 + 9x + 4} \div \dfrac{x^2 + 6x + 9}{2x^2 - x - 1}$

22. $\dfrac{x^2 + 8x + 15}{2x^2 + 11x + 5} \div \dfrac{x^2 + 6x + 9}{2x^2 - 7x - 4}$

To Think About

23. Consider the problem $\dfrac{x + 5}{x - 2} \div \dfrac{x + 7}{x - 6}$. Explain why 2, −7, and 6 are not allowable replacements for the variable x.

24. Consider the problem $\dfrac{x - 8}{x + 5} \div \dfrac{x - 9}{x + 4}$. Explain why −5, 9, and −4 are not allowable replacements for the variable x.

Cumulative Review

25. Solve. $6x^2 + 3x - 18 = 5x - 2 + 6x^2$

26. Multiply. $(7x^2 - x - 1)(x - 3)$

27. ***Correct Dosage*** Suzanne Hartling is a nurse at Meadowbrook Rehabilitation Center. She must give an 80-kilogram patient a medication based on his weight. The dosage is $\frac{1}{16}$ milligram of medication for each kilogram of patient weight. Find the amount of medication she should give this patient.

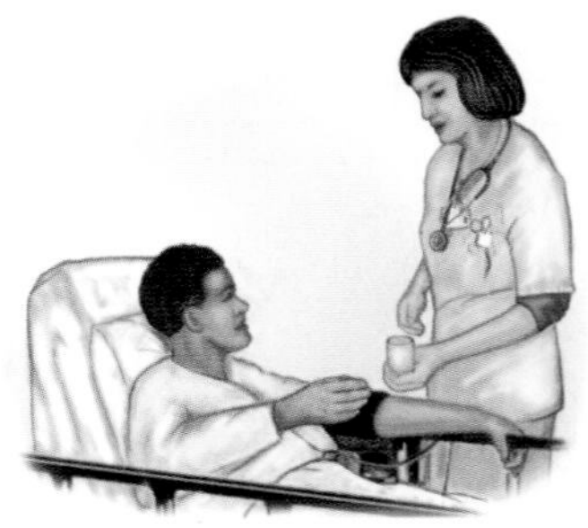

▲ **28.** ***Golden Gate Bridge*** The Golden Gate Bridge has a total length (including approaches) of 8981 feet and a road width of 90 feet. The width of the sidewalk is 10.5 feet. (The sidewalk spans the entire length of the bridge.) Assume it would cost $\$x$ per square foot to resurface the road or the sidewalk. Write an expression for how much more it would cost to resurface the road than the sidewalk.

▲ **29.** ***Garden Design*** Harold Rafton planted a square garden bed. George Avis also planted a garden that was 2 feet less in width, but 3 feet longer in length than Harold's garden. If the area of George's garden was 36 square feet, find the dimensions of each garden.

6.3 Adding and Subtracting Rational Expressions

Adding and Subtracting Rational Expressions with a Common Denominator

If rational expressions have the same denominator, they can be combined in a fashion similar to that used for fractions in arithmetic. The numerators are added or subtracted and the denominator remains the same.

ADDING RATIONAL EXPRESSIONS

For any rational expressions $\frac{a}{b}$ and $\frac{c}{b}$,

$$\frac{a}{b} + \frac{c}{b} = \frac{a + c}{b} \quad \text{where } b \neq 0.$$

EXAMPLE 1 Add. $\frac{5a}{a + 2b} + \frac{6a}{a + 2b}$

Solution

$$\frac{5a}{a + 2b} + \frac{6a}{a + 2b} = \frac{5a + 6a}{a + 2b} = \frac{11a}{a + 2b}$$

Note that the denominators are the same. Only add the numerators. Keep the same denominator.
Do not change the denominator.

Practice Problem 1 Add. $\frac{2s + t}{2s - t} + \frac{s - t}{2s - t}$

SUBTRACTING RATIONAL EXPRESSIONS

For any rational expressions $\frac{a}{b}$ and $\frac{c}{b}$,

$$\frac{a}{b} - \frac{c}{b} = \frac{a - c}{b} \quad \text{where } b \neq 0.$$

EXAMPLE 2 Subtract. $\frac{3x}{(x + y)(x - 2y)} - \frac{8x}{(x + y)(x - 2y)}$

Solution

$$\frac{3x}{(x + y)(x - 2y)} - \frac{8x}{(x + y)(x - 2y)} = \frac{3x - 8x}{(x + y)(x - 2y)}$$ Write as one fraction.

$$= \frac{-5x}{(x + y)(x - 2y)}$$ Simplify.

Practice Problem 2 Subtract. $\frac{b}{(a - 2b)(a + b)} - \frac{2b}{(a - 2b)(a + b)}$

Determining the LCD for Rational Expressions with Different Denominators

How do we add or subtract rational expressions when the denominators are not the same? First we must find the **least common denominator** (LCD). You need to be clear on how to find a least common denominator and how to add and subtract fractions from arithmetic before you attempt this section. Review Sections 0.1 and 0.2 if you have any questions about this topic.

Student Learning Objectives

After studying this section, you will be able to:

1. **Add and subtract rational expressions with a common denominator.**
2. **Determine the LCD for rational expressions with different denominators.**
3. **Add and subtract rational expressions with different denominators.**

NOTE TO STUDENT: Fully worked-out solutions to all of the Practice Problems can be found at the back of the text starting at page SP-1

HOW TO FIND THE LCD OF TWO OR MORE RATIONAL EXPRESSIONS

1. Factor each denominator completely.
2. The LCD is a product containing each *different factor.*
3. If a factor occurs more than once in any one denominator, the LCD will contain that factor repeated the greatest number of times that it occurs in any one denominator.

EXAMPLE 3 Find the LCD. $\frac{5}{2x-4}, \frac{6}{3x-6}$

Solution Factor each denominator.

$$2x - 4 = 2(x - 2) \qquad 3x - 6 = 3(x - 2)$$

The different factors are 2, 3, and $(x - 2)$. Since no factor appears more than once in any one denominator, the LCD is the product of these three factors.

$$\text{LCD} = (2)(3)(x - 2) = 6(x - 2)$$

NOTE TO STUDENT: Fully worked-out solutions to all of the Practice Problems can be found at the back of the text starting at page SP-1

Practice Problem 3 Find the LCD. $\frac{7}{6x+21}, \frac{13}{10x+35}$

EXAMPLE 4 Find the LCD.

(a) $\frac{5}{12ab^2c}, \frac{13}{18a^3bc^4}$ **(b)** $\frac{8}{x^2-5x+4}, \frac{12}{x^2+2x-3}$

Solution If a factor occurs more than once in any one denominator, the LCD will contain that factor repeated the greatest number of times that it occurs in any one denominator.

(a)

$$\begin{aligned} 12ab^2c &= 2 \cdot 2 \cdot 3 \cdot a \cdot b \cdot b \cdot c \\ 18a^3bc^4 &= 2 \cdot 3 \cdot 3 \cdot a \cdot a \cdot a \cdot b \cdot c \cdot c \cdot c \cdot c \\ & \downarrow \\ & 2 \cdot 2 \cdot 3 \cdot 3 \cdot a \cdot a \cdot a \cdot b \cdot b \cdot c \cdot c \cdot c \cdot c \end{aligned}$$

$$\text{LCD} = 2^2 \cdot 3^2 \cdot a^3 \cdot b^2 \cdot c^4 = 36a^3b^2c^4$$

(b)

$$\begin{aligned} x^2 - 5x + 4 &= (x - 4)(x - 1) \\ x^2 + 2x - 3 &= (x - 1)(x + 3) \\ \text{LCD} &= (x - 4)(x - 1)(x + 3) \end{aligned}$$

Practice Problem 4 Find the LCD.

(a) $\frac{3}{50xy^2z}, \frac{19}{40x^3yz}$ **(b)** $\frac{2}{x^2+5x+6}, \frac{6}{3x^2+5x-2}$

Adding and Subtracting Rational Expressions with Different Denominators

If two rational expressions have different denominators, we first change them to equivalent rational expressions with the least common denominator. Then we add or subtract the numerators and keep the common denominator.

EXAMPLE 5 Add. $\frac{5}{xy} + \frac{2}{y}$

Solution The denominators are different. We must find the LCD. The two factors are x and y. We observe that the LCD is xy.

$$\frac{5}{xy} + \frac{2}{y} = \frac{5}{xy} + \frac{2}{y} \cdot \frac{x}{x}$$ Multiply the second fraction by $\frac{x}{x}$.

$$= \frac{5}{xy} + \frac{2x}{xy}$$ Now each fraction has a common denominator of xy.

$$= \frac{5 + 2x}{xy}$$ Write the sum as one fraction.

Practice Problem 5 Add. $\frac{7}{a} + \frac{3}{abc}$

EXAMPLE 6 Add. $\frac{3x}{x^2 - y^2} + \frac{5}{x + y}$

Solution We factor the first denominator so that $x^2 - y^2 = (x + y)(x - y)$. Thus, the factors of the denominators are $(x + y)$ and $(x - y)$. We observe that the LCD $= (x + y)(x - y)$.

$$\frac{3x}{(x + y)(x - y)} + \frac{5}{(x + y)} \cdot \frac{x - y}{x - y}$$ Multiply the second fraction by $\frac{x - y}{x - y}$.

$$= \frac{3x}{(x + y)(x - y)} + \frac{5x - 5y}{(x + y)(x - y)}$$ Now each fraction has a common denominator of $(x + y)(x - y)$.

$$= \frac{3x + 5x - 5y}{(x + y)(x - y)}$$ Write the sum of the numerators over one common denominator.

$$= \frac{8x - 5y}{(x + y)(x - y)}$$ Collect like terms.

Practice Problem 6 Add. $\frac{2a - b}{a^2 - 4b^2} + \frac{2}{a + 2b}$

It is important to remember that the LCD is the smallest algebraic expression into which each denominator can be divided. For rational expressions the LCD must contain *each factor* that appears in any denominator. If the factor is repeated, the LCD must contain that factor the greatest number of times that it appears in any one denominator.

In many cases, the denominators in an addition or subtraction problem are not in factored form. You must factor each denominator to determine the LCD. Collect like terms in the numerator; then determine whether that final numerator can be factored. If so, you may be able to simplify the fraction.

EXAMPLE 7 Add. $\frac{5}{x^2 - y^2} + \frac{3x}{x^3 + x^2y}$

Solution

$\frac{5}{x^2 - y^2} + \frac{3x}{x^3 + x^2y}$ Factor the two denominators. Observe that the LCD is $x^2(x + y)(x - y)$.

$= \frac{5}{(x + y)(x - y)} + \frac{3x}{x^2(x + y)}$

$= \frac{5}{(x + y)(x - y)} \cdot \frac{x^2}{x^2} + \frac{3x}{x^2(x + y)} \cdot \frac{x - y}{x - y}$ Multiply each fraction by the appropriate value to obtain a common denominator of $x^2(x + y)(x - y)$.

$= \frac{5x^2}{x^2(x + y)(x - y)} + \frac{3x^2 - 3xy}{x^2(x + y)(x - y)}$

$= \frac{5x^2 + 3x^2 - 3xy}{x^2(x + y)(x - y)}$ Write the sum of the numerators over one common denominator.

$= \frac{8x^2 - 3xy}{x^2(x + y)(x - y)}$ Collect like terms.

$= \frac{x(8x - 3y)}{x^2(x + y)(x - y)}$ Divide out the common factor x in the numerator and denominator and simplify.

$= \frac{8x - 3y}{x(x + y)(x - y)}$

***NOTE TO STUDENT:** Fully worked-out solutions to all of the Practice Problems can be found at the back of the text starting at page SP-1*

Practice Problem 7 Add. $\frac{7a}{a^2 + 2ab + b^2} + \frac{4}{a^2 + ab}$

It is very easy to make a sign mistake when subtracting two fractions. You will find it helpful to place parentheses around the numerator of the second fraction so that you will not forget to subtract the entire numerator.

EXAMPLE 8 Subtract. $\frac{3x + 4}{x - 2} - \frac{x - 3}{2x - 4}$

Solution Factor the second denominator.

$= \frac{3x + 4}{x - 2} - \frac{x - 3}{2(x - 2)}$ Observe that the LCD is $2(x - 2)$.

$= \frac{2}{2} \cdot \frac{(3x + 4)}{x - 2} - \frac{x - 3}{2(x - 2)}$ Multiply the first fraction by $\frac{2}{2}$ so that the resulting fraction will have the common denominator.

$= \frac{2(3x + 4) - (x - 3)}{2(x - 2)}$ Write the indicated subtraction as one fraction. Note the parentheses around $x - 3$.

$= \frac{6x + 8 - x + 3}{2(x - 2)}$ Remove the parentheses in the numerator.

$= \frac{5x + 11}{2(x - 2)}$ Collect like terms.

Practice Problem 8 Subtract. $\frac{x + 7}{3x - 9} - \frac{x - 6}{x - 3}$

To avoid making errors when subtracting two fractions, some students find it helpful to change subtraction to addition of the opposite of the second fraction. In other words, we use the property that $\frac{a}{b} - \frac{c}{b} = \frac{a}{b} + \frac{-c}{b}$.

EXAMPLE 9 Subtract. $\frac{8x}{x^2 - 16} - \frac{4}{x - 4}$

Solution

$\frac{8x}{x^2 - 16} - \frac{4}{x - 4}$

$= \frac{8x}{(x + 4)(x - 4)} + \frac{-4}{x - 4}$ Factor the first denominator. Use the property that $\frac{a}{b} - \frac{c}{b} = \frac{a}{b} + \frac{-c}{b}$.

$= \frac{8x}{(x + 4)(x - 4)} + \frac{-4}{x - 4} \cdot \frac{x + 4}{x + 4}$ Multiply the second fraction by $\frac{x + 4}{x + 4}$.

$= \frac{8x + (-4)(x + 4)}{(x + 4)(x - 4)}$ Write the sum of the numerators over one common denominator.

$= \frac{8x - 4x - 16}{(x + 4)(x - 4)}$ Remove parentheses.

$= \frac{4x - 16}{(x + 4)(x - 4)}$ Collect like terms. Note that the numerator can be factored.

$= \frac{4\cancel{(x - 4)}}{(x + 4)\cancel{(x - 4)}}$ Since $(x - 4)$ is a *factor* of the numerator *and* the denominator, we may divide out the common factor.

$= \frac{4}{x + 4}$

Practice Problem 9 Subtract and simplify. $\frac{x - 2}{x^2 - 4} - \frac{x + 1}{2x^2 + 4x}$

6.3 Exercises

Student Solutions Manual | CD/ Video | PH Math Tutor Center | MathXL®Tutorials on CD | MathXL® | MyMathLab® | Interactmath.com

Verbal and Writing Skills

1. Suppose two rational expressions have denominators of $(x + 3)(x + 5)$ and $(x + 3)^2$. Explain how you would determine the LCD.

2. Suppose two rational expressions have denominators of $(x - 4)^2(x + 7)$ and $(x - 4)^3$. Explain how you would determine the LCD.

Perform the operation indicated. Be sure to simplify.

3. $\dfrac{x}{x + 5} + \dfrac{2x + 1}{5 + x}$

4. $\dfrac{8}{7 + 2x} + \dfrac{x + 3}{2x + 7}$

5. $\dfrac{3x}{x + 3} - \dfrac{x + 5}{x + 3}$

6. $\dfrac{2x + 7}{x - 8} - \dfrac{x + 1}{x - 8}$

7. $\dfrac{8x + 3}{5x + 7} - \dfrac{6x + 10}{5x + 7}$

8. $\dfrac{5x - 9}{3x + 4} - \dfrac{4x + 14}{3x + 4}$

Find the LCD. Do not combine fractions.

9. $\dfrac{13}{3ab}, \dfrac{7}{a^2b^2}$

10. $\dfrac{12}{5a^2}, \dfrac{9}{a^3}$

11. $\dfrac{5}{18x^2y^5}, \dfrac{7}{30x^3y^3}$

12. $\dfrac{11}{16x^2y^3}, \dfrac{17}{56xy^4}$

13. $\dfrac{8}{5x - 15}, \dfrac{7}{3x - 9}$

14. $\dfrac{9}{2x - 8}, \dfrac{11}{5x - 20}$

15. $\dfrac{8}{x + 3}, \dfrac{15}{x^2 - 9}$

16. $\dfrac{13}{x^2 - 16}, \dfrac{7}{x - 4}$

17. $\dfrac{7}{3x^2 + 14x - 5}, \dfrac{4}{9x^2 - 6x + 1}$

18. $\dfrac{4}{2x^2 - 9x - 35}, \dfrac{3}{4x^2 + 20x + 25}$

Add.

19. $\dfrac{7}{ab} + \dfrac{3}{b}$

20. $\dfrac{8}{cd} + \dfrac{9}{d}$

21. $\dfrac{3}{x + 7} + \dfrac{8}{x^2 - 49}$

22. $\dfrac{5}{x^2 - 2x + 1} + \dfrac{3}{x - 1}$

23. $\dfrac{3y}{y + 2} + \dfrac{y}{y - 2}$

24. $\dfrac{2}{y - 1} + \dfrac{2}{y + 1}$

25. $\dfrac{6}{5a} + \dfrac{5}{3a + 2}$

26. $\dfrac{3}{2a + 5} + \dfrac{4}{7a}$

27. $\dfrac{2}{3xy} + \dfrac{1}{6yz}$

28. $\dfrac{5}{4xy} + \dfrac{5}{12yz}$

Subtract.

29. $\dfrac{5x+6}{x-3} - \dfrac{x-2}{2x-6}$

30. $\dfrac{7x+3}{x-4} - \dfrac{x-3}{2x-8}$

31. $\dfrac{3x}{x^2-25} - \dfrac{2}{x+5}$

32. $\dfrac{7x}{x^2-9} - \dfrac{6}{x+3}$

33. $\dfrac{a+3b}{2} - \dfrac{a-b}{5}$

34. $\dfrac{3b-a}{6} - \dfrac{a+b}{5}$

35. $\dfrac{8}{2x-3} - \dfrac{6}{x+2}$

36. $\dfrac{6}{3x-4} - \dfrac{5}{4x-3}$

37. $\dfrac{x}{x^2+2x-3} - \dfrac{x}{x^2-5x+4}$

38. $\dfrac{1}{x^2-2x} - \dfrac{5}{x^2-4x+4}$

39. $\dfrac{2}{x^2+5x+6} + \dfrac{3}{x^2+7x+10}$

40. $\dfrac{3}{x^2-x-12} + \dfrac{2}{x^2+x-20}$

41. $\dfrac{3x-8}{x^2-5x+6} + \dfrac{x+2}{x^2-6x+8}$

42. $\dfrac{3x+5}{x^2+4x+3} + \dfrac{-x+5}{x^2+2x-3}$

Mixed Practice

Add or subtract the following problems.

43. $\dfrac{6x}{y-2x} - \dfrac{5x}{2x-y}$

44. $\dfrac{8b}{2b-a} - \dfrac{3b}{a-2b}$

45. $\dfrac{3y}{8y^2+2y-1} - \dfrac{5y}{2y^2-9y-5}$

46. $\dfrac{2x}{x^2+5x+6} - \dfrac{x+1}{x^2+2x-3}$

47. $\dfrac{4y}{y^2+4y+3} + \dfrac{2}{y+1}$

48. $\dfrac{y-23}{y^2-y-20} + \dfrac{2}{y-5}$

To Think About

Add the following.

49. $\dfrac{2x}{x-3} + \dfrac{3x}{x+2} + \dfrac{7}{x^2 - x - 6}$

50. $\dfrac{x}{x-4} + \dfrac{5}{x+4} + \dfrac{10}{x^2 - 16}$

Cumulative Review

51. Solve. $\dfrac{1}{3}(x-2) + \dfrac{1}{2}(x+3) = \dfrac{1}{4}(3x+1)$

52. Solve for y. $5ax = 2(ay - 3bc)$

53. Solve for x. $\dfrac{1}{2}x < \dfrac{1}{3}x + \dfrac{1}{4}$

54. Simplify. $(3x^3y^4)^4$

55. ***Commuting Costs*** A subway token costs \$1.50. A monthly unlimited ride subway pass costs \$50. How many days per month would you have to use the subway to go to work (assume one subway token to get to work and one subway token to get back home) in order for it to be cheaper to buy a monthly subway pass?

56. ***Unemployment in Finland*** In Finland the unemployment rate went from 3.5% in 1990 to 14.6% in 1999. (*Source:* United Nations Statistics Division.) If the working age population of Finland was 5,100,000 during this period, how many more people were unemployed in 1999 than in 1990?

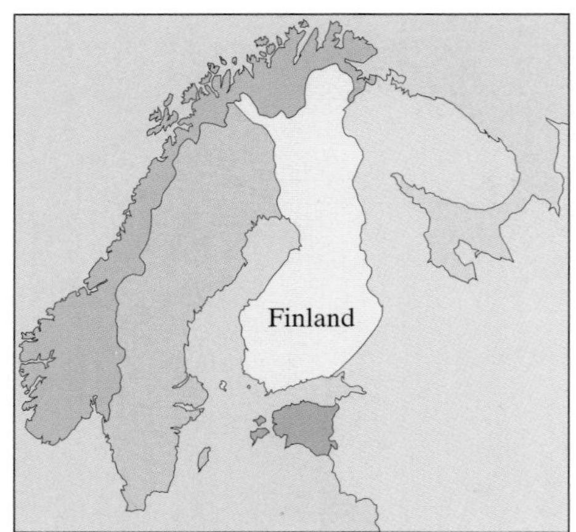

57. ***Anchovy Population*** During the 1972–1973 El Niño weather pattern, the waters around the country of Peru became very warm. The cool-water-loving anchovy fish population dropped from 20 million to 2 million. This particular El Niño lasted 20 months. (*Source:* National Oceanic and Atmospheric Administration.) **(a)** If during this time the population level dropped at a constant rate, how much did it drop per month? **(b)** Fishermen worried that the entire anchovy population would be destroyed. If the weather pattern had continued beyond the 20 months and if the anchovy population had continued to decline at the same rate, how many more months would it have been before the entire anchovy population was destroyed?

58. ***DVD Rentals*** Renting a DVD from the local video store costs \$3.50. If you sign up for a rental service on the Web, you pay \$21.00 each month, plus a \$0.50 mailing charge per DVD. How many DVDs must you rent each month so that the Web service is cheaper than renting locally?

How Am I Doing? Sections 6.1–6.3

How are you doing with your homework assignments in Sections 6.1 to 6.3? Do you feel you have mastered the material so far? Do you understand the concepts you have covered? Before you go further in the textbook, take some time to do each of the following problems.

Simplify.

6.1

1. $\dfrac{8x - 48}{x^2 - 6x}$

2. $\dfrac{2x^2 - 7x - 15}{x^2 - 12x + 35}$

3. $\dfrac{y^2 + 6y + 9}{27x^2 - 3x^2y^2}$

4. $\dfrac{5x^2 - 23x + 12}{5x^2 + 7x - 6}$

6.2

5. $\dfrac{8x^3}{3x + 12} \cdot \dfrac{9x + 36}{16x^2}$

6. $\dfrac{x - 5}{x^2 + 5x - 14} \cdot \dfrac{x^2 + 12x + 35}{15 - 3x}$

7. $\dfrac{x^2 - 9}{2x + 6} \div \dfrac{2x^2 - 5x - 3}{4x^2 - 1}$

8. $\dfrac{3a^2 + 7a + 2}{4a^2 + 11a + 6} \div \dfrac{6a^2 - 13a - 5}{16a^2 - 9}$

6.3

9. $\dfrac{x - 3y}{xy} - \dfrac{4a - y}{ay}$

10. $\dfrac{7}{2x - 4} + \dfrac{-14}{x^2 - 4}$

11. $\dfrac{2x}{x^2 + 10x + 21} + \dfrac{x - 3}{x + 7}$

12. $\dfrac{2}{x^2 + 3x - 10} - \dfrac{5x}{x^2 - 6x + 8}$

Now turn to page SA-14 for the answer to each of these problems. Each answer also includes a reference to the objective in which the problem is first taught. If you missed any of these problems, you should stop and review the Examples and Practice Problems in the referenced objective. A little review now will help you master the material in the upcoming sections of the text.

1. ________________
2. ________________
3. ________________
4. ________________
5. ________________
6. ________________
7. ________________
8. ________________
9. ________________
10. ________________
11. ________________
12. ________________

6.4 Simplifying Complex Rational Expressions

Student Learning Objectives

After studying this section, you will be able to:

1. **Simplify complex rational expressions by adding or subtracting in the numerator and denominator.**
2. **Simplify complex rational expressions using the LCD.**

1 Simplifying Complex Rational Expressions by Adding or Subtracting in the Numerator and Denominator

A **complex rational expression** (also called a **complex fraction**) has a fraction in the numerator or in the denominator, or both.

$$\frac{3 + \frac{2}{x}}{\frac{x}{7} + 2} \qquad \frac{\frac{x}{y} + 1}{2} \qquad \frac{\frac{a+b}{3}}{\frac{x-2y}{4}}$$

The bar in a complex rational expression is both a grouping symbol and a symbol for division.

$$\frac{\frac{a+b}{3}}{\frac{x-2y}{4}} \quad \text{is equivalent to} \quad \left(\frac{a+b}{3}\right) \div \left(\frac{x-2y}{4}\right)$$

We need a procedure for simplifying complex rational expressions.

PROCEDURE TO SIMPLIFY A COMPLEX RATIONAL EXPRESSION ADDING AND SUBTRACTING

1. Add or subtract so that you have a single fraction in the numerator and in the denominator.
2. Divide the fraction in the numerator by the fraction in the denominator. This is done by inverting the fraction in the denominator and multiplying it by the numerator.

EXAMPLE 1 Simplify. $\dfrac{\frac{1}{x}}{\frac{2}{y^2} + \frac{1}{y}}$

Solution

Step 1 Add the two fractions in the denominator.

$$\frac{\frac{1}{x}}{\frac{2}{y^2} + \frac{1}{y}\cdot\frac{y}{y}} = \frac{\frac{1}{x}}{\frac{2+y}{y^2}}$$

Step 2 Divide the fraction in the numerator by the fraction in the denominator.

$$\frac{1}{x} \div \frac{2+y}{y^2} = \frac{1}{x} \cdot \frac{y^2}{2+y} = \frac{y^2}{x(2+y)}$$

Practice Problem 1 Simplify. $\dfrac{\frac{1}{a} + \frac{1}{b}}{\frac{2}{ab^2}}$

NOTE TO STUDENT: Fully worked-out solutions to all of the Practice Problems can be found at the back of the text starting at page SP-1

A complex rational expression may contain two or more fractions in the numerator and the denominator.

EXAMPLE 2 Simplify. $\dfrac{\dfrac{1}{x}+\dfrac{1}{y}}{\dfrac{3}{a}-\dfrac{2}{b}}$

Solution We observe that the LCD of the fractions in the numerator is xy. The LCD of the fractions in the denominator is ab.

$$= \frac{\dfrac{1}{x}\cdot\dfrac{y}{y}+\dfrac{1}{y}\cdot\dfrac{x}{x}}{\dfrac{3}{a}\cdot\dfrac{b}{b}-\dfrac{2}{b}\cdot\dfrac{a}{a}}$$

Multiply each fraction by the appropriate value to obtain common denominators.

$$= \frac{\dfrac{y+x}{xy}}{\dfrac{3b-2a}{ab}}$$

Add the two fractions in the numerator.

Subtract the two fractions in the denominator.

$$= \frac{y+x}{xy}\cdot\frac{ab}{3b-2a}$$

Invert the fraction in the denominator and multiply it by the numerator.

$$= \frac{ab(y+x)}{xy(3b-2a)}$$

Write the answer as one fraction.

Practice Problem 2 Simplify. $\dfrac{\dfrac{1}{a}+\dfrac{1}{b}}{\dfrac{1}{a}-\dfrac{1}{b}}$

For some complex rational expressions, factoring may be necessary to determine the LCD and to combine fractions.

EXAMPLE 3 Simplify. $\dfrac{\dfrac{1}{x^2-1}+\dfrac{2}{x+1}}{x}$

Solution We need to factor $x^2 - 1$.

$$= \frac{\dfrac{1}{(x+1)(x-1)}+\dfrac{2}{(x+1)}\cdot\dfrac{x-1}{x-1}}{x}$$

The LCD for the fractions in the numerator is $(x + 1)(x - 1)$.

$$= \frac{\dfrac{1+2x-2}{(x+1)(x-1)}}{x}$$

Add the two fractions in the numerator.

$$= \frac{2x-1}{(x+1)(x-1)}\cdot\frac{1}{x}$$

Simplify the numerator. Invert the fraction in the denominator and multiply.

$$= \frac{2x-1}{x(x+1)(x-1)}$$

Write the answer as one fraction.

Practice Problem 3 Simplify. $\dfrac{\dfrac{x}{x^2+4x+3}+\dfrac{2}{x+1}}{x+1}$

When simplifying complex rational expressions, always check to see if the final fraction can be reduced or simplified.

EXAMPLE 4 Simplify. $\dfrac{\dfrac{3}{a+b} - \dfrac{3}{a-b}}{\dfrac{5}{a^2-b^2}}$

Solution The LCD of the two fractions in the numerator is $(a+b)(a-b)$.

$$\frac{\dfrac{3}{a+b}\cdot\dfrac{a-b}{a-b} - \dfrac{3}{a-b}\cdot\dfrac{a+b}{a+b}}{\dfrac{5}{a^2-b^2}}$$

$$= \frac{\dfrac{3a-3b}{(a+b)(a-b)} - \dfrac{3a+3b}{(a+b)(a-b)}}{\dfrac{5}{a^2-b^2}}$$

Study carefully how we combine the two fractions in the numerator. Do you see how we obtain $-6b$?

$$= \frac{\dfrac{-6b}{(a+b)(a-b)}}{\dfrac{5}{(a+b)(a-b)}}$$ Factor $a^2 - b^2$ as $(a+b)(a-b)$.

$$= \frac{-6b}{(a+b)(a-b)} \cdot \frac{(a+b)(a-b)}{5}$$ Since $(a+b)(a-b)$ are factors in both numerator and denominator, they may be divided out.

$$= \frac{-6b}{5} \quad \text{or} \quad -\frac{6b}{5}$$

NOTE TO STUDENT: Fully worked-out solutions to all of the Practice Problems can be found at the back of the text starting at page SP-1

Practice Problem 4 Simplify. $\dfrac{\dfrac{6}{x^2-y^2}}{\dfrac{1}{x-y} + \dfrac{3}{x+y}}$

2 Simplifying Complex Rational Expressions Using the LCD

There is another way to simplify complex rational expressions: Multiply the numerator and denominator of the complex fraction by the least common denominator of all the denominators appearing in the complex fraction.

PROCEDURE TO SIMPLIFY A COMPLEX RATIONAL EXPRESSION: MULTIPLYING BY THE LCD

1. Determine the LCD of all individual denominators occurring in the numerator and denominator of the complex rational expression.
2. Multiply both the numerator and the denominator of the complex rational expression by the LCD.
3. Simplify, if possible.

EXAMPLE 5 Simplify by multiplying by the LCD. $\dfrac{\dfrac{5}{ab^2} - \dfrac{2}{ab}}{3 - \dfrac{5}{2a^2b}}$

Solution The LCD of all the denominators in the complex rational expression is $2a^2b^2$.

$$\frac{2a^2b^2\left(\dfrac{5}{ab^2} - \dfrac{2}{ab}\right)}{2a^2b^2\left(3 - \dfrac{5}{2a^2b}\right)}$$

$$= \frac{2a^2b^2\left(\dfrac{5}{ab^2}\right) - 2a^2b^2\left(\dfrac{2}{ab}\right)}{2a^2b^2(3) - 2a^2b^2\left(\dfrac{5}{2a^2b}\right)} \quad \text{Multiply each term by } 2a^2b^2.$$

$$= \frac{10a - 4ab}{6a^2b^2 - 5b} \quad \text{Simplify.}$$

Practice Problem 5 Simplify by multiplying by the LCD. $\dfrac{\dfrac{2}{3x^2} - \dfrac{3}{y}}{\dfrac{5}{xy} - 4}$

So that you can compare the two methods, we will redo Example 4 by multiplying by the LCD.

EXAMPLE 6 Simplify by multiplying by the LCD. $\dfrac{\dfrac{3}{a+b} - \dfrac{3}{a-b}}{\dfrac{5}{a^2 - b^2}}$

Solution The LCD of all individual fractions contained in the complex fraction is $(a + b)(a - b)$.

$$\frac{(a+b)(a-b)\left(\dfrac{3}{a+b}\right) - (a+b)(a-b)\left(\dfrac{3}{a-b}\right)}{(a+b)(a-b)\left(\dfrac{5}{(a+b)(a-b)}\right)} \quad \text{Multiply each term by the LCD.}$$

$$= \frac{3(a-b) - 3(a+b)}{5} \quad \text{Simplify.}$$

$$= \frac{3a - 3b - 3a - 3b}{5} \quad \text{Remove parentheses.}$$

$$= -\frac{6b}{5} \quad \text{Simplify.}$$

Practice Problem 6 Simplify by multiplying by the LCD. $\dfrac{\dfrac{6}{x^2 - y^2}}{\dfrac{7}{x-y} + \dfrac{3}{x+y}}$

6.4 Exercises

Student Solutions Manual | CD/ Video | PH Math Tutor Center | MathXL®Tutorials on CD | MathXL® | MyMathLab® | Interactmath.com

Simplify.

1. $\dfrac{\frac{3}{x}}{\frac{2}{x^2}+\frac{5}{x}}$

2. $\dfrac{\frac{4}{x}}{\frac{7}{x}+\frac{2}{x^2}}$

3. $\dfrac{\frac{1}{x}+\frac{1}{y}}{\frac{1}{xy}}$

4. $\dfrac{\frac{3}{x}+\frac{4}{y}}{\frac{6}{xy}}$

5. $\dfrac{\frac{x}{6}-\frac{1}{3}}{\frac{2}{3x}+\frac{5}{6}}$

6. $\dfrac{\frac{x}{8}-\frac{1}{2}}{\frac{3}{8x}+\frac{3}{4}}$

7. $\dfrac{\frac{7}{5x}-\frac{1}{x}}{\frac{3}{5}+\frac{2}{x}}$

8. $\dfrac{\frac{8}{x}-\frac{2}{3x}}{\frac{2}{3}+\frac{5}{x}}$

9. $\dfrac{\frac{5}{x}+\frac{3}{y}}{3x+5y}$

10. $\dfrac{\frac{1}{x}+\frac{1}{y}}{x+y}$

11. $\dfrac{4-\frac{1}{x^2}}{2+\frac{1}{x}}$

12. $\dfrac{1-\frac{36}{x^2}}{1-\frac{6}{x}}$

13. $\dfrac{\frac{10}{x^2-25}}{\frac{3}{x+5}+\frac{2}{x-5}}$

14. $\dfrac{\frac{8}{x^2-4}}{\frac{7}{x+2}-\frac{3}{x-2}}$

15. $\dfrac{a+\frac{3}{a}}{\frac{a^2+2}{3a}}$

16. $\dfrac{x+\frac{4}{x}}{\frac{x^2+3}{4x}}$

17. $\dfrac{\frac{3}{x-3}}{\frac{1}{x^2-9}+\frac{2}{x+3}}$

18. $\dfrac{\frac{5}{x+4}}{\frac{1}{x-4}-\frac{2}{x^2-16}}$

19. $\dfrac{\frac{2}{y-1}+2}{\frac{2}{y+1}-2}$

20. $\dfrac{\frac{y}{y+1}+1}{\frac{2y+1}{y-1}}$

To Think About

21. Consider the complex fraction $\dfrac{\frac{4}{x+3}}{\frac{5}{x}-1}$. What values are not allowable replacements for the variable x?

22. Consider the complex fraction $\dfrac{\frac{5}{x-2}}{\frac{6}{x}+1}$. What values are not allowable replacements for the variable x?

Cumulative Review

23. Solve for w. $P = 2(l + w)$

24. Solve and graph. $7 + x < 11 + 5x$

5 4 3 2 1 0 1 2 3 4 5 x

25. ***Loan Repayment*** Manuela is paying back a \$4000 loan with no interest from her favorite sister. If Manuela has already paid \$125 per month for 17 months, how much of the loan does she have yet to pay?

26. ***Urban Sprawl*** A neighborhood in Hopewell, New Jersey, is upset because a big office complex is being built in their neighborhood. Many of the citizens of Hopewell moved to their town to get away from urban sprawl. An investment firm will be building a complex planned to cover 3.5 million square feet. This initial estimate could grow to 5.5 million square feet. What percent of increase would this be?

6.5 Solving Equations Involving Rational Expressions

Solving Equations Involving Rational Expressions That Have Solutions

Student Learning Objectives

After studying this section, you will be able to:

1. **Solve equations involving rational expressions that have solutions.**
2. **Determine whether an equation involving rational expressions has no solution.**

In Section 2.4 we developed procedures to solve linear equations containing fractions whose denominators were numerical values. In this section we use a similar approach to solve equations containing fractions whose denominators are polynomials. It would be wise for you to review Section 2.4 briefly *before you begin this section*. It will be especially helpful to carefully study Examples 1 and 2.

TO SOLVE AN EQUATION CONTAINING RATIONAL EXPRESSIONS

1. Determine the LCD of all the denominators.
2. Multiply each term of the equation by the LCD.
3. Solve the resulting equation.
4. Check your solution. Exclude from your solution any value that would make the LCD equal to zero. If such a value is obtained, there is *no solution*.

EXAMPLE 1 Solve for x and check your solution. $\frac{5}{x} + \frac{2}{3} = -\frac{3}{x}$

Solution

$$3x\left(\frac{5}{x}\right) + 3x\left(\frac{2}{3}\right) = 3x\left(-\frac{3}{x}\right) \quad \text{Observe that the LCD is } 3x. \text{ Multiply each term by } 3x.$$

$$15 + 2x = -9$$

$$2x = -9 - 15 \quad \text{Subtract 15 from both sides.}$$

$$2x = -24$$

$$x = -12 \quad \text{Divide both sides by 2.}$$

Check.

$$\frac{5}{-12} + \frac{2}{3} \stackrel{?}{=} -\frac{3}{-12} \quad \text{Replace each } x \text{ by } -12.$$

$$-\frac{5}{12} + \frac{8}{12} \stackrel{?}{=} \frac{3}{12}$$

$$\frac{3}{12} = \frac{3}{12} \checkmark \quad \text{It checks.}$$

Practice Problem 1 Solve for x and check your solution. $\frac{3}{x} + \frac{4}{5} = -\frac{2}{x}$

NOTE TO STUDENT: Fully worked-out solutions to all of the Practice Problems can be found at the back of the text starting at page SP-1

EXAMPLE 2 Solve and check. $\frac{6}{x+3} = \frac{3}{x}$

Solution Observe that the LCD $= x(x + 3)$.

$$x(x+3)\left(\frac{6}{x+3}\right) = x(x+3)\left(\frac{3}{x}\right) \quad \text{Multiply both sides by } x(x+3).$$

$$6x = 3(x + 3) \quad \text{Simplify. Do you see how this is done?}$$

$$6x = 3x + 9 \quad \text{Remove parentheses.}$$

$$3x = 9 \quad \text{Subtract } 3x \text{ from both sides.}$$

$$x = 3 \quad \text{Divide both sides by 3.}$$

Check. $\dfrac{6}{3+3} \stackrel{?}{=} \dfrac{3}{3}$ Replace each x by 3.

$\dfrac{6}{6} = \dfrac{3}{3}$ ✓ It checks.

Practice Problem 2 Solve and check. $\dfrac{4}{2x+1} = \dfrac{6}{2x-1}$

It is sometimes necessary to factor denominators before the correct LCD can be determined.

EXAMPLE 3 Solve and check. $\dfrac{3}{x+5} - 1 = \dfrac{4-x}{2x+10}$

Solution

$$\frac{3}{x+5} - 1 = \frac{4-x}{2(x+5)}$$ Factor $2x + 10$. We determine that the LCD is $2(x + 5)$.

$$2(x+5)\left(\frac{3}{x+5}\right) - 2(x+5)(1) = 2(x+5)\left[\frac{4-x}{2(x+5)}\right]$$ Multiply each term by the LCD.

$$2(3) - 2(x+5) = 4 - x$$ Simplify.

$$6 - 2x - 10 = 4 - x$$ Remove parentheses.

$$-2x - 4 = 4 - x$$ Collect like terms.

$$-4 = 4 + x$$ Add $2x$ to both sides.

$$-8 = x$$ Subtract 4 from both sides.

Check. $\dfrac{3}{-8+5} - 1 \stackrel{?}{=} \dfrac{4-(-8)}{2(-8)+10}$ Replace each x in the original equation by -8.

$$\frac{3}{-3} - 1 \stackrel{?}{=} \frac{4+8}{-16+10}$$

$$-1 - 1 \stackrel{?}{=} \frac{12}{-6}$$

$-2 = -2$ ✓ It checks. The solution is -8.

Practice Problem 3 Solve and check. $\dfrac{x-1}{x^2-4} = \dfrac{2}{x+2} + \dfrac{4}{x-2}$

NOTE TO STUDENT: Fully worked-out solutions to all of the Practice Problems can be found at the back of the text starting at page SP-1

2 Determining Whether an Equation Involving Rational Expressions Has No Solution

Equations containing rational expressions sometimes appear to have solutions when in fact they do not. By this we mean that the "solutions" we get by using completely correct methods are, in actuality, not solutions.

In the case where a value makes a denominator in the equation equal to zero, we say it is not a solution to the equation. Such a value is called an **extraneous solution.** An extraneous solution is an apparent solution that does *not* satisfy the original equation. If all of the apparent solutions of an equation are extraneous solutions, we say that the equation has **no solution.** It is important that you check all apparent solutions in the original equation.

EXAMPLE 4 Solve and check. $\dfrac{y}{y-2} - 4 = \dfrac{2}{y-2}$

Solution Observe that the LCD is $y - 2$.

$$(y-2)\left(\frac{y}{y-2}\right) - (y-2)(4) = (y-2)\left(\frac{2}{y-2}\right)$$ Multiply each term by $(y - 2)$.

$$y - 4(y-2) = 2$$ Simplify. Do you see how this is done?

$$y - 4y + 8 = 2$$ Remove parentheses.

$$-3y + 8 = 2$$ Collect like terms.

$$-3y = -6$$ Subtract 8 from both sides.

$$\frac{-3y}{-3} = \frac{-6}{-3}$$ Divide both sides by -3.

$$y = 2$$ 2 is only an apparent solution.

This equation has no solution.

Why? We can see immediately that $y = 2$ is not a solution for the original equation. When we substitute 2 for y in a denominator, the denominator is equal to zero and the expression is undefined.

Check. $$\frac{y}{y-2} - 4 = \frac{2}{y-2}$$ Suppose that you try to check the apparent solution by substituting 2 for y.

$$\frac{2}{2-2} - 4 \stackrel{?}{=} \frac{2}{2-2}$$

$$\frac{2}{0} - 4 = \frac{2}{0}$$ This does not check since you do not obtain a real number when you divide by zero.

These expressions are not defined.

There is no such number as $2 \div 0$. We see that 2 does *not* check. This equation has **no solution.**

Practice Problem 4 Solve and check. $\dfrac{2x}{x+1} = \dfrac{-2}{x+1} + 1$

6.5 Exercises

Student Solutions Manual | CD/Video | PH Math Tutor Center | MathXL®Tutorials on CD | MathXL® | MyMathLab® | Interactmath.com

Solve and check problems 1–16.

1. $\frac{7}{x} + \frac{3}{4} = \frac{-2}{x}$

2. $\frac{8}{x} + \frac{2}{5} = \frac{-2}{x}$

3. $\frac{-1}{4x} + \frac{3}{2} = \frac{5}{x}$

4. $\frac{1}{3x} + \frac{5}{6} = \frac{2}{x}$

5. $\frac{5x + 3}{3x} = \frac{7}{3} - \frac{9}{x}$

6. $\frac{3x - 7}{4x} = \frac{2}{x} - \frac{9}{4}$

7. $\frac{x + 1}{2x} = \frac{2}{3}$

8. $\frac{x - 2}{4x} = \frac{1}{6}$

9. $\frac{6}{3x - 5} = \frac{3}{2x}$

10. $\frac{1}{x + 6} = \frac{4}{x}$

11. $\frac{2}{2x + 5} = \frac{4}{x - 4}$

12. $\frac{3}{x + 5} = \frac{3}{3x - 2}$

13. $\frac{2}{x} + \frac{x}{x + 1} = 1$

14. $\frac{5}{2} = 3 + \frac{2x + 7}{x + 6}$

15. $\frac{85 - 4x}{x} = 7 - \frac{3}{x}$

16. $\frac{63 - 2x}{x} = 2 - \frac{5}{x}$

Mixed Practice

Solve and check. If there is no solution, so indicate.

17. $\frac{3}{x + 2} - 4 = \frac{4x - 1}{x + 2}$

18. $\frac{4}{x + 3} - 2 = \frac{5x - 9}{x + 3}$

19. $\frac{2}{x - 6} - 5 = \frac{2(x - 5)}{x - 6}$

20. $7 - \frac{x}{x + 5} = \frac{5}{5 + x}$

21. $\frac{2}{x + 1} - \frac{1}{x - 1} = \frac{2x}{x^2 - 1}$

22. $\frac{8x}{4x^2 - 1} = \frac{3}{2x + 1} + \frac{3}{2x - 1}$

23. $\frac{y + 1}{y^2 + 2y - 3} = \frac{1}{y + 3} - \frac{1}{y - 1}$

24. $\frac{6}{x - 5} + \frac{3x + 1}{x^2 - 2x - 15} = \frac{5}{x + 3}$

25. $\frac{2x}{x + 4} - \frac{8}{x - 4} = \frac{2x^2 + 32}{x^2 - 16}$

26. $\frac{4x}{x + 3} - \frac{12}{x - 3} = \frac{4x^2 + 36}{x^2 - 9}$

27. $\dfrac{4}{x^2 - 1} + \dfrac{7}{x + 1} = \dfrac{5}{x - 1}$

28. $\dfrac{7}{4x^2 - 1} + \dfrac{2}{2x + 1} = \dfrac{3}{2x - 1}$

29. $\dfrac{x + 11}{x^2 - 5x + 4} + \dfrac{3}{x - 1} = \dfrac{5}{x - 4}$

30. $\dfrac{6}{x - 3} = \dfrac{-5}{x - 2} + \dfrac{-5}{x^2 - 5x + 6}$

To Think About

In each of the following equations, what values are not allowable replacements for the variable x? Do not solve the equation.

31. $\dfrac{3x}{x - 2} - \dfrac{4x}{x - 4} = \dfrac{3}{x^2 - 6x + 8}$

32. $\dfrac{3x}{x - 1} - \dfrac{5x}{2x + 3} = \dfrac{7}{2x^2 + 5x + 3}$

Cumulative Review

33. Factor. $6x^2 - x - 12$

34. Solve. $4 - (3 - x) = 7(x + 3)$

▲ **35.** ***Geometry*** The perimeter of a rectangular sign is 54 meters. The length is 1 meter less than triple the width. Find the dimensions of the sign.

36. ***Mortgage Payments*** Wally and Adele Panzas plan to purchase a new home and borrow \$115,000. They plan to take out a 25-year mortgage at an annual interest rate of 8.75%. The bank will charge them \$8.23 per month for each \$1000 of mortgage. What will their monthly payments be?

Immigrants *The accompanying bar graph depicts the number of immigrants to the United States from Europe and Latin America for each decade from 1960 to 2010. Use the graph to answer exercises 37–40.*

37. What was the percent of decrease in immigrants from Europe from the decade 1960–1969 to the decade 1970–1979? Round to the nearest tenth.

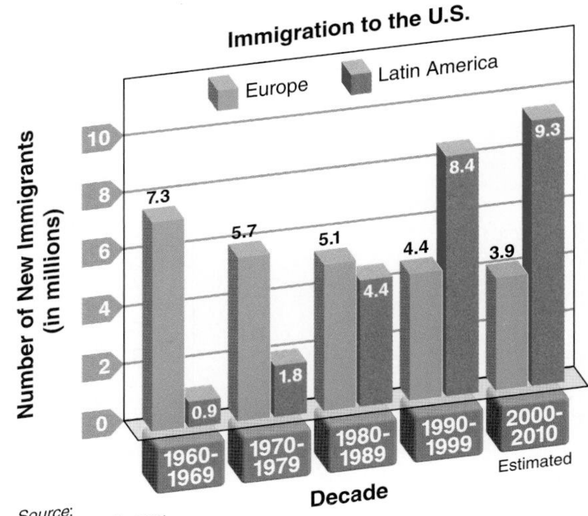

38. What was the percent of increase in immigrants from Latin America from the decade 1980–1989 to the decade 1990–1999? Round to the nearest tenth.

39. If the rate of increase in immigrants from Latin America from the decade starting in 1990 to the decade starting in 2000 continues for another two decades, what will be the expected number of immigrants from Latin America to the United States in 2010? Round to the nearest tenth.

40. If the rate of decrease in immigrants from Europe from the decade starting in 1990 to the decade starting in 2000 continues for another two decades, what will be the expected number of immigrants from Europe to the United States in the decade starting in 2010?

6.6 RATIO, PROPORTION, AND OTHER APPLIED PROBLEMS

Student Learning Objectives

After studying this section, you will be able to:

1. **Solve problems involving ratio and proportion.**
2. **Solve problems involving similar triangles.**
3. **Solve distance problems involving rational expressions.**
4. **Solve work problems.**

1 Solving Problems Involving Ratio and Proportion

A **ratio** is a comparison of two quantities. You may be familiar with ratios that compare miles to hours or miles to gallons. A ratio is often written as a quotient in the form of a fraction. For example, the ratio of 7 to 9 can be written as $\frac{7}{9}$.

A **proportion** is an equation that states that two ratios are equal. For example,

$$\frac{7}{9} = \frac{21}{27}, \quad \frac{2}{3} = \frac{10}{15}, \quad \text{and} \quad \frac{a}{b} = \frac{c}{d} \quad \text{are proportions.}$$

Let's take a closer look at the last proportion. We can see that the LCD of the fractional equation is bd.

$$(bd)\frac{a}{b} = (bd)\frac{c}{d} \qquad \text{Multiply each side by the LCD.}$$

$$da = bc$$

$$ad = bc \qquad \text{Since multiplication is commutative, } da = ad.$$

Thus we have proved the following.

THE PROPORTION EQUATION

If

$$\frac{a}{b} = \frac{c}{d}, \quad \text{then} \quad ad = bc$$

for all real numbers a, b, c, and d, where $b \neq 0$ and $d \neq 0$.

This is sometimes called **cross multiplying.** It can be applied only if you have *one* fraction and nothing else on each side of the equation.

EXAMPLE 1 Michael took 5 hours to drive 245 miles on the turnpike. At the same rate, how many hours will it take him to drive a distance of 392 miles?

Solution

1. ***Understand the problem.*** Let $x =$ the number of hours it will take to drive 392 miles. If 5 hours are needed to drive 245 miles, then x hours are needed to drive 392 miles.
2. ***Write an equation.*** We can write this as a proportion. Compare time to distance in each ratio.

$$\begin{matrix} \text{Time} & \longrightarrow \\ \text{Distance} & \longrightarrow \end{matrix} \frac{5 \text{ hours}}{245 \text{ miles}} = \frac{x \text{ hours}}{392 \text{ miles}} \begin{matrix} \longleftarrow & \text{Time} \\ \longleftarrow & \text{Distance} \end{matrix}$$

3. ***Solve and state the answer.***

$$5(392) = 245x \qquad \text{Cross multiply.}$$

$$\frac{1960}{245} = x \qquad \text{Divide both sides by 245.}$$

$$8 = x$$

It will take Michael 8 hours to drive 392 miles.

4. ***Check.*** Is $\frac{5}{245} = \frac{8}{392}$? Do the computation and see.

Practice Problem 1 It took Brenda 8 hours to drive 420 miles. At the same rate, how long would it take her to drive 315 miles?

NOTE TO STUDENT: Fully worked-out solutions to all of the Practice Problems can be found at the back of the text starting at page SP-1

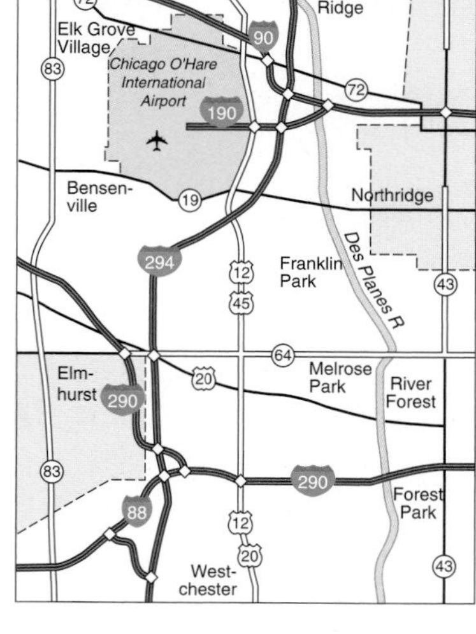

EXAMPLE 2 If $\frac{3}{4}$ inch on a map represents an actual distance of 20 miles, how long is the distance represented by $4\frac{1}{8}$ inches on the same map?

Solution Let x = the distance represented by $4\frac{1}{8}$ inches.

Initial measurement on map $\longrightarrow$ $\frac{3}{4} = \frac{4\frac{1}{8}}{x}$ $\longleftarrow$ Second measurement on the map

Initial distance $\longrightarrow$ 20, x $\longleftarrow$ Second distance

$$\left(\frac{3}{4}\right)(x) = (20)\left(4\frac{1}{8}\right) \quad \text{Cross multiply.}$$

$$\left(\frac{3}{4}\right)(x) = \overset{5}{\cancel{(20)}}\left(\frac{33}{\underset{2}{\cancel{8}}}\right) \quad \text{Write } 4\tfrac{1}{8} \text{ as } \tfrac{33}{8} \text{ and simplify.}$$

$$\frac{3x}{4} = \frac{165}{2} \quad \text{Multiplication of fractions.}$$

$$4\left(\frac{3x}{4}\right) = \overset{2}{\cancel{4}}\left(\frac{165}{\cancel{2}}\right) \quad \text{Multiply each side by 4.}$$

$$3x = 330 \quad \text{Simplify.}$$

$$x = 110 \quad \text{Divide both sides by 3.}$$

$4\frac{1}{8}$ inches on the map represents an actual distance of 110 miles.

Practice Problem 2 If $\frac{5}{8}$ inch on a map represents an actual distance of 30 miles, how long is the distance represented by $2\frac{1}{2}$ inches on the same map?

2 Solving Problems Involving Similar Triangles

Similar triangles are triangles that have the same shape, but may be different sizes. For example, if you draw a triangle on a sheet of paper, place the paper in a photocopy machine, and make a copy that is reduced by 25%, you would create a triangle that is similar to the original triangle. The two triangles will have the same shape. The corresponding sides of the triangles will be proportional. The corresponding angles of the triangles will also be equal.

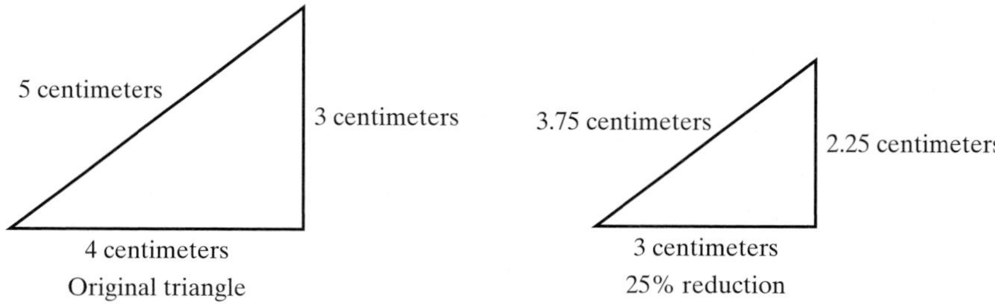

You can use the proportion equation to show that the corresponding sides of the preceding triangles are proportional. In fact, you can use the proportion equation to find an unknown length of a side of one of the two similar triangles.

▲ **EXAMPLE 3** A ramp is 32 meters long and rises up 15 meters. A ramp at the same angle is 9 meters long. How high is the second ramp?

Solution To answer this question, we find the length of side x in the following two similar triangles.

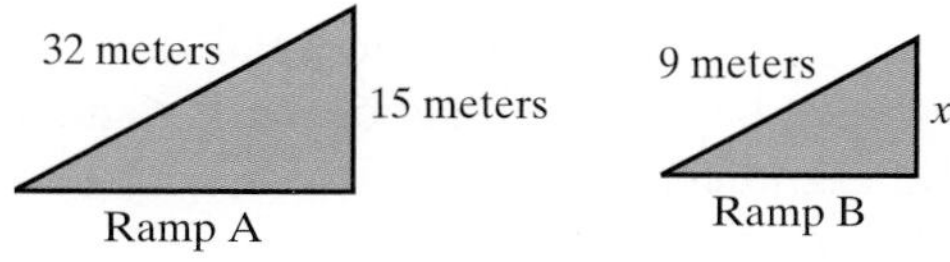

$$\begin{array}{lcl} \text{Ramp A, longest side} \longrightarrow & \dfrac{32}{9} = \dfrac{15}{x} & \longleftarrow \text{Shortest side, ramp A} \\ \text{Ramp B, longest side} \longrightarrow & & \longleftarrow \text{Shortest side, ramp B} \end{array}$$

$$32x = (9)(15) \quad \text{Cross multiply.}$$

$$32x = 135 \quad \text{Multiply.}$$

$$x = \frac{135}{32} \quad \text{Divide both sides by 32.}$$

$$\text{or} \quad x = 4\frac{7}{32} \text{ meters}$$

NOTE TO STUDENT: Fully worked-out solutions to all of the Practice Problems can be found at the back of the text starting at page SP-1

▲ **Practice Problem 3** Triangle C is similar to triangle D. Find the length of side x. Leave your answer as a fraction.

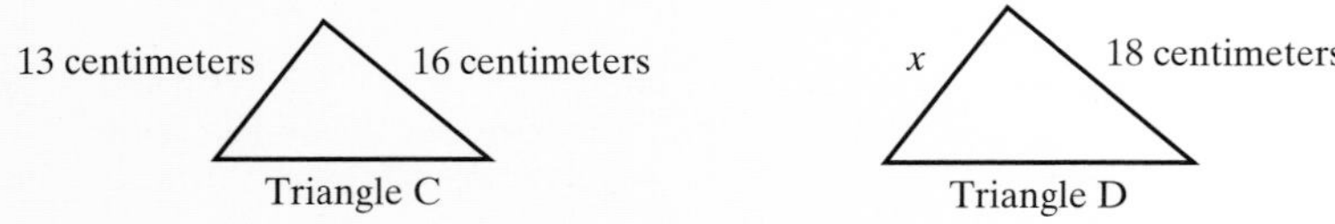

We can also use similar triangles for indirect measurement—for instance, to find the measure of an object that is too tall to measure using standard measuring devices. When the sun shines on two vertical objects at the same time, the shadows and the objects form similar triangles.

▲ **EXAMPLE 4** A woman who is 5 feet tall casts a shadow that is 8 feet long. At the same time of day, a building casts a shadow that is 72 feet long. How tall is the building?

Solution

1. ***Understand the problem.*** First we draw a sketch. We do not know the height of the building, so we call it x.

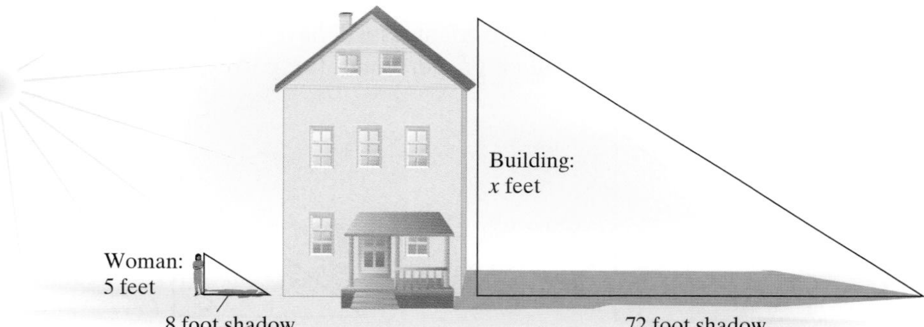

2. ***Write an equation and solve.***

$$\begin{array}{lcl} \text{Height of woman} \longrightarrow & \dfrac{5}{8} = \dfrac{x}{72} & \longleftarrow \text{Height of building} \\ \text{Length of woman's shadow} \longrightarrow & & \longleftarrow \text{Length of building's shadow} \end{array}$$

$$(5)(72) = 8x \quad \text{Cross multiply.}$$

$$360 = 8x$$

$$45 = x$$

The height of the building is 45 feet.

▲ **Practice Problem 4** A man who is 6 feet tall casts a shadow that is 7 feet long. At the same time of day, a large flagpole casts a shadow that is 38.5 feet long. How tall is the flagpole?

In problems such as Example 4, we are assuming that the building and the person are standing exactly perpendicular to the ground. In other words, each triangle is assumed to be a right triangle. In other similar triangle problems, if the triangles are not right triangles you must be careful that the angles between the objects and the ground are the same.

3 Solving Distance Problems Involving Rational Expressions

Some distance problems are solved using equations with rational expressions. We will need the formula Distance = Rate × Time, $D = RT$, which we can write in the form $T = \frac{D}{R}$. In the United States, distances are usually measured in miles. In European countries, distances are usually measured in kilometers.

EXAMPLE 5 A French commuter airline flies from Paris to Avignon. Plane A flies at a speed that is 50 kilometers per hour faster than plane B. Plane A flies 500 kilometers in the amount of time that plane B flies 400 kilometers. Find the speed of each plane.

Solution

1. ***Understand the problem.*** Let $s =$ the speed of plane B in kilometers per hour.
   Let $s + 50 =$ the speed of plane A in kilometers per hour.
   Make a simple table for D, R, and T.

	D	R	$T = \frac{D}{R}$
Plane A	500	$s + 50$	?
Plane B	400	s	?

   Since $T = \frac{D}{R}$, for each plane we divide the expression for D by the expression for R and write it in the table in the column for time.

	D	R	$T = \frac{D}{R}$
Plane A	500	$s + 50$	$\frac{500}{s + 50}$
Plane B	400	s	$\frac{400}{s}$

2. ***Write an equation and solve.*** Each plane flies for the same amount of time. That is, the time for plane A equals the time for plane B.

$$\frac{500}{s + 50} = \frac{400}{s}$$

   You can solve this equation using the methods in Section 6.5 or you may cross multiply. Here we will cross multiply.

$$500s = (s + 50)(400) \quad \text{Cross multiply.}$$
$$500s = 400s + 20{,}000 \quad \text{Remove parentheses.}$$
$$100s = 20{,}000 \quad \text{Subtract } 400s \text{ from each side.}$$
$$s = 200 \quad \text{Divide each side by 100.}$$

Plane B travels 200 kilometers per hour. Since

$$s + 50 = 200 + 50 = 250,$$

plane A travels 250 kilometers per hour.

Practice Problem 5 Two European freight trains traveled toward Paris for the same amount of time. Train A traveled 180 kilometers, while train B traveled 150 kilometers. Train A traveled 10 kilometers per hour faster than train B. What was the speed of each train?

4 Solving Work Problems

Some applied problems involve the length of time needed to do a job. These problems are often referred to as work problems.

EXAMPLE 6 Reynaldo can sort a huge stack of mail on an old sorting machine in 9 hours. His brother Carlos can sort the same amount of mail using a newer sorting machine in 8 hours. How long would it take them to do the job working together? Express your answer in hours and minutes. Round to the nearest minute.

Solution

1. ***Understand the problem.*** Let's do a little reasoning.

   If Reynaldo can do the job in 9 hours, then in *1 hour* he could do $\frac{1}{9}$ of the job.
   If Carlos can do the job in 8 hours, then in *1 hour* he could do $\frac{1}{8}$ of the job.
   Let $x =$ the number of hours it takes Reynaldo and Carlos to do the job together. In *1 hour* together they could do $\frac{1}{x}$ of the job.

2. ***Write an equation and solve.*** The amount of work Reynaldo can do in 1 hour plus the amount of work Carlos can do in 1 hour must be equal to the amount of work they could do together in 1 hour.

Amount of work done by Reynaldo	+	Amount of work done by Carlos	=	Amount of work done together
$\frac{1}{9}$	+	$\frac{1}{8}$	=	$\frac{1}{x}$

Let us solve for x. We observe that the LCD is $72x$.

$$72x\left(\frac{1}{9}\right) + 72x\left(\frac{1}{8}\right) = 72x\left(\frac{1}{x}\right) \quad \text{Multiply each term by the LCD.}$$

$$8x + 9x = 72 \quad \text{Simplify.}$$

$$17x = 72 \quad \text{Collect like terms.}$$

$$x = \frac{72}{17} \quad \text{Divide each side by 17.}$$

$$x = 4\frac{4}{17}$$

To change $\frac{4}{17}$ of an hour to minutes we multiply.

$$\frac{4}{17}\,\cancel{\text{hour}} \times \frac{60 \text{ minutes}}{1\,\cancel{\text{hour}}} = \frac{240}{17} \text{ minutes, which is approximately 14.118 minutes}$$

To the nearest minute this is 14 minutes. Thus doing the job together will take 4 hours and 14 minutes.

Practice Problem 6 John Tobey and Dave Wells obtained night custodian jobs at a local factory while going to college part time. Using the buffer machine, John can buff all the floors in the building in 6 hours. Dave takes a little longer and can do all the floors in the building in 7 hours. Their supervisor bought another buffer machine. How long will it take John and Dave to do all the floors in the building working together, each with his own machine? Express your answer in hours and minutes. Round to the nearest minute.

Calculator

Reciprocals

You can find $\frac{1}{x}$ for any value of x on a scientific calculator by using the key labeled $\boxed{x^{-1}}$ or the key labeled $\boxed{1/x}$. For example, to find $\frac{1}{9}$, we use 9 $\boxed{x^{-1}}$ or 9 $\boxed{1/x}$. The display will read 0.11111111. Therefore we can solve Example 6 as follows:

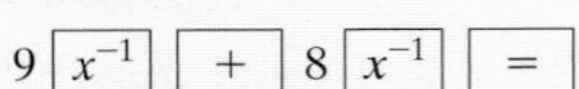

9 $\boxed{x^{-1}}$ $\boxed{+}$ 8 $\boxed{x^{-1}}$ $\boxed{=}$

The display will read 0.2361111.

Thus we have obtained the equation $0.2361111 = \frac{1}{x}$. Now this is equivalent to $x = \frac{1}{0.2361111}$. (Do you see why?) Thus we enter 0.2361111 $\boxed{x^{-1}}$, and the display reads 4.235294118. If we round to the nearest hundredth, we have $x \approx 4.24$ hours, which is approximately equal to our answer of $4\frac{4}{17}$ hours.

NOTE TO STUDENT: Fully worked-out solutions to all of the Practice Problems can be found at the back of the text starting at page SP-1

6.6 Exercises

Student Solutions Manual | CD/Video | PH Math Tutor Center | MathXL®Tutorials on CD | MathXL® | MyMathLab® | Interactmath.com

Solve.

1. $\frac{4}{9} = \frac{8}{x}$

2. $\frac{5}{12} = \frac{x}{8}$

3. $\frac{x}{17} = \frac{12}{5}$

4. $\frac{16}{x} = \frac{3}{4}$

5. $\frac{8}{5} = \frac{x}{7}$

6. $\frac{6}{x} = \frac{45}{12}$

7. $\frac{7}{x} = \frac{40}{130}$

8. $\frac{x}{18} = \frac{13}{2}$

Applications

Use a proportion to answer exercises 9–16.

9. ***Map Scale*** The scale on the AAA map of Colorado is approximately $\frac{3}{4}$ inch to 15 miles. If the distance from Denver to Pueblo measures 5.5 inches on the map, how far apart are the two cities?

10. ***Recipe Ratios*** Nella Coates's recipe for Shoofly Pie contains $\frac{3}{4}$ cup of unsulfured molasses. This recipe makes a small pie that serves 8 people. If she makes the larger pie that serves 12 people and the ratio of molasses to people remains the same, how much molasses will she need for the larger pie?

11. ***Exchange Rates*** Jocelyn Robinson spent a year studying in Australia. The day she arrived, the exchange rate was 1.49 Australian dollars per U.S. dollar. When she arrived she exchanged $700 U.S.

(a) How many Australian dollars were her $700 worth?

(b) Three days later, the value of the Australian dollar rose to 1.68 Australian dollars per U.S. dollar. How much more money would she have received had she waited the three days to exchange her money?

12. ***Exchange Rates*** Sarah Tanguay spent last summer touring thoughout Europe. On the day she landed in Paris, the exchange rate for the Euro was 0.88 Euros per U.S. dollar. Jen converted $650 to euros that day.

(a) How many euros did Jen receive for her $650?

(b) On her way back home, Jen decided to stop in England for a week. She had €250 (250 Euros) that she wanted to change into British pounds for her stay in London. If the exchange rate on the day she landed was 0.69 British pounds per Euro, how many pounds did she receive?

13. ***Speed Units*** Alfonse and Melinda are taking a drive in Mexico. They know that a speed of 100 kilometers per hour is approximately equal to 62 miles per hour. They are now driving on a Mexican road that has a speed limit of 90 kilometers per hour. How many miles per hour is the speed limit? Round to the nearest mile per hour.

14. ***Baggage Weight*** Dick and Anne took a trip to France. Their suitcases were weighed at the airport and the weight recorded was 39 kilograms. If 50 kilograms is equivalent to 110 pounds, how many pounds did their suitcases weigh? Round to the nearest pound.

15. ***Map Scale*** On a map the distance between two mountains is $3\frac{1}{2}$ inches. The actual distance between the mountains is 136 miles. Russ is camped at a location that on the map is $\frac{3}{4}$ inch from the base of the mountain. How many miles is he from the base of the mountain? Round to the nearest mile.

16. ***Construction Scales*** Maria is adding a porch to her house that is 18 feet long. On the drawing done by the carpenter the length is shown as 11 inches. The drawing shows that the width of the porch is 8 inches. How many feet wide will the porch be? Round to the nearest foot.

Geometry *Triangles A and B are similar. Use them to answer exercises 17–20. Leave your answers as fractions.*

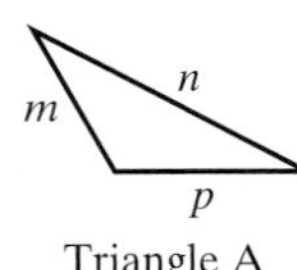

Triangle A

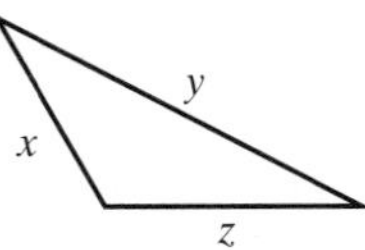

Triangle B

▲ **17.** If $x = 20$ in., $y = 29$ in., and $m = 13$ in., find the length of side n.

▲ **18.** If $p = 14$ in., $m = 17$ in., and $z = 23$ in., find the length of side x.

▲ **19.** If $x = 175$ meters, $n = 40$ meters, and $m = 35$ meters find the length of side y.

▲ **20.** If $z = 18$ cm, $y = 25$ cm, and $n = 9$ cm, find the length of side p.

Geometry *Just as we have discussed similar triangles, other geometric shapes can be similar. Similar geometric shapes will have sides that are proportional. Quadrilaterals abcd and ghjk are similar. Use them to answer exercises 21–24. Leave your answers as fractions.*

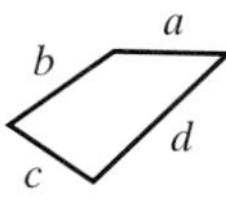

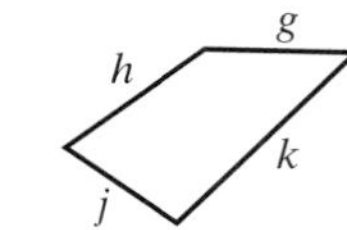

▲ **21.** If $a = 7$ in., $g = 9$ in., and $k = 12$ in., find the length of side d.

▲ **22.** If $b = 8$ ft, $c = 7$ ft, and $j = 11$ ft, find the length of side h.

▲ **23.** If $b = 20$ m, $h = 24$ m, and $d = 32$ m, find the length of side k.

▲ **24.** If $a = 16$ cm, $d = 19$ cm, and $k = 23$ cm, find the length of side g.

Use a proportion to solve.

▲ **25.** ***Geometry*** A rectangle whose width-to-length ratio is approximately 5 to 8 is called a **golden rectangle** and is said to be pleasing to the eye. Using this ratio, what should the length of a rectangular picture be if its width is to be 30 inches?

▲ **26.** ***Shadows*** Jake is 6 feet tall and notices that he casts a shadow of 8 feet. At the same time, the new public sculpture in the park casts a shadow of 23 feet. How tall is the sculpture? (Round your answer to the nearest foot.)

▲ **27.** ***Floral Displays*** Floral designers often create arrangements where the flower height to container ratio is 5 to 3. The FIU Art Museum wishes to create a floral display for the opening of a new show. They know they want to use an antique Chinese vase from their collection that is 13 inches high. How tall will the entire flower arrangement be if they use this standard ratio? (Round your answer to the nearest inch.)

▲ **28.** ***Securing Wires*** A wire line helps to secure a radio transmission tower. The wire measures 23 meters from the tower to the ground anchor pin. The wire is secured 14 meters up on the tower. If a second wire is secured 130 meters up on the tower and is extended from the tower at the same angle as the first wire, how long would the second wire need to be to reach an anchor pin on the ground? Round to the nearest meter.

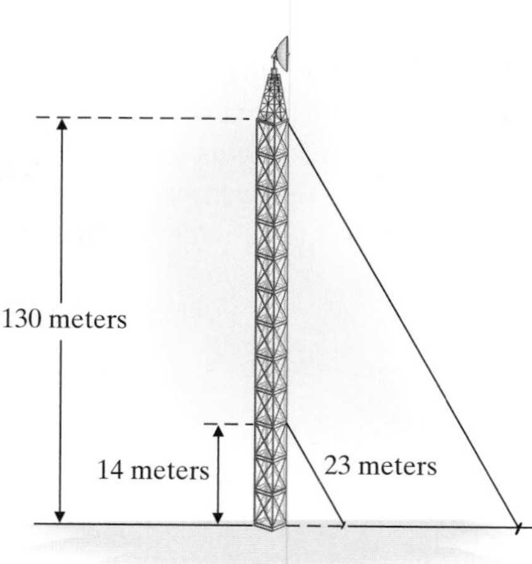

29. ***Acceleration*** Ben Hale is driving his new Toyota Camry on Interstate 90 at 45 miles per hour. He accelerates at the rate of 3 miles per hour every 2 seconds. How fast will he be traveling after accelerating for 11 seconds?

30. ***Braking*** Tim Newitt is driving a U-Haul truck to Chicago. He is driving at 55 miles per hour and has to hit the brakes because of heavy traffic. His truck slows at the rate of 2 miles per hour for every 3 seconds. How fast will he be traveling 10 seconds after he hits the brakes?

31. ***Flight Speeds*** A Montreal commuter airliner travels 40 kilometers per hour faster than the television news helicopter over the city. The commuter airliner travels 1250 kilometers during the same time that the television news helicopter travels only 1050 kilometers. How fast does the commuter airliner fly? How fast does the television news helicopter fly?

32. ***Driving Speeds*** Melissa drove to Dallas while Marcia drove to Houston in the same amount of time. Melissa drove 360 kilometers, while Marcia drove 280 kilometers. Melissa traveled 20 kilometers per hour faster than Marcia on her trip. What was the average speed in kilometers per hour for each woman?

33. ***Fluff Containers*** Marshmallow fluff comes in only two sizes, a $7\frac{1}{2}$ - oz glass jar and a 16-oz plastic tub. At a local market, the 16-oz tub costs \$1.49 and the $7\frac{1}{2}$ - oz jar costs \$0.79.

(a) How much does marshmallow fluff in the glass jar cost per oz? (Round your answer to the nearest cent.)

(b) How much does marshmallow fluff in the plastic tub cost per oz? (Round your answer to the nearest cent.)

(c) If the marshmallow fluff company decided to add a third size, a 40-oz bucket, how much would the price be if it was at the same unit price as the 16-oz plastic tub? (*Hint:* Set up a proportion. Do *not* use your answer from part (b). Round your answer to the nearest cent.)

34. ***Green Tea*** Won Ling is a Chinese tea importer in Boston's Chinatown. He charges \$12.25 for four sample packs of his famous green tea. The packs are in the following sizes: 25 grams, 40 grams, 50 grams, and 60 grams.

(a) How much is Won Ling charging per gram for his green tea?

(b) How much would you pay for a 60-gram pack if he were willing to sell that one by itself?

(c) How much would you pay for an 800-gram package of green tea if it cost the same amount per gram?

35. ***Lawn Mowing*** It takes a person using a large rotary mower 4 hours to mow all the lawns at the town park. It takes a person using a small rotary mower 5 hours to mow these same lawns. How long should it take two people using these mowers to mow these lawns together? Round to the nearest minute.

36. ***Tank Cleaning*** Juan Reyes works at Sea World. Every fish tank needs a thorough cleaning once a week. It takes Juan 5 hours to clean all the tanks in the store. When Juan is not there, Chet James does the cleaning. Since he is not as experienced as Juan, it takes Chet 7 hours to do the same job. At the start of the July sales promotion, the boss wanted all the tanks cleaned as quickly as possible so that Juan could help with the customers. He had both Chet and Juan cleaning the tanks. How long did it take them to do the job? (Round your answer to the nearest minute.)

37. ***Raking Leaves*** When all the leaves have fallen at Fred and Suzie's house in Concord, New Hampshire, Suzie can rake the entire yard in 6 hours. When Fred does it alone, it takes him 8 hours. How long would it take them to rake the yard together? Round to the nearest minute.

38. ***Typing Speed*** Professor Matthews can type his course syllabus in 12 hours. The departmental secretary can type it in 7 hours. How long would it take the two people to type it together? Round to the nearest minute.

Cumulative Review

39. Write in scientific notation. 0.000892465

40. Write in decimal notation. 5.82×10^8

41. Write with positive exponents. $\dfrac{x^{-3}y^{-2}}{z^4w^{-8}}$

42. Evaluate. $\left(\dfrac{2}{3}\right)^{-3}$

Putting Your Skills to Work

Determining Monthly Profit of a Business

Rick and Wally discovered a great need for a calculator store in their city. They opened a store called Calculator Corner in a major shopping mall. As long as they advertised in local newspapers, they discovered that they made a good profit. When they spent \$1000 a month in advertising, the Calculator Corner store made a monthly profit of \$6000. When they spent \$3000 a month in advertising, the store made a monthly profit of \$12,000. The following chart shows the observed relationship between monthly advertising and the monthly profit of the store in thousands of dollars. They measured the profit after subtracting all expenses, including advertising, salaries and benefits of employees, taxes, rent, utilities, and shipping expenses.

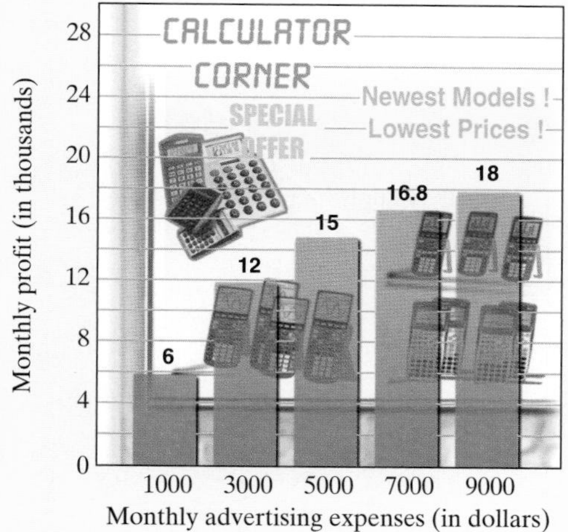

Problems for Individual Investigation and Analysis

1. When they increased the monthly advertising budget from \$3000 to \$5000, how much did the monthly profit of the store increase?

2. When they increased the monthly advertising budget from \$7000 to \$9000, how much did the monthly profit of the store increase?

Problems for Group Investigation and Cooperative Learning

Rich and Wally discovered that the predicted monthly profit of the business (measured in thousands of dollars) could be obtained from the equation

$$P = \frac{24x^2 + 120x}{x^2 + 8x + 15}$$

where x is the number of thousands of dollars in the monthly advertising budget.

3. Using your skills learned in this chapter, factor the numerator and denominator and then simplify the equation.

4. Use the simplified equation obtained in exercise 3 to predict the monthly profit if the monthly advertising budget is \$11,000. (Round to the nearest dollar.)

5. Use the simplified equation obtained in exercise 3 to predict how large a monthly advertising budget would be needed to obtain a monthly profit of \$20,000.

6. Use the simplified equation obtained in exercise 3 to predict how large a monthly advertising budget would be needed to obtain a monthly profit of \$21,000.

Chapter 6 Organizer

Topic	Procedure	Examples
Simplifying rational expressions, p. 356.	**1.** Factor the numerator and denominator. **2.** Divide out any factor common to both the numerator and denominator.	$\frac{36x^2 - 16y^2}{18x^2 + 24xy + 8y^2} = \frac{4(3x - 2y)(3x + 2y)}{2(3x + 2y)(3x + 2y)}$ $= \frac{2(3x - 2y)}{3x - 2y}$
Multiplying rational expressions, p. 362.	**1.** Factor all numerators and denominators and rewrite the product as one fraction. **2.** Simplify the resulting rational expression as described above.	$\frac{x^2 - y^2}{x^2 + 2xy + y^2} \cdot \frac{x^2 + 4xy + 3y^2}{x^2 - 4xy + 3y^2}$ $= \frac{(x + y)(x - y)(x + y)(x + 3y)}{(x + y)(x + y)(x - y)(x - 3y)}$ $= \frac{x + 3y}{x - 3y}$
Dividing rational expressions, p. 363.	**1.** Invert the second fraction and rewrite the problem as a product. **2.** Multiply the rational expressions.	$\frac{14x^2 + 17x - 6}{x^2 - 25} \div \frac{4x^2 - 8x - 21}{x^2 + 10x + 25}$ $= \frac{(2x + 3)(7x - 2)}{(x + 5)(x - 5)} \cdot \frac{(x + 5)(x + 5)}{(2x - 7)(2x + 3)}$ $= \frac{(7x - 2)(x + 5)}{(x - 5)(2x - 7)}$
Adding rational expressions, p. 367.	**1.** If the denominators differ, factor them and determine the least common denominator (LCD). **2.** Change each fraction by multiplication into an equivalent one with the LCD. **3.** Add numerators; put the answer over the LCD. **4.** Simplify as needed.	$\frac{x - 1}{x^2 - 4} + \frac{x - 1}{3x + 6} = \frac{x - 1}{(x + 2)(x - 2)} + \frac{x - 1}{3(x + 2)}$ $\text{LCD} = 3(x + 2)(x - 2)$ $\frac{x - 1}{(x + 2)(x - 2)} = \frac{?}{3(x + 2)(x - 2)}$ Need to multiply by $\frac{3}{3}$. $\frac{(x - 1)}{3(x + 2)} = \frac{?}{3(x + 2)(x - 2)}$ Need to multiply by $\frac{x - 2}{x - 2}$. $\frac{x - 1}{(x + 2)(x - 2)} + \frac{x - 1}{3(x + 2)}$ $= \frac{(x - 1) \cdot 3}{3(x + 2)(x - 2)} + \frac{(x - 1)(x - 2)}{3(x + 2)(x - 2)}$ $= \frac{3x - 3 + x^2 - 3x + 2}{3(x + 2)(x - 2)}$ $= \frac{x^2 - 1}{3(x + 2)(x - 2)}$
Subtracting rational expressions, p. 367.	Move a subtraction sign to the numerator of the second fraction. Add. Simplify if possible. $\frac{a}{b} - \frac{c}{b} = \frac{a}{b} + \frac{-c}{b}$	$\frac{5x}{x - 2} - \frac{3x + 4}{x - 2} = \frac{5x}{x - 2} + \frac{-(3x + 4)}{x - 2}$ $= \frac{5x - 3x - 4}{x - 2}$ $= \frac{2x - 4}{x - 2}$ $= \frac{2(x - 2)}{x - 2} = 2$

Topic	Procedure	Examples
Simplifying complex rational expressions, p. 376.	**1.** Add the two fractions in the numerator. **2.** Add the two fractions in the denominator. **3.** Divide the fraction in the numerator by the fraction in the denominator. This is done by inverting the fraction in the denominator and multiplying by the numerator. **4.** Simplify.	$\dfrac{\dfrac{x}{x^2-4}+\dfrac{1}{x+2}}{\dfrac{3}{x+2}-\dfrac{4}{x-2}}$ $=\dfrac{\dfrac{x}{(x+2)(x-2)}+\dfrac{1(x-2)}{(x+2)(x-2)}}{\dfrac{3(x-2)}{(x+2)(x-2)}+\dfrac{-4(x+2)}{(x+2)(x-2)}}$ $=\dfrac{\dfrac{x+x-2}{(x+2)(x-2)}}{\dfrac{3x-6-4x-8}{(x+2)(x-2)}}$ $=\dfrac{2x-2}{(x+2)(x-2)}\div\dfrac{-x-14}{(x+2)(x-2)}$ $=\dfrac{2(x-1)}{(x+2)(x-2)}\cdot\dfrac{(x+2)(x-2)}{-x-14}$ $=\dfrac{2x-2}{-x-14}$ or $\dfrac{-2x+2}{x+14}$
Solving equations involving rational expressions, p. 381.	**1.** Determine the LCD of all denominators. **2.** Note what values will make the LCD equal to 0. These are excluded from your solutions. **3.** Multiply each side by the LCD, distributing as needed. **4.** Solve the resulting polynomial equation. **5.** Check. Be sure to exclude those values found in step 2.	$\dfrac{3}{x-2}=\dfrac{4}{x+2}$ LCD $=(x-2)(x+2)$. Since LCD $\neq 0$, then $x \neq 2, -2$. $(x-2)(x+2)\dfrac{3}{x-2}=\dfrac{4}{x+2}(x-2)(x+2)$ $3(x+2)=4(x-2)$ $3x+6=4x-8$ $-x=-14$ $x=14$ (Since $x \neq 2, -2$, this solution should check unless an error has been made.) *Check:* $\dfrac{3}{14-2}\stackrel{?}{=}\dfrac{4}{14+2}$ $\dfrac{3}{12}\stackrel{?}{=}\dfrac{4}{16}$ $\dfrac{1}{4}=\dfrac{1}{4}$ ✓
Solving applied problems with proportions, p. 386.	**1.** Organize the data. **2.** Write a proportion equating the respective parts. Let x represent the value that is not known. **3.** Solve the proportion.	Renee can make five cherry pies with 3 cups of flour. How many cups of flour does she need to make eight cherry pies? $\dfrac{5 \text{ cherry pies}}{3 \text{ cups flour}}=\dfrac{8 \text{ cherry pies}}{x \text{ cups flour}}$ $\dfrac{5}{3}=\dfrac{8}{x}$ $5x=24$ $x=\dfrac{24}{5}$ $x=4\dfrac{4}{5}$ $4\dfrac{4}{5}$ cups of flour are needed for eight cherry pies.

Chapter 6 Review Problems

Section 6.1

Simplify.

1. $\dfrac{bx}{bx - by}$

2. $\dfrac{4x - 4y}{5y - 5x}$

3. $\dfrac{2x^2 + 5x - 3}{2x^2 - 9x + 4}$

4. $\dfrac{3x^2 + 7x + 2}{3x^2 + 13x + 4}$

5. $\dfrac{x^2 - 9}{x^2 - 10x + 21}$

6. $\dfrac{2x^2 + 18x + 40}{3x + 15}$

7. $\dfrac{x^3 + 3x^2}{x^3 - 2x^2 - 15x}$

8. $\dfrac{4x^2 + 4x - 3}{4x^2 - 2x}$

9. $\dfrac{2x^2 - 2xy - 24y^2}{2x^2 + 5xy - 3y^2}$

10. $\dfrac{4 - y^2}{3y^2 + 5y - 2}$

11. $\dfrac{5x^3 - 10x^2}{25x^4 + 5x^3 - 30x^2}$

12. $\dfrac{16x^2 - 4y^2}{4x - 2y}$

Section 6.2

Multiply or divide.

13. $\dfrac{3x^2 - 13x - 10}{3x^2 + 2x} \cdot \dfrac{x^2 - 25x}{x^2 - 25}$

14. $\dfrac{2y^2 - 18}{3y^2 + 3y} \div \dfrac{y^2 + 6y + 9}{y^2 + 4y + 3}$

15. $\dfrac{2y^2 + 3y - 2}{2y^2 + y - 1} \div \dfrac{2y^2 + y - 1}{2y^2 - 3y - 2}$

16. $\dfrac{6y^2 + 13y - 5}{9y^2 + 3y} \div \dfrac{4y^2 + 20y + 25}{12y^2}$

17. $\dfrac{3xy^2 + 12y^2}{2x^2 - 11x + 5} \div \dfrac{2xy + 8y}{8x^2 + 2x - 3}$

18. $\dfrac{11}{x - 2} \cdot \dfrac{2x^2 - 8}{44}$

19. $\dfrac{x^2 - 5xy - 24y^2}{2x^2 - 2xy - 24y^2} \cdot \dfrac{4x^2 + 4xy - 24y^2}{x^2 - 10xy + 16y^2}$

20. $\dfrac{2x^2 + 10x + 2}{8x - 8} \cdot \dfrac{3x - 3}{4x^2 + 20x + 4}$

Section 6.3

Add or subtract.

21. $\dfrac{7}{x + 1} + \dfrac{4}{2x}$

22. $5 + \dfrac{1}{x} + \dfrac{1}{x + 1}$

23. $\dfrac{7}{x + 2} + \dfrac{3}{x - 4}$

24. $\dfrac{2}{x^2 - 9} + \dfrac{x}{x + 3}$

25. $\dfrac{x}{y} + \dfrac{3}{2y} + \dfrac{1}{y + 2}$

26. $\dfrac{4}{a} + \dfrac{2}{b} + \dfrac{3}{a + b}$

27. $\dfrac{3x + 1}{3x} - \dfrac{1}{x}$

28. $\dfrac{x + 4}{x + 2} - \dfrac{1}{2x}$

29. $\dfrac{27}{x^2 - 81} + \dfrac{3}{2(x + 9)}$

30. $\dfrac{1}{x^2 + 7x + 10} - \dfrac{x}{x + 5}$

Section 6.4

Simplify.

31. $\dfrac{\dfrac{3}{2y} - \dfrac{1}{y}}{\dfrac{4}{y} + \dfrac{3}{2y}}$

32. $\dfrac{\dfrac{2}{x} + \dfrac{1}{2x}}{x + \dfrac{x}{2}}$

33. $\dfrac{w - \dfrac{4}{w}}{1 + \dfrac{2}{w}}$

34. $\dfrac{1 - \dfrac{w}{w - 1}}{1 + \dfrac{w}{1 - w}}$

35. $\dfrac{1 + \dfrac{1}{y^2 - 1}}{\dfrac{1}{y + 1} - \dfrac{1}{y - 1}}$

36. $\dfrac{\dfrac{1}{y} + \dfrac{1}{x + y}}{1 + \dfrac{2}{x + y}}$

37. $\dfrac{\dfrac{1}{a+b} - \dfrac{1}{a}}{b}$

38. $\dfrac{\dfrac{2}{a+b} - \dfrac{3}{b}}{\dfrac{1}{a+b}}$

39. $\dfrac{x+5y}{x-6y} \div \left(\dfrac{1}{5y} - \dfrac{1}{x+5y}\right)$

40. $\left(\dfrac{1}{x+2y} - \dfrac{1}{x-y}\right) \div \dfrac{2x-4y}{x^2-3xy+2y^2}$

Section 6.5

Solve for the variable. If there is no solution, say so.

41. $\dfrac{8a-1}{6a+8} = \dfrac{3}{4}$

42. $\dfrac{8}{a-3} = \dfrac{12}{a+3}$

43. $\dfrac{2x-1}{x} - \dfrac{1}{2} = -2$

44. $\dfrac{5-x}{x} - \dfrac{7}{x} = -\dfrac{3}{4}$

45. $\dfrac{5}{2} - \dfrac{2y+7}{y+6} = 3$

46. $\dfrac{5}{4} - \dfrac{1}{2x} = \dfrac{1}{x} + 2$

47. $\dfrac{7}{8x} - \dfrac{3}{4} = \dfrac{1}{4x} + \dfrac{1}{2}$

48. $\dfrac{1}{3x} + 2 = \dfrac{5}{6x} - \dfrac{1}{2}$

49. $\dfrac{3}{y-3} = \dfrac{3}{2} + \dfrac{y}{y-3}$

50. $\dfrac{x-8}{x-2} = \dfrac{2x}{x+2} - 2$

51. $\dfrac{9}{2} - \dfrac{7y-4}{y+2} = -\dfrac{1}{4}$

52. $\dfrac{3y-1}{3y} - \dfrac{6}{5y} = \dfrac{1}{y} - \dfrac{4}{15}$

53. $\dfrac{y+18}{y^2-16} = \dfrac{y}{y+4} - \dfrac{y}{y-4}$

54. $\dfrac{4}{x^2-1} = \dfrac{2}{x-1} + \dfrac{2}{x+1}$

55. $\dfrac{9y-3}{y^2+2y} - \dfrac{5}{y+2} = \dfrac{3}{y}$

56. $\dfrac{2}{3-3y} + \dfrac{2}{2y-1} = \dfrac{4}{3y-3}$

Section 6.6

Solve. Leave your answer in decimal form. Round to the nearest tenth.

57. $\frac{x}{4} = \frac{12}{17}$

58. $\frac{8}{5} = \frac{2}{x}$

59. $\frac{33}{10} = \frac{x}{8}$

60. $\frac{5}{x} = \frac{22}{9}$

61. $\frac{13.5}{0.6} = \frac{360}{x}$

62. $\frac{2\frac{1}{2}}{3\frac{1}{4}} = \frac{7}{x}$

Use a proportion to answer each question.

63. ***Paint Needs*** A 5-gallon can of paint will cover 240 square feet. How many gallons of paint will be needed to cover 400 square feet? Round to the nearest tenth of a gallon.

64. ***Recipe Ratios*** Aunt Lexie uses 3 pounds of sugar to make 100 cookies. How many cookies can she make with 5 pounds of sugar? Round to the nearest whole cookie.

65. ***Gas Usage*** Ron found that his car used 7 gallons of gas to travel 200 miles. He plans to drive 1300 miles from his home to Denver, Colorado. How many gallons of gas will he use if his car continues to consume gas at the same rate? Round to the nearest gallon.

66. ***Map Scale*** The distance on a map between two cities is 4 inches. The actual distance between these cities is 122 miles. Two lakes are 3 inches apart on the same map. How many miles apart are these two lakes?

67. ***Travel Speeds*** A train travels 180 miles in the same time that a car travels 120 miles. The speed of the train is 20 miles per hour faster than the speed of the car. Find the speed of the train and the speed of the car.

68. ***Interior Painting*** A professional painter can paint the interior of the Jacksons' house in 5 hours. John Jackson can do the same job in 8 hours. How long would it take these two people working together on the painting job? Round to the nearest minute.

▲ **69.** ***Shadows*** Mary takes a walk across a canyon in New Mexico. She stands 5.75 feet tall and her shadow is 3 feet long. At the same time, the shadow from the peak of the canyon wall casts a shadow that is 95 feet long. How tall is the peak of the canyon? Round to the nearest foot.

▲ **70.** ***Shadows*** A flagpole that is 8 feet tall casts a shadow of 3 feet. At the same time of day, a tall office building in the city casts a shadow of 450 feet. How tall is the office building?

71. ***House Painting*** Fred is an experienced painter. He can paint the sides of an average house in 5 hours. His new assistant is still being trained. It takes the assistant 10 hours to paint the sides of an average house. How long would it take Fred and his assistant to paint the sides of an average house if they worked together?

72. ***Plowing Fields*** Sally runs the family farm in Boone, Iowa. She can plow the fields of the farm in 20 hours. Her daughter Brenda can plow the fields of the farm in 30 hours. If they have two identical tractors, how long would it take Brenda and Sally to plow the fields of the farm if they worked together?

Mixed Practice

Perform the indicated operation. Simplify.

73. $\dfrac{a^2 + a - 12}{48a^2 - 16a^3}$

74. $\dfrac{6b^3 - 24b^2}{b^2 + b - 20}$

75. $\dfrac{x^2 - y^2}{x^2 + 4xy + 3y^2} \cdot \dfrac{x^2 + xy - 6y^2}{x^2 + xy - 2y^2}$

76. $\dfrac{x^2 - 6xy - 16y^2}{x^2 + 4xy - 21y^2} \cdot \dfrac{x^2 - 8xy + 15y^2}{x^2 - 3xy - 10y^2}$

77. $\dfrac{x}{x + 3} + \dfrac{9x + 18}{x^2 + 3x}$

78. $\dfrac{x - 30}{x^2 - 5x} + \dfrac{x}{x - 5}$

79. $\dfrac{a + b}{ax + ay} - \dfrac{a + b}{bx + by}$

80. $\dfrac{\dfrac{5}{3x} + \dfrac{2}{9x}}{\dfrac{3}{x} + \dfrac{8}{3x}}$

81. $\dfrac{\dfrac{4}{5y} - \dfrac{8}{y}}{y + \dfrac{y}{5}}$

82. $\dfrac{x - 3y}{x + 2y} \div \left(\dfrac{2}{y} - \dfrac{12}{x + 3y}\right)$

83. $\dfrac{10}{x - 3} = \dfrac{9}{x - 5}$

84. $\dfrac{7x - 4}{6x - 5} = \dfrac{8}{7}$

85. $2 + \dfrac{4}{b - 1} = \dfrac{4}{b^2 - b}$

86. ***Wire Weight*** If 30 meters of wire weighs 8 kilograms, what will 40 meters of the same kind of wire weigh? Round your answer to the nearest tenth.

87. ***Driving Rates*** Ming drove 270 miles in $4\frac{1}{2}$ hours. At that same rate, how far would she drive in 7 hours?

How Am I Doing? Chapter 6 Test

Remember to use your Chapter Test Prep Video CD to see the worked-out solutions to the test problems you want to review.

Perform the operation indicated. Simplify.

1. $\dfrac{2ac + 2ad}{3a^2c + 3a^2d}$

2. $\dfrac{8x^2 - 2x^2y^2}{y^2 + 4y + 4}$

3. $\dfrac{x^2 + 2x}{2x - 1} \cdot \dfrac{10x^2 - 5x}{12x^3 + 24x^2}$

4. $\dfrac{x + 2y}{12y^2} \cdot \dfrac{4y}{x^2 + xy - 2y^2}$

5. $\dfrac{2a^2 - 3a - 2}{a^2 + 5a + 6} \div \dfrac{a^2 - 5a + 6}{a^2 - 9}$

6. $\dfrac{1}{a^2 - a - 2} + \dfrac{3}{a - 2}$

7. $\dfrac{x - y}{xy} - \dfrac{a - y}{ay}$

8. $\dfrac{3x}{x^2 - 3x - 18} - \dfrac{x - 4}{x - 6}$

9. $\dfrac{\dfrac{x}{3y} - \dfrac{1}{2}}{\dfrac{4}{3y} - \dfrac{2}{x}}$

10. $\dfrac{\dfrac{6}{b} - 4}{\dfrac{5}{bx} - \dfrac{10}{3x}}$

11. $\dfrac{2x^2 + 3xy - 9y^2}{4x^2 + 13xy + 3y^2}$

12. $\dfrac{1}{x + 4} - \dfrac{2}{x^2 + 6x + 8}$

In questions 13–18, solve for x. Check your answers. If there is no solution, say so.

13. $\dfrac{4}{3x} - \dfrac{5}{2x} = 5 - \dfrac{1}{6x}$

14. $\dfrac{x - 3}{x - 2} = \dfrac{2x^2 - 15}{x^2 + x - 6} - \dfrac{x + 1}{x + 3}$

15. $3 - \dfrac{7}{x + 3} = \dfrac{x - 4}{x + 3}$

16. $\dfrac{3}{3x - 5} = \dfrac{7}{5x + 4}$

17. $\dfrac{9}{x} = \dfrac{13}{5}$

18. $\dfrac{9.3}{2.5} = \dfrac{x}{10}$

19. A random check of America West air flights last month showed that 113 of the 150 flights checked arrived on time. If the inspectors check 200 flights next month, how many can be expected to be on time? (Round to the nearest whole number.)

20. In northern Michigan the Gunderson family heats their home with firewood. They used \$100 worth of wood in 25 days. Mr. Gunderson estimates that he needs to burn wood at that rate for about 92 days during the winter. If that is so, how much will the 92-day supply of wood cost?

▲ **21.** A hiking club is trying to construct a rope bridge across a canyon. A 6-foot construction pole held upright casts a 7-foot shadow. At the same time of day, a tree at the edge of the canyon casts a shadow that exactly covers the distance that is needed for the rope bridge. The tree is exactly 87 feet tall. How long should the rope bridge be? Round to the nearest foot.

1. ________
2. ________
3. ________
4. ________
5. ________
6. ________
7. ________
8. ________
9. ________
10. ________
11. ________
12. ________
13. ________
14. ________
15. ________
16. ________
17. ________
18. ________
19. ________
20. ________
21. ________

Cumulative Test for Chapters 0–6

Approximately one-half of this test covers the content of Chapters 0–5. The remainder covers the content of Chapter 6.

1. To the nearest thousandth, how much error can be tolerated in the length of a wire that is supposed to be 2.57 centimeters long if specifications allow an error of no more than 0.25%?

2. There are 252 students in the drama club at Western Community College. If there are 720 students at the Community College, what percent are in the drama club?

3. Carla is thinking of buying a new car for $18,500. Her state presently has a sales tax of 5.5%. In a few weeks the state will raise the sales tax to 6%. How much will she save in sales tax if she purchases the car before the sales tax rate is raised?

4. Solve. $5(x - 3) - 2(4 - 2x) = 7(x - 1) - (x - 2)$

5. Solve for h. $A = \pi r^2 h$

6. Solve and graph on a number line. $4(2 - x) < 3$

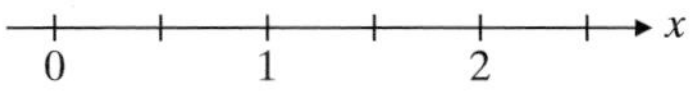

7. Solve for x. $\frac{3}{5}x - 2 \le \frac{1}{2}x + \frac{3}{5}$

8. Factor. $3ax + 3bx - 2ay - 2by$

9. Factor. $8a^3 - 38a^2b - 10ab^2$

10. Simplify. Leave the answer in positive exponents. $\dfrac{-12x^{-2}y^4}{3x^{-5}y^{-8}}$

11. Simplify. $\dfrac{4x^2 - 25}{2x^2 + 9x - 35}$

Perform the indicated operations.

12. $\dfrac{x^2 - 4}{x^2 - 25} \cdot \dfrac{3x^2 - 14x - 5}{3x^2 + 6x}$

13. $\dfrac{2x^2 - 9x + 9}{8x - 12} \div \dfrac{x^2 - 3x}{2x}$

14. $\dfrac{5}{2x + 4} + \dfrac{3}{x - 3}$

15. $\dfrac{8}{c^2 - 4} - \dfrac{2}{c^2 - 5c + 6}$

Solve for x.

16. $\dfrac{3x - 2}{3x + 2} = 2$

17. $\dfrac{x - 3}{x} = \dfrac{x + 2}{x + 3}$

In questions 18 and 19, simplify.

18. $\dfrac{\dfrac{1}{x - 3} + \dfrac{5}{x^2 - 9}}{\dfrac{6x}{x + 3}}$

19. $\dfrac{\dfrac{3}{a} + \dfrac{2}{b}}{\dfrac{5}{a^2} - \dfrac{2}{b^2}}$

20. Solve for x. $\dfrac{2x + 1}{3} = \dfrac{4}{5}$

21. Jane is looking at a road map. The distance between two cities is 130 miles. This distance is represented by $2\frac{1}{2}$ inches on the map. She sees that the distance she has to drive today is a totally straight interstate highway that is 4 inches long on the map. How many miles does she have to drive?

22. Roberto is working as a telemarketing salesperson for a large corporation. In the last 22 telephone calls he has made, he was able to make a sale five times. His goal is to make 110 sales this month. If his rate for making a sale continues as in the past, how many phone calls must he make?

1. ________
2. ________
3. ________
4. ________
5. ________
6. ________
7. ________
8. ________
9. ________
10. ________
11. ________
12. ________
13. ________
14. ________
15. ________
16. ________
17. ________
18. ________
19. ________
20. ________
21. ________
22. ________

Beginning Algebra Glossary

Absolute value of a number (1.1) The absolute value of a number x is the distance between 0 and the number x on the number line. It is written as $|x|$. $|x| = x$ if $x \geq 0$, but $|x| = -x$ if $x < 0$.

Altitude of a geometric figure (1.8) The height of the geometric figure. In the three figures shown the altitude is labeled a.

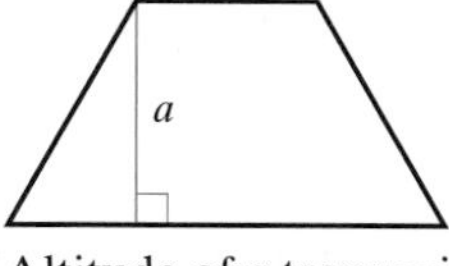

Altitude of a trapezoid

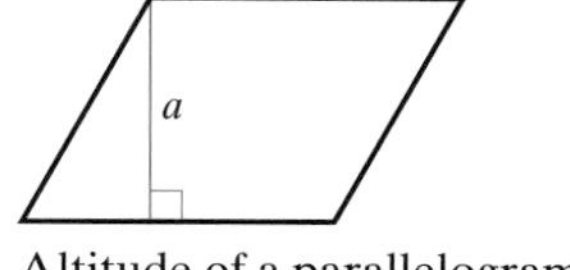

Altitude of a parallelogram

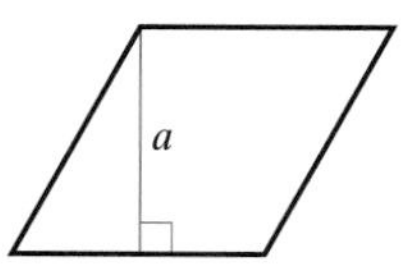

Altitude of a rhombus

Altitude of a triangle (1.8) The height of any given triangle. In the three triangles shown the altitude is labeled a.

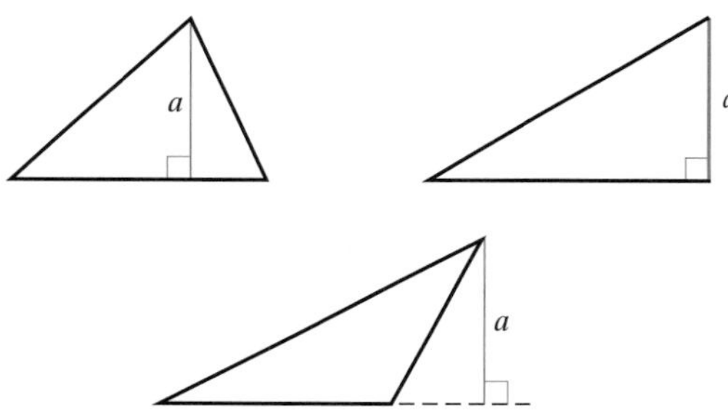

Associative property of addition (1.1) If a, b, and c are real numbers, then

$$a + (b + c) = (a + b) + c.$$

This property states that if three numbers are added it does not matter *which two numbers* are added first, the result will be the same.

Associative property of multiplication (1.3) If a, b, and c are real numbers, then

$$a \times (b \times c) = (a \times b) \times c.$$

This property states that if three numbers are multiplied it does not matter *which two numbers* are multiplied first; the result will be the same.

Base (1.4) The number or variable that is raised to a power. In the expression 2^6, the number 2 is the base.

Base of a triangle (1.8) The side of a triangle that is perpendicular to the altitude.

Binomial (4.3) A polynomial of two terms. The expressions $a + 2b$, $6x^3 + 1$, and $5a^3b^2 + 6ab$ are all binomials.

Circumference of a circle (1.8) The distance around a circle. The circumference of a circle is given by the formula $C = \pi d$ or $C = 2\pi r$, where d is the diameter of the circle and r is the radius of the circle.

Coefficient (4.1) A coefficient is a factor or a group of factors in a product. In the term $4xy$ the coefficient of y is $4x$, but the coefficient of xy is 4. In the term $-5x^3y$ the coefficient of x^3y is -5.

Commutative property for addition (1.1) If a and b are any real numbers, then $a + b = b + a$.

Commutative property for multiplication (1.3) If a and b are any real numbers, then $ab = ba$.

Complex fraction (6.4) A fraction that contains at least one fraction in the numerator or in the denominator or both. These three fractions are complex fractions:

$$\frac{7 + \frac{1}{x}}{x^2 + 2}, \quad \frac{1 + \frac{1}{5}}{2 - \frac{1}{7}}, \quad \text{and} \quad \frac{1}{\frac{3}{4}}.$$

Constant (2.3) Symbol or letter that is used to represent exactly one single quantity during a particular problem or discussion.

Degree of a polynomial (4.3) The degree of the highest-degree term of a polynomial. The degree of the polynomial $5x^3 + 2x^2 - 6x + 8$ is 3. The degree of the polynomial $5x^2y^2 + 3xy + 8$ is 4.

Degree of a term of a polynomial (4.3) The sum of the exponents of the variables in the term. The degree of $3x^3$ is 3. The degree of $4x^5y^2$ is 7.

Denominator (0.1) and (6.1) The bottom number or algebraic expression in a fraction. The denominator of

$$\frac{3x - 2}{x + 4}$$

is $x + 4$. The denominator of $\frac{3}{7}$ is 7. The denominator of a fraction may not be zero.

Diagonal of a four-sided figure (1.8) A line connecting two nonadjacent corners of the figure. In each of the figures shown, line AC is a diagonal.

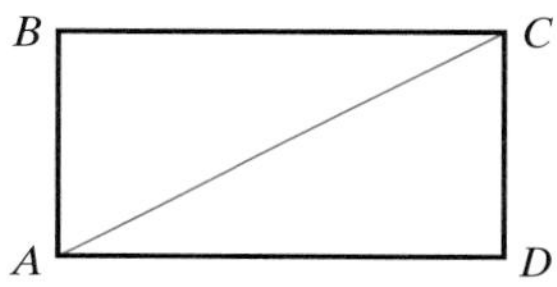

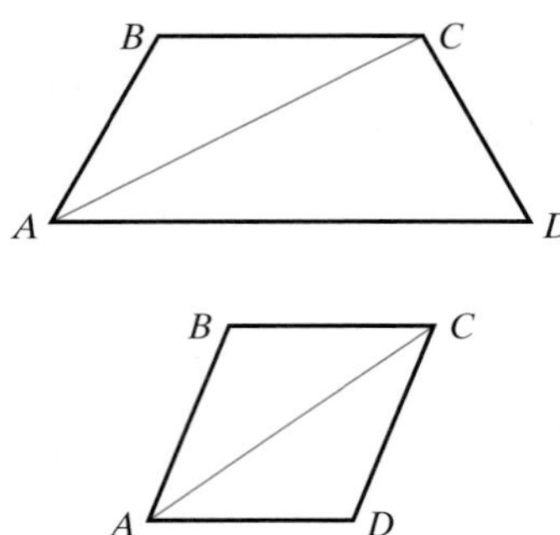

Difference (3.1) The result of subtracting one number or expression from another. The mathematical expression $x - 6$ can be written in words as the difference between x and 6.

Difference-of-two-squares polynomial (5.5) A polynomial of the form $a^2 - b^2$ that may be factored by using the formula

$$a^2 - b^2 = (a + b)(a - b).$$

Distributive property (1.6) For all real numbers a, b, and c, $a(b + c) = ab + ac$.

Dividend (0.4) The number that is to be divided by another. In the problem $30 \div 5 = 6$, the three parts are as follows:

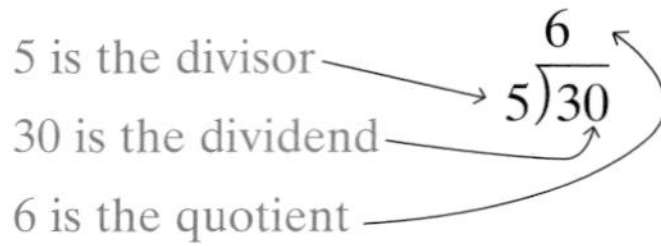

Divisor (0.4) The number you divide into another.

Equilateral triangle (1.8) A triangle with three sides equal in length and three angles that measure 60°. Triangle ABC is an equilateral triangle.

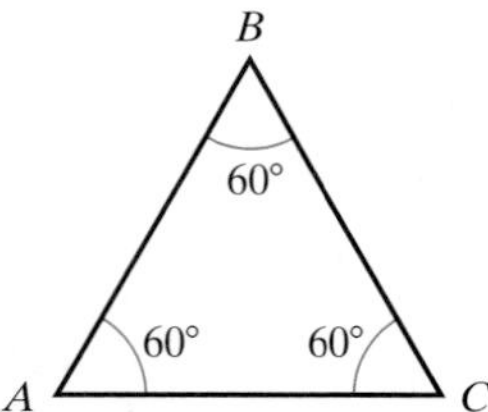

Even integers (1.3) Integers that are exactly divisible by 2, such as $\ldots, -4, -2, 0, 2, 4, 6, \ldots$.

Exponent (1.4) The number that indicates the power of a base. If the number is a positive integer it indicates how many times the base is multiplied. In the expression 2^6, the exponent is 6.

Expression (4.3) A mathematic expression is any quantity using numbers and variables. Therefore, $2x$, $7x + 3$, and $5x^2 + 6x$ are all mathematical expressions.

Extraneous solution (6.5) An obtained solution to an equation that when substituted back into the original equation, does *not* yield an identity. $x = 2$ is an extraneous solution to the equation

$$\frac{x}{x - 2} - 4 = \frac{2}{x - 2}.$$

An extraneous solution is also called an extraneous root.

Factor (0.1) and (5.1) When two or more numbers, variables, or algebraic expressions are multiplied, each is called a factor. If we write $3 \cdot 5 \cdot 2$, the factors are 3, 5, and 2. If we write $2xy$, the factors are 2, x, and y. In the expression $(x - 6)(x + 2)$, the factors are $(x - 6)$ and $(x + 2)$.

Fractions

Algebraic fractions (6.1) The indicated quotient of two algebraic expressions.

$$\frac{x^2 + 3x + 2}{x - 4} \quad \text{and} \quad \frac{y - 6}{y + 8}$$

are algebraic fractions. In these fractions the value of the denominator cannot be zero.

Numerical fractions (0.1) A set of numbers used to describe parts of whole quantities. A numerical fraction can be represented by the quotient of two integers for which the denominator is not zero. The numbers $\frac{1}{5}, -\frac{2}{3}, \frac{8}{2}, -\frac{4}{31}, \frac{8}{1}$, and $-\frac{12}{1}$ are all numerical fractions. The set of rational numbers can be represented by numerical fractions.

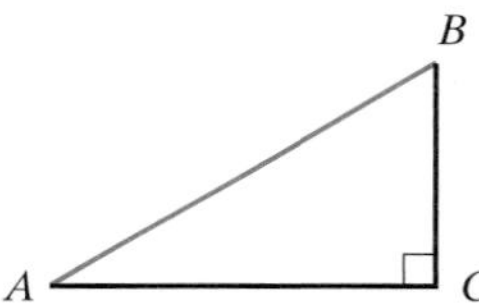

Identity (2.1) A statement that is always true. The equations $5 = 5$, $7 + 4 = 7 + 4$, and $x + 8 = x + 8$ are examples of identities.

Improper fraction (0.1) A numerical fraction whose numerator is larger than or equal to its denominator. $\frac{8}{3}, \frac{5}{2}$, and $\frac{7}{7}$ are improper fractions.

Inequality (2.6) and (2.7) A mathematical relationship between quantities that are not equal. $x \leq -3$, $w > 5$, and $x < 2y + 1$ are mathematical inequalities.

Integers (1.1) The set of numbers $\ldots, -5, -4, -3, -2, -1, 0, 1, 2, 3, 4, 5, \ldots$.

Isosceles triangle (1.8) A triangle with two equal sides and two equal angles. Triangle ABC is an isosceles triangle. Angle BAC is equal to angle ACB. Side AB is equal in length to side BC.

Least common denominator of numerical fractions (0.2) The smallest whole number that is exactly divisible by all denominators of a group of fractions. The least common denominator (LCD) of $\frac{1}{6}, \frac{2}{3}$, and $\frac{3}{5}$ is 30. The least common denominator is also called the lowest common denominator.

Like terms (1.7) Terms that have identical variables and exponents. In the expression $5x^3 + 2xy^2 + 6x^2 - 3xy^2$, the term $2xy^2$ and the term $-3xy^2$ are like terms.

Mixed number (0.1) A number that consists of an integer written next to a proper fraction. $2\frac{1}{3}, 4\frac{6}{7}$, and $3\frac{3}{8}$ are all mixed numbers. Mixed numbers are sometimes called mixed fractions or mixed numerals.

Monomial (4.3) A polynomial of one term. The expressions $3xy, 5a^2b^3cd$, and -6 are all monomials.

Natural numbers (0.1) The set of numbers $1, 2, 3, 4, 5, \ldots$. This set is also called the set of counting numbers.

Numeral (0.1) The symbol used to describe a number.

Numerator (0.1) The top number or algebraic expression in a fraction. The numerator of

$$\frac{x + 3}{5x - 2}$$

is $x + 3$. The numerator of $\frac{12}{13}$ is 12.

Numerical coefficient (4.1) The number that is multiplied by a variable or a group of variables. The numerical coefficient in $5x^3y^2$ is 5. The numerical coefficient in $-6abc$ is -6. The numerical coefficient in x^2y is 1. A numerical coefficient of 1 is not usually written.

Odd integers (1.3) Integers that are not exactly divisible by 2, such as $-3, -1, 1, 3, 5, 7, 9, \ldots$.

Opposite of a number (1.1) Two numbers that are the same distance from zero on the number line but lie on different sides of it are considered opposites. The opposite of -6 is 6. The opposite of $\frac{22}{7}$ is $-\frac{22}{7}$.

Parallelogram (1.8) A four-sided figure with opposite sides parallel. Figure $ABCD$ is a parallelogram.

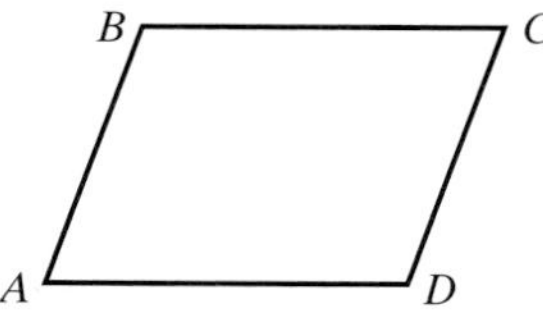

Percent (0.5) Hundredths or "per one hundred"; indicated by the % symbol. Thirty-seven hundredths $\left(\frac{37}{100}\right) = 37\%$ (thirty-seven percent).

Perfect square number (5.5) A number that is the square of an integer. The numbers 1, 4, 9, 16, 25, 36, 49, 64, 81, 100, 121, 144, . . . are perfect square numbers.

Perfect square trinomial (5.5) A polynomial of the form $a^2 + 2ab + b^2$ or $a^2 - 2ab + b^2$ that may be factored using one of the following formulas:

$$a^2 + 2ab + b^2 = (a + b)^2$$

or

$$a^2 - 2ab + b^2 = (a - b)^2.$$

Perimeter (1.8) The distance around any plane figure. The perimeter of this triangle is 13. The perimeter of this rectangle is 20.

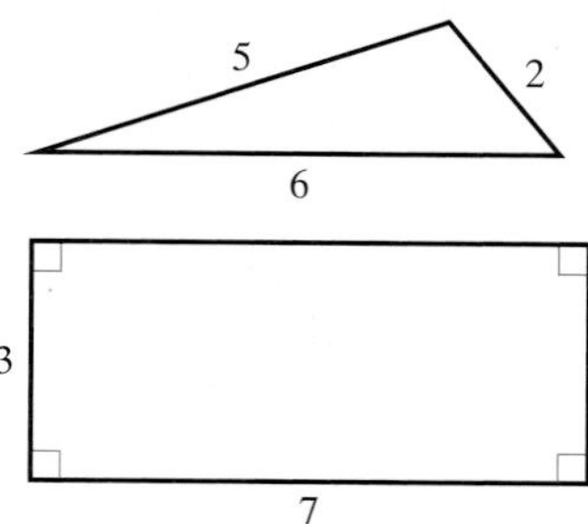

Pi (1.8) An irrational number, denoted by the symbol π, that is approximately equal to 3.141592654. In most cases 3.14 can be used as a sufficiently accurate approximation for π.

Polynomial (4.3) Expressions that contain terms with nonnegative integer exponents. The expressions $5ab + 6, x^3 + 6x^2 + 3, -12$, and $x + 3y - 2$ *are all polynomials.* The expressions $x^{-2} + 2x^{-1}, 2\sqrt{x} + 6$, and $\frac{5}{x} + 2x^2$ *are not polynomials.*

Prime number (0.1) Any natural number greater than 1 whose only natural number factors are 1 and itself. The first eight prime numbers are 2, 3, 5, 7, 11, 13, 17, and 19.

Prime polynomial (5.6) A prime polynomial is a polynomial that cannot be factored by the methods of elementary algebra. $x^2 + x + 1$ is a prime polynomial.

Principal (3.4) In monetary problems, the principal is the original amount of money invested or borrowed.

Proper fraction (0.1) A numerical fraction whose numerator is less than its denominator; $\frac{3}{7}, \frac{2}{5}$, and $\frac{8}{9}$ are proper fractions.

Proportion (6.6) A proportion is an equation stating that two ratios are equal.

$$\frac{a}{b} = \frac{c}{d} \quad \text{where } b, d \neq 0$$

is a proportion.

Quadratic equation (5.7) A quadratic equation is a polynomial equation with one variable that contains at least one term with the variable squared, but no term with the variable raised to a higher power. $5x^2 + 6x - 3 = 0, x^2 = 7$, and $5x^2 = 2x$ are all quadratic equations.

Quotient (0.4) The result of dividing one number or expression by another. In the problem $12 \div 4 = 3$, the quotient is 3.

Ratio (6.6) The ratio of one number a to another number b is the quotient $a \div b$ or $\frac{a}{b}$.

Rational numbers (1.1) A number that can be expressed in the form $\frac{a}{b}$, where a and b are integers and $b \neq 0$. $\frac{7}{3}, -\frac{2}{5}, \frac{7}{-8}, \frac{5}{1}$, 1.62, and 2.7156 are rational numbers.

Rectangle (1.8) A four-sided figure with opposite sides parallel and all interior angles measuring 90°. The opposite sides of a rectangle are equal.

Rhombus (1.8) A parallelogram with four equal sides. Figure $ABCD$ is a rhombus.

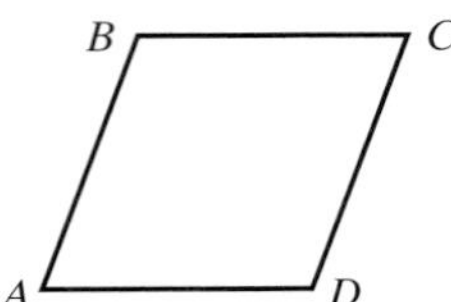

Right angle (1.8) An angle that measures 90°. Right angles are usually labeled in a sketch by using a small square to indicate that it is a right angle. Here angle ABC is a right angle.

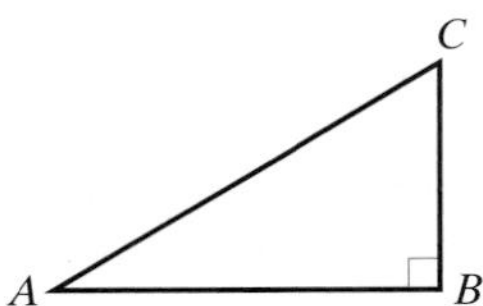

Right triangle (1.8) A triangle that contains a right angle.

Root of an equation (2.1) and (5.7) A value of the variable that makes an equation into a true statement. The root of an equation is also called the solution of an equation.

Scientific notation (4.2) A positive number is written in scientific notation if it is in the form $a \times 10^n$, where $1 \leq a < 10$ and n is an integer.

Solution of an equation (2.1) A number that, when substituted into a given equation, yields an identity. The solution of an equation is also called the root of an equation.

Solution of a linear inequality (2.7) The possible values that make a linear inequality true.

Square (1.8) A rectangle with four equal sides.

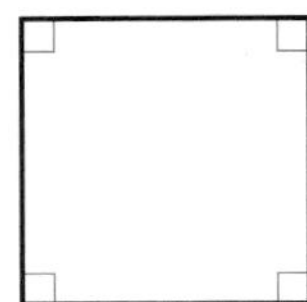

Standard form of a quadratic equation (5.7) A quadratic equation that is in the form $ax^2 + bx + c = 0$.

Subscript of a variable (3.2) A small number or letter written slightly below and to the right of a variable. In the expression $5 = 2(x - x_0)$, the subscript of x is 0. In the expression $t_f = 5(t_a - b)$ the subscript of the first t is f. The subscript of the second t is a. A subscript is used to indicate a different value of the variable.

Term (1.7) A number, a variable, or a product of numbers and variables. For example, in the expression $a^3 - 3a^2b + 4ab^2 + 6b^3 + 8$, there are five terms. They are a^3, $-3a^2b$, $4ab^2$, $6b^3$, and 8. The terms of a polynomial are separated by plus and minus signs.

Trapezoid (1.8) A four-sided figure with two sides parallel. The parallel sides are called the bases of the trapezoid. Figure $ABCD$ is a trapezoid.

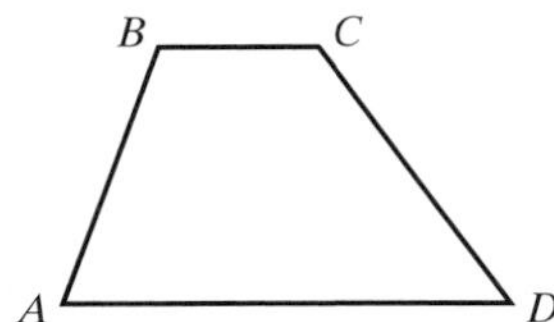

Trinomial (4.3) A polynomial of three terms. The expressions $x^2 + 6x - 8$ and $a + 2b - 3c$ are trinomials.

Variable (1.4) A letter that is used to represent a number or a set of numbers.

Whole numbers (0.1) The set of numbers 0, 1, 2, 3, 4, 5, ...

Appendix A Table of Square Roots

x	$\sqrt{x}$	x	$\sqrt{x}$	x	$\sqrt{x}$	x	$\sqrt{x}$	x	$\sqrt{x}$
1	1.000	**41**	6.403	**81**	9.000	**121**	11.000	**161**	12.689
2	1.414	**42**	6.481	**82**	9.055	**122**	11.045	**162**	12.728
3	1.732	**43**	6.557	**83**	9.110	**123**	11.091	**163**	12.767
4	2.000	**44**	6.633	**84**	9.165	**124**	11.136	**164**	12.806
5	2.236	**45**	6.708	**85**	9.220	**125**	11.180	**165**	12.845
6	2.449	**46**	6.782	**86**	9.274	**126**	11.225	**166**	12.884
7	2.646	**47**	6.856	**87**	9.327	**127**	11.269	**167**	12.923
8	2.828	**48**	6.928	**88**	9.381	**128**	11.314	**168**	12.961
9	3.000	**49**	7.000	**89**	9.434	**129**	11.358	**169**	13.000
10	3.162	**50**	7.071	**90**	9.487	**130**	11.402	**170**	13.038
11	3.317	**51**	7.141	**91**	9.539	**131**	11.446	**171**	13.077
12	3.464	**52**	7.211	**92**	9.592	**132**	11.489	**172**	13.115
13	3.606	**53**	7.280	**93**	9.644	**133**	11.533	**173**	13.153
14	3.742	**54**	7.348	**94**	9.695	**134**	11.576	**174**	13.191
15	3.873	**55**	7.416	**95**	9.747	**135**	11.619	**175**	13.229
16	4.000	**56**	7.483	**96**	9.798	**136**	11.662	**176**	13.266
17	4.123	**57**	7.550	**97**	9.849	**137**	11.705	**177**	13.304
18	4.243	**58**	7.616	**98**	9.899	**138**	11.747	**178**	13.342
19	4.359	**59**	7.681	**99**	9.950	**139**	11.790	**179**	13.379
20	4.472	**60**	7.746	**100**	10.000	**140**	11.832	**180**	13.416
21	4.583	**61**	7.810	**101**	10.050	**141**	11.874	**181**	13.454
22	4.690	**62**	7.874	**102**	10.100	**142**	11.916	**182**	13.491
23	4.796	**63**	7.937	**103**	10.149	**143**	11.958	**183**	13.528
24	4.899	**64**	8.000	**104**	10.198	**144**	12.000	**184**	13.565
25	5.000	**65**	8.062	**105**	10.247	**145**	12.042	**185**	13.601
26	5.099	**66**	8.124	**106**	10.296	**146**	12.083	**186**	13.638
27	5.196	**67**	8.185	**107**	10.344	**147**	12.124	**187**	13.675
28	5.292	**68**	8.246	**108**	10.392	**148**	12.166	**188**	13.711
29	5.385	**69**	8.307	**109**	10.440	**149**	12.207	**189**	13.748
30	5.477	**70**	8.367	**110**	10.488	**150**	12.247	**190**	13.784
31	5.568	**71**	8.426	**111**	10.536	**151**	12.288	**191**	13.820
32	5.657	**72**	8.485	**112**	10.583	**152**	12.329	**192**	13.856
33	5.745	**73**	8.544	**113**	10.630	**153**	12.369	**193**	13.892
34	5.831	**74**	8.602	**114**	10.677	**154**	12.410	**194**	13.928
35	5.916	**75**	8.660	**115**	10.724	**155**	12.450	**195**	13.964
36	6.000	**76**	8.718	**116**	10.770	**156**	12.490	**196**	14.000
37	6.083	**77**	8.775	**117**	10.817	**157**	12.530	**197**	14.036
38	6.164	**78**	8.832	**118**	10.863	**158**	12.570	**198**	14.071
39	6.245	**79**	8.888	**119**	10.909	**159**	12.610	**199**	14.107
40	6.325	**80**	8.944	**120**	10.954	**160**	12.649	**200**	14.142

Unless the value of $\sqrt{x}$ ends in 000, all values are rounded to the nearest thousandth.

Appendix B Metric Measurement and Conversion of Units

Student Learning Objectives

After studying this section, you will be able to:

1. **Convert from one metric unit of measurement to another.**
2. **Convert between metric and U.S. units of measure.**
3. **Convert from one type of unit of measure to another.**

1 Converting from One Metric Unit of Measurement to Another

Metric measurements are becoming more common in the United States. The metric system is used in many parts of the world and in the sciences. The basic unit of length in the metric system is the meter. For smaller measurements, centimeters are commonly used. There are 100 centimeters in 1 meter. For larger measurements, kilometers are commonly used. There are 1000 meters in 1 kilometer. The following tables give the metric units of measurement for length.

METRIC LENGTH

*1 kilometer (km)	=	1000 meters
1 hectometer (hm)	=	100 meters
1 dekameter (dam)	=	10 meters
*1 meter (m)	=	1 meter
1 decimeter (dm)	=	0.1 meter
*1 centimeter (cm)	=	0.01 meter
*1 millimeter (mm)	=	0.001 meter

The four most common units of metric measurement are indicated by an asterisk.

METRIC WEIGHT

1 kilogram (kg)	=	1000 grams
1 gram (g)	=	1 gram
1 milligram (mg)	=	0.001 gram

METRIC VOLUME

1 kiloliter (kL)	=	1000 liters
1 liter (L)	=	1 liter
1 milliliter (mL)	=	0.001 liter

One way to convert from one metric unit to another is to multiply by 1. We know mathematically that to multiply by 1 will yield an equivalent expression since $(a)(1) = a$. In our calculations when solving word problems, we treat dimension symbols much as we treat variables in algebra.

EXAMPLE 1 Fred drove a distance of 5.4 kilometers. How many meters is that?

Solution

$$5.4 \text{ km} \cdot 1 = 5.4 \text{ km} \cdot \frac{1000 \text{ m}}{1 \text{ km}} = \frac{(5.4)(1000)}{1} \cdot \frac{\text{km}}{\text{km}} \cdot \text{m}$$
$$= 5400 \text{ m}$$

The distance is 5400 meters.

***NOTE TO STUDENT:** Fully worked-out solutions to all of the Practice Problems can be found at the back of the text starting at page SP-1*

Practice Problem 1 June's room is 3.4 meters wide. How many centimeters is that?

EXAMPLE 2 A chemist measured 67 milliliters of a solution. How many liters is that?

Solution $$67 \text{ mL} \cdot \frac{0.001 \text{ L}}{1 \text{ mL}} = 0.067 \text{ L}$$

The chemist measured 0.067 liters of the solution.

Practice Problem 2 The container has 125 liters of water. How many kiloliters is that?

Converting between Metric and U.S. Units of Measure

The most common relationships between the U.S. and metric systems are listed in the following table. Most of these values are approximate.

METRIC CONVERSION RATIOS

LENGTH:	1 inch = 2.54 centimeters
	39.37 inches = 1 meter
	1 mile = 1.61 kilometers
	0.62 mile = 1 kilometer
WEIGHT:	1 pound = 454 grams
	2.20 pounds = 1 kilogram
	1 ounce = 28.35 grams
	0.0353 ounce = 1 gram
LIQUID CAPACITY:	1 quart = 946 milliliters
	1.06 quarts = 1 liter
	1 gallon = 3.785 liters

EXAMPLE 3 A box weighs 190 grams. How many ounces is that? Round to the nearest hundredth.

Solution $$190 \text{ g} \cdot \frac{0.0353 \text{ oz}}{1 \text{ g}} = 6.707 \text{ oz}$$

$$\approx 6.71 \text{ oz} \quad \text{(rounded to the nearest hundredth)}$$

The box weighs approximately 6.71 ounces.

Practice Problem 3 A bag of groceries weighs 5.72 pounds. How many kilograms is that?

EXAMPLE 4 Juanita drives 23 kilometers to work each day. How many miles is the trip? Round to the nearest mile.

Solution $23 \text{ km} \cdot \dfrac{0.62 \text{ mi}}{1 \text{ km}} = 14.26 \text{ mi} \approx 14 \text{ mi}$ (rounded to the nearest mile)

Juanita drives approximately 14 miles to work each day.

NOTE TO STUDENT: Fully worked-out solutions to all of the Practice Problems can be found at the back of the text starting at page SP-1

Practice Problem 4 Carlos installed an electrical connection that is 8.00 centimeters long. How many inches long is the connection? Round to the nearest hundredth.

EXAMPLE 5 Anita purchased 42.0 gallons of gasoline for her car last month. How many liters did she purchase? Round to the nearest liter.

Solution $42.0 \text{ gal} \cdot \dfrac{3.785 \text{ L}}{1 \text{ gal}} = 158.97 \text{ L} \approx 159 \text{ L}$ (rounded to the nearest liter)

Anita purchased approximately 159 liters of gasoline last month.

Practice Problem 5 Warren purchased a 3-liter bottle of Coca-Cola. How many quarts of Coca-Cola is that? Round to the nearest hundredth of a quart.

3 Converting from One Type of Unit of Measure to Another

Sometimes you will need to convert from one type of unit of measure to another. For example, you may need to convert days to minutes or miles per hour to feet per second. Recall the U.S. units of measure.

Length	Time
12 inches = 1 foot	60 seconds = 1 minute
3 feet = 1 yard	60 minutes = 1 hour
5280 feet = 1 mile	24 hours = 1 day
1760 yards = 1 mile	7 days = 1 week

Weight	Volume
16 ounces = 1 pound	2 cups = 1 pint
2000 pounds = 1 ton	2 pints = 1 quart
	4 quarts = 1 gallon

EXAMPLE 6 A car was traveling at 50.0 miles per hour. How many feet per second was the car traveling? Round to the nearest tenth of a foot per second.

Solution $\dfrac{50 \text{ mi}}{\text{hr}} \cdot \dfrac{5280 \text{ ft}}{1 \text{ mi}} \cdot \dfrac{1 \text{ hr}}{60 \text{ min}} \cdot \dfrac{1 \text{ min}}{60 \text{ sec}} = \dfrac{(50)(5280) \text{ ft}}{(60)(60) \text{ sec}} = \dfrac{73.333\ldots \text{ ft}}{\text{sec}}$

The car was traveling at 73.3 feet per second, rounded to the nearest tenth of a foot per second.

Practice Problem 6 A speeding car was traveling at 70.0 miles per hour. How many feet per second was the car traveling? Round to the nearest tenth of a foot per second.

B Exercises

Student Solutions Manual

CD/ Video

PH Math Tutor Center
MathXL®Tutorials on CD

MathXL®

MyMathLab®

Interactmath.com

1. How many meters are in 34 km?
2. How many meters are in 128 km?
3. How many centimeters are in 57 m?
4. How many centimeters are in 46 m?
5. How many millimeters are in 25 cm?
6. How many millimeters are in 63 cm?
7. How many meters are in 563 mm?
8. How many meters are in 831 mm?
9. How many milligrams are in 29.4 g?
10. How many milligrams are in 75.2 g?
11. How many kilograms are in 98.4 g?
12. How many kilograms are in 62.7 g?
13. How many milliliters are in 7 L?
14. How many milliliters are in 12 L?
15. How many kiloliters are in 4 mL?
16. How many kiloliters are in 3 mL?

Use the table of metric conversion ratios to find each of the following. Round all answers to the nearest tenth.

17. How many inches are in 4.2 cm?
18. How many inches are in 3.8 cm?
19. How many kilometers are in 14 mi?
20. How many kilometers are in 13 mi?
21. How many meters are in 110 in.?
22. How many meters are in 150 in.?
23. How many centimeters are in 7 in.?
24. How many centimeters are in 9 in.?
25. A box weighing 2.4 lb would weigh how many grams?
26. A box weighing 1.6 lb would weigh how many grams?
27. A man weighs 78 kg. How many pounds does he weigh?
28. A woman weighs 52 kg. How many pounds does she weigh?
29. Ferrante purchased 3 qt of milk. How many liters is that?
30. Wong Tin purchased 1 gal of milk. How many liters is that?

Answer the following questions. Round all answers to the nearest hundredth.

31. How many inches are in 3050 miles?

32. How many inches are in 4500 miles?

33. A truck traveled at a speed of 40 feet per second. How many miles per hour is that?
34. A car traveled at a speed of 55 feet per second. How many miles per hour is that?

35. How many years are in 3,500,000 seconds? (Use the approximate value that 365 days = 1 year.)

36. How many years are in 2,800,000 seconds? (Use the approximate value that 365 days = 1 year.)

Appendix C Interpreting Data from Tables, Charts, and Graphs

Student Learning Objectives

After studying this section, you will be able to interpret data from:

 Tables

2 Charts

3 Pictographs

4 Bar Graphs

5 Line Graphs

6 Pie Graphs and Circle Graphs

NOTE TO STUDENT: Fully worked-out solutions to all of the Practice Problems can be found at the back of the text starting at page SP-1

1 Tables

A table is a device used to organize information into categories. Using it you can readily find details about each category.

EXAMPLE 1

Table of Nutritive Values of Certain Popular "Fast Foods"

Type of Sandwich	Calories	Protein (g)	Fat (g)	Cholesterol (g)	Sodium (mg)
Burger King Whopper	630	27	38	90	880
McDonald's Big Mac	500	25	26	100	890
Wendy's Bacon Cheeseburger	440	22	25	65	870
Burger King BK Broiler (chicken)	280	20	10	50	770
McDonald's McChicken	415	19	20	50	830
Wendy's Grilled Chicken	290	24	7	60	670

Source: U.S. Government Agencies and Food Manufacturers

(a) Which food item has the least amount of fat per serving?

(b) Which beef item has the least amount of calories per serving?

(c) How much more protein does a Burger King Whopper have than a McDonald's Big Mac?

Solution

(a) The least amount of fat, 7 grams, is in the Wendy's Grilled Chicken Sandwich.

(b) The least amount of calories, 440, for a beef sandwich is the Wendy's Bacon Cheeseburger.

(c) The Burger King Whopper has 2 grams of protein more than the McDonald's Big Mac.

Practice Problem 1

(a) Which sandwich has the lowest level of sodium?

(b) Which sandwich has the highest level of cholesterol?

Charts

A chart is a device used to organize information in which not every category is the same. Example 2 illustrates a chart containing different types of data.

EXAMPLE 2 The following chart shows how people in Topsfield indicated they spent their free time.

Survey of Use of Leisure Time

Category	Activity	Hours spent per week
Single men	Gym	6
	Outdoor sports	4
	Dating	7
	Watching pro sports	12
	Reading & TV	3
Single women	Gym	4
	Outdoor sports	2
	Dating	7
	Time with friends	10
	Reading & TV	9
Couples	Time with family	21
	Time as a couple	8
	Time with friends	4
	Reading & TV	9
Children	Watching TV	28
	Playing outside	8
	Reading	1

Use the chart to answer the following questions about people in Topsfield.

(a) What is the average amount of time a couple spends together as a family during the week?

(b) How much more time do children spend watching TV than playing outside?

(c) What activity do single men spend most of their time doing?

Solution

(a) The average amount of time a couple spends together as a family is 21 hours per week.

(b) Children spend 20 more hours per week watching TV than playing outside.

(c) Single men spend more time per week watching pro sports (12 hr) than any other activity.

Practice Problem 2

(a) What two categories do single women spend the most time doing?

(b) What do couples spend most of their time doing?

(c) What is the most significant numerical difference in terms of number of hours per week spent by single women versus single men?

3 Pictographs

A pictograph uses a visually appropriate symbol to represent an amount of items. A pictograph is used in Example 3.

EXAMPLE 3 Consider the following pictograph.

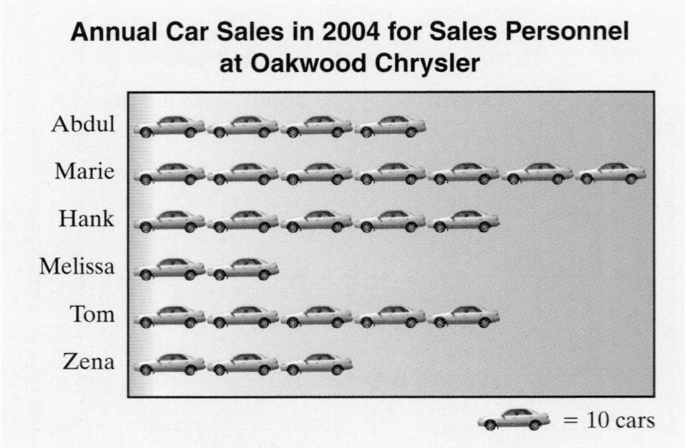

(a) How many cars did Melissa sell in 2004?
(b) Who sold the greatest number of cars?
(c) How many more cars did Tom sell than Zena?

Solution

(a) Melissa sold $2 \times 10 = 20$ cars.
(b) Marie sold the greatest number of cars.
(c) Tom sold $5 \times 10 = 50$ cars. Zena sold $3 \times 10 = 30$ cars. Now $50 - 30 = 20$. Therefore, Tom sold 20 cars more than Zena.

NOTE TO STUDENT: Fully worked-out solutions to all of the Practice Problems can be found at the back of the text starting at page SP-1

Practice Problem 3

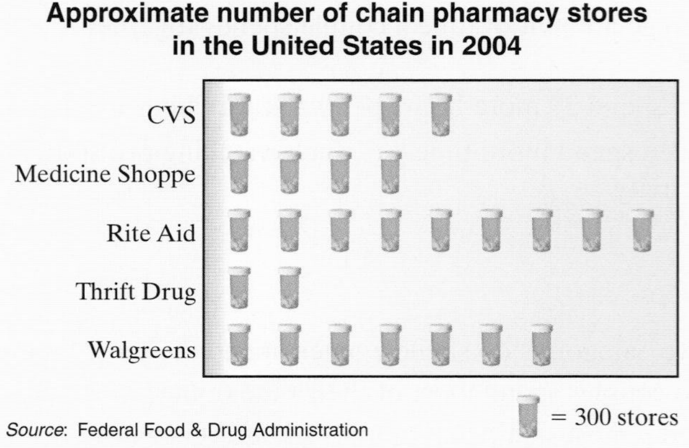

(a) Approximately how many stores does Walgreens have?
(b) Approximately how many more stores does Rite Aid have than CVS?
(c) What is the combined number of Thrift Drug and Medicine Shoppe stores?

4 Bar Graphs

A bar graph is helpful for making comparisons and noting changes or trends. A scale is provided so that the height of the bar graph indicates a specific number. A bar graph is displayed in Example 4. A bar graph may be represented horizontally or vertically. In either case the basic concepts of interpreting a bar graph are the same.

EXAMPLE 4 The approximate population of California by year is given in the following bar graph.

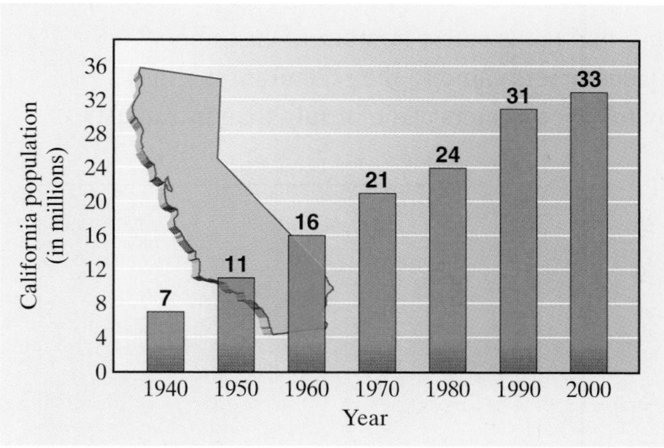

(a) What was the approximate population of California in 2000?

(b) How much greater was the population of California in 1980 than in 1970?

Solution

(a) The approximate population of California in 2000 was about 33 million.

(b) In 1980 it was 24 million. In 1970 it was 21 million. The population was approximately 3 million people more in California in 1980 than in 1970.

Practice Problem 4 The following bar graph depicts the number of fatal accidents for U.S. air carriers for scheduled flight service for aircraft with 30 seats or more.

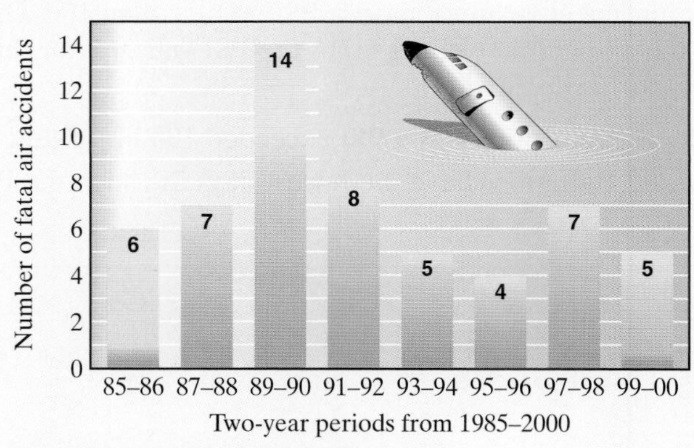

Source: National Transportation Safety Board

(a) What two-year period had the greatest number of fatal accidents?

(b) What was the increase in the number of fatal accidents from the 1987–1988 period to the 1989–1990 period?

(c) What was the decrease in the number of fatal accidents from the 1991–1992 period to the 1993–1994 period?

5 Line Graphs

A line graph is often used to display data when significant changes or trends are present. In a line graph, only a few points are actually plotted from measured values. The points are then connected by straight lines in order to show a trend. The intervening values between points may not exactly lie on the line. A line graph is displayed in Example 5.

EXAMPLE 5 The following line graph shows the number of customers per month coming to a restaurant in a tourist vacation community.

(a) What month had the greatest number of customers?

(b) How many customers came to the restaurant in April?

(c) How many more customers came in July than in August?

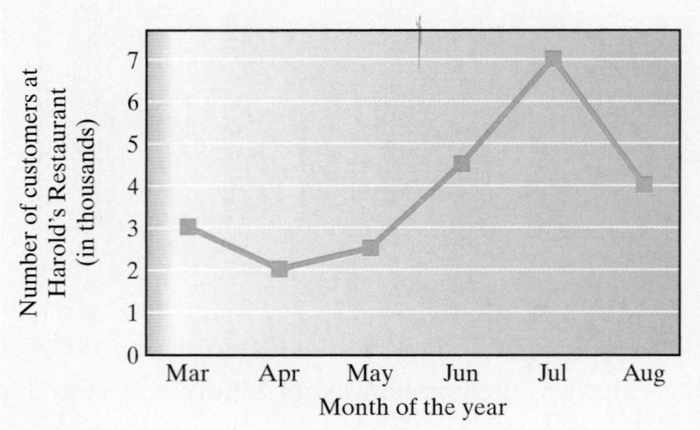

Solution

(a) More customers came during the month of July.

(b) Approximately 2000 customers came in April.

(c) In July there were 7000 customers, while in August there were 4000 customers. Thus, there were 3000 more customers in July than in August.

NOTE TO STUDENT: Fully worked-out solutions to all of the Practice Problems can be found at the back of the text starting at page SP-1

Practice Problem 5 The quality of the air is measured by the Pollutant Standards Index (PSI). To meet the national air quality standards set by the U.S. government, the air in a city cannot have a PSI greater than 100. The following line graph indicates the number of days that the PSI was greater than 100 in the city of Baltimore during an 11-year period.

(a) What was the number of days the PSI exceeded 100 in Baltimore in 1993?

(b) In what year did Baltimore have the fewest days in which the PSI exceeded 100?

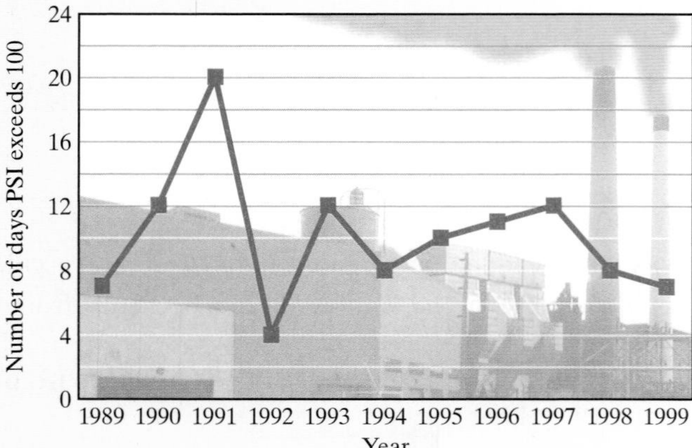

Source: US Environmental Protective Agency

 Pie Graphs and Circle Graphs

A pie graph or a circle graph indicates how a whole quantity is divided into parts. These graphs help you to visualize the size of the relative proportions of parts. Each piece of the pie or circle is called a sector. Example 6 uses a pie graph.

EXAMPLE 6 Together, the Great Lakes form the largest body of fresh water in the world. The total area of these five lakes is about 290,000 square miles, almost all of which is suitable for boating. The percentage of this total area taken up by each of the Great Lakes is shown in the pie graph.

(a) What percentage of the area is taken up by Lake Michigan?

(b) What lake takes up the largest percentage of area?

(c) How many square miles are taken up by Lake Huron and Lake Michigan together?

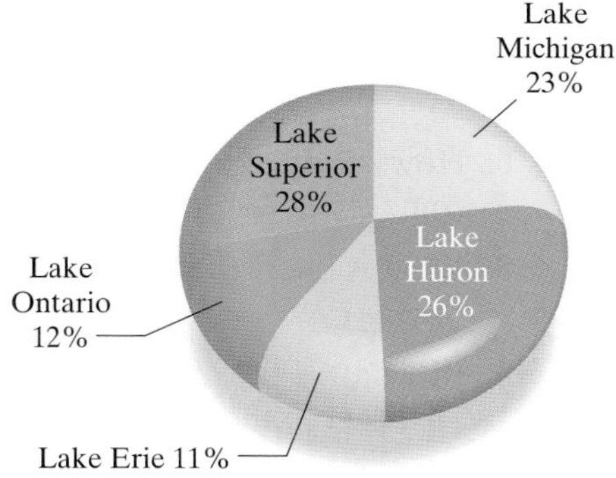

Solution

(a) Lake Michigan takes up 23% of the area.

(b) Lake Superior takes up the largest percentage.

(c) If we add $26 + 23$, we get 49. Thus Lake Huron and Lake Michigan together take up 49% of the total area. 49% of $290,000 = (0.49)(290,000) = 142,100$ square miles.

Practice Problem 6 Seattle receives on average about 37 inches of rain per year. However, the amount of rainfall per month varies significantly. The percent of rainfall that occurs during each quarter of the year is shown by the circle graph.

(a) What percent of the rain in Seattle falls between April and June?

(b) Forty percent of the rainfall occurs in what three-month period?

(c) How many inches of rain fall in Seattle from January to March?

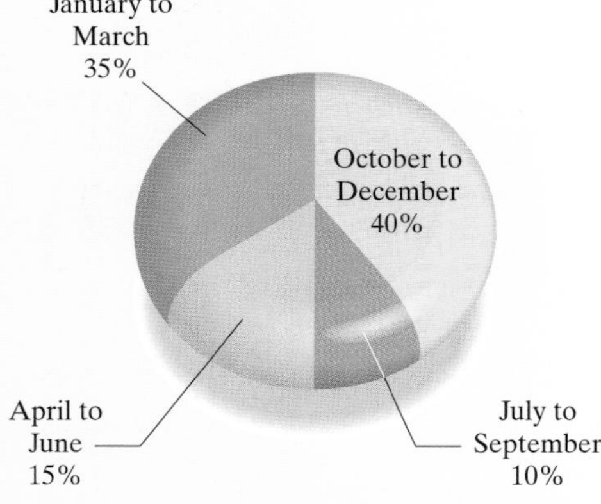

C EXERCISES

Student Solutions Manual | CD/Video | PH Math Tutor Center | MathXL®Tutorials on CD | MathXL® | MyMathLab® | Interactmath.com

In each case study carefully the appropriate visual display, then answer the questions. Consider the following table in answering exercises 1–10.

Table of Facts of the Rocky Mountain States

State	Area in Square Miles	Date Admitted to the Union	Estimated 2002 Population	Number of Representatives in U.S. Congress	Popular Name
Colorado	104,247	1876	4,507,000	7	Centennial State
Idaho	83,557	1890	1,341,000	2	Gem State
Montana	147,138	1889	909,000	1	Treasure State
Nevada	110,540	1864	2,173,000	3	Silver State
Utah	84,916	1896	2,316,000	3	Beehive State
Wyoming	97,914	1890	500,000	1	Equality State

1. What is the area of Utah in square miles?

2. What is the area of Montana in square miles?

3. What is the 2002 estimated population of Colorado?

4. What is the 2002 estimated population of Nevada?

5. How many representatives in the U.S. Congress come from Idaho?

6. How many representatives in the U.S. Congress come from Wyoming?

7. What is the popular name for Montana?

8. What is the popular name for Utah?

9. Which of these six states was the first one to be admitted to the Union?

10. In what year did two of these six states both get admitted to the Union?

Use this pictograph to answer exercises 11–16.

11. How many homes were built in Tarrant County in the year 2004?

12. How many homes were built in Essex County in the year 2004?

13. In what county were the most homes built?

14. How many more homes were built in Tarrant County than Waverly County?

15. How many homes were built in Essex County and Northface County combined?

16. How many homes were built in DuPage County and Waverly County combined?

Number of new homes built in 2004 in each of five counties

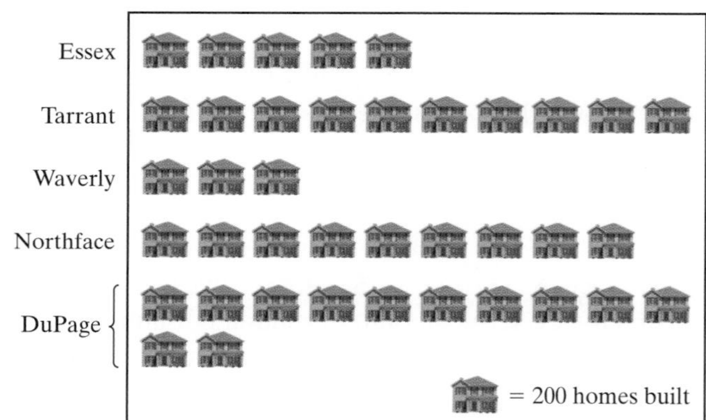

Use this pictograph to answer exercises 17–20.

17. How many apartment units are rented for under $250 per month?

18. How many apartment units are rented for $800–$1249 per month?

19. How many more apartment units are available in the $500–$799 range than in the $800–$1249 range?

20. How many more apartment units are available in the $800–$1249 range than in the $1250 and up range?

Approximate number of apartments in U.S. in 2004

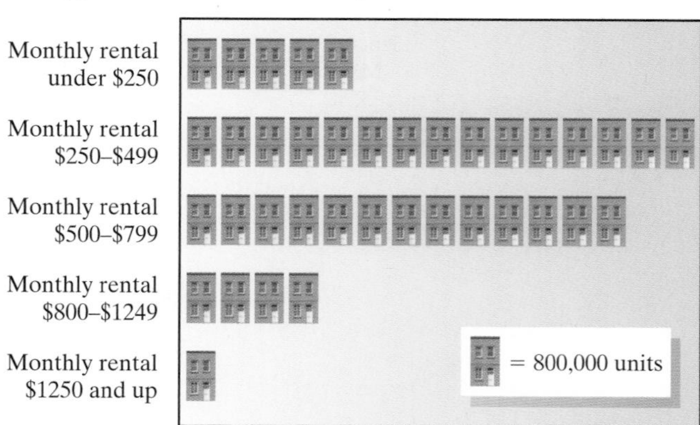

Source: U.S. Bureau of the Census

Use this bar graph to answer exercises 21–26.

21. What was the population in Texas in 1950?

22. What was the population in Texas in 1990?

23. Between what two years was the increase in population the greatest?

24. Between what two years was the increase in population the smallest?

25. How many more people lived in Texas in 1970 than in 1950?

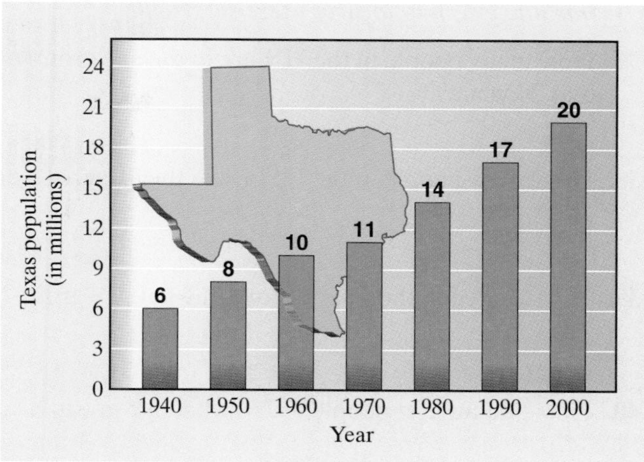

26. How many more people lived in Texas in 1980 than in 1960?

Use this bar graph to answer questions 27–30.

27. According to the bar graph, how many people watched a sports event at least once in the last 12 months?

28. According to the bar graph, how many people were involved in gardening at least once in the last 12 months?

29. What two activities were the most common?

30. What two activities were the least common?

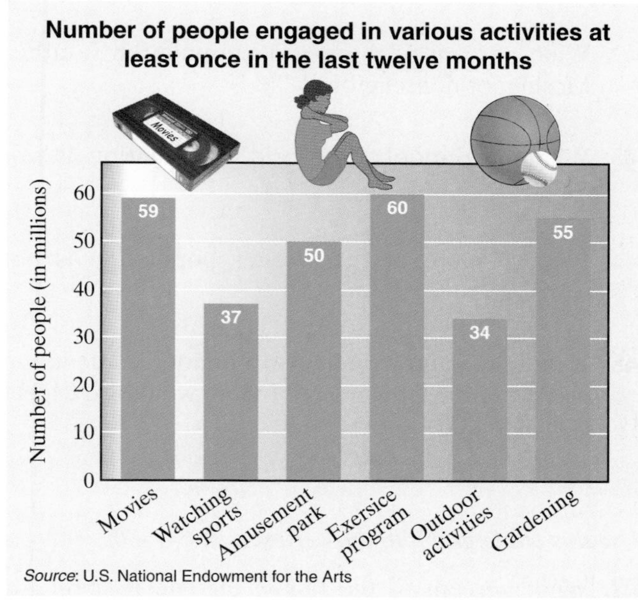

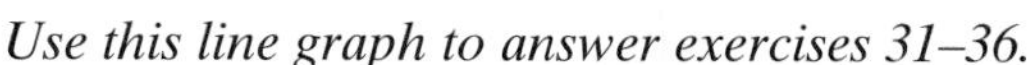

Use this line graph to answer exercises 31–36.

31. What was the profit in 2001?

32. What was the profit in 2000?

33. How much greater was the profit in 2004 than 2003?

34. In what year did the smallest profit occur?

35. Between what two years did the profit decrease the most?

36. Between what two years did the profit increase the most?

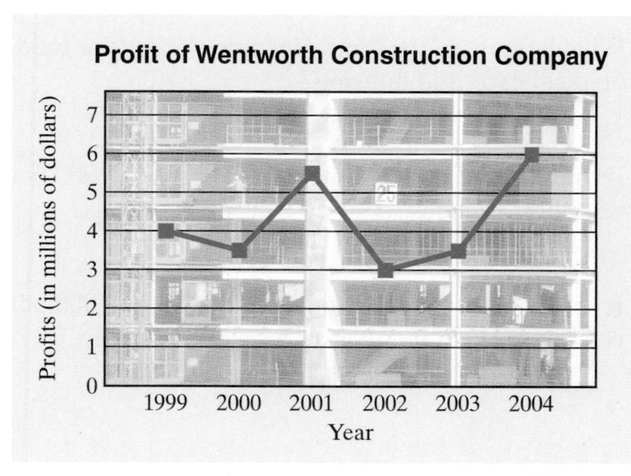

Use this line graph to answer exercises 37–40.

37. How many people in the U.S. are in the age group of 5 to 24 years?

38. How many people in the U.S. are in the age group of 25 to 44 years?

39. Thirty-three million people are in what age group?

40. Fifty-one million people are in what age group?

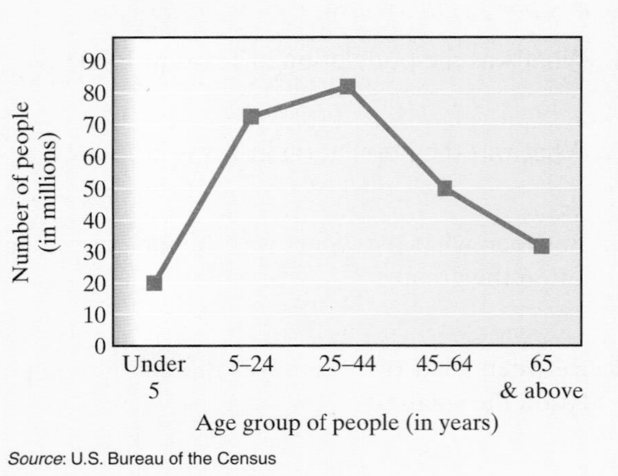

Source: U.S. Bureau of the Census

Use this circle graph to answer exercises 41–46.

41. What percent of the world's population is either Hindu or Buddhist?

42. What percent of the world's population is either Moslem or nonreligious?

43. What percent of the world's population is *not* Moslem?

44. What percent of the world's population is *not* Christian?

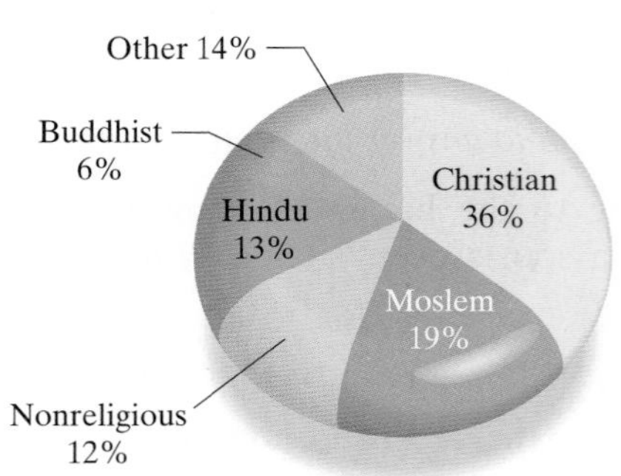

Source: United Nations Statistical Division

45. If there are approximately 6.5 billion people in the world in 2006, how many of them would we expect to be Hindu?

46. If there are approximately 6.9 billion people in the world in 2010, how many of them would we expect to be Moslem?

Use this circle graph to answer exercises 47–50.

47. What percent of the family income is spent for federal, state, and local taxes?

48. What percent of the family income is spent for food, medical care, and housing?

49. If the average two-income family earns \$52,000 per year, how much is spent on transportation?

50. If the average two-income family earns \$52,000 per year, how much is spent on recreation?

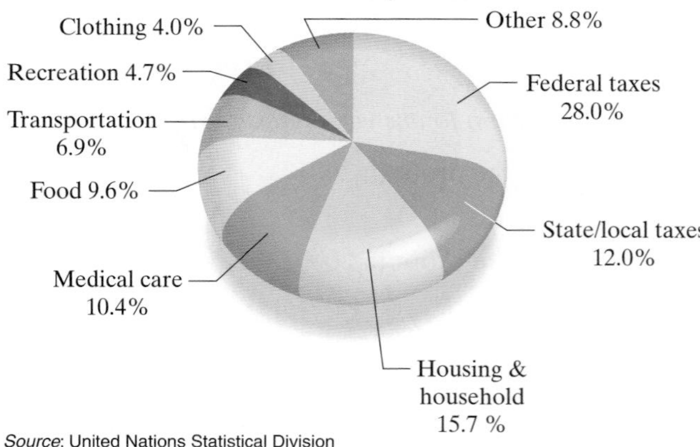

Source: United Nations Statistical Division

Appendix D Inductive and Deductive Reasoning

 Using Inductive Reasoning to Reach a Conclusion

When we reach a conclusion based on specific observations, we are using **inductive reasoning.** Much of our early learning is based on simple cases of inductive reasoning. If a child touches a hot stove or other appliance several times and each time he gets burned, he is likely to conclude, "If I touch something that is hot, I will get burned." This is inductive reasoning. The child has thought about several actions and their outcomes and has made a conclusion or generalization.

The next few examples show how inductive reasoning can be used in mathematics.

Student Learning Objectives

After studying this section, you will be able to:

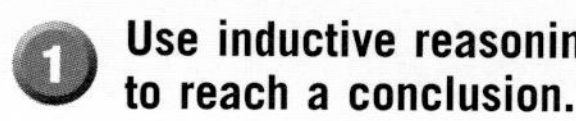

Use inductive reasoning to reach a conclusion.

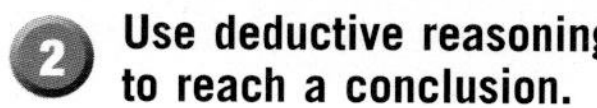

Use deductive reasoning to reach a conclusion.

EXAMPLE 1 Find the next number in the sequence 10, 13, 16, 19, 22, 25, 28, ...

Solution We observe a pattern that each number is 3 more than the preceding number: $10 + 3 = 13$; $13 + 3 = 16$, and so on. Therefore, if we add 3 to 28, we conclude that the next number in the sequence is 31.

Practice Problem 1 Find the next number in the sequence 24, 31, 38, 45, 52, 59, 66, ...

NOTE TO STUDENT: Fully worked-out solutions to all of the Practice Problems can be found at the back of the text starting at page SP-1

EXAMPLE 2 Find the next number in the sequence 1, 8, 27, 64, 125, ...

Solution The sequence can be written as $1^3, 2^3, 3^3, 4^3, 5^3, \ldots$. Each successive integer is cubed. The next number would be 6^3 or 216.

Practice Problem 2 Find the next number in the sequence.

3, 8, 15, 24, 35, 48, 63, 80, ...

EXAMPLE 3 Guess the next seven digits in the following irrational number:

5.636336333633336 . . .

Solution Between 6's there are the digits 3, 33, 333, 3333, and so on. The pattern is that the number of 3's keeps increasing by 1 each time. Thus the next seven digits are 3333363.

Practice Problem 3 Guess the next seven digits in the following irrational number:

6.1213314441 . . .

EXAMPLE 4 Find the next two figures that would appear in the sequence.

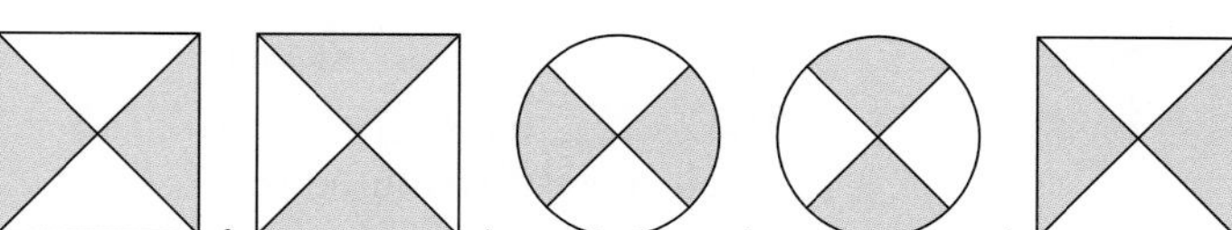

Solution We notice an alternating pattern: square, square, circle, circle, square . . . . We would next expect a square followed by a circle.

We notice a shading pattern of horizontal, vertical, horizontal, vertical, horizontal . . . . We would next expect vertical, then horizontal. Thus, the next two figures are

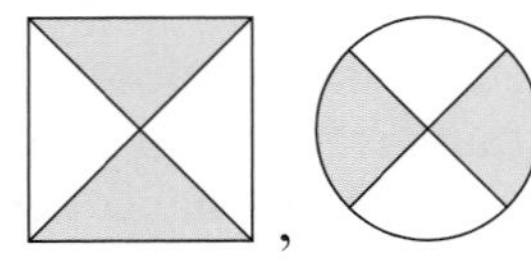

NOTE TO STUDENT: Fully worked-out solutions to all of the Practice Problems can be found at the back of the text starting at page SP-1

Practice Problem 4 Find the next two figures that would appear in the sequence.

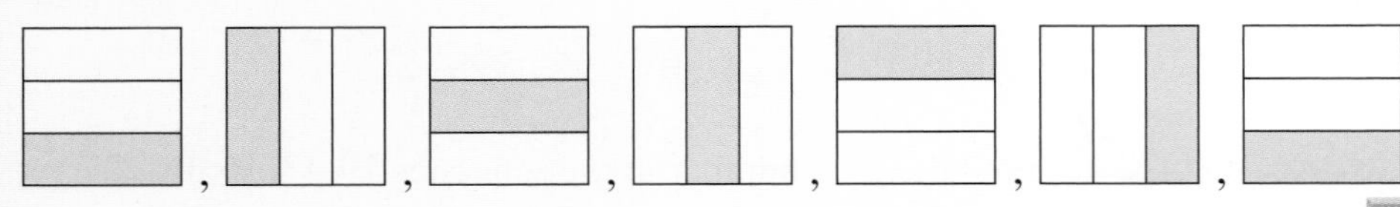

How accurate is inductive reasoning? Do we always come to the right conclusion? Conclusions arrived at by inductive reasoning are always tentative. They may require further investigation. When we use inductive reasoning we are using specific data to reach a general conclusion. However, we may have reached the wrong conclusion. To illustrate:

Take the sequence of numbers 20, 10, 5. What is the next number? You might say 2.5. In the sequence 20, 10, 5, each number appears to be one-half of the preceding number. Thus we would predict 20, 10, 5, 2.5, ...

But wait! There is another possibility. Maybe the sequence is 20, 10, 5, −5, −10, −20, −25, −35, −40, ...

To know for sure which answer is correct, we would need more information, such as more numbers in the sequence to verify the pattern. **You should always treat inductive reasoning conclusions as tentative, requiring further verification.**

2 Using Deductive Reasoning to Reach a Conclusion

Deductive reasoning requires us to take general facts, postulates, or accepted truths and use them to reach a specific conclusion. Suppose we know the following rules or "facts" of algebra:

For all numbers a, b, and c, and for all numbers $d \neq 0$:

1. *Addition principle of equations:* If $a = b$, then $a + c = b + c$.
2. *Division principle of equations:* If $a = b$, then $\frac{a}{d} = \frac{b}{d}$.
3. *Multiplication principle of equations:* If $a = b$, then $ac = bc$.
4. *Distributive property:* $a(b + c) = ab + ac$.

EXAMPLE 5 Use deductive reasoning and the four properties listed in the preceding box to justify each step in solving the equation.

$$2(7x - 2) = 38$$

Solution

Statement	Reason
1. $14x - 4 = 38$	**1.** Distributive property: $a(b + c) = ab + ac$ Here we distributed the 2.
2. $14x = 42$	**2.** Addition principle of equations: If $a = b$, then $a + c = b + c$ Here we added 4 to each side of the equation.

3. $\dfrac{14x}{14} = \dfrac{42}{14}$	3. Division principle of equations:
	If $a = b$, then $\dfrac{a}{d} = \dfrac{b}{d}$
$x = 3$	Here we divided each side by 14.

Practice Problem 5 Use deductive reasoning and the four properties listed in the preceding box to justify each step in solving the equation.

$$\frac{1}{6}x = \frac{1}{3}x + 4$$

Sometimes we need to make conclusions about angles and lines in geometry. The following properties are useful. We will refer to angles 1, 2, 3, 4.

1. If two lines intersect, the opposite angles are equal. Here $\angle 1 = \angle 2$ and $\angle 4 = \angle 3$.

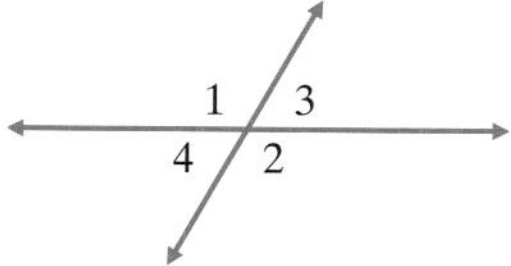

2. If two lines intersect, the adjacent angles are supplementary (they add up to 180°). Here, $\angle 4 + \angle 1 = 180°$, and $\angle 1 + \angle 3 = 180°$, also $\angle 3 + \angle 2 = 180°$, and $\angle 4 + \angle 2 = 180°$.
3. If a transversal (intersecting line) crosses two parallel lines, the alternate interior angles are equal. In the figure at right, line P is a transversal. If line M is parallel to line N, then $\angle 3 = \angle 4$ and $\angle 1 = \angle 2$.

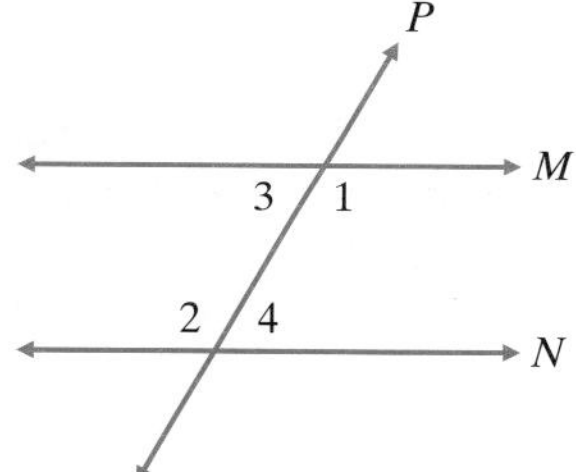

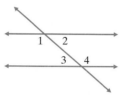

4. If two alternate interior angles on each side of a transversal cutting two straight lines are equal, the two straight lines are parallel. If $\angle 3 = \angle 4$, then line M is parallel to line N.
5. Supplements of equal angles are equal. In the figure at right, if $\angle 1$ and $\angle 2$ are supplementary, and $\angle 3$ and $\angle 4$ are supplementary, then if $\angle 1 = \angle 4$, then $\angle 2 = \angle 3$.
6. Transitive property of equality:

$$\text{If } a = b \text{ and } b = c, \text{ then } a = c.$$

We will now use these facts to prove some geometric conclusions.

EXAMPLE 6 Prove that line M is parallel to line N if $\angle 1 = \angle 3$.

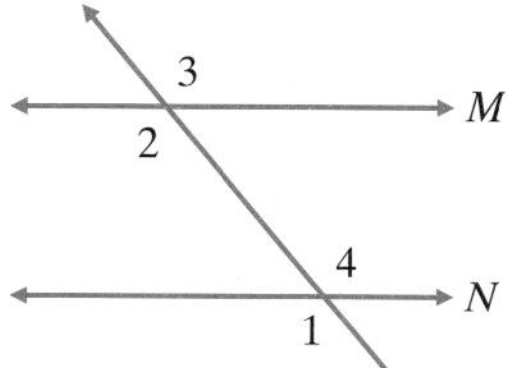

Solution

Statement	Reason
1. $\angle 3 = \angle 2$ and $\angle 4 = \angle 1$	1. If two lines intersect, the opposite angles are equal.
2. $\angle 2 = \angle 4$	2. Transitive property of equality.

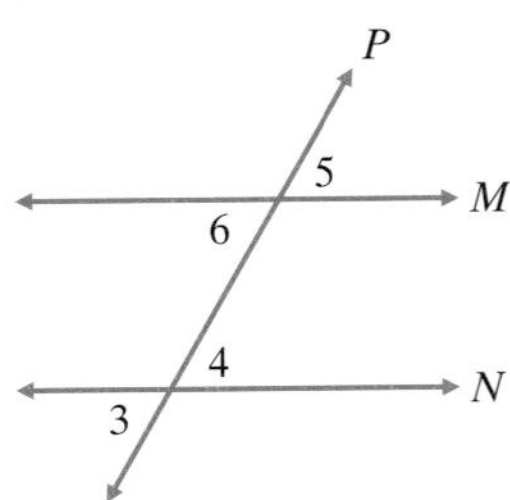

3. Therefore, line M is parallel to line N. (We write this as $M \parallel N$.)	**3.** If two alternate interior angles on each side of a transversal cutting two straight lines are equal, the straight lines are parallel.

Practice Problem 6 Refer to the diagram in the margin. Line M is parallel to line N. $\angle 5 = 26°$. Prove $\angle 4 = 26°$.

Now let us see if we can use deductive reasoning to solve the following problem.

EXAMPLE 7 For next semester, four professors from the psychology department have expressed the following desires for freshman courses. Each professor will teach only *one* freshman course next semester. The four freshman courses are General Psychology, Social Psychology, Psychology of Adjustment, and Educational Psychology.

1. Professors A and B don't want to teach General Psychology.
2. Professor C wants to teach Social Psychology.
3. Professor D will be happy to teach any course.
4. Professor B wants to teach Psychology of Adjustment.

Which professor will teach Educational Psychology, if all professors are given the courses they desire?

Solution Let us organize the facts by listing the four freshman courses and each professor: A, B, C, and D.

General Psychology	Social Psychology	Psychology of Adjustment	Educational Psychology
A	A	A	A
B	B	B	B
C	C	C	C
D	D	D	D

Step	**Reason**
1. We cross off Professors A and B from the General Psychology list.	**1.** Professors A and B don't want to teach General Psychology.

General Psychology			
~~A~~	A	A	A
~~B~~	B	B	B
C	C	C	C
D	D	D	D

2. We cross Professor C off every list (except Social Psychology) and mark that he will teach it.	**2.** Professor C wants to teach Social Psychology.

	Social Psychology		
~~A~~			
~~B~~			
~~C~~	[C]	~~C~~	~~C~~
D			

Step	Reason
3. Professor D is thus the only person who can teach General Psychology. We cross him off every other list and mark that he will teach General Psychology.	**3.** Professor D is happy to teach any course.

~~A~~			
~~B~~			
~~C~~	[C]	~~C~~	~~C~~
[D]	~~D~~	~~D~~	~~D~~

Step	Reason
4. We cross out all courses for Professor B except Psychology of Adjustment.	**4.** Professor B wants to teach Psychology of Adjustment.

		Psychology of Adjustment	
~~A~~	~~A~~	A	A
~~B~~	~~B~~	[B]	~~B~~
~~C~~	[C]	~~C~~	~~C~~
[D]	~~D~~	~~D~~	~~D~~

Step	Reason
5. Professor A will teach Educational Psychology.	**5.** He is the only professor left. All others are assigned.

Educational Psychology
[A]

Practice Problem 7 A Honda, Toyota, Mustang, and Camaro are parked side by side, but not in that order.

1. The Camaro is parked on the right end.
2. The Mustang is between the Honda and the Toyota.
3. The Honda is not next to the Camaro.

Which car is parked on the left end?

NOTE TO STUDENT: Fully worked-out solutions to all of the Practice Problems can be found at the back of the text starting at page SP-1

D Exercises

Student Solutions Manual | CD/Video | PH Math Tutor Center | MathXL®Tutorials on CD | MathXL® | MyMathLab® | Interactmath.com

Find the next number in the sequence.

1. 2, 4, 6, 8, 10, 12, . . .

2. 0, 5, 10, 15, 20, 25, . . .

3. 7, 16, 25, 34, 43, . . .

4. 12, 25, 38, 51, 64, . . .

5. 1, 16, 81, 256, 625, . . .

6. 1, 6, 13, 22, 33, 46, . . .

7. $-7, 3, -6, 4, -5, 5, -4, 6, \ldots$

8. $2, -4, 8, -16, 32, -64, 128, \ldots$

9. $5x, 6x - 1, 7x - 2, 8x - 3, 9x - 4, \ldots$

10. $60x, 30x, 15x, 7.5x, 3.75x, 1.875x, \ldots$

In exercises 11–16, guess the next seven digits in each irrational number.

11. 8.181181118 . . .

12. 3.043004300043 . . .

13. 12.98987987698765 . . .

14. 7.6574839201102938 . . .

15. 2.14916253649 . . .

16. 6.112223333 . . .

17. Find the next row in this triangular pattern.

1

1 1

1 2 1

1 3 3 1

1 4 6 4 1

1 5 10 10 5 1

18. Find the next two figures that would appear in the sequence.

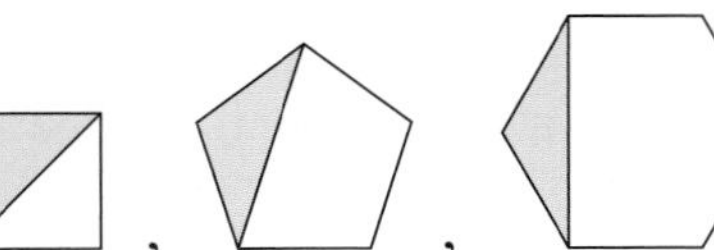
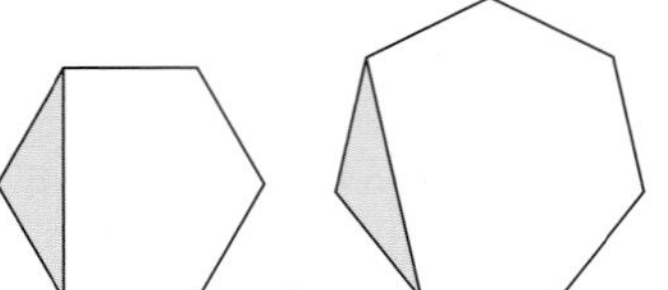

Use deductive reasoning and the four properties discussed in Example 5 to justify each step in solving each equation.

19. $12x - 30 = 6$

20. $3x + 7 = 4$

21. $4x - 3 = 3x - 5$

22. $2x - 9 = 4x + 5$

23. $8x - 3(x - 5) = 30$

24. $3x - 5(x - 1) = -5$

25. $\frac{1}{2}x + 6 = \frac{3}{2} + 6x$

26. $\frac{4}{5}x - 3 = \frac{1}{10}x + \frac{3}{5}$

In exercises 27–28, use deductive reasoning and the properties of geometry discussed in Example 6 to prove each statement.

27. If $\angle 1 = \angle 5$, prove that line P is parallel to line S.

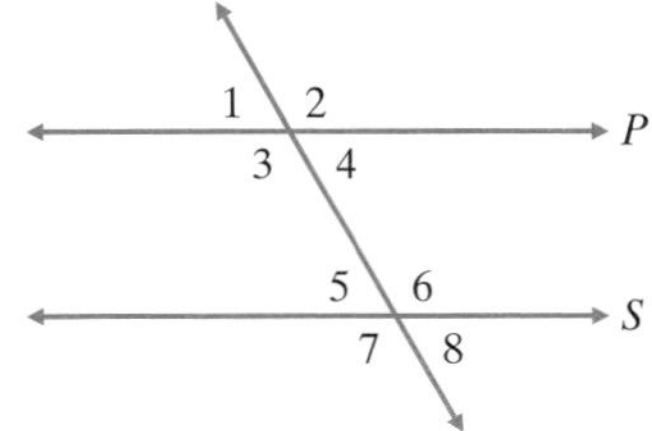

28. If line R is parallel to line S, prove that $\angle 6 = \angle 3$.

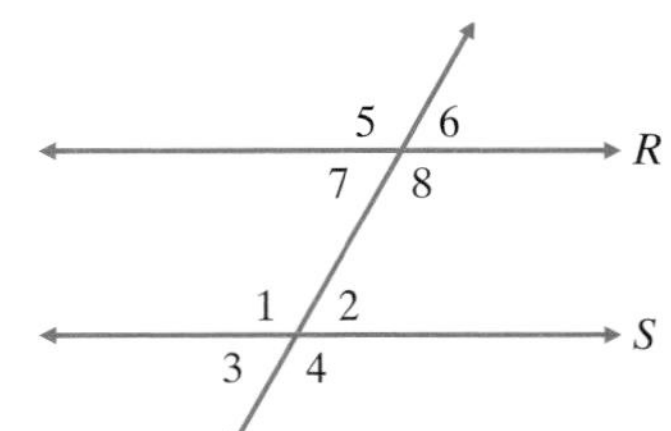

29. William, Brent, Charlie, and Dave competed in the Olympics. These four divers placed first, second, third, and fourth in the competition.

1. James ranked between Brent and Dave.
2. William did better than Brent.
3. Brent did better than Dave.

Who finished in each of the four places?

30. The four floors of Hotel Royale are color-coded.

1. The blue floor is directly below the green floor.
2. The red floor is next to the yellow floor.
3. The green floor is above the red floor.
4. The blue floor is above the yellow floor.
5. There is no floor below the red floor.

What is the order of the colors from top to bottom of Hotel Royale?

31. There are four people named Peter, Michael, Linda and Judy. Each of them has one occupation. They are a teacher, a butcher, a baker, and a candlestick maker.

1. Linda is the baker.
2. The teacher plans to marry the baker in October.
3. Judy and Peter were married last year.

Who is the teacher?

32. A president of a company, a lawyer, a salesman, and a doctor are seated at the head table at a banquet.

1. The lawyer prosecuted the doctor in a malpractice lawsuit and they should not sit together.
2. The salesman should be at one end of the table.
3. The lawyer should be at the far right.

From left to right how should they be seated?

33. John is considering purchasing a new car when he starts his new full-time job. The car with the best gas mileage is a Honda Civic, the car with the most conveniently located dealer is a Toyota Corolla, the car with the lowest price is the Ford Focus and the car that has best handling is the Dodge Neon. His next-door neighbor has a Honda and he does not want to copy his neighbor. If he does not buy a Toyota then he will definitely not go to graduate school. He told his best friend that he probably will not purchase a car based on its handling. He has definitely decided to go to graduate school. What car is he most likely to purchase?

34. Detective Smith recently found a stolen Corvette abandoned near Skull Rocks. A small empty boat was anchored 1 mile offshore with no person in the boat. Divers later found the body of a 35-year-old man $\frac{1}{2}$ mile further out to sea than the boat. If the man entered the water after 10:00 A.M. then the current of the outgoing tide was strong enough to take a dead body a distance of $\frac{1}{2}$ mile further out to sea. The coroner determined when the body was found at 4:00 P.M. that the man had been dead for seven hours. The detective determined that he died instantly when his head hit the rocks directly beneath the anchored boat. Could the man have acted alone based on the facts revealed so far?

35. Dr. Lowe is deciding whether he should do a root canal in order to save Fred's tooth or just remove the tooth and put in a false tooth. If Dr. Lowe works alone on the tooth the procedure will take 2 hours and 15 minutes. Fred wants to save the tooth but he does not want the dental bill for Tuesday's work to be more than \$200. Dr. Lowe charges \$100 per hour for dental procedures. If the bill is under \$150 it is because Dr. Lowe's efficient dental assistant is helping with the oral surgery. The dental procedure is scheduled for Tuesday, when Dr. Lowe does not have any dental assistants available. Will Fred's tooth be saved or will he get a false tooth?

36. If Marcia passes the Bilingual Teacher's exam, she will stay in the Chicago area. If she devotes at least 50 hours of study time to practice her Spanish, she is confident that she can pass the exam. Either Marcia will stay in the Chicago area or she will move back to Massachusetts. If she did not pass the Bilingual Teacher's exam it is because she needed 12 hours of study time per month. Marcia started studying for the exam in April. She will be moving to Massachusetts. When was the Bilingual Teacher's exam given, if we know that Marcia took the exam?

Solutions to Practice Problems

Chapter 0

0.1 Practice Problems

1. (a) $\frac{10}{16} = \frac{2 \times 5}{2 \times 8} = \frac{5}{8}$ **(b)** $\frac{24}{36} = \frac{12 \times 2}{12 \times 3} = \frac{2}{3}$

(c) $\frac{36}{42} = \frac{6 \times 6}{6 \times 7} = \frac{6}{7}$

2. (a) $\frac{4}{12} = \frac{2 \times 2 \times 1}{2 \times 2 \times 3} = \frac{1}{3}$ **(b)** $\frac{25}{125} = \frac{5 \times 5 \times 1}{5 \times 5 \times 5} = \frac{1}{5}$

(c) $\frac{73}{146} = \frac{73 \times 1}{73 \times 2} = \frac{1}{2}$

3. (a) $\frac{18}{6} = \frac{3 \times 6}{6} = 3$ **(b)** $\frac{146}{73} = \frac{73 \times 2}{73} = 2$

(c) $\frac{28}{7} = \frac{7 \times 4}{7} = 4$

4. 56 out of 154 $= \frac{56}{154} = \frac{2 \times 7 \times 4}{2 \times 7 \times 11} = \frac{4}{11}$

5. (a) $\frac{12}{7} = 12 \div 7 = 7\overline{)12} = 1\frac{5}{7}$

$$\begin{array}{r} 1 \\ 7\overline{)12} \\ \underline{7} \\ 5 \end{array} \text{ Remainder}$$

(b) $\frac{20}{5} = 20 \div 5 = 5\overline{)20} = 4$

$$\begin{array}{r} 4 \\ 5\overline{)20} \\ \underline{20} \\ 0 \end{array} \text{ Remainder}$$

6. (a) $3\frac{2}{5} = \frac{(3 \times 5) + 2}{5} = \frac{15 + 2}{5} = \frac{17}{5}$

(b) $1\frac{3}{7} = \frac{(1 \times 7) + 3}{7} = \frac{7 + 3}{7} = \frac{10}{7}$

(c) $2\frac{6}{11} = \frac{(2 \times 11) + 6}{11} = \frac{22 + 6}{11} = \frac{28}{11}$

(d) $4\frac{2}{3} = \frac{(4 \times 3) + 2}{3} = \frac{12 + 2}{3} = \frac{14}{3}$

7. (a) $\frac{3}{8} = \frac{?}{24}$ Observe $8 \times 3 = 24$

$\frac{3 \times 3}{8 \times 3} = \frac{9}{24}$

(b) $\frac{5}{6} = \frac{?}{30}$

$\frac{5 \times 5}{6 \times 5} = \frac{25}{30}$

(c) $\frac{2}{7} = \frac{?}{56}$

$\frac{2 \times 8}{7 \times 8} = \frac{16}{56}$

0.2 Practice Problems

1. (a) $\frac{3}{6} + \frac{2}{6} = \frac{3 + 2}{6} = \frac{5}{6}$ **(b)** $\frac{3}{11} + \frac{8}{11} = \frac{11}{11} = 1$

(c) $\frac{1}{8} + \frac{2}{8} + \frac{1}{8} = \frac{1 + 2 + 1}{8} = \frac{4}{8} = \frac{1}{2}$

(d) $\frac{5}{9} + \frac{8}{9} = \frac{5 + 8}{9} = \frac{13}{9} = 1\frac{4}{9}$

2. (a) $\frac{11}{13} - \frac{6}{13} = \frac{11 - 6}{13} = \frac{5}{13}$

(b) $\frac{8}{9} - \frac{2}{9} = \frac{8 - 2}{9} = \frac{6}{9} = \frac{2}{3}$

3. Find LCD of $\frac{1}{8}$ and $\frac{5}{12}$.

$8 = 2 \cdot 2 \cdot 2$
$12 = \downarrow\ 2 \cdot 2 \cdot 3$
$2 \cdot 2 \cdot 2 \cdot 3 = 24$ LCD $= 24$

4. Find the LCD using prime factors.

$\frac{8}{35}$ and $\frac{6}{15}$

$35 = 7 \cdot 5$
$15 = \ \ \ 5 \cdot 3$
$\downarrow\ \downarrow\ \downarrow$
$7 \cdot 5 \cdot 3$ LCD $= 105$

5. Find LCD of $\frac{5}{12}$ and $\frac{7}{30}$.

$12 = 3 \cdot 2 \cdot 2$
$30 = 3\ \ \ 2 \cdot 5$
$\downarrow\ \downarrow\ \downarrow\ \downarrow$
$3 \cdot 2 \cdot 2 \cdot 5$ LCD $= 60$

6. Find LCD of $\frac{1}{18}, \frac{2}{27}$ and $\frac{5}{12}$.

$12 = 2 \cdot 2 \cdot 3$
$18 = 2\ \ \ 3 \cdot 3$
$27 = \ \ \ 3 \cdot 3 \cdot 3$
$\downarrow\ \downarrow\ \downarrow\ \downarrow\ \downarrow$
$2 \cdot 2 \cdot 3 \cdot 3 \cdot 3$ LCD $= 108$

7. Add $\frac{1}{8} + \frac{5}{12}$

First find the LCD.

$8 = 2 \cdot 2 \cdot 2$
$12 = 2 \cdot 2\ \ \ \cdot 3$
$\downarrow\ \downarrow\ \downarrow\ \downarrow$
$2 \cdot 2 \cdot 2 \cdot 3$ LCD $= 24$

Then change to equivalent fractions and add.

$\frac{1}{8} \times \frac{3}{3} + \frac{5}{12} \times \frac{2}{2} = \frac{3}{24} + \frac{10}{24} = \frac{3 + 10}{24} = \frac{13}{24}$

8. $\frac{3}{5} + \frac{4}{25} + \frac{1}{10}$

First find the LCD.

$5 = \ \ \ 5$
$10 = 2 \cdot 5$
$25 = \ \ \ 5 \cdot 5$
$\downarrow\ \downarrow\ \downarrow$
$2 \cdot 5 \cdot 5$ LCD $= 50$

Then change to equivalent fractions and add.

$\frac{3}{5} \times \frac{10}{10} + \frac{4}{25} \times \frac{2}{2} + \frac{1}{10} \times \frac{5}{5} = \frac{30}{50} + \frac{8}{50} + \frac{5}{50}$

$= \frac{30 + 8 + 5}{50} = \frac{43}{50}$

9. Add $\frac{1}{49} + \frac{3}{14}$

First find the LCD.

$14 = 2 \cdot 7$
$49 = \ \ \ 7 \cdot 7$
$\downarrow\ \downarrow\ \downarrow$
$2 \cdot 7 \cdot 7$ LCD $= 98$

Then change to equivalent fractions and add.

$\frac{1}{49} \times \frac{2}{2} + \frac{3}{14} \times \frac{7}{7} = \frac{2}{98} + \frac{21}{98} = \frac{2 + 21}{98} = \frac{23}{98}$

10. $\frac{1}{12} - \frac{1}{30}$

First find the LCD.

$12 = 2 \cdot 2 \cdot 3$

$30 = \quad 2 \cdot 3 \cdot 5$

$2 \cdot 2 \cdot 3 \cdot 5 \qquad \text{LCD} = 60$

Then change to equivalent fractions and subtract.

$$\frac{1}{12} \times \frac{5}{5} - \frac{1}{30} \times \frac{2}{2} = \frac{5}{60} - \frac{2}{60} = \frac{5-2}{60} = \frac{3}{60} = \frac{1}{20}$$

11. $\frac{2}{3} + \frac{3}{4} - \frac{3}{8}$

First find the LCD.

$3 = \qquad 3$

$4 = 2 \cdot 2$

$8 = 2 \cdot 2 \cdot 2$

$2 \cdot 2 \cdot 2 \cdot 3 \qquad \text{LCD} = 24$

Then change to equivalent fractions and add and subtract.

$$\frac{2}{3} \times \frac{8}{8} + \frac{3}{4} \times \frac{6}{6} - \frac{3}{8} \times \frac{3}{3}$$

$$= \frac{16}{24} + \frac{18}{24} - \frac{9}{24} = \frac{16+18-9}{24} = \frac{25}{24} = 1\frac{1}{24}$$

12. (a) $1\frac{2}{3} + 2\frac{4}{5} = \frac{5}{3} + \frac{14}{5} = \frac{5}{3} \times \frac{5}{5} + \frac{14}{5} \times \frac{3}{3} = \frac{25}{15} + \frac{42}{15}$

$$= \frac{25+42}{15} = \frac{67}{15} = 4\frac{7}{15}$$

(b) $5\frac{1}{4} - 2\frac{2}{3} = \frac{21}{4} - \frac{8}{3} = \frac{21}{4} \times \frac{3}{3} - \frac{8}{3} \times \frac{4}{4} = \frac{63}{12} - \frac{32}{12}$

$$= \frac{63-32}{12} = \frac{31}{12} = 2\frac{7}{12}$$

13.

$6\frac{1}{2}$

$4\frac{1}{5}$ $\qquad$ $4\frac{1}{5}$

$6\frac{1}{2}$

$$4\frac{1}{5} + 4\frac{1}{5} + 6\frac{1}{2} + 6\frac{1}{2}$$

$$= \frac{21}{5} + \frac{21}{5} + \frac{13}{2} + \frac{13}{2}$$

LCD = 10

$$\frac{21}{5} \times \frac{2}{2} + \frac{21}{5} \times \frac{2}{2} + \frac{13}{2} \times \frac{5}{5} + \frac{13}{2} \times \frac{5}{5}$$

$$= \frac{42}{10} + \frac{42}{10} + \frac{65}{10} + \frac{65}{10} = \frac{42+42+65+65}{10} = \frac{214}{10} = 21\frac{2}{5}$$

The perimeter is $21\frac{2}{5}$ cm.

0.3 Practice Problems

1. (a) $\frac{2}{7} \times \frac{5}{11} = \frac{2 \cdot 5}{7 \cdot 11} = \frac{10}{77}$

(b) $\frac{1}{5} \times \frac{7}{10} = \frac{1 \times 7}{5 \times 10} = \frac{7}{50}$

(c) $\frac{9}{5} \times \frac{1}{4} = \frac{9 \times 1}{5 \times 4} = \frac{9}{20}$

(d) $\frac{8}{9} \times \frac{3}{10} = \frac{8 \times 3}{9 \times 10} = \frac{24}{90} = \frac{4}{15}$

2. (a) $\frac{3}{5} \times \frac{4}{3} = \frac{3 \cdot 4}{5 \cdot 3} = \frac{4}{5}$

(b) $\frac{9}{10} \times \frac{5}{12} = \frac{3 \cdot 3}{2 \cdot 5} \times \frac{5}{2 \cdot 2 \cdot 3} = \frac{3}{8}$

3. (a) $4 \times \frac{2}{7} = \frac{4}{1} \times \frac{2}{7} = \frac{4 \cdot 2}{1 \cdot 7} = \frac{8}{7} = 1\frac{1}{7}$

(b) $12 \times \frac{3}{4} = \frac{12}{1} \times \frac{3}{4} = \frac{2 \cdot 2 \cdot 3}{1} \times \frac{3}{2 \cdot 2} = 9$

4. Multiply. $5\frac{3}{5}$ times $3\frac{3}{4}$

$$5\frac{3}{5} \times 3\frac{3}{4} = \frac{28}{5} \times \frac{15}{4} = \frac{2 \cdot 2 \cdot 7}{5} \times \frac{3 \cdot 5}{2 \cdot 2} = \frac{21}{1} = 21$$

21 square miles

5. $3\frac{1}{2} \times \frac{1}{14} \times 4 = \frac{7}{2} \times \frac{1}{14} \times \frac{4}{1} = \frac{7}{2} \times \frac{1}{2 \cdot 7} \times \frac{2 \cdot 2}{1} = 1$

6. (a) $\frac{2}{5} \div \frac{1}{3} = \frac{2}{5} \times \frac{3}{1} = \frac{6}{5}$

(b) $\frac{12}{13} \div \frac{4}{3} = \frac{2 \cdot 2 \cdot 3}{13} \times \frac{3}{2 \cdot 2} = \frac{9}{13}$

7. (a) $\frac{3}{7} \div 6 = \frac{3}{7} \div \frac{6}{1} = \frac{3}{7} \times \frac{1}{6} = \frac{3}{42} = \frac{1}{14}$

(b) $8 \div \frac{2}{3} = \frac{8}{1} \times \frac{3}{2} = 12$

8. (a) $\dfrac{\frac{3}{11}}{\frac{5}{7}} = \frac{3}{11} \div \frac{5}{7} = \frac{3}{11} \times \frac{7}{5} = \frac{21}{55}$

(b) $\dfrac{\frac{12}{5}}{\frac{8}{15}} = \frac{12}{5} \div \frac{8}{15} = \frac{2 \cdot 2 \cdot 3}{5} \times \frac{3 \cdot 5}{2 \cdot 2 \cdot 2} = \frac{9}{2} = 4\frac{1}{2}$

9. (a) $1\frac{2}{5} \div 2\frac{1}{3} = \frac{7}{5} \div \frac{7}{3} = \frac{7}{5} \times \frac{3}{7} = \frac{3}{5}$

(b) $4\frac{2}{3} \div 7 = \frac{14}{3} \times \frac{1}{7} = \frac{2 \cdot 7}{3} \times \frac{1}{7} = \frac{2}{3}$

(c) $\dfrac{1\frac{1}{5}}{1\frac{2}{7}} = 1\frac{1}{5} \div 1\frac{2}{7} = \frac{6}{5} \div \frac{9}{7} = \frac{6}{5} \times \frac{7}{9} = \frac{2 \cdot 3}{5} \times \frac{7}{3 \cdot 3} = \frac{14}{15}$

10. $64 \div 5\frac{1}{3} = 64 \div \frac{16}{3} = 64 \times \frac{3}{16} = 12$ jars

11. $25\frac{1}{2} \times 5\frac{1}{4} = \frac{51}{2} \times \frac{21}{4} = \frac{1071}{8} = 133\frac{7}{8}$ miles

0.4 Practice Problems

1. (a) $0.9 = \frac{9}{10}$ = nine tenths **(b)** $\frac{9}{100}$ = nine hundredths.

(c) $0.731 = \frac{731}{1000}$ = seven hundred thirty-one thousandths

(d) $1.371 = 1\frac{371}{1000}$ = one and three hundred seventy-one thousandths

(e) $0.0005 = \frac{5}{10{,}000}$ = five ten-thousandths

2. (a) $\frac{3}{8}$

```
   0.375
8)3.000
  2 4
    60
    56
     40
     40
      0
```

(b) $\frac{7}{200}$

```
     0.035
200)7.000
    6 00
    1 000
    1 000
        0
```

(c) $\frac{33}{20}$

```
    1.65
20)33.00
   20
   13 0
   12 0
    1 00
    1 00
       0
```

3. (a) $\frac{1}{6}$ $\quad 6\overline{)1.000} = 0.166 = 0.1\overline{6}$

```
     0.166 = 0.16̄
  6)1.000
    6
    40
    36
     40
     36
      4
```

(b) $\frac{5}{11}$ $\quad 11\overline{)5.0000} = 0.4545 = .\overline{45}$

```
      0.4545 = .45̄
  11)5.0000
     4 4
      60
      55
       50
       44
        60
        55
         5
```

4. (a) $0.8 \quad \frac{8}{10} = \frac{2 \cdot 2 \cdot 2}{2 \cdot 5} = \frac{4}{5}$

(b) $0.88 \quad \frac{88}{100} = \frac{11 \cdot 2 \cdot 2 \cdot 2}{5 \cdot 5 \cdot 2 \cdot 2} = \frac{22}{25}$

(c) $0.45 \quad \frac{45}{100} = \frac{5 \cdot 3 \cdot 3}{5 \cdot 5 \cdot 2 \cdot 2} = \frac{9}{20}$

(d) $0.148 \quad \frac{148}{1000} = \frac{2 \cdot 2 \cdot 37}{5 \cdot 5 \cdot 5 \cdot 2 \cdot 2 \cdot 2} = \frac{37}{250}$

(e) $0.612 \quad \frac{612}{1000} = \frac{17 \cdot 3 \cdot 3 \cdot 2 \cdot 2}{5 \cdot 5 \cdot 5 \cdot 2 \cdot 2 \cdot 2} = \frac{153}{250}$

(f) $0.016 \quad \frac{16}{1000} = \frac{2 \cdot 2 \cdot 2 \cdot 2}{5 \cdot 5 \cdot 5 \cdot 2 \cdot 2 \cdot 2} = \frac{2}{125}$

5. (a)
```
  3.12
  5.08
  1.42
  ----
  9.62
```
(b)
```
   152.003
  -136.118
  --------
    15.885
```
(c)
```
  1.1
  3.16
  5.123
  -----
  9.383
```
(d)
```
   1.0052
  -0.1234
  -------
   0.8818
```

6. (a)
```
  0.061
  5.0008
  1.3
  ------
  6.3618
```
(b)
```
   18.000
  - 0.126
  -------
   17.874
```

7.
```
    0.5
  × 0.3
  -----
   0.15
```

8.
```
    0.12
  ×  0.4
  ------
   0.048
```

9. (a)
```
      1.23
  × 0.005
  -------
  0.00615
```
(b)
```
     0.00002
  ×    0.003
  ----------
  0.00000006
```

10.
```
    $5.26
  6)31.56
    30
     15
     12
      36
      36
       0
```
$5.26 for each box of paper

11.
```
        30,000.
  .06.)1800.00.
```

12.
```
  4.9.)0.0.1764

       0.0036
  49)0.1764
       147
        294
        294
          0
```

13. (a) $0.0016 \times 100 = 0.16$
Move decimal point 2 places to the right.

(b) $2.34 \times 1000 = 2340$
Move decimal point 3 places to the right.

(c) $56.75 \times 10{,}000 = 567{,}500$
Move decimal point 4 places to the right.

14. (a) $\frac{5.82}{10}$ (Move decimal point 1 place to the left.) 0.582

(b) $\frac{123.4}{1000}$ (Move decimal point 3 places to the left.) 0.1234

(c) $\frac{0.00614}{10{,}000}$ (Move decimal point 4 places to the left.)
0.000000614

0.5 Practice Problems

1. (a) $0.92 = 92\%$ **(b)** $0.418 = 41.8\%$ **(c)** $0.7 = 70\%$

2. (a) $0.0019 = 0.19\%$ **(b)** $0.0736 = 7.36\%$
(c) $0.0003 = 0.03\%$

3. (a) 304% **(b)** 518.6% **(c)** 210%

4. (a) 0.07 **(b)** 0.093 **(c)** 0.002

5. (a) 1.31 **(b)** 3.016 **(c)** 0.0004

6. Change % to decimal and multiply.
(a) $0.18 \times 50 = 9$
(b) $0.04 \times 64 = 2.56$
(c) $1.56 \times 35 = 54.6$

7. $4.2\% \times 38{,}000 = 0.042 \times 38{,}000$
(a) $1596 **(b)** 38,000 + 1596 = $39,596

8. $\frac{37}{148}$ reduces to $\frac{37 \cdot 1}{37 \cdot 2 \cdot 2} = \frac{1}{4} = 0.25 = 25\%$

9. (a) $\frac{24}{48} = \frac{2 \cdot 2 \cdot 2 \cdot 3}{2 \cdot 2 \cdot 2 \cdot 2 \cdot 3} = \frac{1}{2} = 0.5 = 50\%$

(b) $\frac{4}{25} = 0.16 = 16\%$

10. $\frac{430}{1256} = \frac{215}{628} \approx 0.342 \approx 34\%$

0.6 Practice Problems

1. $100{,}000 \times 400 = 40{,}000{,}000$

2. $12\frac{1}{2} \rightarrow 10$; $9\frac{3}{4} \rightarrow 10$; First room $10 \times 10 = 100$ square feet.

$14\frac{1}{4} \rightarrow 15$; $18\frac{1}{2} \rightarrow 20$; Second room $15 \times 20 = 300$ square feet.

Both rooms $100 + 300 = 400$ square feet.

3. (a) $422.8 \rightarrow 400$ miles $\quad 19.3 \rightarrow 20$ gallons of gas

$\frac{400}{20} = 20$ miles/gallon

(b) $1.69\frac{9}{10} \rightarrow \$2.00$ per gallon $\quad 3862 \rightarrow 4000$ miles

$\frac{4000 \text{ miles}}{20 \text{ mi/gallon}} = 200$ gallons

200 gallons × $2.00 per gallon = $400.00

4. (a) 3,580,000,000 estimate → $\frac{4{,}000{,}000{,}000 \text{ miles}}{40{,}000 \text{ mi/hour}}$
43,300 estimate →
100,000 hours

(b) 24 hours/day estimate → $\frac{100{,}000}{20} = 5000$ days

5. 56.93% estimate → 60% → 0.6

293,567.12 estimate → 300,000
$0.6 \times 300{,}000 = \$180{,}000$

0.7 Practice Problems

1.

Mathematics Blueprint for Problem Solving			
Gather the Facts	**What Am I Solving for?**	**What Must I Calculate?**	**Key Points to Remember**
Living Room measures $16\frac{1}{2}$ ft $\times$ $10\frac{1}{2}$ ft. The carpet costs \$20.00 per square yard.	Area of room in square feet. Area of room in square yards. Cost of the carpet.	Multiply $16\frac{1}{2}$ ft by $10\frac{1}{2}$ ft to get the area in square feet. Divide the number of square feet by 9 to get the number of square yards. Multiply the number of square yards by \$20.00.	9 sq feet = 1 square yard

$16\frac{1}{2} \times 10\frac{1}{2} = 173\frac{1}{4}$ square feet

$173\frac{1}{4} \div 9 = 19\frac{1}{4}$ square yards

$19\frac{1}{4} \times 20 = \$385.00$ total cost of carpet

Check:

Estimate area of room $16 \times 10 = 160$ square feet
Estimate area in square yards $160 \div 10 = 16$
Estimate the cost $16 \times 20 = \$320.00$
This is close to our answer of \$385.00. Our answer seems reasonable.

2. (a) $\frac{10}{55} \approx 0.181 \approx 18\%$ (b) $\frac{3{,}660{,}000}{13{,}240{,}000} \approx 0.276 \approx 28\%$

(c) $\frac{15}{55} \approx 0.273 \approx 27\%$ (d) $\frac{3{,}720{,}000}{13{,}240{,}000} \approx 0.281 \approx 28\%$

(e) We notice that 18% of the company's sales force is located in the Northwest, and they were responsible for 28% of the sales volume. The percent of sales compared to the percent of sales force is about 150%. 27% of the company's sales force is located in the Southwest, and they were responsible for 28% of the sales volume. The percent of sales compared to the percent of sales force is approximately 100%. It would appear that the Northwest sales force is more effective.

Chapter 1

1.1 Practice Problems

1.

	Number	Integer	Rational Number	Irrational Number	Real Number
(a)	$-\frac{2}{5}$		X		X
(b)	1.515151...		X		X
(c)	−8	X	X		X
(d)	π			X	X

2. (a) Population growth of 1,259 is +1,259.
(b) Depreciation of 763 is −763.00.
(c) Wind chill factor of minus 10 is −10.

3. (a) The additive inverse of $+\frac{2}{5}$ is $-\frac{2}{5}$.
(b) The additive inverse of −1.92 is +1.92.
(c) The opposite of a loss of 12 yards on a football play is a gain of 12 yards on the play.

4. (a) $|-7.34| = 7.34$

(b) $\left|\frac{5}{8}\right| = \frac{5}{8}$ (c) $\left|\frac{0}{2}\right| = \frac{0}{2} = 0$

1.1 Practice Problems (*continued*)

5. (a) $37 + 19$
$37 + 19 = 56$
$37 + 19 = +56$

(b) $-23 + (-35)$
$23 + 35 = 58$
$-23 + (-35) = -58$

6. $-\frac{3}{5} + \left(-\frac{4}{7}\right)$
$-\frac{21}{35} + \left(-\frac{20}{35}\right)$
$-\frac{21}{35} + \left(-\frac{20}{35}\right) = -\frac{41}{35}$

7. $-12.7 + (-9.38)$
$12.7 + 9.38 = 22.08$
$-12.7 + (-9.38) = -22.08$

8. $-7 + (-11) + (-33)$
$= -18 + (-33)$
$= -51$

9. $-9 + 15$
$15 - 9 = 6$
$-9 + 15 = 6$

10. $-\frac{5}{12} + \frac{7}{12} + \left(-\frac{11}{12}\right)$
$= \frac{2}{12} + \left(-\frac{11}{12}\right) = -\frac{9}{12} = -\frac{3}{4}$

11. $-6.3 + (-8.0) + 3.5$
$= -14.3 + 3.5$
$= -10.8$

12. $-6 + 5 + (-7) + (-2) + 5 + 3$

−6	+ 5
−7	+ 5
−2	+ 3
−15	13

$-15 + 13 = -2$

13. (a) $-2.9 + (-5.7) = -8.6$ (b) $\frac{2}{3} + \left(-\frac{1}{4}\right)$
$= \frac{8}{12} + \left(-\frac{3}{12}\right) = \frac{5}{12}$

1.2 Practice Problems

1. $9 - (-3) = 9 + (+3) = 12$
2. $-12 - (-5) = -12 + (+5) = -7$
3. (a) $\frac{5}{9} - \frac{7}{9} = \frac{5}{9} + \left(-\frac{7}{9}\right) = -\frac{2}{9}$

(b) $-\frac{5}{21} - \left(-\frac{3}{7}\right) = -\frac{5}{21} + \left(+\frac{3}{7}\right) = -\frac{5}{21} + \left(+\frac{9}{21}\right) = +\frac{4}{21}$

4. $-17.3 - (-17.3)$
$= -17.3 + 17.3$
$= 0$

5. (a) $-21 - 9$
$= -21 + (-9)$
$= -30$

(b) $17 - 36$
$= 17 + (-36)$
$= -19$

(c) $12 - (-15)$
$= 12 + (+15)$
$= 27$

(d) $\frac{3}{5} - 2$
$= \frac{3}{5} + (-2)$
$= \frac{3}{5} + \left(-\frac{10}{5}\right) = -\frac{7}{5}$ or $-1\frac{2}{5}$

6. $350 - (-186)$
$= 350 + 186$
$= 536$ The helicopter is 536 feet from the sunken vessel.

1.3 Practice Problems

1. (a) $(-6)(-2) = 12$
(b) $(7)(9) = 63$
(c) $\left(-\frac{3}{5}\right)\left(\frac{2}{7}\right) = -\frac{6}{35}$
(d) $\left(\frac{5}{6}\right)(-7) = \left(\frac{5}{6}\right)\left(-\frac{7}{1}\right) = -\frac{35}{6}$

2. $(-5)(-2)(-6)$
$= (+10)(-6) = -60$

3. (a) positive; $-2(-3) = 6$

(b) negative; $(-1)(-3)(-2)$
$= 3(-2)$
$= -6$

(c) positive; $-4\left(-\frac{1}{4}\right)(-2)(-6)$
$= 1(-2)(-6)$
$= -2(-6)$
$= +12$ or 12

4. (a) $-36 \div (-2) = 18$
(b) $-49 \div 7 = -7$
(c) $\frac{50}{-10} = -5$
(d) $\frac{-39}{13} = -3$

5. (a) $-12.6 \div (-1.8) = 7$
(b) $0.45 \div (-0.9) = -0.5$

6. $-\frac{5}{16} \div \left(-\frac{10}{13}\right) = \left(-\frac{5}{16}\right)\left(-\frac{13}{10}\right) = \left(-\frac{\overset{1}{\cancel{5}}}{16}\right)\left(-\frac{13}{\underset{2}{\cancel{10}}}\right) = \frac{13}{32}$

7. (a) $\frac{-12}{-\frac{4}{5}} = -12 \div \left(-\frac{4}{5}\right) = -12\left(-\frac{5}{4}\right) = \left(-\frac{\overset{3}{\cancel{12}}}{1}\right)\left(-\frac{5}{\underset{1}{\cancel{4}}}\right) = 15$

(b) $\frac{-\frac{2}{9}}{\frac{8}{13}} = -\frac{2}{9} \div \frac{8}{13} = -\frac{\overset{1}{\cancel{2}}}{9}\left(\frac{13}{\underset{4}{\cancel{8}}}\right) = -\frac{13}{36}$

8. (a) $6(-10) = -60$ yards
(b) $7(15) = 105$ yards
(c) $-60 + 105 = 45$ yards

1.4 Practice Problems

1. (a) $6(6)(6)(6) = 6^4$
(b) $-2(-2)(-2)(-2)(-2) = (-2)^5$
(c) $108(108)(108) = 108^3$
(d) $-11(-11)(-11)(-11)(-11)(-11) = (-11)^6$
(e) $(w)(w)(w) = w^3$
(f) $(z)(z)(z)(z) = z^4$

2. (a) $3^5 = (3)(3)(3)(3)(3) = 243$
(b) $2^2 + 3^3$
$2^2 = (2)(2) = 4$
$3^3 = (3)(3)(3) = 27$
$4 + 27 = 31$

3. (a) $(-3)^3 = -27$
(b) $(-2)^6 = 64$
(c) $-2^4 = -(2^4) = -16$
(d) $-(3^6) = -729$

4. (a) $\left(\frac{1}{3}\right)^3 = \left(\frac{1}{3}\right)\left(\frac{1}{3}\right)\left(\frac{1}{3}\right) = \frac{1}{27}$
(b) $(0.3)^4 = (0.3)(0.3)(0.3)(0.3) = 0.0081$
(c) $\left(\frac{3}{2}\right)^4 = \left(\frac{3}{2}\right)\left(\frac{3}{2}\right)\left(\frac{3}{2}\right)\left(\frac{3}{2}\right) = \frac{81}{16}$
(d) $(3)^4(4)^2$
$3^4 = (3)(3)(3)(3) = 81$
$4^2 = (4)(4) = 16$
$(81)(16) = 1296$
(e) $4^2 - 2^4 = 16 - 16 = 0$

1.5 Practice Problems

1. $25 \div 5 \cdot 6 + 2^3$
$= 25 \div 5 \cdot 6 + 8$
$= 5 \cdot 6 + 8$
$= 30 + 8$
$= 38$

2. $(-4)^3 - 2^6$
$= -64 - 64$
$= -128$

3. $6 - (8 - 12)^2 + 8 \div 2$
$= 6 - (-4)^2 + 8 \div 2$
$= 6 - (16) + 8 \div 2$
$= 6 - 16 + 4$
$= -10 + 4$
$= -6$

4. $\left(-\frac{1}{7}\right)\left(-\frac{14}{5}\right) + \left(-\frac{1}{2}\right) \div \left(\frac{3}{4}\right)$
$= \left(-\frac{1}{7}\right)\left(-\frac{14}{5}\right) + \left(-\frac{1}{2}\right) \times \left(\frac{4}{3}\right)$
$= \frac{2}{5} + \left(-\frac{2}{3}\right)$
$= \frac{2 \cdot 3}{5 \cdot 3} + \left(-\frac{2 \cdot 5}{3 \cdot 5}\right)$
$= \frac{6}{15} + \left(-\frac{10}{15}\right) = -\frac{4}{15}$

1.6 Practice Problems

1. (a) $3(x + 2y) = 3x + 6y$
(b) $-a(a - 3b) = -a(a) + (-a)(-3b) = -a^2 + 3ab$

2. (a) $-(-3x + y) = (-1)(-3x + y) = (-1)(-3x) + (-1)(y)$
$= 3x - y$

3. (a) $\frac{3}{5}(a^2 - 5a + 25) = \left(\frac{3}{5}\right)(a^2) + \left(\frac{3}{5}\right)(-5a) + \left(\frac{3}{5}\right)(25)$
$= \frac{3}{5}a^2 - 3a + 15$

(b) $2.5(x^2 - 3.5x + 1.2)$
$= (2.5)(x^2) + (2.5)(-3.5x) + (2.5)(1.2)$
$= 2.5x^2 - 8.75x + 3$

4. $-4x(x - 2y + 3) = (-4)(x)(x) - (-4)(x)(2)(y) + (-4)(x)(3)$
$= -4x^2 + 8xy - 12x$

5. $(3x^2 - 2x)(-4) = (3x^2)(-4) - (2x)(-4) = -12x^2 + 8x$

6. $400(6x + 9y) = 400(6x) + 400(9y)$
$= 2400x + 3600y$

1.7 Practice Problems

1. (a) $5a$ and $8a$ are like terms.
   $2b$ and $-4b$ are like terms.
   (b) y^2 and $-7y^2$ are like terms. These are the only like terms.
2. (a) $16y^3 + 9y^3 = (16 + 9)y^3 = 25y^3$
   (b) $5a + 7a + 4a = (5 + 7 + 4)a = 16a$
3. $-8y^2 - 9y^2 + 4y^2 = (-8 - 9 + 4)y^2 = -13y^2$
4. (a) $1.3x + 3a - 9.6x + 2a = -8.3x + 5a$
   (b) $5ab - 2ab^2 - 3a^2b + 6ab = 5ab + 6ab - 2ab^2 - 3a^2b$
   $= 11ab - 2ab^2 - 3a^2b$
   (c) $7x^2y - 2xy^2 - 3x^2y - 4xy^2 + 5x^2y$
   $= 7x^2y - 3x^2y + 5x^2y - 2xy^2 - 4xy^2 = 9x^2y - 6xy^2$
5. $5xy - 2x^2y + 6xy^2 - xy - 3xy^2 - 7x^2y$
   $= 5xy - xy - 2x^2y - 7x^2y + 6xy^2 - 3xy^2$
   $= 4xy - 9x^2y + 3xy^2$
6. $\frac{1}{7}a^2 + 2a^2 = \frac{1}{7}a^2 + \frac{2}{1}a^2 = \frac{1}{7}a^2 + \frac{2 \cdot 7}{1 \cdot 7}a^2$
   $= \frac{1}{7}a^2 + \frac{14}{7}a^2 = \frac{15}{7}a^2$
   $-\frac{5}{12}b - \frac{1}{3}b = -\frac{5}{12}b - \frac{1 \cdot 4}{3 \cdot 4}b = -\frac{5}{12}b - \frac{4}{12}b$
   $= -\frac{9}{12}b = -\frac{3}{4}b$
   Thus, our solution is $\frac{15}{7}a^2 - \frac{3}{4}b$
7. $5a(2 - 3b) - 4(6a + 2ab) = 10a - 15ab - 24a - 8ab$
   $= -14a - 23ab$

1.8 Practice Problems

1. $4 - \frac{1}{2}x = 4 - \frac{1}{2}(-8)$
   $= 4 + 4$
   $= 8$
2. (a) $4x^2 = 4(-3)^2 = 4(9) = 36$
   (b) $(4x)^2 = [4(-3)]^2 = [-12]^2 = 144$
3. $2x^2 - 3x = 2(-2)^2 - 3(-2)$
   $= 2(4) - 3(-2)$
   $= 8 + 6$
   $= 14$
4. Area of a triangle is
   $A = \frac{1}{2}ba$
   altitude = 3 meters (m)
   base = 7 meters (m)
   $A = \frac{1}{2}(7\text{ m})(3\text{ m})$
   $= \frac{1}{2}(7)(3)(m)(m)$
   $= \left(\frac{7}{2}\right)(3)(m)^2$
   $= \frac{21}{2}(\text{m})^2$
   $= 10.5$ square meters
5. Area of a circle is
   $A = \pi r^2$
   $r = 3$ meters
   $A \approx 3.14(3\text{ m})^2$
   $= 3.14(9)(\text{m})^2$
   $= 28.26$ square meters
6. Formula $C = \frac{5}{9}(F - 32)$
   $= \frac{5}{9}(68 - 32)$
   $= \frac{5}{9}(36)$
   $= 5(4)$
   $= 20°$ Celsius
7. Use the formula.
   $k = 1.61\,(r)$ Replace r by 35.
   $k = 1.61\,(35)$
   $k = 56.35$ The truck is violating the minimum speed limit.

1.9 Practice Problems

1. $5[4x - 3(y - 2)]$
   $= 5[4x - 3y + 6]$
   $= 20x - 15y + 30$
2. $-3[2a - (3b - c) + 4a]$
   $= -3[2a - 3b + c + 4a]$
   $= -3[6a - 3b + c]$
   $= -18a + 9b - 3c$
3. $3[4x - 2(1 - x)] - [3x + (x - 2)]$
   $= 3[4x - 2 + 2x] - [3x + x - 2]$
   $= 12x - 6 + 6x - 3x - x + 2$
   $= 14x - 4$
4. $-2\{5x - 3x[2x - (x^2 - 4x)]\}$
   $= -2\{5x - 3x[2x - x^2 + 4x]\}$
   $= -2\{5x - 3x[6x - x^2]\}$
   $= -2\{5x - 18x^2 + 3x^3\}$
   $= -10x + 36x^2 - 6x^3$
   $= -6x^3 + 36x^2 - 10x$

Chapter 2

2.1 Practice Problems

1. $x + 14 = 23$
   $x + 14 + (-14) = 23 + (-14)$
   $x + 0 = 9$
   $x = 9$
   Check. $9 + 14 = 23$
   $23 = 23$
2. $17 = x - 5$
   $+5 \quad +5$
   $22 = x$
   Check. $17 \stackrel{?}{=} 22 - 5$
   $17 = 17$
3. $0.5 - 1.2 = x - 0.3$
   $-0.7 = x - 0.3$
   $+0.3 \quad +0.3$
   $-0.4 = x$
   Check. $0.5 - 1.2 \stackrel{?}{=} -0.4 - 0.3$
   $-0.7 = -0.7$
4. $x + 8 = -22 + 6$
   $x = -2$
   Check. $-2 + 8 \stackrel{?}{=} -22 + 6$
   $6 \neq -16$ This is not true.
   Thus $x = -2$ is not a solution. Solve to find the solution.
   $x + 8 = -22 + 6 = -16$
   $x = -16 - 8$
   $x = -24$

5. $\frac{1}{20} - \frac{1}{2} = x + \frac{3}{5}$

$\frac{1}{20} - \frac{1 \cdot 10}{2 \cdot 10} = x + \frac{3 \cdot 4}{5 \cdot 4}$

$\frac{1}{20} - \frac{10}{20} = x + \frac{12}{20}$

$-\frac{9}{20} = x + \frac{12}{20}$

$-\frac{9}{20} - \frac{12}{20} = x + \frac{12}{20} - \frac{12}{20}$

$-\frac{21}{20} = -1\frac{1}{20} = x$

Check.

$\frac{1}{20} - \frac{1}{2} \stackrel{?}{=} -1\frac{1}{20} + \frac{3}{5}$

$\frac{1}{20} - \frac{10}{20} \stackrel{?}{=} -\frac{21}{20} + \frac{12}{20}$

$-\frac{9}{20} = -\frac{9}{20}$ ✓

2.2 Practice Problems

1. $(\cancel{8})\frac{1}{\cancel{8}}x = -2(8)$

$x = -16$

2. $\frac{\cancel{9}x}{\cancel{9}} = \frac{72}{9}$

$x = 8$

3. $\frac{\cancel{6}x}{\cancel{6}} = \frac{50}{6}$

$x = \frac{25}{3}$

4. $\frac{-\cancel{27}x}{-\cancel{27}} = \frac{54}{-27}$

$x = -2$

5. $\frac{-x}{-1} = \frac{36}{-1}$

$x = -36$

6. $\frac{-51}{-6} = \frac{-6x}{-6}$

$\frac{17}{2} = x$

7. $16.2 = 5.2x - 3.4x$

$16.2 = 1.8x$

$\frac{16.2}{1.8} = \frac{1.8x}{1.8}$

$9 = x$

2.3 Practice Problems

1. $9x + 2 = 38$

$\quad - 2 \quad -2$

$\frac{9x}{9} = \frac{36}{9}$

$x = 4$

Check. $9(4) + 2 \stackrel{?}{=} 38$

$36 + 2 \stackrel{?}{=} 38$

$38 = 38$ ✓

2. $13x = 2x - 66$

$-2x \quad -2x$

$\frac{11x}{11} = \frac{-66}{11}$

$x = -6$

Check. $13(-6) \stackrel{?}{=} 2(-6) - 66$

$-78 \stackrel{?}{=} -12 - 66$

$-78 = -78$ ✓

3. $3x + 2 = 5x + 2$

$\quad -2 \quad -2$

$3x = 5x$

$-5x \quad -5x$

$-2x = 0$

$x = 0$

Check. $3(0) + 2 \stackrel{?}{=} 5(0) + 2$

$2 = 2$ ✓

4. $-z + 8 - z = 3z + 10 - 3$

$-2z + 8 = 3z + 7$

$-3z \quad -3z$

$-5z + 8 = 7$

$-8 = -8$

$\frac{-5z}{-5} = \frac{-1}{-5}$

$z = \frac{1}{5}$

5. $4x - (x + 3) = 12 - 3(x - 2)$

$4x - x - 3 = 12 - 3x + 6$

$3x - 3 = -3x + 18$

$+3x \quad +3x$

$6x - 3 = 18$

$+3 \quad +3$

$\frac{6x}{6} = \frac{21}{6}$

$x = \frac{21}{6} = \frac{7}{2}$ or $3\frac{1}{2}$

Check. $4\left(\frac{7}{2}\right) - \left(\frac{7}{2} + 3\right) \stackrel{?}{=} 12 - 3\left(\frac{7}{2} - 2\right)$

$14 - \frac{13}{2} \stackrel{?}{=} 12 - 3\left(\frac{3}{2}\right)$

$\frac{28}{2} - \frac{13}{2} \stackrel{?}{=} \frac{24}{2} - \frac{9}{2}$; $\quad \frac{15}{2} = \frac{15}{2}$ ✓

6. $4(-2x - 3) = -5(x - 2) + 2$

$-8x - 12 = -5x + 10 + 2$

$-8x - 12 = -5x + 12$

$+5x \quad +5x$

$-3x - 12 = 12$

$+12 = +12$

$\frac{-3x}{-3} = \frac{24}{-3}$

$x = -8$

7. $0.3x - 2(x + 0.1) = 0.4(x - 3) - 1.1$

$0.3x - 2x - 0.2 = 0.4x - 1.2 - 1.1$

$-1.7x - 0.2 = 0.4x - 2.3$

$-0.4x \quad -0.4x$

$-2.1x - 0.2 = -2.3$

$+0.2 \quad +0.2$

$\frac{-2.1x}{-2.1} = \frac{-2.1}{-2.1}$

$x = 1$

8. $5(2z - 1) + 7 = 7z - 4(z + 3)$

$10z - 5 + 7 = 7z - 4z - 12$

$10z + 2 = 3z - 12$

$-3z \quad -3z$

$7z + 2 = -12$

$-2 \quad -2$

$\frac{7z}{7} = -\frac{14}{7}$

$z = -2$

Check. $5[2(-2) - 1] + 7 \stackrel{?}{=} 7(-2) - 4[-2 + 3]$

$5(-5) + 7 \stackrel{?}{=} -14 - 4(1)$

$-25 + 7 \stackrel{?}{=} -18$

$-18 = -18$ ✓

2.4 Practice Problems

1. $\frac{3}{8}x - \frac{3}{2} = \frac{1}{4}x$

$3x - 12 = 2x$

$-2x \quad -2x$

$x - 12 = 0$

$+12 \quad +12$

$x = 12$

2. $\frac{5x}{4} - 1 = \frac{3x}{4} + \frac{1}{2}$

$5x - 4 = 3x + 2$

$-3x \quad -3x$

$2x - 4 = +2$

$+4 = +4$

$\frac{2x}{2} = \frac{6}{2}$

$x = 3$

Check. $\frac{5(3)}{4} - 1 \stackrel{?}{=} \frac{3(3)}{4} + \frac{1}{2}$

$\frac{15}{4} - 1 \stackrel{?}{=} \frac{9}{4} + \frac{1}{2}$

$\frac{15}{4} - \frac{4}{4} \stackrel{?}{=} \frac{9}{4} + \frac{2}{4}$

$\frac{11}{4} = \frac{11}{4}$ ✓

3.
$$\frac{x+6}{9} = \frac{x}{6} + \frac{1}{2}$$
$$\frac{x}{9} + \frac{6}{9} = \frac{x}{6} + \frac{1}{2}$$
$$18\left(\frac{x}{9}\right) + 18\left(\frac{6}{9}\right) = 18\left(\frac{x}{6}\right) + 18\left(\frac{1}{2}\right)$$
$$2x + 12 = 3x + 9$$
$$\underline{-2x \qquad -2x}$$
$$12 = x + 9$$
$$\underline{-9 \qquad -9}$$
$$3 = x$$

4. $\frac{1}{3}(x-2) = \frac{1}{4}(x+5) - \frac{5}{3}$
$$\frac{1}{3}x - \frac{2}{3} = \frac{1}{4}x + \frac{5}{4} - \frac{5}{3}$$
$$4x - 8 = 3x + 15 - 20$$
$$4x - 8 = 3x - 5$$
$$\underline{-3x \qquad = -3x}$$
$$x - 8 = -5$$
$$\underline{+8 \qquad +8}$$
$$x = 3$$

Check. $\frac{1}{3}(3-2) \stackrel{?}{=} \frac{1}{4}(3+5) - \frac{5}{3}$
$$\frac{1}{3}(1) \stackrel{?}{=} \frac{1}{4}(8) - \frac{5}{3}$$
$$\frac{1}{3} \stackrel{?}{=} 2 - \frac{5}{3}$$
$$\frac{1}{3} \stackrel{?}{=} \frac{6}{3} - \frac{5}{3}$$
$$\frac{1}{3} = \frac{1}{3} \checkmark$$

5.
$$2.8 = 0.3(x-2) + 2(0.1x - 0.3)$$
$$2.8 = 0.3x - 0.6 + 0.2x - 0.6$$
$$10(2.8) = 10(0.3x) - 10(0.6) + 10(0.2x) - 10(0.6)$$
$$28 = 3x - 6 + 2x - 6$$
$$28 = 5x - 12$$
$$\underline{+12 \qquad + 12}$$
$$40 = 5x$$
$$8 = x$$

2.5 Practice Problems

1.
$$d = rt$$
$$\frac{4565}{8.3} = \frac{8.3r}{8.3}$$
$$550 \text{ mph} = r$$

2. Solve for m. $\frac{E}{c^2} = \frac{mc^2}{c^2} \qquad \frac{E}{c^2} = m$

3. Solve for y. $8 - 2y + 3x = 0$
$$\underline{-3x = \quad -3x}$$
$$8 - 2y \quad = \quad -3x$$
$$\underline{-8 \qquad\qquad -8}$$
$$\frac{-2y}{-2} = \frac{-3x-8}{-2}$$
$$y = \frac{3x+8}{2} \text{ or } y = \frac{3}{2}x + 4$$

4. Solve for d. $C = \pi d$
$$\frac{C}{\pi} = \frac{\pi d}{\pi}$$
$$\frac{C}{\pi} = d$$

2.6 Practice Problems

1. **(a)** $7 > 2$ **(b)** $-3 > -4$ **(c)** $-1 < 2$
(d) $-8 < -5$ **(e)** $0 > -2$ **(f)** $\frac{2}{5} > \frac{3}{8}$

2. **(a)** $x > 5$; x is greater than 5

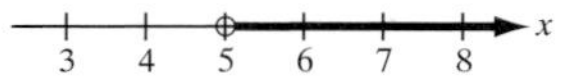

(b) $x \le -2$; x is less than or equal to -2

(c) $3 > x$; 3 is greater than x (or x is less than 3)

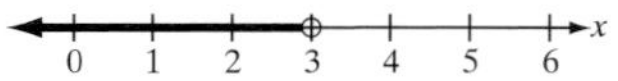

(d) $x \ge -\frac{3}{2}$; x is greater than or equal to $-\frac{3}{2}$

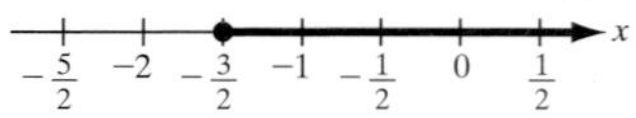

3. **(a)** $t \le 180$ **(b)** $d < 15{,}000$

2.7 Practice Problems

1. **(a)** $9 + 4 > 6 + 4$
$$13 > 10$$
(b) $-2 - 3 < 5 - 3$
$$-5 < 2$$
(c) $1(2) > -3(2)$
$$2 > -6$$
(d) $\frac{10}{5} < \frac{15}{5}$
$$2 < 3$$

2. **(a)** $7 > 2$
$$-14 < -4$$
(b) $-3 < -1$
$$3 > 1$$
(c) $-10 \ge -20$
$$1 \le 2$$
(d) $-15 \le -5$
$$3 \ge 1$$

3. $8x - 2 < 3$
$$\underline{+2 \qquad +2}$$
$$\frac{8x}{8} < \frac{5}{8}$$
$$x < \frac{5}{8}$$

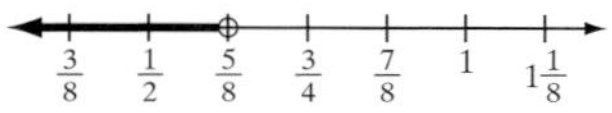

4. $4 - 5x > 7$
$$\underline{-4 \qquad -4}$$
$$\frac{-5x}{-5} < \frac{3}{-5}$$
$$x < \frac{-3}{5}$$

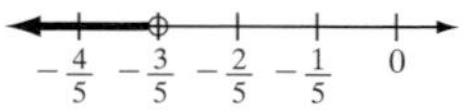

5. $\frac{1}{2}x + 3 < \frac{2}{3}x$
$$3x + 18 < 4x$$
$$\underline{-4x \qquad -4x}$$
$$-x + 18 < 0$$
$$\underline{-18 \qquad -18}$$
$$\frac{-x}{-1} > \frac{-18}{-1}$$
$$x > 18$$

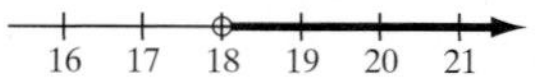

6. $\frac{1}{2}(3 - x) \le 2x + 5$
$$\frac{3}{2} - \frac{1}{2}x \le 2x + 5$$
$$3 - x \le 4x + 10$$
$$-5x \le 7$$
$$x \ge -\frac{7}{5}$$

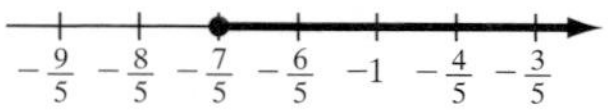

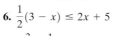

7. $2000n - 700{,}000 \ge 2{,}500{,}000$
$$2{,}000n \ge 3{,}200{,}000$$
$$n \ge 1{,}600$$

Chapter 3

3.1 Practice Problems

1. **(a)** $x + 4$ **(b)** $3x$ **(c)** $x - 8$ **(d)** $\frac{1}{4}x$

2. **(a)** $3x + 8$ **(b)** $3(x + 8)$ **(c)** $\frac{1}{3}(x + 4)$

3. Let a = Ann's hours per week.
Then $a - 17$ = Marie's hours per week.

4. $l = 2w + 5$, w
width $= w$
length $= 2w + 5$

5. 1st angle $= s - 16$
2nd angle $= s$
3rd angle $= 2s$

$2s$, s, $s - 16$

6. Let x = the number of students in the fall.
$\frac{2}{3}x$ = the number of students in the spring.
$\frac{1}{5}x$ = the number of students in the summer.

3.2 Practice Problems

1. $\frac{3}{4}x = -81$
$x = -108$

2. $3x - 2 = 49$
$3x = 51$
$x = 17$

3. $x + (3x - 12) = 24$
$4x - 12 = 24$
$4x = 36$
$x = 9$
First number is 9. Second number $= 3(9) - 12 = 15$.

4. Let rainfall in Canada $= x$
Then rainfall in Texas $= 3x - 14$
$3x - 14 = 43$
$+14 \quad +14$
$\frac{3x}{3} = \frac{57}{3}$
$x = 19$
19 inches in Canada
43 inches in Texas

5. **(a)** $\frac{220}{4} = 55$ mph **(b)** $\frac{225}{4.5} = 50$ mph
(c) The trip leaving the city by 5 mph.

6. $\frac{x + x + 78 + 80 + 100 + 96}{6} = 90$
$354 + 2x = 540$
$2x = 186$
$x = 93$
She needs a 93 on the final exam.

3.3 Practice Problems

1. short piece $= x$
long piece $= x + 17$
$x + (x + 17) = 89$
$2x + 17 = 89$
$2x = 72$
$x = 36$ feet
Therefore, Short piece 36 feet
Long piece $36 + 17 = 53$ feet

2. Family 1 $= x + 360$
Family 2 $= x$
Family 3 $= 2x - 200$
$(x) + (x + 360) + (2x - 200) = 3960$
$4x + 160 = 3960$
$x = 950$
Therefore, Family #2 $= \$950.00$
Family #3 $= 2(950) - 200 = \$1700.00$
Family #1 $= 950 + 360 = \$1310.00$

3. Let the second side $= x$
first side $= x - 30$
third side $= \frac{1}{2}x$
$x + x - 30 + \frac{1}{2}x = 720$
$5x - 60 = 1440$
$5x = 1500$
$x = 300$
Therefore the
second side = 300 meters
first side = 270 meters
third side = 150 meters

3.4 Practice Problems

1. $3(25) + (0.20)m = 350$
$75 + 0.20m = 350$
$0.20m = 275$
$m = 1375$ miles

2. $0.38x = 4560$
$x = \$12{,}000.00$

3. $x + 0.07x = 13{,}910$
$1.07x = 13{,}910$
$x = \$13{,}000.00$

4. $x = 7000(0.12)(1)$
$x = \$840.00$

5. $0.09x + 0.07(8000 - x) = 630$
$0.09x + 560 - 0.07x = 630$
$0.02x + 560 = 630$
$0.02x = 70$
$x = \$3500$
Therefore, she invested \$3500.00 at 9%.
$(8000 - 3500) = \$4500.00$ at 7%

6. x = Dimes
$x + 5$ = Quarters
$0.10x + 0.25(x + 5) = 5.10$
$0.10x + 0.25x + 1.25 = 5.10$
$0.35x + 1.25 = 5.10$
$0.35x = 3.85$
$x = 11$
Therefore, she has 11 dimes and 16 quarters.

7. Nickels $= 2x$
Dimes $= x$
Quarters $= x + 4$
$0.05(2x) + 0.10(x) + 0.25(x + 4) = 2.35$
$0.1x + 0.10x + 0.25x + 1 = 2.35$
$0.45x + 1 = 2.35$
$0.45x = 1.35$
$x = 3$
Therefore, the boy has 3 dimes, 6 nickels, and 7 quarters.

3.5 Practice Problems

1. $A = \frac{1}{2}ab$
$= \frac{1}{2}(20)(14)$
$= (10)(14)$
$= 140$ square inches

2. $A = lw$
$120 = l(8)$
$\frac{120}{8} = l$
$l = 15$ yards

3. $A = \frac{1}{2}a(b_1 + b_2)$

$256 = \frac{1}{2}a(12 + 20)$

$256 = \frac{1}{2}(a)(32)$

$256 = 16a$

$\frac{256}{16} = a$

$a = 16$ feet

4. $C = 2\pi r$
$C = 2(3.14)(15)$
$C = 94.2$
$C \approx 94$ meters

5. $P = a + b + c$
$P = 15 + 15 + 15$
$P = 45$ cm

6.

132°, x, x

$132° + x + x = 180°$
$132° + 2x = 180°$
$2x = 48°$
$x = 24°$

7. Surface Area $= 4\pi r^2$
$= 4(3.14)(5)^2$
$= 314 \text{ m}^2$

8. $V = \pi r^2 h$
$V = 3.14(3)^2(4) \approx 113 \text{ ft}^3$

9. Calculate the area of the pool.
$A = lw$
$A = 12 \times 8 = 96$ sq. ft.
Now add 6 feet to the length and 6 feet to the width of the pool and calculate the area.
$A = lw$
$A = 18 \times 14 = 252$ sq. ft.
Now subtract the areas.
$252 - 96 = 156$ sq. ft. at \$12 a square foot.
$156 \times 12 = \$1872$

10. $V = lwh$
$V = (6)(5)(8) = 240 \text{ ft}^3$
Weight $= 240 \text{ ft}^3 \times \frac{62.4 \text{ lb}}{1 \text{ ft}^3} = 14{,}976 \text{ lb} \approx 15{,}000 \text{ lb}$

3.6 Practice Problems

1. (a) height ≤ 6
(b) speed > 65
(c) area ≥ 560
(d) profit margin ≥ 50

2. $\frac{1050 + 1250 + 950 + x}{4} \ge 1100$

$\frac{x + 3250}{4} \ge 1100$

$x + 3250 \ge 4400$
$x \ge 1150$

The rope must hold at least 1150 pounds.

3. $1400 + 0.02x > 2200$
$0.02x > 800$
$x > 40{,}000$
Rita must sell more than \$40,000 worth of products each month.

Chapter 4

4.1 Practice Problems

1. (a) $a^7 \cdot a^5 = a^{7+5} = a^{12}$ **(b)** $w^{10} \cdot w = w^{10+1} = w^{11}$

2. (a) $x^3 \cdot x^9 = x^{3+9} = x^{12}$ **(b)** $3^7 \cdot 3^4 = 3^{7+4} = 3^{11}$
(c) $a^3 \cdot b^2 = a^3 \cdot b^2$ (cannot be simplified)

3. (a) $(-a^8)(a^4) = (-1 \cdot 1)(a^8 \cdot a^4)$
$= -1(a^8 \cdot a^4)$
$= -1a^{12} = -a^{12}$
(b) $(3y^2)(-2y^3) = (3)(-2)(y^2 \cdot y^3) = -6y^5$
(c) $(-4x^3)(-5x^2) = (-4)(-5)(x^3 \cdot x^2) = 20x^5$

4. $(2xy)\left(-\frac{1}{4}x^2y\right)(6xy^3) = (2)\left(-\frac{1}{4}\right)(6)(x \cdot x^2 \cdot x)(y \cdot y \cdot y^3)$
$= -3x^4y^5$

5. (a) $\frac{10^{13}}{10^7} = 10^{13-7} = 10^6$ **(b)** $\frac{x^{11}}{x} = x^{11-1} = x^{10}$
(c) $\frac{y^{18}}{y^8} = y^{18-8} = y^{10}$

6. (a) $\frac{c^3}{c^4} = \frac{1}{c^{4-3}} = \frac{1}{c}$ **(b)** $\frac{10^{31}}{10^{56}} = \frac{1}{10^{56-31}} = \frac{1}{10^{25}}$
(c) $\frac{z^{15}}{z^{21}} = \frac{1}{z^{21-15}} = \frac{1}{z^6}$

7. (a) $\frac{-7x^7}{-21x^9} = \frac{1}{3x^{9-7}} = \frac{1}{3x^2}$ **(b)** $\frac{15x^{11}}{-3x^4} = -5x^{11-4} = -5x^7$
(c) $\frac{23x^8}{46x^9} = \frac{1}{2x^{9-8}} = \frac{1}{2x}$

8. (a) $\frac{x^7y^9}{y^{10}} = \frac{x^7}{y}$ **(b)** $\frac{12x^5y^6}{-24x^3y^8} = -\frac{x^2}{2y^2}$

9. (a) $\frac{10^7}{10^7} = 1$
(b) $\frac{12a^4}{15a^4} = \frac{4}{5}\left(\frac{a^4}{a^4}\right) = \frac{4}{5}(1) = \frac{4}{5}$

10. (a) $\frac{-20a^3b^8c^4}{28a^3b^7c^5} = -\frac{5a^0b}{7c} = -\frac{5(1)b}{7c} = -\frac{5b}{7c}$
(b) $\frac{5x^0y^6}{10x^4y^8} = \frac{5(1)y^6}{10x^4y^8} = \frac{1}{2x^4y^2}$

11. $\frac{(-6ab^5)(3a^2b^4)}{16a^5b^7} = \frac{-18a^3b^9}{16a^5b^7} = -\frac{9b^2}{8a^2}$

12. (a) $(a^4)^3 = a^{4 \cdot 3} = a^{12}$
(b) $(10^5)^2 = 10^{5 \cdot 2} = 10^{10}$ **(c)** $(-1)^{15} = -1$

13. (a) $(3xy)^3 = (3)^3x^3y^3 = 27x^3y^3$
(b) $(yz)^{37} = y^{37}z^{37}$
(c) $(-3x^3)^2 = (-3)^2(x^3)^2 = 9x^6$

14. (a) $\left(\frac{x}{5}\right)^3 = \frac{x^3}{5^3} = \frac{x^3}{125}$
(b) $\left(\frac{4a}{b}\right)^6 = \frac{4^6a^6}{b^6} = \frac{4096a^6}{b^6}$

15. $\left(\frac{-2x^3y^0z}{4xz^2}\right)^5 = \left(\frac{-x^2}{2z}\right)^5 = \frac{(-1)^5(x^2)^5}{2^5z^5} = -\frac{x^{10}}{32z^5}$

4.2 Practice Problems

1. (a) $x^{-12} = \frac{1}{x^{12}}$ **(b)** $w^{-5} = \frac{1}{w^5}$ **(c)** $z^{-2} = \frac{1}{z^2}$

2. (a) $4^{-3} = \frac{1}{4^3} = \frac{1}{64}$ **(b)** $2^{-4} = \frac{1}{2^4} = \frac{1}{16}$

3. (a) $\frac{3}{w^{-4}} = 3w^4$ **(b)** $\frac{x^{-6}y^4}{z^{-2}} = \frac{y^4z^2}{x^6}$ **(c)** $x^{-6}y^{-5} = \frac{1}{x^6y^5}$

4. (a) $(2x^4y^{-5})^{-2} = 2^{-2}x^{-8}y^{10} = \frac{y^{10}}{2^2x^8} = \frac{y^{10}}{4x^8}$
(b) $\frac{y^{-3}z^{-4}}{y^2z^{-6}} = \frac{z^6}{y^2y^3z^4} = \frac{z^6}{y^5z^4} = \frac{z^2}{y^5}$

5. (a) $78{,}200 = 7.82 \times 10{,}000 = 7.82 \times 10^4$
(b) $4{,}786{,}000 = 4.786 \times 1{,}000{,}000 = 4.786 \times 10^6$

6. (a) $0.98 = 9.8 \times 10^{-1}$
(b) $0.000092 = 9.2 \times 10^{-5}$

7. (a) $1.93 \times 10^6 = 1.93 \times 1{,}000{,}000 = 1{,}930{,}000.0$
(b) $8.562 \times 10^{-5} = 8.562 \times \dfrac{1}{100{,}000} = 0.00008562$

8. $30{,}900{,}000{,}000{,}000{,}000 = 3.09 \times 10^{16}$ meters

9. (a)
$$(56{,}000)(1{,}400{,}000{,}000) = (5.6 \times 10^4)(1.4 \times 10^9) = (5.6)(1.4)(10^4)(10^9) = 7.84 \times 10^{13}$$
(b)
$$\frac{0.000111}{0.00000037} = \frac{1.11 \times 10^{-4}}{3.7 \times 10^{-7}} = \frac{1.11}{3.7} \times \frac{10^{-4}}{10^{-7}} = \frac{1.11}{3.7} \times \frac{10^7}{10^4} = 0.3 \times 10^3 = 3.0 \times 10^2$$

10.
$$159 \text{ parsecs} = (159 \text{ parsecs})\frac{(3.09 \times 10^{13} \text{ kilometers})}{1 \text{ parsec}} = 491.31 \times 10^{13} \text{ kilometers}$$
$$d = r \times t$$
$$491.31 \times 10^{13} \text{ km} = \frac{50{,}000 \text{ km}}{1 \text{ hr}} \times t$$
$$4.9131 \times 10^{15} \text{ km} = \frac{5 \times 10^4 \text{ km}}{1 \text{ hr}} \times t$$
$$\frac{4.9131 \times 10^{15} \text{ km}}{\dfrac{5 \times 10^4 \text{ km}}{1 \text{ hr}}} = t$$
$$\frac{4.9131 \times 10^{15} \text{ km (1 hr)}}{5.0 \times 10^4 \text{ km}} = t$$
$$0.98262 \times 10^{11} \text{ hr} = t$$
9.83×10^{10} hours

4.3 Practice Problems

1. (a) This polynomial is of degree 5. It has two terms, so it is a binomial.
(b) This polynomial is of degree 7, since the sum of the exponents is $3 + 4 = 7$. It has one term, so it is a monomial.
(c) This polynomial is of degree 3. It has three terms, so it is a trinomial.

2.
$$(-8x^3 + 3x^2 + 6) + (2x^3 - 7x^2 - 3)$$
$$= [-8x^3 + 2x^3] + [3x^2 - 7x^2] + [6 - 3]$$
$$= [(-8 + 2)x^3] + [(3 - 7)x^2] + [6 - 3]$$
$$= -6x^3 - 4x^2 + 3$$

3.
$$\left(-\frac{1}{3}x^2 - 6x - \frac{1}{12}\right) + \left(\frac{1}{4}x^2 + 5x - \frac{1}{3}\right)$$
$$= \left[-\frac{1}{3}x^2 + \frac{1}{4}x^2\right] + [-6x + 5x] + \left[-\frac{1}{12} - \frac{1}{3}\right]$$
$$= \left[\left(-\frac{1}{3} + \frac{1}{4}\right)x^2\right] + [(-6 + 5)x] + \left[-\frac{1}{12} - \frac{1}{3}\right]$$
$$= \left[\left(-\frac{4}{12} + \frac{3}{12}\right)x^2\right] + [-x] + \left[-\frac{1}{12} - \frac{4}{12}\right]$$
$$= -\frac{1}{12}x^2 - x - \frac{5}{12}$$

4.
$$(3.5x^3 - 0.02x^2 + 1.56x - 3.5) + (-0.08x^2 - 1.98x + 4)$$
$$= 3.5x^3 + [-0.02 - 0.08]x^2 + [1.56 - 1.98]x + [-3.5 + 4]$$
$$= 3.5x^3 - 0.1x^2 - 0.42x + 0.5$$

5.
$$(5x^3 - 15x^2 + 6x - 3) - (-4x^3 - 10x^2 + 5x + 13)$$
$$= (5x^3 - 15x^2 + 6x - 3) + (4x^3 + 10x^2 - 5x - 13)$$
$$= [5 + 4]x^3 + [-15 + 10]x^2 + [6 - 5]x + [-3 - 13]$$
$$= 9x^3 - 5x^2 + x - 16$$

6.
$$(x^3 - 7x^2y + 3xy^2 - 2y^3) - (2x^3 + 4xy - 6y^3)$$
$$= [1 - 2]x^3 - 7x^2y + 3xy^2 - 4xy + [-2 + 6]y^3$$
$$= -x^3 - 7x^2y + 3xy^2 - 4xy + 4y^3$$

7. (a) 1974 is 4 years later than 1970, so $x = 4$.
$$0.03(4) + 5.4 = 0.12 + 5.4 = 5.52$$
We estimate that the average truck in 1974 obtained 5.52 miles per gallon.
(b) 2006 is 36 years later than 1970, so $x = 36$.
$$0.03(36) + 5.4 = 1.08 + 5.4 = 6.48$$
We predict that the average truck in 2006 will obtain 6.48 miles per gallon.

4.4 Practice Problems

1.
$$4x^3(-2x^2 + 3x) = 4x^3(-2x^2) + 4x^3(3x) = 4(-2)(x^3)(x^2) + 4(3)(x^3)(x) = -8x^5 + 12x^4$$

2. (a) $-3x(x^2 + 2x - 4) = -3x^3 - 6x^2 + 12x$
(b) $6xy(x^3 + 2x^2y - y^2) = 6x^4y + 12x^3y^2 - 6xy^3$

3. $(-6x^3 + 4x^2 - 2x)(-3xy) = 18x^4y - 12x^3y + 6x^2y$

4. $(5x - 1)(x - 2) = 5x^2 - 10x - x + 2 = 5x^2 - 11x + 2$

5. $(8a - 5b)(3a - b) = 24a^2 - 8ab - 15ab + 5b^2 = 24a^2 - 23ab + 5b^2$

6. $(3a + 2b)(2a - 3c) = 6a^2 - 9ac + 4ab - 6bc$

7. $(3x - 2y)(3x - 2y) = 9x^2 - 6xy - 6xy + 4y^2 = 9x^2 - 12xy + 4y^2$

8. $(2x^2 + 3y^2)(5x^2 + 6y^2) = 10x^4 + 12x^2y^2 + 15x^2y^2 + 18y^4 = 10x^4 + 27x^2y^2 + 18y^4$

9.
$$A = (\text{length})(\text{width}) = (7x + 3)(2x - 1) = 14x^2 - 7x + 6x - 3 = 14x^2 - x - 3$$
There are $(14x^2 - x - 3)$ square feet in the room.

4.5 Practice Problems

1. $(6x + 7)(6x - 7) = (6x)^2 - (7)^2 = 36x^2 - 49$

2. $(3x + 5y)(3x - 5y) = (3x)^2 - (5y)^2 = 9x^2 - 25y^2$

3. (a) $(4a - 9b)^2 = (4a)^2 - 2(4a)(9b) + (9b)^2 = 16a^2 - 72ab + 81b^2$
(b) $(5x + 4)^2 = (5x)^2 + 2(5x)(4) + (4)^2 = 25x^2 + 40x + 16$

4. $(4x^3 - 2x^2 + x)(x^2 + 3x - 2)$
$$\begin{array}{r} 4x^3 - 2x^2 + x \\ x^2 + 3x - 2 \\ \hline -8x^3 + 4x^2 - 2x \\ 12x^4 - 6x^3 + 3x^2 \\ 4x^5 - 2x^4 + x^3 \\ \hline 4x^5 - 10x^4 - 13x^3 + 7x^2 - 2x \end{array}$$

5.
$$(2x^2 + 5x + 3)(x^2 - 3x - 4)$$
$$= 2x^2(x^2 - 3x - 4) + 5x(x^2 - 3x - 4) + 3(x^2 - 3x - 4)$$
$$= 2x^4 - 6x^3 - 8x^2 + 5x^3 - 15x^2 - 20x + 3x^2 - 9x - 12$$
$$= 2x^4 - x^3 - 20x^2 - 29x - 12$$

6.
$$(3x - 2)(2x + 3)(3x + 2) = (3x - 2)(3x + 2)(2x + 3) = [(3x)^2 - 2^2](2x + 3) = (9x^2 - 4)(2x + 3)$$
$$\begin{array}{r} 9x^2 - 4 \\ 2x + 3 \\ \hline 27x^2 + 0x - 12 \\ 18x^3 + 0x^2 - 8x \\ \hline 18x^3 + 27x^2 - 8x - 12 \end{array}$$
Thus we have
$(3x - 2)(2x + 3)(3x + 2) = 18x^3 + 27x^2 - 8x - 12.$

4.6 Practice Problems

1. $\dfrac{15y^4 - 27y^3 - 21y^2}{3y^2} = \dfrac{15y^4}{3y^2} - \dfrac{27y^3}{3y^2} - \dfrac{21y^2}{3y^2} = 5y^2 - 9y - 7$

2. $$\begin{array}{r|l} & x^2 + 6x + 7 \\ x + 4 & x^3 + 10x^2 + 31x + 35 \\ & x^3 + 4x^2 \\ & \quad 6x^2 + 31x \\ & \quad 6x^2 + 24x \\ & \qquad 7x + 35 \\ & \qquad 7x + 28 \\ & \qquad\quad 7 \end{array}$$
Ans. $x^2 + 6x + 7 + \dfrac{7}{x + 4}$

3. $$\begin{array}{r|l} & 2x^2 + x + 1 \\ x - 1 & 2x^3 - x^2 + 0x + 1 \\ & 2x^3 - 2x^2 \\ & \quad x^2 + 0x \\ & \quad x^2 - x \\ & \qquad x + 1 \\ & \qquad x - 1 \\ & \qquad\quad 2 \end{array}$$
Ans. $2x^2 + x + 1 + \dfrac{2}{x - 1}$

4. $$\begin{array}{r|l} & 5x^2 + x - 2 \\ 4x - 3 & 20x^3 - 11x^2 - 11x + 6 \\ & 20x^3 - 15x^2 \\ & \quad 4x^2 - 11x \\ & \quad 4x^2 - 3x \\ & \qquad -8x + 6 \\ & \qquad -8x + 6 \\ & \qquad\quad 0 \end{array}$$
Ans. $5x^2 + x - 2$

Check. $(4x - 3)(5x^2 + x - 2)$
$= 20x^3 + 4x^2 - 8x - 15x^2 - 3x + 6$
$= 20x^3 - 11x^2 - 11x + 6$

Chapter 5

5.1 Practice Problems

1. **(a)** $7(3a - b)$
   (b) $5xy + 8x$
   $= x(5y + 8)$
2. $4a(3a + 4b^2 - 3ab)$
3. **(a)** $8(2a^3 - 3b^3)$
   (b) $r^3(s^2 - 4rs + 7r^2)$
4. $9ab^2c(2a^2 - 3bc - 5ac)$
5. $6xy^2(5x^2 - 4x + 1) = 30x^3y^2 - 24x^2y^2 + 6xy^2$
6. $3(a + 5b) + x(a + 5b)$
   $= (a + 5b)(3 + x)$
7. $(9y^2 - 2)(8y - 1)$
8. $\pi b^2 - \pi a^2 = \pi(b^2 - a^2)$

5.2 Practice Problems

1. $(2x - 7)(3y - 8)$
2. $3x(2x - 5) + 2(2x - 5)$
   $= (2x - 5)(3x + 2)$
3. $a(x + 2) + 4b(x + 2)$
   $= (x + 2)(a + 4b)$
4. $6a^2 + 3ac + 10ab + 5bc$
   $= 3a(2a + c) + 5b(2a + c)$
   $= (2a + c)(3a + 5b)$
5. $6xy + 14x - 15y - 35$
   $= 2x(3y + 7) - 5(3y + 7)$
   $= (3y + 7)(2x - 5)$
6. $3x + 6y - 5ax - 10ay$
   $= 3(x + 2y) - 5a(x + 2y)$
   $= (3 - 5a)(x + 2y)$
7. $10ad + 27bc - 6bd - 45ac$
   $= 10ad - 6bd - 45ac + 27bc$
   $= 2d(5a - 3b) - 9c(5a - 3b)$
   $= (2d - 9c)(5a - 3b)$
   Check: $10ad - 6bd - 45ac + 27bc$

5.3 Practice Problems

1. $(x + 6)(x + 2)$
2. $(x + 2)(x + 15)$
3. $(x - 9)(x - 2)$
4. $x^2 - 11x + 24 = (x - 8)(x - 3)$ or $(x - 3)(x - 8)$
5. $x^2 - 5x - 24 = (x - 8)(x + 3)$ or $(x + 3)(x - 8)$
6. $y^2 + 17y - 60 = (y + 20)(y - 3)$ or $(y - 3)(y + 20)$
7. $(x + 5)(x - 12)$
8. $(a^2 + 7)(a^2 - 6)$
9. $3x^2 + 45x + 150$
   $= 3(x^2 + 15x + 50)$
   $= 3(x + 5)(x + 10)$
10. $4x^2 - 8x - 140$
    $= 4(x^2 - 2x - 35)$
    $= 4(x + 5)(x - 7)$
11. $x(x + 1) - 4(5)$
    $= x^2 + x - 20$
    $= (x + 5)(x - 4)$

5.4 Practice Problems

1. $(2x + 5)(x + 1)$
2. $(9x - 1)(x - 7)$
3. $(3x - 7)(x + 2)$
4. $2x^2 + 7x + 5 = 2x^2 + 5x + 2x + 5$
   $= x(2x + 5) + 1(2x + 5)$
   $= (2x + 5)(x + 1)$
5. $9x^2 - 63x - x + 7$
   $= 9x(x - 7) - 1(x - 7)$
   $= (x - 7)(9x - 1)$
6. $3x^2 + 6x - 2x - 4$
   $= 3x(x + 2) - 2(x + 2)$
   $= (x + 2)(3x - 2)$
7. $8x^2 + 8x - 6 = 2(4x^2 + 4x - 3)$
   $= 2[4x^2 - 2x + 6x - 3]$
   $= 2[2x(2x - 1) + 3(2x - 1)]$
   $= 2(2x - 1)(2x + 3)$
8. $24x^2 - 38x + 10$
   $= 2(12x^2 - 19x + 5)$
   $= 2(12x^2 - 4x - 15x + 5)$
   $= 2[4x(3x - 1) - 5(3x - 1)]$
   $= 2(4x - 5)(3x - 1)$

5.5 Practice Problems

1. $64x^2 - 1 = (8x - 1)(8x + 1)$
2. $(6x + 7)(6x - 7)$
3. $(10x + 9y)(10x - 9y)$
4. $(x^4 + 1)(x^4 - 1)$
   $= (x^4 + 1)(x^2 + 1)(x^2 - 1)$
   $= (x^4 + 1)(x^2 + 1)(x + 1)(x - 1)$
5. $x^2 + 10x + 25 = (x + 5)(x + 5)$ or $(x + 5)^2$
6. $25x^2 - 30x + 9 = (5x - 3)(5x - 3) = (5x - 3)^2$
7. **(a)** $25x^2 + 60xy + 36y^2 = (5x + 6y)^2$
   (b) $64x^6 - 48x^3 + 9 = (8x^3 - 3)^2$
8. $9x^2 + 15x + 4 = (3x + 1)(3x + 4)$
9. $20x^2 - 45$
   $= 5(4x^2 - 9)$
   $= 5(2x - 3)(2x + 3)$
10. $3(25x^2 - 20x + 4)$
    $= 3(5x - 2)(5x - 2)$
    $= 3(5x - 2)^2$

5.6 Practice Problems

1. (a) $3(x^2 - 12x + 36)$
$= 3(x - 6)(x - 6)$
$= 3(x - 6)^2$

(b) $9y^2(x^4 - 1)$
$= 9y^2(x^2 + 1)(x^2 - 1)$
$= 9y^2(x^2 + 1)(x + 1)(x - 1)$

(c) $5x(x^2 - 3xy + 2x - 6y)$
$= 5x[x(x - 3y) + 2(x - 3y)]$
$= 5x(x + 2)(x - 3y)$

(d) $-(4x^2 - 12x + 9)$
$= -(2x - 3)(2x - 3)$
$= -(2x - 3)^2$

2. $x^2 - 9x - 8$
The factors of -8 are $(-2)(4) = -8$, $(2)(-4) = -8$, $(-8)(1) = -8$, $(-1)(8) = -8$
None of these pairs will add up to be the coefficient of the middle term. Thus the polynomial cannot be factored. It is prime.

3. $25x^2 + 82x + 4$
Check to see if this is a perfect square trinomial.
$2[(5)(2)] = 2(10) = 20$
This is not the coefficient of the middle term. The grouping number equals 100. No factors add to 82. It is prime.

5.7 Practice Problems

1. $10x^2 - x - 2 = 0$
$(5x + 2)(2x - 1) = 0$ $\quad 5x + 2 = 0$ $\quad 2x - 1 = 0$
$5x = -2 \qquad 2x = 1$
$x = -\frac{2}{5} \qquad x = \frac{1}{2}$

Check. $10\left(-\frac{2}{5}\right)^2 - \left(-\frac{2}{5}\right) - 2 \stackrel{?}{=} 0 \qquad 10\left(\frac{1}{2}\right)^2 - \frac{1}{2} - 2 \stackrel{?}{=} 0$
$10\left(\frac{4}{25}\right) + \frac{2}{5} - 2 \stackrel{?}{=} 0 \qquad 10\left(\frac{1}{4}\right) - \frac{1}{2} - 2 \stackrel{?}{=} 0$
$\frac{8}{5} + \frac{2}{5} - 2 \stackrel{?}{=} 0 \qquad \frac{5}{2} - \frac{1}{2} - 2 \stackrel{?}{=} 0$
$\frac{10}{5} - \frac{10}{5} \stackrel{?}{=} 0 \qquad \frac{4}{2} - 2 \stackrel{?}{=} 0$
$0 = 0 \qquad 2 - 2 \stackrel{?}{=} 0$
$0 = 0$

Thus $-\frac{2}{5}$ and $\frac{1}{2}$ are both roots for the equation.

2. $3x^2 + 11x - 4 = 0$
$(3x - 1)(x + 4) = 0 \quad 3x - 1 = 0 \quad x + 4 = 0$
$3x = 1 \qquad x = -4$
$x = \frac{1}{3}$

3. $7x^2 + 11x = 0 \qquad x = 0 \qquad 7x + 11 = 0$
$x(7x + 11) = 0 \qquad 7x = -11$
$x = \frac{-11}{7}$

4. $x^2 - 6x + 4 = -8 + x \qquad x - 3 = 0 \qquad x - 4 = 0$
$x^2 - 7x + 12 = 0 \qquad x = 3 \qquad x = 4$
$(x - 3)(x - 4) = 0$

5. $\frac{2x^2 - 7x}{3} = 5$
$2x^2 - 7x = 15 \qquad 2x + 3 = 0 \qquad x - 5 = 0$
$2x^2 - 7x - 15 = 0 \qquad x = -\frac{3}{2} \qquad x = 5$
$(2x + 3)(x - 5) = 0$

6. Let w = width, then
$3w + 2$ = length.
$(3w + 2)w = 85 \qquad 3w + 17 = 0 \qquad w - 5 = 0$
$3w^2 + 2w = 85 \qquad w = -\frac{17}{3} \qquad w = 5$
$3w^2 + 2w - 85 = 0$
$(3w + 17)(w - 5) = 0$
The only valid answer is width = 5 meters.
length $= 3(5) + 2 = 17$ meters

7. Let b = base.
$b - 3$ = altitude.
$\frac{b(b - 3)}{2} = 35$
$b^2 - 3b = 70$
$b^2 - 3b - 70 = 0$
$(b + 7)(b - 10) = 0$
$b + 7 = 0$
$b = -7$
This is not a valid answer.
$b - 10 = 0$
$b = 10$
Thus the base = 10 centimeters.
altitude $= 10 - 3 = 7$ centimeters

8. $-5t^2 + 45 = 0$
$-5(t^2 - 9) = 0$
$t^2 - 9 = 0$
$(t + 3)(t - 3) = 0$
$t = 3 \qquad t = -3 \qquad t = -3$ is not a valid answer
Thus it will be 3 seconds before he breaks the water's surface.

Chapter 6

6.1 Practice Problems

1. $\frac{28}{63} = \frac{7 \times 2 \times 2}{7 \times 3 \times 3} = \frac{4}{9}$

2. $\frac{12x - 6}{14x - 7} = \frac{6(2x - 1)}{7(2x - 1)} = \frac{6}{7}$

3. $\frac{4x^2 - 9}{2x^2 - x - 3} = \frac{(2x - 3)(2x + 3)}{(2x - 3)(x + 1)} = \frac{2x + 3}{x + 1}$

4. $\frac{x^3 - 16x}{x^3 - 2x^2 - 8x} = \frac{x(x^2 - 16)}{x(x^2 - 2x - 8)} = \frac{x(x + 4)(x - 4)}{x(x - 4)(x + 2)} = \frac{x + 4}{x + 2}$

5. $\frac{2x - 5}{5 - 2x} = \frac{-1(-2x + 5)}{(5 - 2x)} = \frac{-1(5 - 2x)}{(5 - 2x)} = -1$

6. $\frac{4x^2 + 3x - 10}{25 - 16x^2} = \frac{(4x - 5)(x + 2)}{(5 + 4x)(5 - 4x)} = \frac{(4x - 5)(x + 2)}{-1(4x - 5)(5 + 4x)}$
$= \frac{x + 2}{-1(5 + 4x)} = -\frac{x + 2}{5 + 4x}$

7. $\frac{4x^2 - 9y^2}{4x^2 + 12xy + 9y^2} = \frac{(2x + 3y)(2x - 3y)}{(2x + 3y)(2x + 3y)} = \frac{2x - 3y}{2x + 3y}$

8. $\frac{25a^2 - 16b^2}{10a^2 + 3ab - 4b^2} = \frac{(5a + 4b)(5a - 4b)}{(5a + 4b)(2a - b)} = \frac{5a - 4b}{2a - b}$

6.2 Practice Problems

1. $\frac{6x^2 + 7x + 2}{x^2 - 7x + 10} \cdot \frac{x^2 + 3x - 10}{2x^2 + 11x + 5}$
$= \frac{(2x + 1)(3x + 2)}{(x - 5)(x - 2)} \cdot \frac{(x + 5)(x - 2)}{(2x + 1)(x + 5)} = \frac{3x + 2}{x - 5}$

2. $\frac{2y^2 - 6y - 8}{y^2 - y - 2} \cdot \frac{y^2 - 5y + 6}{2y^2 - 32}$
$\frac{2(y^2 - 3y - 4)}{(y - 2)(y + 1)} \cdot \frac{(y - 3)(y - 2)}{2(y^2 - 16)}$
$\frac{2(y - 4)(y + 1)}{(y - 2)(y + 1)} \cdot \frac{(y - 3)(y - 2)}{2(y - 4)(y + 4)} = \frac{y - 3}{y + 4}$

3. $\frac{x^2 + 5x + 6}{x^2 + 8x} \div \frac{2x^2 + 5x + 2}{2x^2 + x}$
$= \frac{(x + 2)(x + 3)}{x(x + 8)} \cdot \frac{x(2x + 1)}{(2x + 1)(x + 2)} = \frac{x + 3}{x + 8}$

4. $\frac{x + 3}{x - 3} \div (9 - x^2) = \frac{x + 3}{x - 3} \cdot \frac{1}{(3 + x)(3 - x)}$
$= \frac{1}{(x - 3)(3 - x)}$

6.3 Practice Problems

1. $\dfrac{2s+t}{2s-t}+\dfrac{s-t}{2s-t}=\dfrac{2s+t+s-t}{2s-t}=\dfrac{3s}{2s-t}$

2. $\dfrac{b}{(a-2b)(a+b)}-\dfrac{2b}{(a-2b)(a+b)}=\dfrac{b-2b}{(a-2b)(a+b)}$
$=\dfrac{-b}{(a-2b)(a+b)}$

3. $\dfrac{7}{6x+21},\ \dfrac{13}{10x+35}$ $\quad 6x+21=3(2x+7)$
$10x+35=5(2x+7)$
$\text{LCD}=3\cdot 5\cdot(2x+7)=15(2x+7)$

4. (a) $\dfrac{3}{50xy^2z},\ \dfrac{19}{40x^3yz}$ $\quad 50xy^2z=2\cdot 5^2\cdot x\cdot y^2\cdot z$
$40x^3yz=2^3\cdot 5\cdot x^3\cdot y\cdot z$
$\text{LCD}=2^3\cdot 5^2\cdot x^3\cdot y^2\cdot z$
$\text{LCD}=200x^3y^2z$

(b) $\dfrac{2}{x^2+5x+6},\ \dfrac{6}{3x^2+5x-2}$
$x^2+5x+6=(x+3)(x+2)$
$3x^2+5x-2=(3x-1)(x+2)$
$\text{LCD}=(x+2)(x+3)(3x-1)$

5. $\dfrac{7}{a}+\dfrac{3}{abc}=\dfrac{7bc+3}{abc}$ $\quad \text{LCD}=abc$

6. $\dfrac{2a-b}{a^2-4b^2}+\dfrac{2}{a+2b}$ $\quad \text{LCD}=(a+2b)(a-2b)$
$=\dfrac{2a-b}{(a+2b)(a-2b)}+\dfrac{2(a-2b)}{(a+2b)(a-2b)}$
$=\dfrac{2a-b}{(a+2b)(a-2b)}+\dfrac{2a-4b}{(a+2b)(a-2b)}$
$=\dfrac{2a-b+2a-4b}{(a+2b)(a-2b)}$
$=\dfrac{4a-5b}{(a+2b)(a-2b)}$

7. $\dfrac{7a}{a^2+2ab+b^2}+\dfrac{4}{a^2+ab}$
$=\dfrac{7a}{(a+b)(a+b)}+\dfrac{4}{a(a+b)}$ $\quad \text{LCD}=a(a+b)^2$
$=\dfrac{7a^2}{a(a+b)(a+b)}+\dfrac{4(a+b)}{a(a+b)(a+b)}=\dfrac{7a^2+4a+4b}{a(a+b)^2}$

8. $\dfrac{x+7}{3x-9}-\dfrac{x-6}{x-3}=\dfrac{x+7}{3(x-3)}-\dfrac{x-6}{x-3}$ $\quad \text{LCD}=3(x-3)$
$=\dfrac{x+7-3(x-6)}{3(x-3)}=\dfrac{x+7-3x+18}{3(x-3)}=\dfrac{-2x+25}{3(x-3)}$

9. $\dfrac{x-2}{x^2-4}-\dfrac{x+1}{2x^2+4x}=\dfrac{x-2}{(x+2)(x-2)}-\dfrac{x+1}{2x(x+2)}$
$\text{LCD}=2x(x+2)(x-2)$
$=\dfrac{2x(x-2)}{2x(x+2)(x-2)}-\dfrac{(x-2)(x+1)}{2x(x+2)(x-2)}$
$=\dfrac{2x^2-4x-(x^2-x-2)}{2x(x+2)(x-2)}=\dfrac{2x^2-4x-x^2+x+2}{2x(x+2)(x-2)}$
$=\dfrac{x^2-3x+2}{2x(x+2)(x-2)}=\dfrac{(x-2)(x-1)}{2x(x+2)(x-2)}=\dfrac{x-1}{2x(x+2)}$

6.4 Practice Problems

1. $\dfrac{\frac{1}{a}+\frac{1}{b}}{\frac{2}{ab^2}}=\dfrac{\frac{b+a}{ab}}{\frac{2}{ab^2}}$
$=\dfrac{b+a}{ab}\div\dfrac{2}{ab^2}=\dfrac{b+a}{ab}\cdot\dfrac{ab^2}{2}=\dfrac{ab^2(a+b)}{2\,ab}=\dfrac{b(a+b)}{2}$

2. $\dfrac{\frac{1}{a}+\frac{1}{b}}{\frac{1}{a}-\frac{1}{b}}=\dfrac{\frac{b+a}{ab}}{\frac{b-a}{ab}}=\dfrac{b+a}{ab}\cdot\dfrac{ab}{b-a}=\dfrac{b+a}{b-a}$

3. $\dfrac{\frac{x}{x^2+4x+3}+\frac{2}{x+1}}{x+1}=\dfrac{\frac{x}{(x+1)(x+3)}+\frac{2}{x+1}}{x+1}$
$=\dfrac{\frac{x+2(x+3)}{(x+1)(x+3)}}{x+1}=\dfrac{\frac{x+2x+6}{(x+1)(x+3)}}{(x+1)}$
$=\dfrac{3x+6}{(x+1)(x+3)}\cdot\dfrac{1}{(x+1)}=\dfrac{3(x+2)}{(x+1)^2(x+3)}$

4. $\dfrac{\frac{6}{x^2-y^2}}{\frac{1}{x-y}+\frac{3}{x+y}}=\dfrac{\frac{6}{(x+y)(x-y)}}{\frac{(x+y)+3(x-y)}{(x+y)(x-y)}}$
$=\dfrac{6}{(x+y)(x-y)}\div\dfrac{x+y+3x-3y}{(x+y)(x-y)}$
$=\dfrac{6}{(x+y)(x-y)}\cdot\dfrac{(x+y)(x-y)}{4x-2y}$
$=\dfrac{6}{(x+y)(x-y)}\cdot\dfrac{(x+y)(x-y)}{2(2x-y)}=\dfrac{3}{2x-y}$

5. $\dfrac{\frac{2}{3x^2}-\frac{3}{y}}{\frac{5}{xy}-4}$ $\quad \text{LCD}=3x^2y$
$\dfrac{3x^2y\left(\frac{2}{3x^2}\right)-3x^2y\left(\frac{3}{y}\right)}{3x^2y\left(\frac{5}{xy}\right)-3x^2y(4)}=\dfrac{2y-3x^2(3)}{3x(5)-12x^2y}$
$=\dfrac{2y-9x^2}{15x-12x^2y}$

6. $\dfrac{\frac{6}{x^2-y^2}}{\frac{7}{x-y}+\frac{3}{x+y}}=\dfrac{\frac{6}{(x+y)(x-y)}}{\frac{7}{x-y}+\frac{3}{x+y}}$
$\text{LCD}=(x+y)(x-y)$
$\dfrac{(x+y)(x-y)\left(\frac{6}{(x+y)(x-y)}\right)}{(x+y)(x-y)\left(\frac{7}{x-y}\right)+(x+y)(x-y)\left(\frac{3}{x+y}\right)}$
$=\dfrac{6}{7(x+y)+3(x-y)}=\dfrac{6}{7x+7y+3x-3y}$
$=\dfrac{6}{10x+4y}$
$=\dfrac{3}{5x+2y}$

6.5 Practice Problems

1. $\dfrac{3}{x}+\dfrac{4}{5}=\dfrac{-2}{x}$ $\quad \text{LCD}=5x$
$=15+4x=-10$
$4x=-10-15$
$4x=-25$
$x=-\dfrac{25}{4}$

Check.
$\dfrac{3}{\frac{-25}{4}}+\dfrac{4}{5}\stackrel{?}{=}\dfrac{-2}{\frac{-25}{4}}$
$\dfrac{12}{-25}+\dfrac{4}{5}\stackrel{?}{=}\dfrac{-2}{\frac{-25}{4}}$
$-\dfrac{12}{25}+\dfrac{20}{25}\stackrel{?}{=}\dfrac{8}{25}$
$\dfrac{8}{25}=\dfrac{8}{25}$ ✓

2. $\frac{4}{2x+1} = \frac{6}{2x-1}$ LCD $= (2x+1)(2x-1)$

$$(2x+1)(2x-1)\left[\frac{4}{2x+1}\right] = (2x+1)(2x-1)\left[\frac{6}{2x-1}\right]$$
$$4(2x-1) = 6(2x+1)$$
$$8x - 4 = 12x + 6$$
$$-4x = 10$$
$$x = -\frac{5}{2}$$

Check.

$$\frac{4}{2\left(-\frac{5}{2}\right)+1} \stackrel{?}{=} \frac{6}{2\left(-\frac{5}{2}\right)-1}$$
$$\frac{4}{-5+1} \stackrel{?}{=} \frac{6}{-5-1}$$
$$\frac{4}{-4} \stackrel{?}{=} \frac{6}{-6}$$
$$-1 = -1 \checkmark$$

3. $\frac{x-1}{x^2-4} = \frac{2}{x+2} + \frac{4}{x-2}$

$\frac{x-1}{(x+2)(x-2)} = \frac{2}{x+2} + \frac{4}{x-2}$ LCD $= (x+2)(x-2)$

$$(x+2)(x-2)\left[\frac{x-1}{(x+2)(x-2)}\right]$$
$$= (x+2)(x-2)\left[\frac{2}{x+2}\right] + (x+2)(x-2)\left[\frac{4}{x-2}\right]$$
$$x - 1 = 2(x-2) + 4(x+2)$$
$$x - 1 = 2x - 4 + 4x + 8$$
$$x - 1 = 6x + 4$$
$$-5x = 5$$
$$x = -1$$

Check.

$$\frac{-1-1}{(-1)^2-4} \stackrel{?}{=} \frac{2}{-1+2} + \frac{4}{-1-2}$$
$$\frac{-2}{-3} \stackrel{?}{=} \frac{2}{1} + \frac{4}{-3}$$
$$\frac{2}{3} \stackrel{?}{=} \frac{6}{3} - \frac{4}{3}$$
$$\frac{2}{3} = \frac{2}{3} \checkmark$$

4. $\frac{2x}{x+1} = \frac{-2}{x+1} + 1$ LCD $= (x+1)$

$$(x+1)\left[\frac{2x}{x+1}\right] = (x+1)\left[\frac{-2}{x+1}\right] + (x+1)[1]$$
$$2x = -2 + x + 1$$
$$2x = x - 1$$
$$x = -1$$

Check.

$$\frac{2(-1)}{-1+1} \stackrel{?}{=} \frac{-2}{-1+1} + 1$$
$$\frac{-2}{0} \stackrel{?}{=} \frac{-2}{0} + 1$$

These expressions are not defined; therefore, there is no solution to this problem.

6.6 Practice Problems

1. $\frac{8}{420} = \frac{x}{315}$

$$8(315) = 420x$$
$$2520 = 420x$$
$$x = 6$$

It would take Brenda 6 hours to drive 315 miles.

2. $\frac{\frac{5}{8}}{30} = \frac{2\frac{1}{2}}{x}$

$$\frac{5}{8}x = 30\left(2\frac{1}{2}\right)$$
$$\frac{5}{8}x = 75$$
$$x = 120$$

Therefore $2\frac{1}{2}$ inches would represent 120 miles.

3. $\frac{13}{x} = \frac{16}{18}$

$$13(18) = 16x$$
$$234 = 16x$$
$$x = 14\frac{5}{8} \text{ cm}$$

4. $\frac{6}{7} = \frac{x}{38.5}$

$$6(38.5) = 7x$$
$$231 = 7x$$
$$x = 33 \text{ feet}$$

5. Train A time $= \frac{180}{x+10}$ Train B time $= \frac{150}{x}$

$$\frac{180}{x+10} = \frac{150}{x}$$
$$180x = 150(x+10)$$
$$180x = 150x + 1500$$
$$30x = 1500$$
$$x = 50$$

Train B travels 50 kilometers per hour. Train A travels $50 + 10 = 60$ kilometers per hour.

6.

	Number of Hours	Part of the Job Done in One Hour
John	6 hours	$\frac{1}{6}$
Dave	7 hours	$\frac{1}{7}$
John & Dave Together	x	$\frac{1}{x}$

$\frac{1}{6} + \frac{1}{7} = \frac{1}{x}$ LCD $= 42x$

$$7x + 6x = 42$$
$$13x = 42$$

$x = 3\frac{3}{13}$ $\frac{3}{13}$ hour $\times \frac{60 \text{ min}}{1 \text{ hour}} = \frac{180}{13}$ min $= 13.846$ min

Thus, doing the job together will take 3 hours and 14 minutes.

Appendix B

Practice Problems

1. $3.4 \text{ m} \cdot 1 = 3.4 \text{ m} \cdot \frac{100 \text{ cm}}{1 \text{ m}} = \frac{(3.4)(100)}{1} \cdot \frac{\text{m}}{\text{m}} \cdot \text{cm} = 340 \text{ cm}$

2. $125 \text{ L} \cdot \frac{0.001 \text{ kL}}{1 \text{ L}} = \frac{(125)(0.001)}{1} \cdot \frac{\text{L}}{\text{L}} \cdot \text{kL} = 0.125 \text{ kL}$

3. $5.72 \text{ lb} \cdot \frac{1 \text{ kg}}{2.20 \text{ lb}} = 2.6 \text{ kg}$

4. $8 \text{ cm} \cdot \frac{1 \text{ in.}}{2.54 \text{ cm}} \approx 3.15 \text{ in.}$

5. $3 \text{ L} \cdot \frac{1.06 \text{ qt}}{1 \text{ L}} = 3.18 \text{ qt}$

6. $\frac{70 \text{ mi}}{\text{hr}} \cdot \frac{5280 \text{ ft}}{1 \text{ mi}} \cdot \frac{1 \text{ hr}}{60 \text{ min}} \cdot \frac{1 \text{ min}}{60 \text{ sec}} = \frac{(70)(5280) \text{ ft}}{(60)(60) \text{ sec}}$

≈ 102.7 ft/sec

Appendix C

Practice Problems

1. **(a)** The lowest level of sodium, 670 mg, is in the Wendy's Grilled Chicken Sandwich.
   (b) The highest level of cholesterol, 100 g, is in the McDonald's Big Mac.
2. **(a)** The two activities single women spend the most time doing are spending time with friends, and reading and watching TV.
   (b) Couples spend more time per week with their family (21 hr) than any other activity.
   (c) The greatest difference between single men and single women is the time spent reading and watching TV (6 hr).
3. **(a)** Walgreens has $7 \times 300 = 2100$ stores.
   (b) Rite Aid has $9 \times 300 = 2700$ stores. CVS has $5 \times 300 = 1500$ stores. Since $2700 - 1500 = 1200$, Rite Aid has 1200 more stores than CVS.
   (c) Thrift Drug has $2 \times 300 = 600$ stores, and Medicine Shoppe has $4 \times 300 = 1200$ stores. There are $600 + 1200 = 1800$ total Thrift Drug and Medicine Shoppe stores.
4. **(a)** The greatest number of fatal accidents, 14, occurred during the 1989–1990 period.
   (b) During the 1987–1988 period there were 7 accidents. During 1989–1990 there were 14 accidents. The increase in the number of fatal accidents from 1987–1988 to 1989–1990 was 7.
   (c) During the 1991–1992 period there were 8 accidents. During 1993–1994 there were 5 accidents. The decrease in the number of fatal accidents from 1991–1992 to 1993–1994 was 3.
5. **(a)** There were 12 days in 1993 in which the PSI exceeded 100.
   (b) The year with the fewest days in which the PSI exceeded 100 was 1992.
6. **(a)** 15% of Seattle's rainfall falls between April and June.
   (b) 40% of Seattle's rainfall occurs from October to December.
   (c) 35% of the total rainfall occurs from January to March. This is $35\% \times 37 = 0.35 \times 37 = 12.95$ inches.

Appendix D

Practice Problems

1. Each number is 7 more than the preceding number. The next number in the sequence is $66 + 7 = 73$.
2. The sequence could be written $2^2 - 1, 3^2 - 1, 4^2 - 1, 5^2 - 1, \ldots$. The next number would be $10^2 - 1 = 99$.
3. Between 1's there are one 2, two 3's, and three 4's. Next would come four 5's, a 1, and then five 6's. The next seven digits are 5555166.
4. In the first figure, the bottom rectangle is shaded and the figure is rotated 90° clockwise to get the second figure. Then, in the third figure, the middle rectangle is shaded. This is rotated 90° clockwise to get the fourth figure. Then, the top rectangle is shaded and the figure is rotated. In the last figure, the bottom rectangle is shaded again and the sequence is repeated.
   The next two figures are

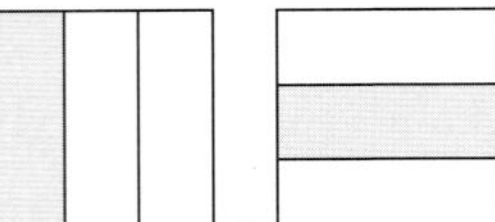

5.

Statement	Reason
1. $x = 2x + 24$	1. Multiplication principle: If $a = b$, then $ac = bc$. Here we multiplied by 6.
2. $-x = 24$	2. Addition principle: If $a = b$, then $a + c = b + c$. Here we added $-2x$ to each side of the equation.
3. $x = -24$	3. Multiplication principle: If $a = b$, then $ac = bc$. Here we multiplied each side by -1.

6.

Statement	Reason
1. $\angle 6 = \angle 5 = 26°$	1. If two lines intersect, the opposite angles are equal.
2. $\angle 4 = \angle 6 = 26°$	2. If a transversal crosses two parallel lines, the alternate interior angles are equal.

7. Let us organize the facts by listing the cars and each possible position: 1, 2, 3, 4, in which position 1 means far left and position 4 means far right.

Honda	Toyota	Mustang	Camaro
1	1	1	1
2	2	2	2
3	3	3	3
4	4	4	4

Step	Reason
1. We indicate that the Camaro is in position 4 and cross out the other 4's since no other car can be in position 4. We also cross out positions 1, 2, and 3 for the Camaro.	1. The Camaro is parked on the right end.

Honda	Toyota	Mustang	Camaro
1	1	1	~~1~~
2	2	2	~~2~~
3	3	3	~~3~~
~~4~~	~~4~~	~~4~~	$\boxed{4}$

Step	Reason
2. The Mustang cannot be in position 1 since it's between two cars. It also cannot be in position 3 as that would place it next to the Camaro. Therefore, the Mustang must be in position 2. Cross off the 2's in all other columns.	2. The Mustang is between the Honda and the Toyota.

Honda	Toyota	Mustang	Camaro
1	1	~~1~~	~~1~~
~~2~~	~~2~~	$\boxed{2}$	~~2~~
3	3	~~3~~	~~3~~
~~4~~	~~4~~	~~4~~	$\boxed{4}$

Step	Reason
3. The Honda must be in position 1 since it cannot be in position 3, next to the Camaro. This leaves position 3 for the Toyota.	3. The Honda is not next to the Camaro.

Honda	Toyota	Mustang	Camaro
$\boxed{1}$	~~1~~	~~1~~	~~1~~
~~2~~	~~2~~	$\boxed{2}$	~~2~~
~~3~~	$\boxed{3}$	~~3~~	~~3~~
~~4~~	~~4~~	~~4~~	$\boxed{4}$

The Honda, in position 1, is the car parked on the left end.

Answers to Selected Exercises

Chapter 0

0.1 Exercises

1. 12 **3.** When two or more numbers are multiplied, each number that is multiplied is called a factor. In 2×3, 2 and 3 are factors.
5. 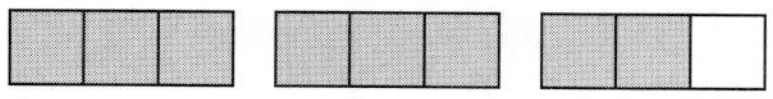 **7.** $\frac{3}{4}$ **9.** $\frac{1}{3}$ **11.** 5 **13.** $2\frac{5}{6}$ **15.** $12\frac{1}{3}$ **17.** $5\frac{3}{7}$ **19.** $\frac{16}{5}$

21. $\frac{33}{5}$ **23.** 8 **25.** 12 **27.** 21 **29.** 12 **31.** $22\frac{16}{17}$ **33.** $\frac{33}{160}$ **35.** $\frac{1}{4}$ **37.** $\frac{1}{2}$

39. Aaron Dunsay $\frac{3}{5}$, Paul Banks $\frac{2}{5}$, Tom Re $\frac{4}{5}$ **41.** $\frac{13}{16}$

0.2 Exercises

1. Answers may vary. A sample answer is: 8 is exactly divisible by 4.
3. 105 **5.** 20 **7.** 54 **9.** 90

11. $\frac{5}{8}$ **13.** $\frac{2}{7}$ **15.** $\frac{29}{24}$ or $1\frac{5}{24}$ **17.** $\frac{31}{63}$ **19.** $\frac{11}{15}$ **21.** $\frac{17}{36}$ **23.** $\frac{3}{2}$ or $1\frac{1}{2}$ **25.** $\frac{1}{2}$ **27.** $7\frac{11}{15}$ **29.** $1\frac{35}{72}$ **31.** $4\frac{11}{12}$
33. $6\frac{13}{28}$ **35.** $5\frac{19}{24}$ **37.** $4\frac{3}{7}$ **39.** $8\frac{7}{8}$ **41.** $\frac{29}{18}$ or $1\frac{11}{18}$ **43.** $\frac{83}{14}$ or $5\frac{13}{14}$ **45.** $\frac{10}{21}$ **47.** $\frac{27}{10}$ or $2\frac{7}{10}$ **49.** $10\frac{7}{24}$ miles
51. $4\frac{1}{12}$ hours **53.** A = 12 inches, B = $15\frac{7}{8}$ inches **55.** $1\frac{5}{8}$ inches **57.** $\frac{9}{11}$ **58.** $\frac{133}{5}$

0.3 Exercises

1. First, change each number to an improper fraction. Look for a common factor in the numerator and denominator to divide by, and, if one is found, peform the division. Multiply the numerators. Multiply the denominators.
3. $\frac{20}{7}$ or $2\frac{6}{7}$ **5.** $\frac{17}{30}$ **7.** $\frac{6}{25}$ **9.** $\frac{12}{5}$ or $2\frac{2}{5}$ **11.** $\frac{18}{5}$ or $3\frac{3}{5}$ **13.** $\frac{3}{5}$ **15.** $\frac{1}{7}$ **17.** 14 **19.** $\frac{7}{6}$ or $1\frac{1}{6}$ **21.** $\frac{15}{14}$ or $1\frac{1}{14}$ **23.** $\frac{8}{35}$
25. $\frac{4}{3}$ or $1\frac{1}{3}$ **27.** $\frac{7}{12}$ **29.** $\frac{8}{15}$ **31.** 1 **33.** $\frac{5}{4}$ or $1\frac{1}{4}$ **35.** $\frac{219}{4}$ or $54\frac{3}{4}$ **37.** $\frac{17}{2}$ or $8\frac{1}{2}$ **39.** 28 **41.** $\frac{3}{16}$ **43.** $71\frac{1}{2}$ yards
45. $2\frac{4}{5}$ miles **47.** $\frac{29}{31}$ **48.** $\frac{3}{7}$

0.4 Exercises

1. 10; 100; 10,000; and so on **3.** three, left **5.** 0.625 **7.** 0.2 **9.** $0.\overline{63}$ **11.** $\frac{4}{5}$ **13.** $\frac{5}{8}$ **15.** $\frac{13}{5}$ or $2\frac{3}{5}$ **17.** 2.09 **19.** 10.82
21. 261.208 **23.** 131.79 **25.** 30.282 **27.** 0.10575 **29.** 219.7 **31.** 2.64 **33.** 261.5 **35.** 0.257 **37.** 3450 **39.** 0.0076
41. 73,600 **43.** 0.73892 **45.** 1.425 **47.** 11.7257 **49.** 2.12 **51.** 768.3 **53.** 24.13 cm **55.** \$212.75
57. No, there were 0.3 milligrams of copper in excess. **59.** $\frac{2}{3}$ **60.** $\frac{1}{6}$ **61.** $\frac{93}{100}$ **62.** $\frac{11}{10}$ or $1\frac{1}{10}$

How Am I Doing? Sections 0.1–0.4

1. $\frac{3}{11}$ (obj. 0.1.2) **2.** $\frac{2}{5}$ (obj. 0.1.2) **3.** $3\frac{3}{4}$ (obj. 0.1.3) **4.** $\frac{33}{7}$ (obj. 0.1.3) **5.** 6 (obj. 0.1.4) **6.** 35 (obj. 0.1.4)

7. 120 = LCD (obj. 0.2.2) **8.** $\frac{5}{7}$ (obj. 0.2.1) **9.** $\frac{19}{42}$ (obj. 0.2.3) **10.** $8\frac{5}{12}$ (obj. 0.2.4) **11.** $\frac{7}{18}$ (obj. 0.2.3)

12. $\frac{4}{21}$ (obj. 0.2.3) **13.** $1\frac{33}{40}$ (obj. 0.2.4) **14.** $\frac{10}{9}$ or $1\frac{1}{9}$ (obj. 0.3.1) **15.** $\frac{21}{2}$ or $10\frac{1}{2}$ (obj. 0.3.1) **16.** $\frac{7}{2}$ or $3\frac{1}{2}$ (obj. 0.3.2)

17. $\frac{28}{39}$ (obj. 0.3.2) **18.** 0.875 (obj. 0.4.2) **19.** $0.\overline{5}$ (obj. 0.4.2) **20.** 0.015 (obj. 0.4.2) **21.** 19.651 (obj. 0.4.4)
22. 2.0664 (obj. 0.4.5) **23.** 0.45 (obj. 0.4.6) **24.** 2.246 (obj. 0.4.4)

0.5 Exercises

1. Answers may vary. Sample answers are below. 19% means 19 out of 100 parts. Percent means per 100. 19% is really a fraction with a denominator of 100. In this case it would be $\frac{19}{100}$.
3. 28% **5.** 56.8% **7.** 7.6% **9.** 239% **11.** 0.03 **13.** 0.004 **15.** 2.5 **17.** 0.074 **19.** 5.2 **21.** 13 **23.** 72.8
25. 150% **27.** 5% **29.** 250% **31.** 85% **33.** $4.92 tip $37.72 total **35.** approximately 21% **37.** 540
39. $1 an hour raise; $13.50 per hour **41.** $29,640 sales commission; $35,040 annual salary **43.** $2.97 **45.** $538.13
46. $6220.50 **47.** 22 miles per gallon **48.** 4.0 inches

0.6 Exercises

1. 210,000 **3.** 18,000,000 **5.** 240 **7.** 20,000 **9.** 0.1 **11.** $4000.00 **13.** $400 **15.** $6400 **17.** 25 miles per gallon
19. $1666.67 **21.** $60,000,000,000 **23.** $4000 **25.** 10% **27.** $240 **29.** 2.1 **30.** 56.25% **31.** $6.73 **32.** 270 tires

0.7 Exercises

1. $269.17 **3.** **(a)** $82\frac{1}{3}$ feet **(b)** 90 feet; $17.90 **5.** jog, $2\frac{2}{3}$ miles; walk $3\frac{1}{9}$ miles rest, $4\frac{4}{9}$ minutes; walk, $1\frac{7}{9}$ miles

7. Betty; Melinda increases each activity by $\frac{2}{3}$ by day 3 but Betty increases each activity by $\frac{7}{9}$ by day 3. **9.** $4\frac{1}{2}$ miles

11. $98,969.00 **13.** **(a)** $36,000 **(b)** $11,160 **15.** 18% **17.** 69%

Putting Your Skills to Work

1. 12,700 sq mi **2.** 9400 sq mi **3.** About 4 times **4.** About 319 times

Chapter 0 Review Problems

1. $\frac{3}{4}$ **2.** $\frac{3}{10}$ **3.** $\frac{18}{41}$ **4.** $\frac{3}{5}$ **5.** $\frac{23}{5}$ **6.** $6\frac{4}{5}$ **7.** $6\frac{1}{2}$ **8.** 15 **9.** 5 **10.** 40 **11.** 22 **12.** $\frac{17}{20}$ **13.** $\frac{29}{24}$ or $1\frac{5}{24}$
14. $\frac{4}{15}$ **15.** $\frac{13}{30}$ **16.** $\frac{173}{30}$ or $5\frac{23}{30}$ **17.** $\frac{79}{20}$ or $3\frac{19}{20}$ **18.** $2\frac{29}{36}$ **19.** $\frac{23}{12}$ or $1\frac{11}{12}$ **20.** $\frac{30}{11}$ or $2\frac{8}{11}$ **21.** $\frac{21}{2}$ or $10\frac{1}{2}$ **22.** $\frac{19}{8}$ or $2\frac{3}{8}$
23. $\frac{20}{7}$ or $2\frac{6}{7}$ **24.** $\frac{1}{16}$ **25.** $\frac{24}{5}$ or $4\frac{4}{5}$ **26.** $\frac{3}{20}$ **27.** 6 **28.** 7.201 **29.** 7.737 **30.** 29.561 **31.** 4.436 **32.** 0.03745
33. 362,341 **34.** 0.07956 **35.** 10.368 **36.** 0.00186 **37.** 0.07132 **38.** 1.3075 **39.** 90 **40.** 1.82 **41.** 0.5 **42.** 0.375
43. $\frac{9}{25}$ **44.** 0.014 **45.** 0.361 **46.** 0.0002 **47.** 1.253 **48.** 510 **49.** 3.96 **50.** 64% **51.** 12.5% **52.** 60%
53. 16,324,803 **54.** 75% **55.** 400,000,000,000 **56.** 2500 **57.** 300,000 **58.** 19 **59.** $12,000 **60.** 30 **61.** $240
62. $300 **63.** $349.07 **64.** 8% **65.** 1840 miles; 1472 miles **66.** 1500 miles; 1050 miles **67.** $7\frac{1}{2}$ cubic inches **68.** 200 boxes
69. $462.80 **70.** 46 packages **71.** $1585.50 **72.** $371.20

How Am I Doing? Chapter 0 Test

1. $\frac{8}{9}$ (obj. 0.1.2) **2.** $\frac{4}{3}$ (obj. 0.1.2) **3.** $\frac{45}{7}$ (obj. 0.1.3) **4.** $11\frac{2}{3}$ (obj. 0.1.3) **5.** $\frac{15}{8}$ or $1\frac{7}{8}$ (obj. 0.2.3) **6.** $\frac{39}{8}$ or $4\frac{7}{8}$ (obj. 0.2.4)
7. $\frac{5}{6}$ (obj. 0.2.4) **8.** $\frac{4}{3}$ or $1\frac{1}{3}$ (obj. 0.3.1) **9.** $\frac{5}{24}$ (obj. 0.3.1) **10.** $\frac{7}{2}$ or $3\frac{1}{2}$ (obj. 0.3.2) **11.** $\frac{65}{8}$ or $8\frac{1}{8}$ (obj. 0.3.1)
12. $\frac{43}{22}$ or $1\frac{21}{22}$ (obj. 0.3.2) **13.** 14.64 (obj. 0.4.4) **14.** 3.9897 (obj. 0.4.4) **15.** 1.312 (obj. 0.4.5) **16.** 73.85 (obj. 0.4.5)
17. 230 (obj. 0.4.6) **18.** 263,259 (obj. 0.4.7) **19.** 7.3% (obj. 0.5.2) **20.** 1.965 (obj. 0.5.3) **21.** 6.3 (obj. 0.5.4)
22. 0.336 (obj. 0.5.4) **23.** 6% (obj. 0.5.5) **24.** 30% (obj. 0.5.5) **25.** 18 (obj. 0.3.2) **26.** 100 (obj. 0.6.1) **27.** 700 (obj. 0.6.1)
28. 65% (obj. 0.7.1) **29.** 60 tiles (obj. 0.7.1)

Chapter 1

1.1 Exercises

1. Whole number, rational number, real number **3.** Irrational number, real number **5.** Rational number, real number
7. Rational number, real number **9.** Irrational number, real number **11.** −20,000 **13.** $-37\frac{1}{2}$ **15.** +7 **17.** −8 **19.** 2.73
21. 1.3 **23.** $\frac{5}{6}$ **25.** −11 **27.** −31 **29.** $\frac{1}{4}$ **31.** $-\frac{7}{13}$ **33.** $\frac{1}{35}$ **35.** −3.8 **37.** 0.4 **39.** −14.16 **41.** −6 **43.** −5

45. $-\frac{4}{15}$ **47.** -8 **49.** -3 **51.** 59 **53.** $\frac{7}{18}$ **55.** $\frac{2}{5}$ **57.** 0.76 **59.** 12 **61.** 0 **63.** 15.94 **65.** $167 profit **67.** $-\$3800$ **69.** 3 yard gain **71.** 3500 **73.** $32,000,000 **75.** 18 **77.** 6 yards **79.** $\frac{2}{3}$ **80.** $\frac{8}{27}$ **81.** $\frac{1}{12}$ **82.** $\frac{25}{34}$ **83.** 1.52 **84.** 0.65 **85.** 1.141 **86.** 0.26

1.2 Exercises

1. First change subtracting -3 to adding a positive three. Then use the rules for addition of two real numbers with different signs. Thus, $-8 - (-3) = -8 + 3 = -5$. **3.** -17 **5.** -5 **7.** -11 **9.** 8 **11.** 5 **13.** 0 **15.** -3 **17.** $-\frac{2}{5}$ **19.** $\frac{27}{20}$ or $1\frac{7}{20}$ **21.** $-\frac{19}{12}$ or $-1\frac{7}{12}$ **23.** -0.9 **25.** 4.47 **27.** $-\frac{17}{5}$ or $-3\frac{2}{5}$ **29.** $\frac{40}{7}$ or $5\frac{5}{7}$ **31.** -53 **33.** -73 **35.** 7.1 **37.** $8\frac{3}{4}$ **39.** $-6\frac{1}{6}$ **41.** $-\frac{21}{20}$ or $-1\frac{1}{20}$ **43.** -8.5 **45.** $-5\frac{4}{5}$ **47.** 8.162 **49.** -5.047 **51.** 7 **53.** -48 **55.** -2 **57.** 11 **59.** -62 **61.** 1.6 **63.** 38 **65.** $149 **67.** 6051 meters **69.** -21 **70.** -51 **71.** -19 **72.** -8°C **73.** $6\frac{2}{3}$ miles were snow covered

1.3 Exercises

1. To multiply two real numbers, multiply the absolute values. The sign of the result is positive if both numbers have the same sign, but negative if the two numbers have opposite signs. **3.** -20 **5.** 0 **7.** 24 **9.** 0.264 **11.** -1.75 **13.** $-\frac{3}{2}$ or $-1\frac{1}{2}$ **15.** $\frac{9}{11}$ **17.** $-\frac{5}{26}$ **19.** 4 **21.** 6 **23.** 20 **25.** -12 **27.** -130 **29.** -0.6 **31.** -0.9 **33.** $-\frac{3}{10}$ **35.** $\frac{20}{3}$ or $6\frac{2}{3}$ **37.** $\frac{7}{10}$ **39.** 14 **41.** $-\frac{5}{4}$ or $-1\frac{1}{4}$ **43.** $\frac{15}{16}$ **45.** -24 **47.** 24 **49.** -16 **51.** -0.00018 **53.** $-\frac{8}{35}$ **55.** $\frac{2}{27}$ **57.** 9 **59.** -2 **61.** 17 **63.** -72 **65.** -1 **67.** He gave $4.40 to each boy and to himself. **69.** $328.50 **71.** 20 yards **73.** 70 yards **75.** The Panthers gained 20 yards **77.** The Panthers would have gained 105 fewer yards. **78.** -6.69 **79.** $-\frac{11}{6}$ or $-1\frac{5}{6}$ **80.** -15 **81.** -88 **82.** 266 square yards

1.4 Exercises

1. The base is 4 and the exponent is 4. Thus you multiply $(4)(4)(4)(4) = 256$.
3. The answer is negative. When you raise a negative number to an odd power the result is always negative.
5. If you have parentheses surrounding the -2, then the base is -2 and the exponent is 4. The result is 16. If you do not have parentheses, then the base is 2. You evaluate to obtain 16 and then take the negative of 16, which is -16. Thus $(-2)^4 = 16$ but $-2^4 = -16$. **7.** 5^7 **9.** w^2 **11.** p^4 **13.** $(3q)^3$ or 3^3q^3 **15.** 27 **17.** 81 **19.** 216 **21.** -27 **23.** 16 **25.** -25 **27.** $\frac{1}{16}$ **29.** $\frac{8}{125}$ **31.** 1.21 **33.** 0.0016 **35.** 256 **37.** -256 **39.** 161 **41.** 116 **43.** -91 **45.** 23 **47.** -576 **49.** -512 **51.** 16,777,216 **53.** -7 **55.** -19 **56.** $-\frac{5}{3}$ or $-1\frac{2}{3}$ **57.** -8 **58.** 2.52 **59.** $1672

1.5 Exercises

1. $3(4) + 6(5)$ **3.** (a) 90 (b) 42 **5.** 12 **7.** 13 **9.** -29 **11.** 24 **13.** 21 **15.** 13 **17.** -6 **19.** 42 **21.** $\frac{9}{4}$ or $2\frac{1}{4}$ **23.** 0.848 **25.** $\frac{3}{10}$ **27.** 5 **29.** $-\frac{23}{2}$ or $-11\frac{1}{2}$ **31.** 7.56 **33.** $\frac{1}{4}$ **35.** $3(-2) + 9(-1) + 5(0) + 1(1)$ **37.** 1 above par **39.** 0.125 **40.** $-\frac{19}{12}$ or $-1\frac{7}{12}$ **41.** -1 **42.** $\frac{72}{125}$ **43.** 45 ounces **44.** 0.684 **45.** 0.54

How Am I Doing? Sections 1.1–1.5

1. -9 (obj. 1.1.4) **2.** $-\frac{41}{24}$ or $-1\frac{17}{24}$ (obj. 1.1.3) **3.** 1.24 (obj. 1.1.3) **4.** -7.1 (obj. 1.1.4) **5.** 11 (obj. 1.2.1) **6.** $-\frac{17}{15}$ or $-1\frac{2}{15}$ (obj. 1.2.1) **7.** 12.3 (obj. 1.2.1) **8.** 10 (obj. 1.2.1) **9.** -96 (obj. 1.3.1) **10.** $\frac{10}{11}$ (obj. 1.3.1) **11.** -0.9 (obj. 1.3.3) **12.** $-\frac{10}{17}$ (obj. 1.3.3) **13.** 0.343 (obj. 1.4.2) **14.** 256 (obj. 1.4.2) **15.** -256 (obj. 1.4.2) **16.** $\frac{8}{27}$ (obj. 1.4.2) **17.** 141 (obj. 1.4.2) **18.** 7 (obj. 1.5.1) **19.** 10 (obj. 1.5.1) **20.** 11 (obj. 1.5.1) **21.** -3.3 (obj. 1.5.1) **22.** $-\frac{9}{20}$ (obj. 1.5.1)

1.6 Exercises

1. variable **3.** Here we are multiplying 4 by x by x. Since we know from the definition of exponents that x multiplied by x is x^2, this gives us an answer of $4x^2$.
5. Yes, $a(b - c)$ can be written as $a[b + (-c)]$

$3(10 - 2) = (3 \times 10) - (3 \times 2)$
$3 \times 8 = 30 - 6$
$24 = 24$

7. $3x - 6y$ **9.** $-8a + 6b$ **11.** $9x + 3y$ **13.** $-10a - 15b$ **15.** $-x + 3y$ **17.** $-81x + 45y - 72$ **19.** $-10x + 2y - 12$
21. $10x^2 - 20x + 15$ **23.** $\frac{x^2}{5} + 2xy - \frac{4x}{5}$ **25.** $5x^2 + 10xy + 5xz$ **27.** $-4x + 6$ **29.** $18x^2 + 3xy - 3x$
31. $-3x^2y - 2xy^2 + xy$ **33.** $6x^2y + 9xy^2 - 6xy$ **35.** $9.43x^2 - 5.29x + 0.92$ **37.** $0.36x^3 + 0.09x^2 - 0.15x$
39. $0.3x^2 + 0.4xy - 2.5x$ **41.** $800(5x + 14y) = 4000x + 11{,}200y$ square feet **43.** $8xy - 20y$ dollars
45. $4x(3000 - 2y) = 12{,}000 - 8xy$ square feet **46.** -16 **47.** 64 **48.** 14 **49.** 4 **50.** 10 **51.** 56% **52.** 14 days

1.7 Exercises

1. A term is a number, a variable, or a product of numbers and variables.
3. The two terms $5x$ and $-8x$ are like terms because they both have the variable x with the exponent of one.
5. The only like terms are $7xy$ and $-14xy$ because the other two have different exponents even though they have the same variables.
7. $-25b^2$ **9.** $18x^4 + 7x^2$ **11.** $-5x - 5y$ **13.** $7.1x - 3.5y$ **15.** $-2x - 8.7y$ **17.** $5p + q - 18$ **19.** $5bc - 6ac$
21. $x^2 - 10x + 3$ **23.** $-10y^2 - 16y + 12$ **25.** $-\frac{1}{15}x - \frac{2}{21}y$ **27.** $\frac{11}{20}a^2 - \frac{5}{6}b$ **29.** $-8ab - 3a - 6b$ **31.** $28a - 20b$
33. $-27ab - 11b^2$ **35.** $-8x^2 - 39y$ **37.** $32x + 23$ **39.** $7a + 9b$ **41.** $7a + 7b + 3$ centimeters **43.** $36x - 20$ inches
45. $-\frac{2}{15}$ **46.** $-\frac{5}{6}$ **47.** $\frac{23}{50}$ **48.** $-\frac{15}{98}$ **49.** 0.2 liter

1.8 Exercises

1. -5 **3.** -11 **5.** $\frac{25}{2}$ or $12\frac{1}{2}$ **7.** -26 **9.** -1.3 **11.** $\frac{25}{4}$ or $6\frac{1}{4}$ **13.** 10 **15.** 3 **17.** -24 **19.** -20 **21.** 9 **23.** 39
25. -2 **27.** 15 **29.** 42 **31.** -9 **33.** 29 **35.** 49 **37.** 32 **39.** $-\frac{1}{2}$ **41.** 352 square feet **43.** 1.24 square centimeters
45. 32 square inches **47.** 56,000 square feet **49.** 50.24 square centimeters **51.** -78.5°C **53.** \$2340.00 **55.** -58°F to 140°F
57. 1.4 miles; air is thin, oxygen is lacking **59.** 16 **60.** $-x^2 + 2x - 4y$ **61.** 6.2 minutes/song
62. 53.5 = 54 papers each approximately

1.9 Exercises

1. $-(3x + 2y)$ **3.** distributive **5.** $3x + 6y$ **7.** $5a + 3b$ **9.** $x - 7y$ **11.** $8x^3 - 4x^2 + 12x$ **13.** $-2x + 26y$
15. $4x - 6y - 3$ **17.** $15a - 60ab$ **19.** $12a^3 - 19a^2 - 22a$ **21.** $3a^2 + 16b + 12b^2$ **23.** $-7a + 8b$ **25.** $9b^2 + 36b - 12$
27. $12a^2 - 8b$ **29.** 219 unsuccessful; 8541 successful **31.** 97.52°F **32.** 453,416 square feet **33.** 300,000 sq feet; \$16,500.00
34. 11.375 sq ft \$1387.75 **35.** Great Danes weigh 264.4 to 330.75 kg on average. **36.** Miniature Pinschers weigh on average 19.845 to 30.87 kg.

Putting Your Skills to Work

1. about 21,190,964 **2.** about 9,518,000 **3.** 846,622,338 people **4.** 76,598,250 people **5.** 92,190,000 **6.** 105,690,000

Chapter 1 Review Problems

1. -8 **2.** -4.2 **3.** -9 **4.** 1.9 **5.** $-\frac{1}{3}$ **6.** $-\frac{7}{22}$ **7.** $\frac{1}{6}$ **8.** $\frac{22}{15}$ or $1\frac{7}{15}$ **9.** 8 **10.** 13 **11.** -33 **12.** 9.2
13. $-\frac{13}{8}$ or $-1\frac{5}{8}$ **14.** $\frac{1}{2}$ **15.** -22.7 **16.** -88 **17.** -3 **18.** 18 **19.** 32 **20.** $-\frac{2}{3}$ **21.** $-\frac{25}{7}$ or $-3\frac{4}{7}$ **22.** -72
23. 30 **24.** -30 **25.** -4 **26.** 16 **27.** -29 **28.** 1 **29.** $-\frac{1}{2}$ **30.** $-\frac{4}{7}$ **31.** -30 **32.** -5 **33.** -9.1 **34.** 0.9
35. 10.1 **36.** -1.2 **37.** 1.9 **38.** -1.3 **39.** 24 yards **40.** -22°F **41.** 7363 feet **42.** $2\frac{1}{4}$ point loss **43.** -243
44. -128 **45.** 625 **46.** $\frac{8}{27}$ **47.** -81 **48.** 0.36 **49.** $\frac{25}{36}$ **50.** $\frac{27}{64}$ **51.** -44 **52.** 30 **53.** 1 **54.** $15x - 35y$
55. $6x^2 - 14xy + 8x$ **56.** $-7x^2 + 3x - 11$ **57.** $-6xy^2 - 3xy + 3y^2$ **58.** $-5a^2b + 3bc$ **59.** $-3x - 4y$ **60.** $-5x^2 - 35x - 9$
61. $10x^2 - 8x - \frac{1}{2}$ **62.** -55 **63.** 1 **64.** -4 **65.** -15 **66.** 10 **67.** -16 **68.** $\frac{32}{5}$ **69.** \$810 **70.** 86°F
71. \$2119.50 **72.** \$8580.00 **73.** 100,000 sq ft \$200,000 **74.** 10.45 sq feet \$689.70 **75.** $-2x + 42$ **76.** $-17x - 18$ **77.** $-2 + 10x$

78. $-12x^2 + 63x$ **79.** $5xy^3 - 6x^3y - 13x^2y^2 - 6x^2y$ **80.** $x - 10y + 35 - 15xy$ **81.** $10x - 22y - 36$
82. $-10a + 25ab - 15b^2 - 10ab^2$ **83.** $-3x - 9xy + 18y^2$ **84.** $10x + 8xy - 32y$ **85.** -2.3 **86.** 8 **87.** $-\frac{22}{15}$ or $-1\frac{7}{15}$
88. $-\frac{1}{8}$ **89.** -1 **90.** -0.5 **91.** $\frac{3}{2}$ or $1\frac{1}{2}$ **92.** 6 **93.** 240 **94.** -25.42 **95.** \$600 **96.** 0.0081
97. -0.0625 **98.** 10 **99.** $-4.9x + 4.1y$ **100.** $-\frac{1}{9}$ **101.** $-\frac{2}{3}$ **102.** The dog doesn't have a fever. 101.48° is below normal.
103. $3y^2 + 12y - 7x - 28$ **104.** $-12x + 6y + 12xy$

How Am I Doing? Chapter 1 Test

1. -0.3 (obj. 1.1.4) **2.** 2 (obj. 1.2.1) **3.** $-\frac{14}{3}$ or $-4\frac{2}{3}$ (obj. 1.3.1) **4.** -70 (obj. 1.3.1) **5.** 4 (obj. 1.3.3) **6.** -3 (obj. 1.3.3)
7. -64 (obj. 1.4.2) **8.** 2.56 (obj. 1.4.2) **9.** $\frac{16}{81}$ (obj. 1.4.2) **10.** 6.8 (obj. 1.5.1) **11.** -25 (obj. 1.5.1)
12. $-5x^2 - 10xy + 35x$ (obj. 1.6.1) **13.** $6a^2b^2 + 4ab^3 - 14a^2b^3$ (obj. 1.6.1) **14.** $2a^2b + \frac{15}{2}ab$ (obj. 1.7.2)
15. $-1.8x^2y - 4.7xy^2$ (obj. 1.7.2) **16.** $5a + 30$ (obj. 1.7.2) **17.** $14x - 16y$ (obj. 1.7.2) **18.** 122 (obj. 1.8.1) **19.** 37 (obj. 1.8.1)
20. $\frac{13}{6}$ or $2\frac{1}{6}$ (obj. 1.8.1) **21.** 96.6 kilometers/hr (obj. 1.8.2) **22.** 22,800 sq ft (obj. 1.8.2) **23.** \$23.12 (obj. 1.8.2) **24.** 3 cans (obj. 1.8.2)
25. $3x - 6xy - 21y^2$ (obj. 1.9.1) **26.** $-3a - 9ab + 3b^2 - 3ab^2$ (obj. 1.9.1)

Chapter 2

2.1 Exercises

1. equals, equal **3.** solution **5.** answers vary **7.** $x = 4$ **9.** $x = 12$ **11.** $x = 17$ **13.** $x = -5$ **15.** $x = -13$ **17.** $x = 62$
19. $x = 15$ **21.** $x = 21$ **23.** $x = 0$ **25.** $x = -7$ **27.** $x = 21$ **29.** no, $x = 9$ **31.** no, $x = -13$ **33.** yes **35.** yes
37. $x = -1.8$ **39.** $x = 2.5$ **41.** $x = 1$ **43.** $x = -\frac{1}{4}$ **45.** $x = -7$ **47.** $x = \frac{17}{6}$ or $2\frac{5}{6}$ **49.** $x = \frac{13}{12}$ or $1\frac{1}{12}$ **51.** $x = 7.2$
53. $x = 1.4906$ **55.** $-2x - 4y$ **56.** $-2y^2 - 4y + 4$ **57.** yes, this was $1.9\% < 3\%$ **58.** \$14.92 **59.** 117 feet

2.2 Exercises

1. 6 **3.** 7 **5.** $x = 36$ **7.** $x = -27$ **9.** $x = 80$ **11.** $x = -15$ **13.** $x = 4$ **15.** $x = 8$ **17.** $x = -\frac{8}{3}$ or $-2\frac{2}{3}$
19. $x = 50$ **21.** $x = 15$ **23.** $x = -7$ **25.** $x = 0.2$ or $\frac{1}{5}$ **27.** $x = 4$ **29.** no, $x = -7$ **31.** yes **33.** $y = -0.03$
35. $t = \frac{8}{3}$ or $2\frac{2}{3}$ **37.** $y = -0.7$ **39.** $x = 3$ **41.** $x = -4$ **43.** $x = \frac{7}{9}$ **45.** $x = 1$ **47.** $x = 3$ **49.** $x = 27$
51. $x = -5.26$ **53.** To solve an equation, we are performing steps to get an equivalent equation that has the same solution. Now $a = b$ and $a(0) = b(0)$ are not equivalent equations because they do not have the same solution. So we must have the requirement that when we multiply both sides of the equation by c, it is absolutely essential that c is nonzero.
55. $48 - 6 = 42$ **56.** $-27 - 10 = -37$ **57.** $5 + 16 = 21$ **58.** $93\frac{1}{3}\%$ **59.** \$632 **60.** 104 calves **61.** 27 earthquakes

2.3 Exercises

1. $x = 2$ **3.** $x = 6$ **5.** $x = -4$ **7.** $x = 13$ **9.** $x = 3.1$ **11.** $x = 40$ **13.** $x = -27$ **15.** $x = 8$ **17.** $x = 3$ **19.** $x = 7$
21. $x = -9$ **23.** yes **25.** no, $x = -11$ **27.** $x = -1$ **29.** $x = 7$ **31.** $y = 1$ **33.** $x = 16$ **35.** $y = 3$ **37.** $x = 4$
39. $x = -\frac{1}{3}$ **41.** $x = 2.5$ or $2\frac{1}{2}$ **43.** $x = 6.5$ or $6\frac{1}{2}$ **45.** $x = 8$ **47.** $x = -3.2$ or $-3\frac{1}{5}$ **49.** $y = 2$ **51.** $x = -4$ **53.** $z = 5$
55. $a = -6.5$ **57.** $x = -\frac{2}{3}$ **59.** $x = -0.25$ or $-\frac{1}{4}$ **61.** $x = 8$ **63.** $x = -4.5$ **65.** $x = \frac{7}{6}$ or $1\frac{1}{6}$ **67.** $x = -4.23$
69. $14x^2 - 14xy$ **70.** $-10x - 60$ **71.** $\$844\frac{1}{4}$ or \$844.25 **72.** (a) \$91.00 (b) \$94.50

2.4 Exercises

1. $x = -1$ **3.** $x = 1$ **5.** $x = 1$ **7.** $x = 24$ **9.** $y = 20$ **11.** $x = 3$ **13.** $x = \frac{7}{3}$ or $2\frac{1}{3}$ **15.** $x = -3.5$ **17.** yes **19.** no
21. $x = 1$ **23.** $x = 8$ **25.** $x = 2$ **27.** $x = -3$ **29.** $y = 4$ **31.** $x = -22$ **33.** $x = 2$ **35.** $x = -12$ **37.** $x = -\frac{5}{3}$ or $-1\frac{2}{3}$
39. $x = 0.4$ **41.** no solution **43.** infinite number of solutions **45.** $x = 0$ **47.** no solution **49.** $\frac{27}{14}$ or $1\frac{13}{14}$ **50.** $\frac{19}{20}$
51. $-\frac{52}{3}$ or $-17\frac{1}{3}$ **52.** $\frac{22}{5}$ or $4\frac{2}{5}$ **53.** 264 pairs **54.** 3173 seats **55.** \$226.08 **56.** \$108

How Am I Doing? Sections 2.1–2.4

1. $x = -9$ (obj. 2.1.1) **2.** $x = -10.9$ (obj. 2.1.1) **3.** $x = 9$ (obj. 2.2.2) **4.** $x = -8$ (obj. 2.2.2) **5.** $x = \frac{2}{3}$ (obj. 2.3.1) **6.** $x = \frac{7}{26}$ (obj. 2.3.2) **7.** $x = \frac{3}{5}$ (obj. 2.3.3) **8.** $x = 3.75$ (obj. 2.3.3) **9.** $x = -1.6$ or $-1\frac{3}{5}$ (obj. 2.3.3) **10.** $x = \frac{8}{9}$ (obj. 2.4.1) **11.** $x = -3$ (obj. 2.4.1) **12.** $x = \frac{9}{11}$ (obj. 2.4.1) **13.** $x = 5$ (obj. 2.4.1) **14.** $x = -\frac{1}{3}$ (obj. 2.4.1)

2.5 Exercises

1. Multiply each term by 5. Then add -160 to each side. Then divide each side by 9. We would obtain $\frac{5F - 160}{9} = C$.

3. (a) 10 meters **(b)** 16 meters **5. (a)** $y = -\frac{4}{3}x + 6$ or $y = \frac{18 - 4x}{3}$ **(b)** $y = 10$ **7.** $b = \frac{2A}{h}$ **9.** $P = \frac{I}{rt}$ **11.** $m = \frac{y - b}{x}$ **13.** $y = \frac{2}{3}x - 2$ **15.** $x = -\frac{3}{2}y + 6$ **17.** $y = \frac{c - ax}{b}$ **19.** $r^2 = \frac{A}{\pi}$ **21.** $g = \frac{2s}{t^2}$ **23.** $t = \frac{A - P}{pr}$ **25.** $h = \frac{S - 2\pi r^2}{2\pi r}$ **27.** $h = \frac{V}{\pi r^2}$ **29.** $L = \frac{V}{WH}$ **31.** $r^2 = \frac{3V}{\pi h}$ **33.** $w = \frac{P - 2L}{2}$ **35.** $a^2 = c^2 - b^2$ **37.** $C = \frac{5F - 160}{9}$ **39.** $R = \frac{E^2}{P}$ **41.** $S = \frac{360A}{\pi r^2}$ **43.** 0.8 mile **45.** 30 feet **47. (a)** $x = \frac{V - 7050}{1100}$ **(b)** 2002 **49.** A doubles **51.** A increases 4 times **53.** 31.2 **54.** 0.096 **55.** 1250 feet of fencing **56.** 2.5% **57.** 39,000 square feet **58.** $10\frac{7}{12}$ hours

2.6 Exercises

1. Yes, both statements imply 5 is to the right of -6 on the number line. **3.** $>$ **5.** $<$ **7.** $>$ **9.** $<$ **11.** $<$ **13.** $<$ **15.** 0.0247 **17.** 

19. 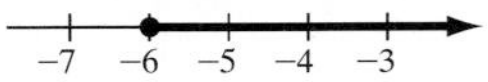

21. 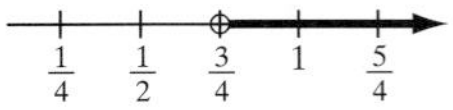

23. 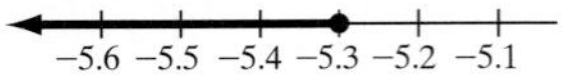

25. 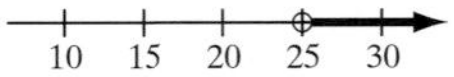

27. $x \geq -\frac{2}{3}$ **29.** $x < -20$ **31.** $x > 2.8$ **33.** $W > 175$ **35.** $h \geq 37$ **37.** $h \geq 48$ **39.** 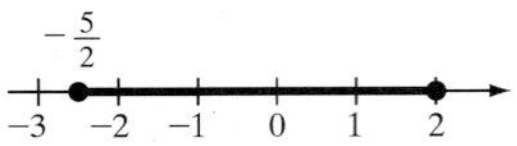

41. 6.08 **42.** 15% **43.** 2% **44.** 37.5% **45.** \$15 **46.** 495 feet

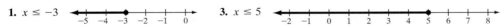

2.7 Exercises

1. $x \leq -3$ 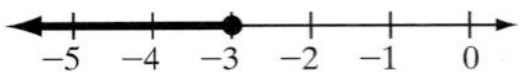

3. $x \leq 5$ 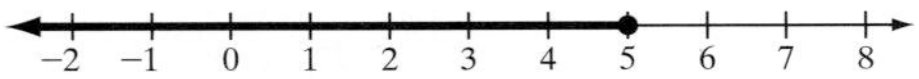

5. $x > -9$ 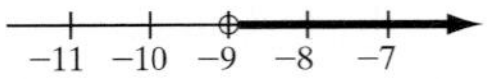

7. $x \geq 8$ 

9. $x < -12$ 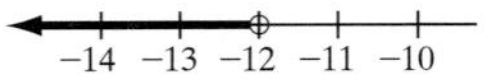

11. $x < \frac{7}{2}$ 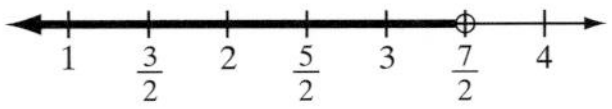

13. $x \geq -2$ 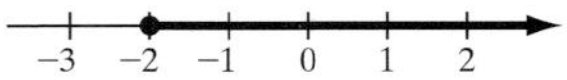

15. $x < \frac{3}{2}$ 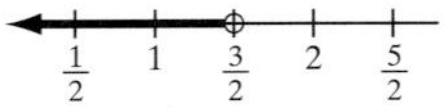

17. $x > -6$ 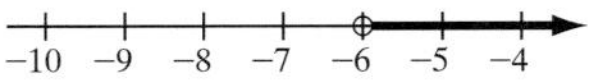

19. $x > \frac{1}{3}$ 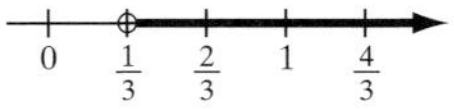

21. $3 > 1$ Adding any number to both sides of an inequality doesn't reverse the direction. **23.** $x > 3$ **25.** $x \geq 4$ **27.** $x < -1$ **29.** $x \leq 14$ **31.** $x < -3$ **33.** $x > -\frac{4}{11}$ **35.** 76 or greater **37.** 8 days or more **39.** 260 feet **40.** width = 6.5 inches height = 3.6 inches **41.** 63.6 sq inches **42.** 15,600 sq feet

Putting Your Skills to Work

1. 8.4 gallons per hour **2.** 252 gallons **3.** 32.3 gallons per hour **4.** 55 miles per hour **5.** $x = \frac{y + 0.1}{0.5}$ or $2y + 0.2 = x$ **6.** 35 mph

Chapter 2 Review Problems

1. -7 **2.** -3 **3.** 2 **4.** -3 **5.** 2.75 or $2\frac{3}{4}$ **6.** -13 **7.** 40.4 **8.** -7 **9.** -2 **10.** -27 **11.** 20 **12.** -9 **13.** -3 **14.** -1 **15.** 4 **16.** 3 **17.** 3 **18.** -7 **19.** 3 **20.** $-\frac{7}{2}$ or $-3\frac{1}{2}$ or -3.5 **21.** -3 **22.** 2.1 **23.** 5 **24.** 1 **25.** 20 **26.** $\frac{2}{3}$ **27.** 5 **28.** $\frac{35}{11}$ or $3\frac{2}{11}$ **29.** 4 **30.** -17 **31.** $\frac{2}{5}$ or 0.4 **32.** 32 **33.** $\frac{26}{7}$ or $3\frac{5}{7}$ **34.** -1 **35.** $\frac{1}{5}$ **36.** $\frac{3}{4}$ **37.** -17 **38.** -2.5 **39.** 23 **40.** -32 **41.** $-3\frac{2}{5}$ or $-\frac{17}{5}$ or -3.4 **42.** 9 **43.** $-\frac{16}{13}$ or $-1\frac{3}{13}$ **44.** 9.75 or $9\frac{3}{4}$ **45.** $y = 3x - 10$

46. $y = \frac{-5x - 7}{2}$ **47.** $r = \frac{A - P}{Pt}$ **48.** $h = \frac{A - 4\pi r^2}{2\pi r}$ **49.** $P = \frac{3H - a - 3}{2}$ **50.** $y = \frac{c - ax}{b}$ **51. (a)** $T = \frac{1000c}{WR}$ **(b)** $T = 6000$ **52. (a)** $y = \frac{5}{3}x - 4$ **(b)** $y = 11$ **53. (a)** $h = \frac{V}{lw}$ **(b)** $h = 6$ **54.** $x \le 2$ 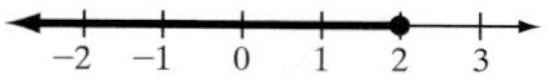 **55.** $x \ge 1$  **56.** $x < -4$ **57.** $x > -3$ 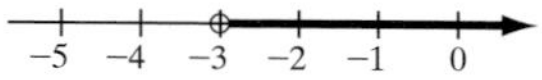 **58.** $x \ge 6$ 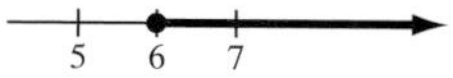 **59.** $x < 5$ **60.** $x < 10$ **61.** $x > -3$ 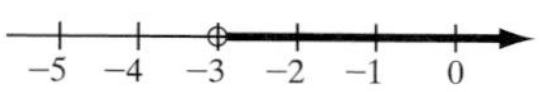 **62.** $x > \frac{17}{2}$ 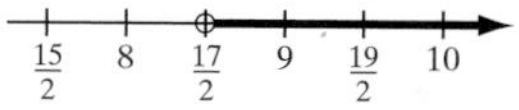 **63.** $x > \frac{7}{5}$ 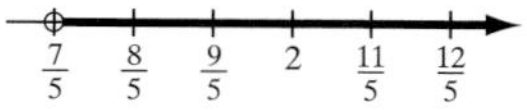 **64.** $h \le 32$ hours **65.** $n \le 17$ **66.** $-\frac{7}{3}$ or $-2\frac{1}{3}$ **67.** $-\frac{2}{7}$ **68.** 0 **69.** 4 **70.** 4 **71.** -5 **72.** $d = \frac{6c - H}{5}$ **73.** $b = \frac{4H - 3c}{2}$ **74.** $x < 2$ **75.** $x \le -8$ **76.** $x \ge \frac{19}{7}$ **77.** $x \ge -15$

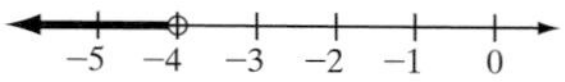

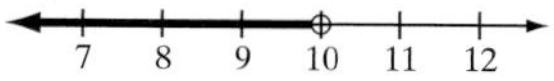

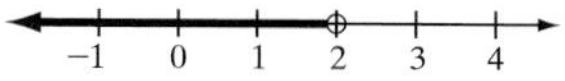

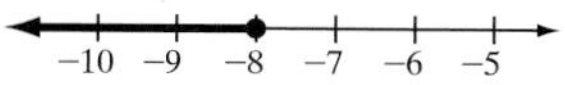

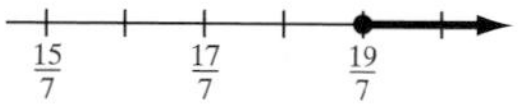

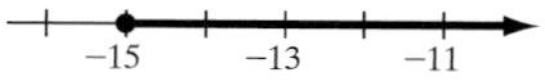

How Am I Doing? Chapter 2 Test

1. $x = 2$ (obj. 2.3.1) **2.** $x = \frac{1}{3}$ (obj. 2.3.2) **3.** $y = -\frac{7}{2}$ or $-3\frac{1}{2}$ or -3.5 (obj. 2.3.3) **4.** $y = 8.4$ or $8\frac{2}{5}$ or $\frac{42}{5}$ (obj. 2.4.1) **5.** $x = 1$ (obj. 2.3.3) **6.** $x = -1.2$ (obj. 2.3.3) **7.** $y = 7$ (obj. 2.4.1) **8.** $y = \frac{7}{3}$ or $2\frac{1}{3}$ (obj. 2.3.3) **9.** $x = 13$ (obj. 2.3.3) **10.** $x = 20$ (obj. 2.3.3) **11.** $x = 10$ (obj. 2.3.3) **12.** $x = -4$ (obj. 2.3.3) **13.** $x = 12$ (obj. 2.3.3) **14.** $x = -\frac{1}{5}$ or -0.2 (obj. 2.4.1) **15.** $x = 3$ (obj. 2.4.1) **16.** $x = 2$ (obj. 2.4.1) **17.** $x = -2$ (obj. 2.4.1) **18.** $w = \frac{A - 2P}{3}$ (obj. 2.5.1) **19.** $w = \frac{6 - 3x}{4}$ (obj. 2.5.1) **20.** $a = \frac{2A - hb}{h}$ (obj. 2.5.1) **21.** $y = \frac{10ax - 5}{8ax}$ (obj. 2.5.1) **22.** $B = \frac{3V}{h}$ (obj. 2.5.1) **23.** $B = 30$ sq. in. (obj. 2.5.1) **24.** $x \le -3$ (obj. 2.7.1) 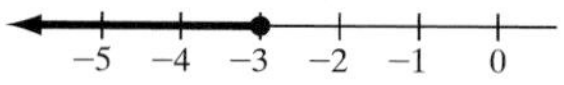 **25.** $x > -\frac{5}{4}$ (obj. 2.7.1)  **26.** $x < 2$ (obj. 2.7.1) **27.** $x \ge \frac{1}{2}$ (obj. 2.7.1)

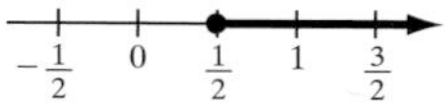

Cumulative Test for Chapters 0–2

1. $\frac{4}{21}$ **2.** $\frac{79}{20}$ or $3\frac{19}{20}$ **3.** $\frac{32}{15}$ or $2\frac{2}{15}$ **4.** 0.6888 **5.** 0.12 **6.** 35.69 **7.** 30 **8.** $12ab - 28ab^2$ **9.** $25x^2$ **10.** $6x - 40 + 48y - 24xy$ **11.** $x = \frac{40}{11}$ or $3\frac{7}{11}$ **12.** $x = 4$ **13.** $y = 1$ **14.** $a = \frac{6 + 8b}{3}$ **15.** $b = \frac{3H - 8a}{2}$ **16.** $t = \frac{I}{Pr}$ **17.** $a = \frac{2A}{h} - b$ **18.** $x < 5$ **19.** $x \le 3$ **20.** $x > -15$ 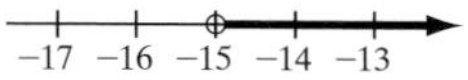 **21.** $x \le -1$ 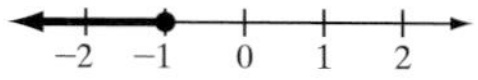 **22.** $x \le 1$  **23.** 92

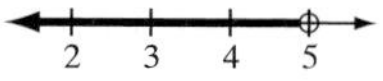

Chapter 3

3.1 Exercises

1. $x + 5$ **3.** $x - 6$ **5.** $\frac{1}{8}x$ or $\frac{x}{8}$ **7.** $2x$ **9.** $3 + \frac{1}{2}x$ **11.** $2x + 9$ **13.** $\frac{1}{3}(x + 7)$ **15.** $\frac{1}{3}x - 2x$ **17.** $3x - 7$

19. x = value of a share of AT&T stock
$x + 74.50$ = value of a share of IBM stock

21. $2w + 7$ = length
w = width

23. x = number of boxes sold by Keiko
$x - 43$ = number of boxes sold by Sarah
$x + 53$ = number of boxes sold by Imelda

25. 1st angle = $s - 16$
2nd angle = s
3rd angle = $2s$

27. v = value of exports of Canada
$2v$ = value of exports of Japan

29. 1st angle = $3x$
2nd angle = x
3rd angle = $x - 14$

31. A = area of Minnesota
$\frac{1}{2}A$ = area of Kentucky
$\frac{2}{5}A$ = area of Maine

33. x = points for an arrow in the blue ring.
$3x - 6$ = points awarded for an arrow in the gold ring.

35. x = men aged 16–24
$x + 51$ = men aged 25–34
$x - 60$ = men aged 35–44
$x - 132$ = men aged 45 and above

37. $x = 7$ **38.** $x = -\frac{5}{2}$ or $-2\frac{1}{2}$ **39.** $x = 12$ **40.** $w = 7$

3.2 Exercises

1. 1261 **3.** 2368 **5.** 182 **7.** 43 **9.** 9 **11.** −5 **13.** 12 **15.** 15 used bikes **17.** 34,415 wildfires **19.** 6 CDs **21.** 4 items **23.** 320.2 miles per hour **25.** 550 lb **27.** 5 miles **29.** She traveled 52 mph on the mountain road. It was 12 mph faster on the highway route. **31.** 105 degrees F **33.** 9 miles per gallon **35. (a)** $F - 40 = \frac{x}{4}$ **(b)** 200 chirps **(c)** 77°F **36.** $10x^3 - 30x^2 - 15x$ **37.** $-2a^2b + 6ab - 10a^2$ **38.** $-5x - 6y$ **39.** $-4x^2y - 7xy^2 - 8xy$ **40.** 3000 apples **41.** 60 people

3.3 Exercises

1. The long piece is 32 meters long.
The short piece is 15 meters long.

3. Dave earned $34,300 per year.
Elsie earned $36,900 per year.

5. David worked 30 hours.
Sarah worked 45 hours.
Kate worked 25 hours.

7. 11 students born in Oklahoma.
19 students born in Texas.
2 students born in Arizona.

9. Length is 13 meters.
Width is 8 meters.

11. Length is 41 centimeters.
Width is 7 centimeters.

13. width = 32.5 cm
length = 62.5 cm

15. The cheetah can run 70 mph.
The jackal can run 35 mph.
The elk can run 45 mph.

17. Length A = 20 inches
Length B = 15 inches
Length C = 10 inches
Length D = 13 inches

19. (a) 18 hours (b) 21 hours (c) 19 mph

21. original square was 11 m × 11 m

23. $-8x^3 + 12x^2 - 32x$ **24.** $5a^2b + 30ab - 10a^2$ **25.** $-19x + 2y - 2$ **26.** $9x^2y - 6xy^2 + 7xy$ **27.** 82% **28.** 20%

How Am I Doing? Sections 3.1–3.3

1. $3x - 40$ (obj. 3.1.2) **2.** $\frac{1}{2}x + 12$ (obj. 3.1.2) **3.** $\frac{5x}{12}$ or $\frac{5}{12}x$ (obj. 3.1.2) **4.** $\frac{1}{4}(x + 10)$ or $\frac{x + 10}{4}$ (obj. 3.1.2)
5. −26 (obj. 3.2.1) **6.** 104 (obj. 3.2.1) **7.** 40 months (obj. 3.2.2) **8.** 5 hours (obj. 3.2.2)

9. The fourth person earns $60,000 per year.
The fifth person earns $62,500 per year. (obj. 3.2.2)

10. The long piece is 62 feet.
The short piece is 22 feet. (obj. 3.3.1)

11. Sunday = 50 pages
Monday = 75 pages
Tuesday = 135 pages (obj. 3.3.1)

12. 1st field = 360 hours
2nd field = 120 hours
3rd field = 30 hours (obj. 3.3.1)

3.4 Exercises

1. 11 bags **3.** 7 hours **5.** 12 weeks **7.** $360 **9.** $22,000 **11.** $6000 **13.** $3000 @ 7%, $2000 @ 5% **15.** Conservative fund = $250,000, growth fund = $150,000

17. $12,000 **19.** 13 quarters, 9 nickels **21.** 18 nickels, 6 dimes, 9 quarters **23.** 30 regular stamps, 22 breast cancer stamps **25.** $10 bills = 8, $20 bills = 16, $100 bills = 11 **27.** $925,000 worth of furniture

29. more than 225 miles **31.** 12 **32.** −17 **33.** −28 **34.** −25 **35.** $95.20 **36.** $19,040

3.5 Exercises

1. distance around **3.** surface **5.** 180° **7.** 156 in.^2 **9.** 98 in.^2 **11.** 10 feet **13.** 9 inches **15.** 153.86 sq ft **17.** 9520.48 miles **19.** 24 inches **21.** 134,400 sq meters **23.** 5 centimeters **25.** 200.96 cm **27.** 74° **29.** equal angles = 80°, 3rd angle = 20°

31. 71° each **33.** 1st angle = 46°, 2nd angle = 23°, 3rd angle = 111° **35.** 52° **37.** 6 feet **39.** 2512 in.^3 **41.** Yes **43.** $V = 452.16 \text{ cm}^3$, $S = 376.8 \text{ cm}^2$ **45.** 163.28 ft^2

47. (a) 22.77 sq. yd (b) $56.93 **49.** (a) 73.96 inches (b) 181.93 cubic inches **51.** 9.3 feet wide and 34.2 feet long **53.** no; the perimeter may be 19 feet or it may be 15.5 feet **55.** 6.28 ft **56.** $3x^2 + 8x - 24$ **57.** $-11x - 17$ **58.** $-4x - 9$ **59.** $22x - 84$

3.6 Exercises

1. $x > 67{,}000$ **3.** $x \leq 120$ **5.** $h \leq 1500$ **7.** $x \geq 93$ **9.** It must be less than or equal to 140 cm. **11.** 22 or more deliveries **13.** Depth can be no more than 7.5 feet. **15.** $x \leq 384.6$ miles **17.** $F < 230°$ **19.** The budget will exceed $307.1 billion after 2005.

21. It will be 8 hours or less **23.** 455 or more discs would need to be sold. **25.** $x < -4$ **26.** $x \leq 3$ **27.** $x \geq 4\frac{2}{3}$ **28.** $x > -4$ **29.** (a) 2920 gallons (b) $24.82

Putting Your Skills to Work

1. $a = \frac{7463}{4} = 1865.75$
$b = 15{,}303$
$y = 1866x + 15{,}303$

2. The herd is approximately 32,097 for 1995.
The herd is approximately 11,571 for 1984.

3. The equation is fairly accurate.
The equation predicts 47,025 and the measured value is 3650 lower.

4. $a = 1651$ approximately
$y = 1651x + 15{,}303$

Chapter 3 Review Problems

1. $x + 19$ **2.** $\frac{2}{3}x$ **3.** $\frac{1}{2}x$ or $\frac{x}{2}$ **4.** $x - 18$ **5.** $3(x + 4)$ **6.** $2x - 3$ **7.** r = the number of retired people; $4r$ = the number of working people; $0.5r$ = the number of unemployed people **8.** $3w + 5$ = the length; w = the width
9. b = the number of degrees in angle B; $2b$ = the number of degrees in angle A; $b - 17$ = the number of degrees in angle C
10. a = the number of students in algebra; $a + 29$ = the number of students in biology; $0.5a$ = the number of students in geology
11. $x = 5$ **12.** $x = 7$ **13.** \$40 **14.** 16 years old **15.** 6.6 hours; 6 hours **16.** 90 **17.** 23 feet
18. 1st angle = 32°; 2nd angle = 96°; 3rd angle = 52° **19.** 31.25 yd; 18.75 yd **20.** Jon = \$30,000; Lauren = \$18,000
21. 310 kilowatt-hours **22.** 280 miles **23.** \$3000 **24.** \$200 **25.** \$7000 at 12%; \$2000 at 8%
26. \$2000 at 4.5%; \$3000 at 6% **27.** 18 nickels; 6 dimes; 9 quarters **28.** 7 nickels; 8 dimes; 10 quarters
29. S.A. = 3215.36 sq. in. **30.** P = 24 feet **31.** 71° **32.** 42 sq. mi. **33.** 1920 ft^3 **34.** 113.04 cm^3 **35.** 254.34 cm^2
36. 12 in. **37.** \$3440 **38.** \$23,864 **39.** 200 miles or less **40.** more than \$300,000 **41.** CP distance = 630 miles; UP distance = 960 miles
42. less than \$16.15 **43.** $24\frac{4}{5}$ min **44.** 4 ounces **45.** more than 3 years **46.** more than 60 months
47. The height is 4 feet. The width is 10 feet. **48.** It will take 10 years. **49.** They made 27 field goals and 9 free throws.
50. The width is 16 feet and the length is 22 feet. **51.** Carl = 12 hours; Ryan = 16 hours **52.** \$13,600 @ 9.75%; \$15,600 @ 8.5%
53. first angle measures 60°; second angle measures 40°; third angle measures 80°; **54.** \$1224 **55.** 94 **56.** No, she traveled 9000 miles for business. Her correct deduction was \$2970. **57.** It can travel 640 miles in one hour. It would take approximately 169 minutes.
58. 12 seconds **59.** 5 Explorers and 10 Caravans **60.** smallest angle = 32°; largest angle = 96°; third angle = 52° **61.** 183.26 kg

How Am I Doing? Chapter 3 Test

1. 35 (obj. 3.2.1) **2.** 36 (obj. 3.2.1) **3.** −4 (obj. 3.2.1) **4.** first side = 20 m; second side = 30 m; third side = 16 m (obj. 3.2.2)
5. width = 20 m; length = 47 m (obj. 3.2.2) **6.** 1st pollutant = 8 ppm; 2nd pollutant = 4 ppm; 3rd pollutant = 3 ppm (obj. 3.4.2)
7. 15 months (obj. 3.4.1) **8.** \$21,000 (obj. 3.4.2) **9.** \$1400 at 14%; \$2600 at 11% (obj. 3.4.3)
10. 16 nickels; 7 dimes; 8 quarters (obj. 3.4.4) **11.** 213.52 in. (obj. 3.5.1) **12.** 192 square inches (obj. 3.5.1) **13.** 4187 $in.^3$ (obj. 3.5.2)
14. 96 cm^2 (obj. 3.5.1) **15.** \$450 (obj. 3.5.3) **16.** at least an 82 (obj. 3.6.2) **17.** more than \$110,000 (obj. 3.6.2)
18. 600 hours (obj. 3.6.2)

Cumulative Test for Chapters 0–3

1. 3.69 **2.** $\frac{31}{24}$ or $1\frac{7}{24}$ **3.** $-23y + 18$ **4.** 21 **5.** $\frac{2H - 3a}{5} = b$ **6.** $x \geq -3$;

7. −7
8. Psychology students = 50; World Hist. students = 84 **9.** width = 7 cm; length = 32 cm **10.** \$135,000
11. \$3000 at 15%; \$4000 at 7% **12.** 7 nickels; 12 dimes; 4 quarters **13.** A = 162.5 m^2; \$731.25
14. V = 113.04 cubic inches; 169.56 pounds **15.** 25 days

Chapter 4

4.1 Exercises

1. When multiplying exponential expressions with the same base, keep the base the same and add the exponents.
3. $\frac{2^2}{2^3} = \frac{2 \cdot 2}{2 \cdot 2 \cdot 2} = \frac{1}{2}$ $= \frac{1}{2^{3-2}}$ **5.** 6; x; y: 11 and 1 **7.** 2^2a^3b **9.** $-3a^2b^2c^3$ **11.** 7^{10} **13.** 5^{26} **15.** x^{12} **17.** w^{32} **19.** $-20x^6$
21. $50x^3$ **23.** $24x^5y^4$ **25.** $\frac{2}{15}x^3y^5$ **27.** $-2.75x^3yz$ **29.** 0 **31.** $80x^3y^7$ **33.** $-24x^4y^7$ **35.** 0 **37.** $-24a^4b^3x^2y^5$
39. $-30x^3y^4z^6$ **41.** y^7 **43.** $\frac{1}{y^3}$ **45.** $\frac{1}{11^{12}}$ **47.** 3^4 **49.** $\frac{a^8}{4}$ **51.** $\frac{x^7}{y^6}$ **53.** $2x^4$ **55.** $-\frac{x^3}{2y^2}$ **57.** $\frac{f^2}{30g^5}$ **59.** $-3x^3$ **61.** $\frac{y^2}{16x^3}$
63. $\frac{3a}{4}$ **65.** $\frac{17a^2b}{9c^3}$ **67.** $-27x^5yz^3$ **69.** x^{12} **71.** x^7y^{14} **73.** r^6s^{12} **75.** $27a^9b^6c^3$ **77.** $9a^8$ **79.** $\frac{x^7}{128m^{28}}$ **81.** $\frac{25x^2}{49y^4}$
83. $81a^8b^{12}$ **85.** $-8x^9z^3$ **87.** $\frac{9}{x}$ **89.** $27a^4b^7$ **91.** $\frac{64}{y^{10}}$ **93.** $\frac{16x^4}{y^{12}}$ **95.** $\frac{a^4b^8}{c^{12}d^{16}}$ **97.** $-3x^3y^4z^7$ **99.** −11 **100.** −46
101. $-\frac{7}{4}$ **102.** 5 **103.** approximately 17.6% **104.** approximately 47.6% of rain forest has been lost
105. 34,500 sq km of rain forest lost

4.2 Exercises

1. $\frac{1}{x^4}$ **3.** $\frac{1}{81}$ **5.** y^8 **7.** $\frac{z^6}{x^4y^5}$ **9.** $\frac{y^6}{x^5}$ **11.** $\frac{x^9}{8}$ **13.** $\frac{3}{x^2}$ **15.** $\frac{1}{16x^4y^2}$ **17.** $\frac{3xz^3}{y^2}$ **19.** $3x$ **21.** $\frac{wy^3}{x^5z^2}$ **23.** $\frac{1}{8}$ **25.** $\frac{z^8}{9y^4}$ **27.** $\frac{1}{x^6y}$ **29.** 1.2378×10^5 **31.** 6.3×10^{-2} **33.** 8.8961×10^{11} **35.** 1.963×10^{-8} **37.** 302,000 **39.** 0.00047 **41.** 983,000 **43.** 2.37×10^{-5} mph **45.** 0.000007 meters **47.** 4.368×10^{19} **49.** 1.0×10^1 **51.** 8.1×10^{-11} **53.** 4.5×10^5 **55.** 2.33×10^4 dollars **57.** 1.90×10^{11} hours **59.** 6.6×10^{-5} miles **61.** $\$1.6 \times 10^8$ **63.** 159.3% **65.** -0.8 **66.** -1 **67.** $-\frac{1}{28}$

68. Candidate 1 shook 2524 hands.
Candidate 2 shook 1016 hands.

69. Mario = \$36,094
Alfonso = \$27,352
Gina = \$48,554

4.3 Exercises

1. A polynomial in x is the sum of a finite number of terms of the form ax^n, where a is any real number and n is a whole number. An example is $3x^2 - 5x - 9$. **3.** The degree of a polynomial in x is the largest exponent of x in any of the terms of the polynomial.

5. degree 4; monomial **7.** degree 5; trinomial **9.** degree 5; binomial **11.** $5x - 28$ **13.** $-2x^2 + 2x - 1$ **15.** $\frac{5}{6}x^2 + \frac{1}{2}x - 9$ **17.** $3.4x^3 + 2.2x^2 - 13.2x - 5.4$ **19.** $5x - 24$ **21.** $\frac{1}{15}x^2 - \frac{1}{14}x + 11$ **23.** $-2x^3 + 5x - 10$ **25.** $-4.7x^4 - 0.7x^2 - 1.6x + 0.4$ **27.** $-8x + 7$ **29.** $-3x^2y + 6xy^2 - 4$ **31.** $x^4 - 3x^3 - 4x^2 - 24$ **33.** 5.4 **35.** 2020 **37.** 727,000 **39.** 434,400 **41.** $3x^2 + 12x$ **43.** $x = \frac{3y - 2}{8}$ **44.** $B = \frac{3A}{2CD}$ **45.** $\frac{2A}{h} - c = b$ **46.** $d = \frac{5xy}{B}$ **47.** approximately 696.8 billion dollars **48.** 300% increase

How Am I Doing? Sections 4.1–4.3

1. $-15x^3y^6$ (obj. 4.1.1) **2.** $-\frac{7y^3}{5x^7}$ (obj. 4.1.2) **3.** $\frac{4x^5}{y^9}$ (obj. 4.1.2) **4.** $81x^{20}y^4$ (obj. 4.1.3) **5.** $\frac{x^6}{16y^8}$ (obj. 4.2.1) **6.** $\frac{y^{15}}{3x^3}$ (obj. 4.2.1) **7.** 5.874×10^4 (obj. 4.2.2) **8.** 9.362×10^{-5} (obj. 4.2.2) **9.** $2.3x^2 - 0.4x - 5.4$ (obj. 4.3.2) **10.** $7x^2 + 17x - 26$ (obj. 4.3.3) **11.** $\frac{1}{6}x^3 + \frac{3}{8}x^2 + 3x$ (obj. 4.3.3) **12.** $\frac{5}{16}x^2 - \frac{3}{10}x - \frac{3}{8}$ (obj. 4.3.2)

4.4 Exercises

1. $-12x^4 + 2x^2$ **3.** $21x^3 - 9x^2$ **5.** $6x^7 - 4x^6 + 10x^4 - 2x^3$ **7.** $x + \frac{3}{2}x^2 + \frac{5}{2}x^3$ **9.** $-15x^4y^2 + 6x^3y^2 - 18x^2y^2$ **11.** $9x^4y + 3x^3y - 24x^2y$ **13.** $3x^4 - 9x^3 + 15x^2 - 6x$ **15.** $-2x^3y^3 + 12x^2y^3 - 16xy$ **17.** $-28x^5y + 12x^4y + 8x^3y - 4x^2y$ **19.** $-6c^2d^5 + 8c^2d^3 - 12c^2d$ **21.** $12x^7 - 6x^5 + 18x^4 + 54x^3$ **23.** $-35x^7 + 56x^6 - 21x^5$ **25.** $x^2 + 13x + 30$ **27.** $x^2 + 8x + 12$ **29.** $x^2 - 6x - 16$ **31.** $x^2 - 9x + 20$ **33.** $-20x^2 - 7x + 6$ **35.** $7x^2 + 14xy - 4x - 8y$ **37.** $15x^2 - 5xy + 6x - 2y$ **39.** $20y^2 - 7y - 3$ **41.** The signs are incorrect. The result is $-3x + 6$. **43.** $20x$ **45.** $20x^2 - 23xy + 6y^2$ **47.** $49x^2 - 28x + 4$ **49.** $16a^2 + 16ab + 4b^2$ **51.** $0.8x^2 + 11.94x - 0.9$ **53.** $\frac{1}{4}x^2 + \frac{1}{24}x - \frac{1}{12}$ **55.** $2ax - 10ab - 3bx + 15b^2$ **57.** $35x^2 + 78xy + 27y^2$ **59.** $20y^2 - 22yz + 6z^2$ **61.** $28x^2 - 30x - 18$ **62.** $x = -10$ **63.** $w = -\frac{25}{7}$ or $-3\frac{4}{7}$ **64.** 7

65. 24 tiger's eye marbles
48 cat's eye marbles

66. 9 twenties
8 tens
23 fives

67. 18.4 hrs **68.** 20.8 hrs **69.** 35.2 hrs **70.** 36.4 hrs

4.5 Exercises

1. binomial **3.** The middle term is missing. The answer should be $16x^2 - 56x + 49$. **5.** $y^2 - 49$ **7.** $x^2 - 81$ **9.** $49x^2 - 16$ **11.** $4x^2 - 49$ **13.** $25x^2 - 9y^2$ **15.** $0.36x^2 - 9$ **17.** $9y^2 + 6y + 1$ **19.** $25x^2 - 40x + 16$ **21.** $49x^2 + 42x + 9$ **23.** $9x^2 - 42x + 49$ **25.** $\frac{4}{9}x^2 + \frac{1}{3}x + \frac{1}{16}$ **27.** $81x^2y^2 + 72xyz + 16z^2$ **29.** $49x^2 - 9y^2$ **31.** $49c^2 - 84cd + 36d^2$ **33.** $81a^2 - 100b^2$ **35.** $25x^2 + 90xy + 81y^2$ **37.** $x^3 + 3x^2 - 13x + 6$ **39.** $4x^4 - 7x^3 + 2x^2 - 3x - 1$ **41.** $a^4 + a^3 - 13a^2 + 17a - 6$ **43.** $3x^3 - 2x^2 - 25x + 24$ **45.** $3x^3 - 13x^2 - 6x + 40$ **47.** $2a^3 + 3a^2 - 50a - 75$ **49.** $24x^3 + 14x^2 - 11x - 6$

51. \$11,000 @ 7%
\$7,000 @ 11%

52. width = 7 m
length = 10 m

53. -28.12°F **54.** 2.0625×10^5 meters

4.6 Exercises

1. $5x^3 - 3x + 4$ **3.** $2y^2 - 3y - 1$ **5.** $9x^4 - 4x^2 - 7$ **7.** $8x^4 - 9x + 6$ **9.** $3x + 5$ **11.** $x - 3 - \frac{32}{x - 5}$ **13.** $3x^2 - 4x + 8 - \frac{10}{x + 1}$ **15.** $2x^2 - 3x - 2 - \frac{5}{2x + 5}$ **17.** $2x^2 + 3x - 1$ **19.** $6y^2 + 3y - 8 + \frac{7}{2y - 3}$

21. $y^2 - 4y - 1 - \frac{9}{y + 3}$ **23.** $y^3 + 2y^2 - 5y - 10 - \frac{25}{y - 2}$ **25.** $2y^2 + \frac{1}{2}y + \frac{7}{8} - \frac{\frac{49}{8}}{4y - 1}$ **27.** 77,000 gallons

28. 1965: $0.75
1970: $0.86
1971: $0.82
29. 200 cats **30.** pages 519 and 520 **31. (a)** 4.2 **(b)** 7.4 **(c)** 76.2% **(d)** 13.0

Putting Your Skills to Work

1. $13,526 **2.** $568,082 **3.** 35.4% **4.** $136,777 **5.** $45,272 **6.** $43,912

Chapter 4 Review Problems

1. $-18a^7$ **2.** 5^{23} **3.** $6x^4y^6$ **4.** $-14x^4y^9$ **5.** $\frac{1}{7^{12}}$ **6.** $\frac{1}{x^5}$ **7.** y^{14} **8.** $\frac{1}{9^{11}}$ **9.** $-\frac{3}{5x^5y^4}$ **10.** $-\frac{2a}{3b^6}$ **11.** x^{24} **12.** b^{30} **13.** $9a^6b^4$ **14.** $81x^{12}y^4$ **15.** $\frac{25a^2b^4}{c^6}$ **16.** $\frac{y^9}{64w^{15}z^6}$ **17.** $\frac{b^5}{a^3}$ **18.** $\frac{m^8}{p^5}$ **19.** $\frac{2y^3}{x^6}$ **20.** $\frac{x^8}{9y^6}$ **21.** $\frac{y^8}{25x^4}$ **22.** $\frac{3y^2}{x^3}$ **23.** $\frac{4w^2}{x^5y^6z^8}$ **24.** $\frac{b^5c^3d^4}{27a^2}$ **25.** 1.563402×10^{11} **26.** 1.79632×10^5 **27.** 7.8×10^{-3} **28.** 6.173×10^{-5} **29.** 120,000 **30.** 6,034,000 **31.** 3,000,000 **32.** 0.25 **33.** 0.0000432 **34.** 0.000000006 **35.** 2.0×10^{13} **36.** 9.36×10^{19} **37.** 9.6×10^{-10} **38.** 7.8×10^{-11} **39.** 3.504×10^8 kilometers **40.** 7.94×10^{14} cycles **41.** 6×10^9 **42.** $11.4x^2 - 7.3x + 5.3$ **43.** $6.7x^2 - 11x + 3$ **44.** $-x^3 + 2x^2 - x + 8$ **45.** $7x^3 - 3x^2 - 6x + 4$ **46.** $\frac{1}{10}x^2y - \frac{13}{21}x + \frac{5}{12}$ **47.** $\frac{1}{4}x^2 - \frac{1}{4}x + \frac{1}{10}$ **48.** $-x^2 - 2x + 10$ **49.** $-6x^2 - 6x - 3$ **50.** $15x^2 + 2x - 1$ **51.** $28x^2 - 29x + 6$ **52.** $20x^2 + 48x + 27$ **53.** $10x^3 - 30x^2 + 15x$ **54.** $-18x^4 + 6x^3 - 3x^2 + 12x$ **55.** $-6x^3y^3 + 9x^3y^2 + 12x^2y^2$ **56.** $5a^2 - 8ab - 21b^2$ **57.** $8x^4 - 10x^2y - 12x^2 + 15y$ **58.** $-15x^6y^2 - 9x^4y + 6x^2y$ **59.** $9x^2 - 12x + 4$ **60.** $25x^2 - 9$ **61.** $49x^2 - 36y^2$ **62.** $25a^2 - 20ab + 4b^2$ **63.** $64x^2 + 144xy + 81y^2$ **64.** $4x^3 + 27x^2 + 5x - 3$ **65.** $2x^3 - 7x^2 - 42x + 72$ **66.** $2y^2 + 3y + 4$ **67.** $6x^3 + 7x^2 - 18x$ **68.** $4x^2y - 6x + 8y$ **69.** $53x^3 - 12x^2 + 19x + 13$ **70.** $3x - 2$ **71.** $3x - 7$ **72.** $3x^2 + 2x + 4 + \frac{9}{2x - 1}$ **73.** $2x^2 - 5x + 13 - \frac{27}{x + 2}$ **74.** $4x + 1$ **75.** $4x - 5 + \frac{11}{2x + 1}$ **76.** $x^2 + 3x + 8$ **77.** $2x^2 + 4x + 5 + \frac{11}{x - 2}$ **78.** 4^{29} **79.** 6^{15} **80.** $125x^8y^{14}$ **81.** $-\frac{2x^5}{y^3}$ **82.** $-64x^{15}y^{18}$ **83.** 7.86×10^{-5} **84.** $-4x^3 - 12x + 17$ **85.** $-12x^5 - 30x^4 + 12x^2$ **86.** $14x^3 + 15x^2 - 23x + 6$ **87.** $2x^2 + 5x + 3 + \frac{4}{3x - 2}$ **88.** $46.07 per person **89.** 1.263×10^9 people **90.** 2.733×10^{-23} gram **91.** 3.3696×10^{31} joules **92.** $3xy + 2x$ **93.** $2x^2 - 4y^2$

How Am I Doing? Chapter 4 Test

1. 3^{34} (obj. 4.1.1) **2.** $\frac{1}{25^{16}}$ (obj. 4.1.7) **3.** 8^{24} (obj. 4.1.3) **4.** $12x^4y^{10}$ (obj. 4.1.1) **5.** $-\frac{7x^3}{5}$ (obj. 4.1.2) **6.** $-125x^3y^{18}$ (obj. 4.1.3) **7.** $\frac{49a^{14}b^4}{9}$ (obj. 4.1.3) **8.** $\frac{3x^4}{4}$ (obj. 4.1.3) **9.** $\frac{1}{64}$ (obj. 4.2.1) **10.** $\frac{6c^5}{a^4b^3}$ (obj. 4.2.1) **11.** $3xy^7$ (obj. 4.2.1) **12.** 5.482×10^{-4} (obj. 4.2.2) **13.** 582,000,000 (obj. 4.2.2) **14.** 2.4×10^{-6} (obj. 4.2.2) **15.** $-2x^2 + 5x$ (obj. 4.3.2) **16.** $-11x^3 - 4x^2 + 7x - 8$ (obj. 4.3.3) **17.** $-21x^5 + 28x^4 - 42x^3 + 14x^2$ (obj. 4.4.1) **18.** $15x^4y^3 - 18x^3y^2 + 6x^2y$ (obj. 4.4.1) **19.** $10a^2 + 7ab - 12b^2$ (obj. 4.4.2) **20.** $6x^3 - 11x^2 - 19x - 6$ (obj. 4.5.3) **21.** $49x^4 + 28x^2y^2 + 4y^4$ (obj. 4.5.2) **22.** $25s^2 - 121t^2$ (obj. 4.5.1) **23.** $12x^4 - 14x^3 + 25x^2 - 29x + 10$ (obj. 4.5.3) **24.** $3x^4 + 4x^3y - 15x^2y^2$ (obj. 4.5.1) **25.** $3x^3 - x + 5$ (obj. 4.6.1) **26.** $2x^2 - 7x + 4$ (obj. 4.6.2) **27.** $2x^2 + 6x + 12$ (obj. 4.6.2) **28.** 3.044×10^9 barrels per year (obj. 4.2.2) **29.** 4.18×10^6 miles (obj. 4.2.2)

Cumulative Test for Chapters 0–4

1. $-\frac{11}{24}$ **2.** -0.74 **3.** $-\frac{6}{7}$ **4.** 110.55 **5.** $2x^2 - 13x$ **6.** 35 **7.** $x = -\frac{9}{2}$ **8.** $x = 15$ **9.** $x > -1$ **10.** $d = \frac{3y - 8x}{11}$ **11.** 12,400 employees **12.** $199.20 **13.** $20x^2 + 9x - 18$ **14.** $9x^2 - 30x + 25$ **15.** $6x^3 - 17x^2 - 26x - 8$ **16.** $-20x^5y^8$ **17.** $-\frac{2x^3}{3y^9}$ **18.** $16x^{12}y^8$ **19.** $\frac{9z^8}{w^2x^3y^4}$ **20.** 1.36×10^{15} **21.** 5.6×10^{-4} **22.** 4.0×10^{-35} **23.** $5x^3 + 7x^2 - 6x + 50$ **24.** $-36x^3y^2 + 18x^2y^3 - 48xy^4$ **25.** $6x^3 - 19x^2 + 18x - 5$ **26.** $x + 5 + \frac{3}{x - 3}$

Chapter 5

5.1 Exercises

1. factors **3.** no, $6a^3 + 3a^2 - 9a$ has a common factor of $3a$. **5.** $3a(a + 1)$ **7.** $7ab(3 - 2b)$ **9.** $2\pi r(h + r)$ **11.** $5x(x^2 + 5x - 3)$ **13.** $4(3ab - 7bc + 5ac)$ **15.** $8x^2(2x^3 + 3x - 4)$ **17.** $7x(2xy - 5y - 9)$ **19.** $9x(6x - 5y + 2)$ **21.** $y(3xy - 2a + 5x - 2)$ **23.** $8xy(3x - 5y)$ **25.** $7x^2y^2(x + 3)$ **27.** $9xy(x - 2y - 3)$ **29.** $(x + 2y)(7a - b)$ **31.** $(x - 4)(3x - 2)$ **33.** $(2a - 3c)(6b - 5d)$ **35.** $(b - a^2)(7c - 5d + 2f)$ **37.** $(xy - 3)(2a - 4 - z)$ **39.** $(a - 3b)(4a^3 + 1)$ **41.** $(2a + 3)(1 - 7x)$ **43.** $A = 2.786(a + b + c + d)$ sq. in. **45.** 17, 19, 21 **47.** 2.24 feet per minute **48.** 23,220,000 tons **49.** 38,700,000 tons **50.** approximately 815 pounds per person **51.** approximately 445 pounds per person

5.2 Exercises

1. We must remove a common factor of 5 from the last two terms. This will give us $3x(x - 2y) + 5(x - 2y)$. Then our final answer is $(x - 2y)(3x + 5)$. **3.** $(a + 4)(b - 3)$ **5.** $(x - 4)(x^2 + 3)$ **7.** $(a + 3b)(2x - y)$ **9.** $(3a + b)(x - 2)$ **11.** $(a + 2b)(5 + 6c)$ **13.** $(a - b)(5 - 2x)$ **15.** $(y - 2)(y - 3)$ **17.** $(7 + y)(2 - y)$ **19.** $(3x + y)(2a - 1)$ **21.** $(2x - 3)(x + 4)$ **23.** $(t - 1)(t^2 + 1)$ **25.** $(4x + 3w)(7x + 2y^2)$ **27.** We must rearrange the terms in a different order so that the expression in the parentheses is the same in each case. We use the order $6a^2 - 8ad + 9ab - 12bd$ to factor $2a(3a - 4d) + 3b(3a - 4d) = (3a - 4d)(2a + 3b)$. **29.** 8 seconds **30.** \$420 **31.** \$126.9 million **32.** 390 floor seats; 510 balcony seats **33.** 7,315,000 tons in 2000; 9,363,200 tons in 2005

5.3 Exercises

1. product, sum **3.** $(x + 1)(x + 1)$ **5.** $(x + 2)(x + 10)$ **7.** $(x - 3)(x - 1)$ **9.** $(x - 7)(x - 4)$ **11.** $(x + 5)(x - 4)$ **13.** $(x - 14)(x + 1)$ **15.** $(x + 7)(x - 5)$ **17.** $(x - 6)(x + 4)$ **19.** $(x + 8)(x + 4)$ **21.** $(x - 6)(x - 4)$ **23.** $(x + 3)(x + 10)$ **25.** $(x - 5)(x - 1)$ **27.** $(a + 8)(a - 2)$ **29.** $(x - 4)(x - 8)$ **31.** $(x + 7)(x - 3)$ **33.** $(x + 7)(x + 8)$ **35.** $(x + 2)(x - 23)$ **37.** $(x + 12)(x - 3)$ **39.** $(x + 3y)(x - 5y)$ **41.** $(x - 7y)(x - 9y)$ **43.** $4(x + 5)(x + 1)$ **45.** $6(x + 1)(x + 2)$ **47.** $2(x - 3)(x - 7)$ **49.** $3(x + 4)(x - 6)$ **51.** $7(x + 5)(x - 2)$ **53.** $3(x - 1)(x - 5)$ **55.** $A = x^2 - \frac{\pi x^2}{4} = x^2\left(1 - \frac{\pi}{4}\right)$; A = 13.76 sq in **57.** $(12 + x)(10 - x)$ **59.** $t = \frac{A - P}{Pr}$ **60.** $x \geq -\frac{5}{3}$ 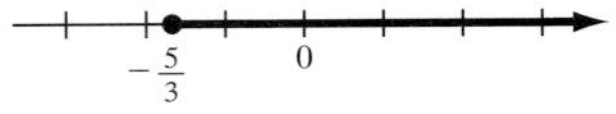

61. 120 miles **62.** \$130,000 **63.** 1:30 A.M. **64.** 9:00 P.M. **65.** 25°C **66.** June

5.4 Exercises

1. $(4x + 1)(x + 3)$ **3.** $(5x + 2)(x + 1)$ **5.** $(3x - 7)(x + 1)$ **7.** $(2x + 1)(x - 3)$ **9.** $(3x + 1)(3x + 2)$ **11.** $(3x - 5)(5x - 3)$ **13.** $(2x - 5)(x + 4)$ **15.** $(4x - 1)(2x + 3)$ **17.** $(3x + 2)(2x - 3)$ **19.** $(3x + 5)(2x - 3)$ **21.** $(x - 2)(7x + 9)$ **23.** $(9y - 4)(y - 1)$ **25.** $(5a + 2)(a - 3)$ **27.** $(7x - 5)(2x + 1)$ **29.** $(5x - 2)(3x + 2)$ **31.** $(6x + 5)(2x + 3)$ **33.** $(6x + 1)(2x - 3)$ **35.** $(2x^2 - 1)(x^2 + 8)$ **37.** $(2x + 5y)(x + 3y)$ **39.** $(5x - 4y)(x + 4y)$ **41.** $2(2x + 3)(x + 7)$ **43.** $2(4x - 1)(x - 3)$ **45.** $5(2x + 1)(x - 3)$ **47.** $3x(2x - 5)(x + 4)$ **49.** $(5x - 2)(x + 1)$ **51.** $2(3x - 2)(2x - 5)$ **53.** $(6x - 1)(2x - 3)$ **55.** $2(2x - 1)(2x + 5)$ **57.** $x = \frac{1}{10}$ **58.** $x = \frac{5 + 3y}{7}$ **59.** 26.5% **60.** 45.4% **61.** China **62.** from 1995 to 2000

How Am I Doing? Sections 5.1–5.4

1. $3(2xy - 5z + 7)$ (obj. 5.1.1) **2.** $4x(5x - 8y + 3)$ (obj. 5.1.1) **3.** $(4x - 5)(7 - b)$ (obj. 5.1.1) **4.** $(8y + 3z)(2x - 5y)$ (obj. 5.1.1) **5.** $(6 + x)(3 - y)$ (obj. 5.2.1) **6.** $(3x + 4w)(5 - 3b)$ (obj. 5.2.1) **7.** $(x - 5)(x^2 - 3)$ (obj. 5.2.1) **8.** $(a + 3b)(7 + 2b)$ (obj. 5.2.1) **9.** $(x - 7)(x - 8)$ (obj. 5.3.1) **10.** $(x + 16)(x - 4)$ (obj. 5.3.1) **11.** $(x + 8y)(x + 5y)$ (obj. 5.3.1) **12.** $7(x + 5)(x - 7)$ (obj. 5.3.2) **13.** $(5x - 2)(2x + 1)$ (obj. 5.4.1) **14.** $(x - 7)(3x - 2)$ (obj. 5.4.1) **15.** $(2x + 3y)(3x + 4y)$ (obj. 5.4.2) **16.** $2x(7x + 4)(x - 2)$ (obj. 5.4.3)

5.5 Exercises

1. $(3x + 1)(3x - 1)$ **3.** $(9x - 4)(9x + 4)$ **5.** $(x + 7)(x - 7)$ **7.** $(2x - 5)(2x + 5)$ **9.** $(x + 5)(x - 5)$ **11.** $(1 - 4x)(1 + 4x)$ **13.** $(4x - 7y)(4x + 7y)$ **15.** $(6x - 13y)(6x + 13y)$ **17.** $(9x + 10)(9x - 10)$ **19.** $(5a + 9b)(5a - 9b)$ **21.** $(3x + 1)^2$ **23.** $(y - 5)^2$ **25.** $(6x - 5)^2$ **27.** $(7x + 2)^2$ **29.** $(x + 7)^2$ **31.** $(5x - 4)^2$ **33.** $(9x + 2y)^2$ **35.** $(5x - 3y)^2$ **37.** $(4a + 9b)^2$ **39.** $(7x - 3y)^2$ **41.** $(7x + 3)^2$ **43.** $(7x + 3)(7x - 3)$ **45.** $(x^2 + 6)(x^2 - 6)$ **47.** $(3x^2 - 2)^2$ **49.** No two binomials can be multiplied to obtain $9x^2 + 1$. **51.** 49, one answer **53.** $4(2x - 3)(2x + 3)$ **55.** $3(7x - y)(7x + y)$ **57.** $3(2x - 3)^2$ **59.** $2(7x + 3)^2$ **61.** $(x - 11)(x - 4)$ **63.** $(2x - 1)(x + 3)$ **65.** $(4x - 11)(4x + 11)$ **67.** $(3x + 7)^2$ **69.** $3(x + 5)(x - 3)$ **71.** $5(x - 4)(x + 4)$ **73.** $7(x + 3)^2$ **75.** $2(x - 9)(x - 7)$ **77.** $x^2 + 3x + 4 + \frac{-3}{x - 2}$ **78.** $2x^2 + x - 5$ **79.** 1.2 ounces of greens; 1.05 ounces of bulk vegetables; 0.75 ounce of fruit **80.** 1.44 ounces of greens; 1.26 ounces of bulk vegetables; 0.9 ounce of fruit **81.** 3838 feet above sea level **82.** 5 miles

5.6 Exercises

1. $a(6a + 2b - 3)$ **3.** $(4x - 5y)(4x + 5y)$ **5.** $(3x - 2y)^2$ **7.** $(x + 5)(x + 3)$ **9.** $(3x + 2)(5x - 1)$ **11.** $(a - 3c)(x + 3y)$ **13.** $(y + 7)^2$ **15.** $(2x - 3)^2$ **17.** $(2x - 3)(x - 4)$ **19.** $(x - 10y)(x + 7y)$ **21.** $(a + 3)(x - 5)$ **23.** $5x(3 - x)(3 + x)$ **25.** $5xy^3(x - 1)^2$ **27.** $3xy(3z + 2)(3z - 2)$ **29.** $3(x + 7)(x - 5)$ **31.** $3x(x + 4)(x - 3)$ **33.** $-1(2x^2 + 1)(x + 2)(x - 2)$ **35.** prime **37.** $5(x^2 + 2xy - 6y)$ **39.** $3x(2x + y)(5x - 2y)$ **41.** $2(3x - 5)(4x - 3)$ **43.** prime **45.** \$78.24 **46.** 372 live strains **47.** \$74 **48.** \$86 **49.** $y = 0.8x + 57$ **50.** $y = -3.3x + 144$

5.7 Exercises

1. $x = -3, 7$ **3.** $x = -13, x = -3$ **5.** $x = \frac{3}{2}, 2$ **7.** $x = \frac{2}{3}, \frac{3}{2}$ **9.** $x = 0, -13$ **11.** $x = 3, -3$ **13.** $x = 0, 1$ **15.** $x = \frac{2}{3}, 2$
17. $x = -3, 2$ **19.** $x = -\frac{1}{2}$ **21.** $x = 0, -2$ **23.** $x = -3, -4$ **25.** $x = -\frac{3}{2}, 4$ **27.** You can always factor out x.
29. $L = 14$ m; $W = 10$ m **31.** 66 groups **33.** 10 students **35.** 12 meters above ground after 2 sec **37.** 5 additional helicopters
39. 2415 telephone calls **41.** 18 people **43.** $-10x^5y^4$ **44.** $12a^{10}b^{13}$ **45.** $-\frac{3a^4}{2b^2}$ **46.** $\frac{1}{3x^5y^4}$

Putting Your Skills to Work

1. 402 **2.** 114 **3.** Increased from 29% to 34% **4.** Decreased from 34% to 32% **5.** 354 **6.** 132 **7.** $y = 6(5x + 49)$
8. $y = 11(x + 9)$

Chapter 5 Review Problems

1. $4x^2(3x - 5y)$ **2.** $5x^3(2 - 7y)$ **3.** $7xy(x - 2y - 3x^2y^2)$ **4.** $25a^4b^4(2b - 1 + 3ab)$ **5.** $3a(a^2 + 2a - 3b + 4)$
6. $2(x - 2y + 3z + 6)$ **7.** $(a + 3b)(2a - 5)$ **8.** $3xy(5x^2 + 2y + 1)$ **9.** $(3x - 7)(a - 2)$ **10.** $(a + 5b)(a - 4)$
11. $(x^2 + 3)(y - 2)$ **12.** $3(2x - y)(5a + 7)$ **13.** $(5x - 1)(3x + 2)$ **14.** $(5w - 3)(6w + z)$ **15.** $(x - 7)(x + 5)$
16. $(x - 4)(x - 6)$ **17.** $(x + 6)(x + 8)$ **18.** $(x + 3y)(x + 5y)$ **19.** $(x^2 + 7)(x^2 + 6)$ **20.** $(x^2 - 7)(x^2 + 5)$
21. $6(x + 2)(x + 3)$ **22.** $3(x + 1)(x + 12)$ **23.** $2(x - 6)(x - 8)$ **24.** $4(x - 5)(x - 6)$ **25.** $(4x - 5)(x + 3)$
26. $(3x - 1)(4x + 5)$ **27.** $(5x + 4)(3x - 1)$ **28.** $(3x - 2)(2x - 3)$ **29.** $(2x - 3)(x + 1)$ **30.** $(3x - 4)(x + 2)$
31. $(10x - 1)(2x + 5)$ **32.** $(5x - 1)(4x + 5)$ **33.** $(3a - 2)(2a + 5)$ **34.** $(3a - 2)(2a - 5)$ **35.** $2(x - 1)(3x + 5)$
36. $2(x + 1)(3x - 5)$ **37.** $2(2x - 3)(x - 5)$ **38.** $4(x - 9)(x + 4)$ **39.** $2(3x + 2)(2x - 5)$ **40.** $3(3x - 2)(2x + 7)$
41. $(3x - 2y)(2x - 5y)$ **42.** $2(3x - y)(x - 5y)$ **43.** $(7x + y)(7x - y)$ **44.** $4(2x - 3y)(2x + 3y)$ **45.** $(5x + 3)^2$
46. $(7x - 2)^2$ **47.** $(5x - 6)(5x + 6)$ **48.** $(10x - 3)(10x + 3)$ **49.** $(y - 6x)(y + 6x)$ **50.** $(3y - 5x)(3y + 5x)$ **51.** $(6x + 1)^2$
52. $(5x - 2)^2$ **53.** $(4x - 3y)^2$ **54.** $(7x - 2y)^2$ **55.** $2(x - 3)(x + 3)$ **56.** $3(x - 5)(x + 5)$ **57.** $7(2x + 5)^2$ **58.** $8(3x - 4)^2$
59. $(2x + 3y)(2x - 3y)$ **60.** $(x + 3)^2$ **61.** $(x - 3)(x - 6)$ **62.** $(x + 15)(x - 2)$ **63.** $(x - 1)(6x + 7)$ **64.** $(5x - 2)(2x + 1)$
65. $12(2x - 5)$ **66.** $4xy(2xy - 1)$ **67.** $10x^2y^2(5x + 2)$ **68.** $13ab(2a^2 - b^2 + 4ab^3)$ **69.** $x(x - 8)^2$ **70.** $2(x + 10)^2$
71. $3(x - 3)^2$ **72.** $x(5x - 6)^2$ **73.** $(7x + 5)(x - 2)$ **74.** $(4x + 3)(x - 4)$ **75.** $xy(3x + 2y)(3x - 2y)$
76. $x^3a(3a + 4x)(a - 5x)$ **77.** $2(3a + 5b)(2a - b)$ **78.** $(11a + 3b)^2$ **79.** $(a - 1)(7 - b)$ **80.** $(4b - 5)(2 + 7c)$
81. $(6b - 7)(3 - 2x)$ **82.** $(b - 7)(5x + 4y)$ **83.** $x(2a - 1)(a - 7)$ **84.** $x(x + 4)(x - 4)(x + 1)(x - 1)$
85. $(x^2 + 9y^6)(x + 3y^3)(x - 3y^3)$ **86.** $(3x^2 - 5)(2x^2 + 3)$ **87.** $yz(14 - x)(2 - x)$ **88.** $x(3x + 2)(4x + 3)$
89. $(2w + 1)(8w - 5)$ **90.** $3(2w - 1)^2$ **91.** $2y(2y - 1)(y + 3)$ **92.** $(5y - 1)(2y + 7)$ **93.** $8y^8(y^2 - 2)$
94. $9(x^2 + 4)(x - 2)(x + 2)$ **95.** prime **96.** prime **97.** $4y(2y^2 - 5)(y^2 + 3)$ **98.** $3x(3y + 7)(y - 2)$ **99.** $(4x^2y - 7)^2$
100. $2xy(8x + 1)(8x - 1)$ **101.** $(2x + 5)(a - 2b)$ **102.** $(2x + 1)(x + 3)(x - 3)$ **103.** $-3, 6$ **104.** $-4, \frac{3}{2}$ **105.** $0, \frac{1}{6}$
106. $4, -3$ **107.** $-5, \frac{1}{2}$ **108.** $-8, -3$ **109.** $-5, -9$ **110.** $-\frac{3}{5}, 2$ **111.** -3 **112.** $-3, \frac{3}{4}$ **113.** $\frac{1}{5}, 2$
114. base = 10 cm; altitude = 7 cm **115.** width = 7 feet, length = 15 feet **116.** 6 seconds **117.** 8 amperes, 12 amperes

How Am I Doing? Chapter 5 Test

1. $(x + 14)(x - 2)$ (obj. 5.3.1) **2.** $(4x + 9)(4x - 9)$ (obj. 5.5.1) **3.** $(5x + 1)(2x + 5)$ (obj. 5.4.2) **4.** $(3a - 5)^2$ (obj. 5.5.2)
5. $x(7 - 9x + 14y)$ (obj. 5.1.1) **6.** $(2x + 3b)(5y - 4)$ (obj. 5.4.2) **7.** $2x(3x - 4)(x - 2)$ (obj. 5.6.1)
8. $c(5a - 1)(a - 2)$ (obj. 5.6.1) **9.** $(9x + 10)(9x - 10)$ (obj. 5.5.1) **10.** $(3x - 1)(3x - 4)$ (obj. 5.6.1)
11. $5(2x - 3)(2x + 3)$ (obj. 5.6.1) **12.** prime (obj. 5.6.2) **13.** $x(3x + 5)(x + 2)$ (obj. 5.6.1) **14.** $-5y(2x - 3y)^2$ (obj. 5.6.1)
15. $(9x + 1)(9x - 1)$ (obj. 5.5.1) **16.** $(9y^2 + 1)(3y - 1)(3y + 1)$ (obj. 5.5.1) **17.** $(x + 3)(2a - 5)$ (obj. 5.6.1)
18. $(a + 2b)(w + 2)(w - 2)$ (obj. 5.6.1) **19.** $3(x - 6)(x + 5)$ (obj. 5.6.1) **20.** $x(2x + 5)(x - 3)$ (obj. 5.6.1) **21.** $-5, -9$ (obj. 5.7.1)
22. $-\frac{7}{3}, -2$ (obj. 5.7.1) **23.** $-\frac{5}{2}, 2$ (obj. 5.7.1) **24.** $x = 7, -4$ (obj. 5.7.1) **25.** width = 7 miles; length = 13 miles (obj. 5.7.2)

Cumulative Test for Chapters 0–5

1. 15% **2.** 0.494 **3.** 5.8 **4.** $8x^4y^{10}$ **5.** 81 **6.** $27x^2 + 6x - 8$ **7.** $2x^3 - 12x^2 + 19x - 3$ **8.** $x \leq -3$ **9.** 2 **10.** -15
11. $q = \frac{p + 3}{5}$ **12.** $(3x - 1)(2x - 1)$ **13.** $(3x + 4)(2x - 1)$ **14.** $(3x + 2)(3x - 1)$ **15.** $(11x + 8y)(11x - 8y)$
16. $-4(5x + 6)(4x - 5)$ **17.** prime **18.** $x(4x + 5)^2$ **19.** $(9x^2 + 4b^2)(3x + 2b)(3x - 2b)$ **20.** $(2x + 3)(a - 2b)$
21. $3(5x - 3)(x + 1)$ **22.** $-8, 3$ **23.** $\frac{5}{3}, 2$ **24.** length = 20 ft
width = 15 ft

Chapter 6

6.1 Exercises

1. 3 **3.** $\frac{6}{x}$ **5.** $\frac{3x + 1}{1 - 3x}$ **7.** $\frac{a(a - 2b)}{2b}$ **9.** $\frac{x + 2}{x}$ **11.** $\frac{x - 5}{3x - 1}$ **13.** $\frac{x - 3}{x(x - 7)}$ **15.** $\frac{3x - 2}{x + 4}$ **17.** $\frac{3x - 5}{4x - 1}$ **19.** $\frac{x - 5}{x + 1}$
21. $-\frac{1}{2x}$ **23.** $\frac{-2x - 3}{x + 5}$ **25.** $\frac{4x + 5}{2x - 1}$ **27.** $\frac{2x - 3}{-x + 5}$ **29.** $\frac{a - b}{2a - b}$ **31.** $\frac{3x - 2y}{3x + 2y}$ **33.** $\frac{x(x + a)}{b(x + c)}$ **35.** $9x^2 - 42x + 49$

36. $49x^2 - 36y^2$ **37.** $2x^3 - 9x^2 - 2x + 24$ **38.** $2x^4 - 5x^3 - 10x^2 - 14x - 15$ **39.** $1\frac{5}{8}$ acre **40.** 6 hrs, 25 min

41. 874,000,000 people **42.** 358,000,000 people

6.2 Exercises

1. factor numerator and denominator completely and divide out common factors **3.** $\frac{2(x+4)}{x-4}$ **5.** $\frac{3x^2}{4(x-3)}$ **7.** $\frac{x-2}{x+3}$ **9.** $\frac{(x+6)(x+2)}{x+5}$

11. $x + 2$ **13.** $\frac{3(x+2y)}{4(x+3y)}$ **15.** $\frac{(x+5)(x-2)}{3x-1}$ **17.** $\frac{-5(x+3)}{2(x-2)}$ or $\frac{5(x+3)}{-2(x-2)}$ or $-\frac{5(x+3)}{2(x-2)}$ **19.** 1 **21.** $\frac{x-1}{x+3}$

23. The denominator cannot be zero. So x cannot be 2, −7, or 6. **25.** $x = -8$ **26.** $7x^3 - 22x^2 + 2x + 3$ **27.** 5 milligrams

28. $79.5(8981)x = \$713{,}989.5x$ **29.** Harold's is 6 ft by 6 ft. George's is 9 ft by 4 ft.

6.3 Exercises

1. The LCD would be a product that contains each factor. However, any repeated factor in any one denominator must be repeated the greatest number of times it occurs in any one denominator. So the LCD would be $(x + 5)(x + 3)^2$.

3. $\frac{3x+1}{x+5}$ **5.** $\frac{2x-5}{x+3}$ **7.** $\frac{2x-7}{5x+7}$ **9.** $3a^2b^2$ **11.** $90x^3y^5$ **13.** $15(x-3)$ **15.** $x^2 - 9$ **17.** $(x+5)(3x-1)^2$

19. $\frac{7+3a}{ab}$ **21.** $\frac{3x-13}{(x+7)(x-7)}$ **23.** $\frac{4y^2-4y}{(y+2)(y-2)}$ **25.** $\frac{43a+12}{5a(3a+2)}$ **27.** $\frac{4z+x}{6xyz}$ **29.** $\frac{9x+14}{2(x-3)}$ **31.** $\frac{x+10}{(x+5)(x-5)}$

33. $\frac{3a+17b}{10}$ **35.** $\frac{-4x+34}{(2x-3)(x+2)}$ **37.** $\frac{-7x}{(x+3)(x-1)(x-4)}$ **39.** $\frac{5x+19}{(x+2)(x+3)(x+5)}$ **41.** $\frac{4x-13}{(x-4)(x-3)}$

43. $\frac{11x}{y-2x}$ **45.** $\frac{-17y^2-10y}{(4y-1)(2y+1)(y-5)}$ **47.** $\frac{6}{y+3}$ **49.** $\frac{5x^2-5x+7}{(x-3)(x+2)}$ **51.** $x = -7$ **52.** $y = \frac{5ax+6bc}{2a}$

53. $x < \frac{3}{2}$ **54.** $81x^{12}y^{16}$ **55.** at least 17 days **56.** 566,100 more people **57. (a)** 900,000 fish **(b)** three more months

58. more than 7 videos per month

How Am I Doing? Sections 6.1–6.3

1. $\frac{8}{x}$ (obj. 6.1.1) **2.** $\frac{2x+3}{x-7}$ (obj. 6.1.1) **3.** $\frac{y+3}{3x^2(3-y)}$ (obj. 6.1.1) **4.** $\frac{x-4}{x+2}$ (obj. 6.1.1) **5.** $\frac{3x}{2}$ (obj. 6.2.1)

6. $-\frac{x+5}{3(x-2)}$ or $\frac{x+5}{-3(x-2)}$ (obj. 6.2.1) **7.** $\frac{2x-1}{2}$ (obj. 6.2.2) **8.** $\frac{4a-3}{2a-5}$ (obj. 6.2.2) **9.** $\frac{xy-3ax-3ay}{axy}$ (obj. 6.3.3)

10. $\frac{7}{2(x+2)}$ (obj. 6.3.3) **11.** $\frac{x^2+2x-9}{(x+3)(x+7)}$ (obj. 6.3.3) **12.** $\frac{-5x^2-23x-8}{(x+5)(x-2)(x-4)}$ (obj. 6.3.3)

6.4 Exercises

1. $\frac{3x}{2+5x}$ **3.** $y + x$ **5.** $\frac{x^2-2x}{4+5x}$ **7.** $\frac{2}{3x+10}$ **9.** $\frac{1}{xy}$ **11.** $\frac{2x-1}{x}$ **13.** $\frac{2}{x-1}$ **15.** $\frac{3a^2+9}{a^2+2}$ **17.** $\frac{3x+9}{2x-5}$

19. $\frac{y+1}{-y+1}$ **21.** No expression in any denominator can be zero because division by zero is undefined. So −3, 5, and 0 are not allowed.

23. $w = \frac{p-2l}{2}$ **24.** $x > -1$ 

25. \$1875 **26.** approximately 57%

6.5 Exercises

1. −12 **3.** 3.5 or $\frac{7}{2}$ **5.** 15 **7.** 3 **9.** −5 **11.** $-\frac{14}{3}$ or $-4\frac{2}{3}$ **13.** −2 **15.** 8 **17.** −0.5 or $-\frac{1}{2}$ **19.** no solution

21. −3 **23.** −5 **25.** no solution **27.** 4 **29.** no solution **31.** 2, 4 **33.** $(3x+4)(2x-3)$ **34.** $-\frac{10}{3}$ **35.** width = 7 m, length = 20 m

36. \$946.45 **37.** 21.9% **38.** 90.9% **39.** 10.3 million people **40.** 3.5 million people

6.6 Exercises

1. 18 **3.** $\frac{204}{5}$ or $40\frac{4}{5}$ **5.** $\frac{56}{5}$ or 11.2 **7.** $\frac{91}{4}$ or 22.75 **9.** 110 miles **11. (a)** 1043 Australian dollars **(b)** 133 more Australian dollars

13. 56 mph **15.** 29 miles **17.** $18\frac{17}{20}$ inches **19.** 200 meters **21.** $9\frac{1}{3}$ in. **23.** $38\frac{2}{5}$ m **25.** 48 in. **27.** 35 inches

29. 61.5 mph **31.** commuter = 250 km/hr, helicopter = 210 km/hr **33. (a)** \$0.11 **(b)** \$0.09 **(c)** \$3.73 **35.** $2\frac{2}{9}$ hours or 2hrs, 13 min **37.** $3\frac{3}{7}$ hours or 3 hrs, 26 min

39. 8.92465×10^{-4} **40.** 582,000,000 **41.** $\frac{w^8}{x^3y^2z^4}$ **42.** $\frac{27}{8}$ or $3\frac{3}{8}$

Putting Your Skills to Work

1. \$3000 **2.** \$1200 **3.** $P = \frac{24x}{x+3}$ **4.** \$18,857 **5.** \$15,000 **6.** \$21,000

Chapter 6 Review Problems

1. $\frac{x}{x-y}$ **2.** $-\frac{4}{5}$ **3.** $\frac{x+3}{x-4}$ **4.** $\frac{x+2}{x+4}$ **5.** $\frac{x+3}{x-7}$ **6.** $\frac{2(x+4)}{3}$ **7.** $\frac{x}{x-5}$ **8.** $\frac{2x+3}{2x}$ **9.** $\frac{2(x-4y)}{2x-y}$ **10.** $\frac{2-y}{3y-1}$ **11.** $\frac{x-2}{(5x+6)(x-1)}$ **12.** $4x+2y$ **13.** $\frac{x-25}{x+5}$ **14.** $\frac{2(y-3)}{3y}$ **15.** $\frac{(y+2)(2y+1)(y-2)}{(2y-1)(y+1)^2}$ **16.** $\frac{4y(3y-1)}{(3y+1)(2y+5)}$ **17.** $\frac{3y(4x+3)}{2(x-5)}$ **18.** $\frac{x+2}{2}$ **19.** $\frac{2(x+3y)}{x-4y}$ **20.** $\frac{3}{16}$ **21.** $\frac{9x+2}{x(x+1)}$ **22.** $\frac{5x^2+7x+1}{x(x+1)}$ **23.** $\frac{10x-22}{(x+2)(x-4)}$ **24.** $\frac{(x-1)(x-2)}{(x+3)(x-3)}$ **25.** $\frac{2xy+4x+5y+6}{2y(y+2)}$ **26.** $\frac{(2a+b)(a+4b)}{ab(a+b)}$ **27.** $\frac{3x-2}{3x}$ **28.** $\frac{2x^2+7x-2}{2x(x+2)}$ **29.** $\frac{3}{2(x-9)}$ **30.** $\frac{1-2x-x^2}{(x+5)(x+2)}$ **31.** $\frac{1}{11}$ **32.** $\frac{5}{3x^2}$ **33.** $w-2$ **34.** 1 **35.** $-\frac{y^2}{2}$ **36.** $\frac{x+2y}{y(x+y+2)}$ **37.** $\frac{-1}{a(a+b)}$ or $-\frac{1}{a(a+b)}$ **38.** $\frac{-3a-b}{b}$ or $-\frac{3a+b}{b}$ **39.** $\frac{5y(x+5y)^2}{x(x-6y)}$ **40.** $\frac{-3y}{2(x+2y)}$ or $-\frac{3y}{2(x+2y)}$ **41.** 2 **42.** 15 **43.** $\frac{2}{7}$ **44.** −8 **45.** −4 **46.** −2 **47.** $\frac{1}{2}$ **48.** $\frac{1}{5}$ **49.** no solution **50.** $x=-4$; $x=6$ **51.** 6 **52.** 2 **53.** −2 **54.** no solution **55.** 9 **56.** 0 **57.** 2.8 **58.** 1.3 **59.** 26.4 **60.** 2 **61.** 16 **62.** 9.1 **63.** 8.3 gallons **64.** 167 cookies **65.** 46 gallons **66.** 91.5 miles **67.** train = 60 mph car = 40 mph **68.** 3 hrs, 5 min **69.** 182 ft **70.** 1200 ft **71.** 3 hrs, 20 min **72.** 12 hrs **73.** $-\frac{a+4}{16a^2}$ **74.** $\frac{6b^2}{b+5}$ **75.** $\frac{x-2y}{x+2y}$ **76.** $\frac{x-8y}{x+7y}$ **77.** $\frac{x+6}{x}$ **78.** $\frac{x+6}{x}$ **79.** $\frac{b^2-a^2}{ab(x+y)}$ **80.** $\frac{1}{3}$ **81.** $-\frac{6}{y^2}$ **82.** $\frac{y(x+3y)}{2(x+2y)}$ **83.** 23 **84.** −12 **85.** −2 **86.** 10.7 kg **87.** 420 miles

How Am I Doing? Chapter 6 Test

1. $\frac{2}{3a}$ (obj. 6.1.1) **2.** $\frac{2x^2(2-y)}{(y+2)}$ (obj. 6.1.1) **3.** $\frac{5}{12}$ (obj. 6.2.1) **4.** $\frac{1}{3y(x-y)}$ (obj. 6.2.1) **5.** $\frac{2a+1}{a+2}$ (obj. 6.2.2) **6.** $\frac{3a+4}{(a+1)(a-2)}$ (obj. 6.3.3) **7.** $\frac{x-a}{ax}$ (obj. 6.3.3) **8.** $-\frac{x+2}{x+3}$ (obj. 6.3.3) **9.** $\frac{x}{4}$ (obj. 6.4.2) **10.** $\frac{6x}{5}$ (obj. 6.4.1) **11.** $\frac{2x-3y}{4x+y}$ (obj. 6.1.1) **12.** $\frac{x}{(x+2)(x+4)}$ (obj. 6.3.3) **13.** $-\frac{1}{5}$ (obj. 6.5.1) **14.** $x=4$ (obj. 6.5.1) **15.** no solution (obj. 6.5.2) **16.** $x=\frac{47}{6}$ (obj. 6.5.1) **17.** $x=\frac{45}{13}$ (obj. 6.6.1) **18.** $x=37.2$ (obj. 6.6.1) **19.** 151 flights (obj. 6.6.1) **20.** $368 (obj. 6.6.1) **21.** 102 feet (obj. 6.6.2)

Cumulative Test for Chapters 0–6

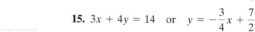

1. 0.006 cm **2.** 35% **3.** $92.50 **4.** $x=6$ **5.** $h=\frac{A}{\pi r^2}$ **6.** $x>1.25$

7. $x \le 26$ **8.** $(a+b)(3x-2y)$ **9.** $2a(4a+b)(a-5b)$ **10.** $-4x^3y^{12}$ **11.** $\frac{2x+5}{x+7}$ **12.** $\frac{(x-2)(3x+1)}{3x(x+5)}$ **13.** $\frac{1}{2}$ **14.** $\frac{11x-3}{2(x+2)(x-3)}$ **15.** $\frac{6c-28}{(c+2)(c-2)(c-3)}$ **16.** $x=-2$ **17.** $x=-\frac{9}{2}$ **18.** $\frac{x+8}{6x(x-3)}$ **19.** $\frac{3ab^2+2a^2b}{5b^2-2a^2}$ **20.** $x=\frac{7}{10}$ **21.** 208 miles **22.** 484 phone calls

Practice Final Examination

1. $-2x+21y+18xy+6y^2$ **2.** 14 **3.** $18x^5y^5$ **4.** $2x^2y-8xy$ **5.** $x=\frac{8}{5}$ **6.** $b=\frac{p-2a}{2}$ **7.** $x \ge 2.6$

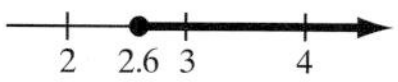

8. $2x^3-5x^2y+xy^2+2y^3$ **9.** $2(2x+1)(x-5)$ **10.** $3x(x-5)(x+2)$ **11.** $\frac{6x-11}{(x+2)(x-3)}$ **12.** $\frac{11(x+2)}{2x(x+4)}$ **13.** $-\frac{12}{5}$ **14.** slope $=\frac{5}{2}$

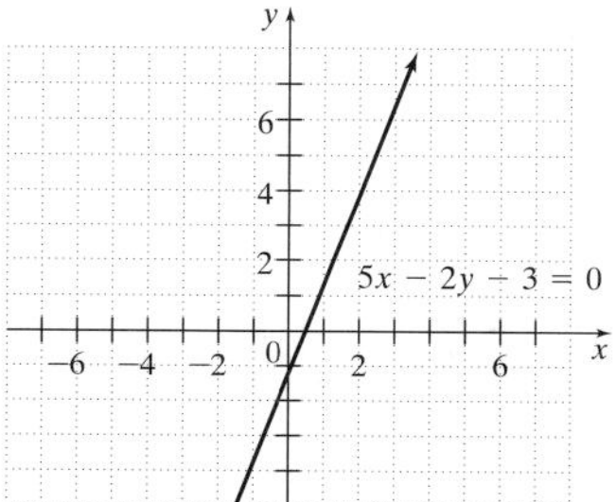

15. $3x+4y=14$ or $y=-\frac{3}{4}x+\frac{7}{2}$

16. 38.13 sq in. **17.** $x = -5, y = 2$ **18.** $a = -2, b = -3$ **19.** $x\sqrt{5x}$ **20.** $6\sqrt{3} - 12 + 12\sqrt{2}$ **21.** $-\frac{\sqrt{15} + \sqrt{35} + \sqrt{21} + 7}{2}$
22. $x = \frac{2}{3}, x = -\frac{1}{4}$ **23.** $y = \frac{3 \pm \sqrt{7}}{2}$ **24.** $x = \pm 2$ **25.** $\sqrt{39}$ **26.** 5 **27.** width 7 meters, length 12 meters
28. \$3000 at 10%, \$4000 at 14% **29.** 200 reserved-seat tickets, 160 general admission tickets **30.** base 8 meters, altitude 17 meters

Appendix B Exercises

1. 34,000 m **3.** 5700 cm **5.** 250 mm **7.** 0.563 m **9.** 29,400 mg **11.** 0.0984 kg **13.** 7000 mL **15.** 0.000004 kL
17. 1.7 in. **19.** 22.5 km **21.** 2.8 m **23.** 17.8 cm **25.** 1089.6 g **27.** 171.6 lb **29.** 2.8 L **31.** 193,248,000 in.
33. 27.27 miles per hour **35.** 0.11 yr

Appendix C Exercises

1. 84,916 square miles **3.** 4,507,000 **5.** 2 **7.** Treasure State **9.** Nevada **11.** 2000 homes **13.** Dupage County
15. 2800 homes **17.** 4,000,000 apartment units **19.** 7,200,000 more apartment units **21.** 8,000,000 **23.** It is a three-way tie. The increase was 3 million in three cases. It occurred between 1970 and 1980, and again between 1980 and 1990, and finally again between 1990 and 2000. **25.** 3 million more **27.** 37 million **29.** Movies and an Exercise Program **31.** \$5.6 million **33.** \$2.5 million greater
35. Between 2001 and 2002 **37.** 74 million **39.** an age group of 65 years and above **41.** 19% **43.** 83% **45.** 754 million people
47. 40% **49.** \$3588

Appendix D Exercises

1. 14 **3.** 52 **5.** 1296 **7.** -3 **9.** $10x - 5$ **11.** 1111811 **13.** 9876549 **15.** 6481100 **17.** 1 6 15 20 15 6 1
19. $x = 3$, steps will vary **21.** $x = -2$, steps will vary **23.** $x = 3$, steps will vary **25.** $x = \frac{9}{11}$, steps will vary **27.** answers will vary
29. William was first, Brent was second, James was third, Dave was fourth **31.** The teacher is Michael **33.** Toyota Corolla
35. Unless Fred is willing to pay over \$200 for Tuesday's procedure, he will probably get a false tooth.

Applications Index

Subject Index

Photo Credits

CHAPTER 0 **CO** © Paul Almasy/Corbis Bettmann **p. 31** Stockbyte **p. 40** Adam Jones/Photo Researchers, Inc. **p. 44** Peter Hvizdak/The Image Works

CHAPTER 1 **CO** SuperStock, Inc. **p. 69** Peter Skinner/Photo Researchers, Inc. **p. 90** Tony Freeman/PhotoEdit **p. 101** AP Wide World Photos **p. 116** John Coletti/Stock Boston **p. 124** Photo Researchers, Inc. **p.125** Elizabeth Crews/ The Image Works

CHAPTER 2 **CO** © Bill Schid/Corbis Bettmann **p. 145** Mark Downy/Getty Images, Inc. **p. 145** C. Allan Morgan/Peter Arnold, Inc. **p. 146** Jerry Wachter/Photo Researchers, Inc. **p. 179** Jeffrey Dunn/Stock Boston **p. 182** Stephen J. Krasemann/Photo Researchers, Inc.

CHAPTER 3 **CO** © Kennan Ward/Corbis Bettmann **p. 201** Ken Graham/Getty Images, Inc. **p. 205** NASA/Science Source/Photo Researchers, Inc. **p. 206** Townsend P. Dickinson/The Image Works **p. 207** Bob Daemmrich/Stock Boston **p. 208** Dennis MacDonald/PhotoEdit **p. 212** Dave Bartruff/Corbis Bettmann **p. 226** AP Wide World Photos **p. 237** George Ranalli/Photo Researchers, Inc. **p. 234** NASA/Johnson Space Center

CHAPTER 4 **CO** Rob Crandall/Stock Boston **p. 265** NASA/John F. Kennedy Space Center

CHAPTER 5 **CO** Jim Cummins/Getty Images, Inc. **p. 306** Malcolm Fielding, Johnson Matthey PLC/Science Photo Library/Photo Researchers, Inc. **p. 308** Luis Veiga/Getty Images, Inc. **p. 333** Alok Kavan/Photo Researchers, Inc. **p. 343** Philip H. Coblentz/World Travel Images, Inc. **p. 347** AP Wide World Photos

CHAPTER 6 **CO** Philippe Hays/Peter Arnold, Inc.

Minimum System Requirements

Windows	Macintosh
Pentium II 300 MHz processor	Power PC G3 233 MHz or better
Windows 98 or later	Mac OS 9.x or 10.x
64 MB RAM	64 MB RAM
800 x 600 resolution	800 x 600 resolution
8x or faster CD-ROM drive	8x or faster CD-ROM drive
Quick Time 6.0 or later	Quick Time 6.0 or later

PROPERTIES OF REAL NUMBERS

	Addition	Multiplication
Commutative Properties	$a + b = b + a$	$ab = ba$
Associative Properties	$(a + b) + c = a + (b + c)$	$(ab)c = a(bc)$
Identity Properties	$a + 0 = 0 + a = a$	$a \cdot 1 = 1 \cdot a = a$
Inverse Properties	$a + (-a) = -a + a = 0$	$a \cdot \frac{1}{a} = \frac{1}{a} \cdot a = 1 \ (a \neq 0)$

Distributive Property $\quad a(b + c) = ab + ac$

PROPERTIES OF EXPONENTS

If $x, y \neq 0$, then

$$x^a \cdot x^b = x^{a+b}$$

$$\frac{x^a}{x^b} = x^{a-b} \text{ if } a \geq b$$

$$\frac{x^a}{x^b} = \frac{1}{x^{b-a}} \text{ if } a < b$$

$$x^0 = 1$$

$$(x^a)^b = x^{ab}$$

$$(xy)^a = x^a y^a$$

$$\left(\frac{x}{y}\right)^a = \frac{x^a}{y^a}$$

ABSOLUTE VALUE

Definition

$$|x| = \begin{cases} x \text{ if } x \geq 0 \\ -x \text{ if } x < 0 \end{cases}$$

INEQUALITIES

If $a < b$, then for all values of c, $a + c < b + c$ and $a - c < b - c$.

If $a < b$ when c is a **positive number** $(c > 0)$, then $ac < bc$ and $\frac{a}{c} < \frac{b}{c}$.

If $a < b$ when c is a **negative number** $(c < 0)$, then $ac > bc$ and $\frac{a}{c} > \frac{b}{c}$.

FACTORING AND MULTIPLYING FORMULAS

Perfect-Square Trinomials	$a^2 + 2ab + b^2 = (a + b)^2$ $a^2 - 2ab + b^2 = (a - b)^2$
Difference of Two Squares	$a^2 - b^2 = (a + b)(a - b)$
Sum of Two Squares	$a^2 + b^2$ *cannot be factored*

PROPERTIES OF LINES AND SLOPES

The **slope** of any nonvertical line passing through (x_1, y_1) and (x_2, y_2) is $m = \frac{y_2 - y_1}{x_2 - x_1} (x_1 \neq x_2)$.

The **standard form** of the equation of a straight line is $Ax + By = C$.

The **slope–intercept** form of the equation of a straight line with slope m and y-intercept $(0, b)$ is $y = mx + b$.

A **horizontal line** has a slope of zero. The equation of a horizontal line can be written as $y = b$.

A **vertical line** has no slope (the slope is not defined for a vertical line).

The equation of a vertical line can be written as $x = a$.